solid state theory

MENDEL SACHS
Associate Professor of Physics
Boston University

solid state theory

McGraw-Hill Book Company
new york san francisco london toronto

solid state theory

Library of Congress Catalog Card Number 62-21804

II

54379

preface

The conditions of temperature and pressure that prevail on the surface of the earth are conducive to the formation of most chemical species into the solid state of matter. The resulting solid may be viewed phenomenologically from the point of view of its macroscopic properties alone. However, to derive these properties from a fundamental approach, we must consider the solid as a condensed assemblage of a very large number of interacting elementary units—the individual atomic species and their daughter electrons. It is the purpose of this text to initiate a study of solids from such a fundamental point of view.

Since the constituent elements of a solid—the atoms and electrons—are described most accurately (for the purposes at hand) by nonrelativistic quantum mechanics, it will be assumed from the outset that the reader is acquainted with (or is studying concurrently) the elements and calculational techniques of this subject. Also, in view of the fact that we are interested in the average properties of a very large number of microscopic systems, some knowledge of elementary statistical mechanics is desirable as a prerequisite. In addition, it will be assumed that the reader has a familiarity with the material that is covered in the undergraduate courses in thermodynamics and in electricity and magnetism.

The range of properties of solids is very broad indeed; on the other hand, this is a consequence of a very small number of basic physical principles. The approach adopted in writing this book was based on an exploitation of some of these principles for the purpose of explaining general features of the nature of matter that is in the solid state phase. Thus, no attempt is made here to display the wide variety of known properties of solids.

While the material contained in this book is designed primarily for a graduate course in physics, with the assumption of a certain amount of mathematical sophistication on the part of the reader, the major emphasis is on physical models. Thus there are portions of the book, describing a physical model, that do not require very much mathematical background and could be read by those who have not yet reached the graduate level. However, the further exploitation of these models does require a more advanced background. Hence, while the over-all text may appear to present a spread of material that is not at a uniform level, it is chosen primarily to give the graduate student a simple physical picture, unobscured by mathematics, along with the mathematical development.

There are essentially two basic features of solids whose implications are investigated in this book. These are (1) the symmetry properties of the crystalline state of matter and (2) the electronic-energy-band structure of solids, the latter being a consequence of the former. Chapter 1 introduces the subject by presenting a simple physical picture of the different types of solids from the point of view of bonding mechanisms and a description of the perfect and imperfect crystal lattices. Chapters 2, 4, and 5 exploit the symmetry aspects of solids in (1) the determination of different crystal symmetry types that appear in nature, (2) crystal field theory, and (3) the determination and implications of the splitting of atomic energy levels in crystals. The latter is applied in Chap. 5 to a discussion of paramagnetism in solids. The last part of Chap. 5 discusses collective magnetism (i.e., ferro-, antiferro-, and ferrimagnetism).

Along with these chapters (which effectively treat each constituent atom separately in its crystalline environment) is Chap. 3 which gives a semiclassical picture of the ionic crystal, emphasizing as much as possible the physical features of the model. It is shown there how the electronic-energy-band scheme emerges.

Chapters 6 through 10 deal with mobile electrons in solids. After the development of the free-electron model (classical and quantum-mechanical) in Chap. 6, the one-dimensional periodic potential is introduced in Chap. 7. It is shown there how the energy-band scheme emerges from an S-matrix approach—a description that considers the transmission of electron waves through a periodic array of potential barriers. It is also shown in this chapter how foreign impurities in the crystal imply extra energy levels in the forbidden energy region, to be calculated from the poles of the S matrix.

In Chap. 8 the symmetry properties of the three-dimensional periodic potential are exploited in a discussion of Brillouin zones and of degenerate and nondegenerate energy bands in the weak- and tight-binding approximations. The energy-band properties of solids are applied to three cases in Chap. 9. These are (1) semiconductor theory, (2) the coupling to time-dependent electromagnetic fields (including a discussion of cyclotron resonance in semiconductors and in metals), and (3) a description of the physical properties of metal-vacuum, metal-semiconductor, and semiconductor-semiconductor contacts.

Finally, Chap. 10 is devoted to a study of the cohesive energy of metallic solids, including the contribution that is due to the correlation of the positions of the electrons (i.e., the correlation energy). The Wigner-Seitz theory is first outlined. A discussion is then given of the collective behavior of an electron gas and of plasma oscillations. The Bohm-Pines theory is outlined, and the correlation energy is derived. While somewhat more general approaches to the derivation of the correlation energy exist, the Bohm-Pines approach is described here because of the pedagogical advantage in the presentation of a very physical description. It is hoped that this discussion may serve as a stimulus for those who may be interested in entering into studies of the many-body problem.

There are three appendices at the end of the text. Appendix A presents a proof of Kramers' theorem in terms of the matrix elements of the irreducible representations of the rotation group. (This is unpublished work done in collaboration with R. A. Satten and A. G. Mencher.) Appendix B presents a brief discussion of statistical mechanics from the density-matrix point of view. Appendix C develops some of the general properties of the S matrix.

Rather than presenting extensive bibliographies at the end of each chapter, references are given throughout the text for pedagogical reasons only—to aid the reader in understanding a particular point.

It is hoped that this text will appeal to three groups of students and research workers: first, those who are interested in acquiring a sufficient theoretical background to allow further exploration into theoretical and/or experimental research in solid state physics; second, students of theoretical physics who wish to widen their scope of knowledge and also to acquire an introduction to other tangential fields in theoretical physics (e.g., the theory of groups applied to physical problems, scattering theory, the many-body problem); and finally, students and researchers in allied fields (e.g., chemistry, metallurgy, electrical engineering) who may derive some insight into their own studies of solids from the point of view of fundamental physics.

This textbook grew out of lecture notes for a course that I taught, initially, at San Jose State College. The aspects of the textbook dealing with statistical mechanics were taken from my lectures at McGill University, and the final material was presented in lectures at Boston University. I should like to express gratitude to my students at these institutions for their response to the lectures—a response that was very helpful during the various stages of development of the manuscript. I am grateful to Prof. Leonard I. Schiff of Stanford University for the time that he spent in reading the manuscript during its process of development and for his many pertinent and valuable suggestions.

On specific sections of the book, I should like to thank Prof. Robert Satten and Dr. Alan Mencher for their collaboration on the work dealing with Kramers' theorem (Appendix A) and Prof. David Pines for his comments and suggestions regarding electron correlations (Chap. 10) and for permission to use illustrative material from his own publications.

For permission to use other illustrative material in the text, I also wish to thank Dr. E. S. Rittner, Prof. E. U. Condon, Dr. G. Dresselhaus, Dr. J. K. Galt, Prof. J. Bardeen, Dr. W. C. Dash, Dr. R. N. Dexter, and Dr. F. J. Morin.

Most sincere thanks are due the directors of the Research Laboratory of the Lockheed Missiles and Space Company in Palo Alto, California, for granting me time to work on the manuscript while I was employed at their laboratory and for supplying secretarial help for typing a part of the rough draft of the manuscript.

Finally, I should like to express most heartfelt appreciation to my wife Yetty and to our children Robert, Daniel, and Carolyn for the many hours of my time that they sacrificed in order that I could write this book.

MENDEL SACHS

contents

solid
state
theory

1 an introduction to the solid state

WE BEGIN our study of the theory of solids by viewing a macroscopic solid as a cohesion of a very large number of (almost immobile) atoms. The fundamental physical theories that must be exploited in this study are therefore (1) *the quantum theory*, to describe the individual constituent atoms, and (2) *statistical mechanics*, to describe the average properties of a large ensemble of atoms. Along with some of the elementary techniques of these theories, use will also be made of *group theory* in order to deduce some of the implications of the high degree of symmetry that is exhibited by those solids that are in the crystalline state.[1]

It is observed that under the conditions of temperature and pressure that prevail on the surface of our planet, most chemical species are in the solid state. From the standpoint of physics, this means that the total inherent energy in the system of atoms is a minimum when these atoms coalesce into a solid. Clearly, the solid state of matter is more ordered than are the liquid and gaseous states, since the (equilibrium) positions

[1] It will be assumed that the reader has been introduced to (or is studying concurrently with this subject) some of the elementary concepts and calculational procedures of quantum mechanics and statistical mechanics. The latter is discussed somewhat (from the density-matrix point of view) in Appendix B. Group theory will be introduced in Chaps. 2 and 4.

There are numerous excellent texts on quantum mechanics. Among them, this author has consulted most frequently the texts by L. I. Schiff, "Quantum Mechanics," McGraw-Hill Book Company, Inc., New York, 1955; L. Landau and E. Lifshitz, "Quantum Mechanics—Nonrelativistic Theory," Addison-Wesley Publishing Company, Inc., Reading, Mass., 1958; and P. A. M. Dirac, "Quantum Mechanics," 3d ed., Oxford University Press, Fair Lawn, N.J., 1947.

Similarly, there are many excellent texts on statistical mechanics. A classic treatise on the subject that emphasizes theory is R. C. Tolman, "The Principles of Statistical Mechanics," Oxford University Press, Fair Lawn, N.J., 1938, and very good texts that emphasize applications are D. ter Haar, "Elements of Statistical Mechanics," Holt, Rinehart and Winston, Inc., New York, 1954, and L. Landau and E. Lifshitz, "Statistical Physics," Addison-Wesley Publishing Company, Inc., Reading, Mass., 1958.

of each of the atoms are fixed in a solid and are random in liquids and gases. (An exception to this is the amorphous solid, such as glass. This will be discussed later in the chapter.) We shall see that the extreme order in the solid state allows simplifications to be made which then permit quantitative computations of the properties of this many-body system in terms of one particle at a time. This is analogous to the study of the gaseous state in which a complete lack of order allows an analysis to be made with regard to the *average* properties of each of the constituent atoms. The liquid state, lying between these two extremes, has been the most difficult to understand, because of the necessity of treating all the constituent atoms together (i.e., this is a many-body problem that must be treated as such).

Let us now imagine that the environmental conditions slowly approach those which are most conducive to the formation of matter in the solid state. The first question that might be asked is: What is the source of the forces that bind the constituent atoms in the solid? The answer to this question is that the source of the binding forces is electromagnetic, since it arises from the interaction of a great number of atoms, each of which is made up of a positively charged nucleus and negatively charged electrons.

The next question would then be: If the cohesion of the atoms in a solid depends on the coupling of atomic electrons, which are in turn characterized by the different atomic states, should one not expect that the nature of binding would differ when one compares solids that are composed of atoms with characteristically different types of shell structures? This is indeed the case. The type of binding mechanism in a solid depends sensitively on the portions of the periodic table that characterize the constituent atoms.

Before going into the details which are evoked by the theory in explaining the behavior of different types of solids, we shall devote this chapter to a qualitative discussion of the major physical mechanisms of binding in solids and the associated structural characteristics.

1.1 The ionic bond

In comparison with other types of solids, ionic crystals are characterized by a relatively strong bond. This is revealed by the relative hardness, high melting point, and low coefficient of expansion of these crystals.

The ionic bond characteristically describes the origin of the binding of salts (i.e., those compounds which are made up of combinations of the atomic species that are found in the right- and left-hand portions of the periodic table). A typical group of such salts are the alkali halides. The origin of the bonding mechanism lies in the relative ease with which the atoms that are characterized by nearly closed-shell configura-

1s	1 H																			2 He $1s^2$
2s	3 Li	4 Be													2p	5 B	6 C	7 N	8 O	9 F	10 Ne
3s	11 Na	12 Mg													3p	13 Al	14 Si	15 P	16 S	17 Cl	18 Ar
4s	19 K	20 Ca	3d	21 Sc	22 Ti	23 V	24 Cr $4s3d^5$	25 Mn	26 Fe	27 Co	28 Ni	29 Cu $4s^1 3d^{10}$	30 Zn	4p	31 Ga	32 Ge	33 As	34 Se	35 Br	36 Kr
5s	37 Rb	38 Sr	4d	39 Y	40 Zr	41 Nb $5s^1 4d^4$	42 Mo $5s^1 4d^5$	43 Tc	44 Ru $5s^1 4d^7$	45 Rh $5s^1 4d^8$	46 Pd $5s^0 4d^{10}$	47 Ag $5s^1 4d^{10}$	48 Cd	5p	49 In	50 Sn	51 Sb	52 Te	53 I	54 Xe
6s	55 Cs	56 Ba	5d	57 La R.E.*	72 Hf	73 Ta	74 W	75 Re	76 Os	77 Ir	78 Pt $6s^1 5d^9$	79 Au $6s^1 5d^{10}$	80 Hg	6p	81 Tl	82 Pb	83 Bi	84 Po	85 At	86 Rn
7s	87 Fr	88 Ra	6d	89 Ac	90 Th H.E.†															
	s^1	s^2		d^1	d^2	d^3	d^4	d^5	d^6	d^7	d^8	d^9	d^{10}		p^1	p^2	p^3	p^4	p^5	p^6

* Rare earths 4f	58 Ce $5d^1$		59 Pr $5d^0$	60 Nd $5d^0$	61 Pm $5d^0$?	62 Sm $5d^0$	63 Eu $5d^0$	64 Gd $5d^1 4f^7$	65 Tb $5d^1 4f^8$	66 Dy $5d^0$?	67 Ho $5d^0$?	68 Er $5d^0$?	69 Tm $5d^0$	70 Yb $5d^0$	71 Lu $5d^1 4f^{14}$
	f^1	f^2	f^3	f^4	f^5	f^6	f^7	f^8	f^9	f^{10}	f^{11}	f^{12}	f^{13}	f^{14}	f^{14}
† Heaviest elements 5f		91 Pa $6d^1$?	92 U $6d^1$	93 Np $6d^1$?	94 Pu $6d^1$?	95 Am $6d^1$?	96 Cm $6d^1$?	97 Bk $6d^1$?	98 Cf $6d^1$?	99 Es	100 Fm	101 Md	102 No		

Examples:

22 Ti:	$1s^2$	$2s^2$	$2p^6$	$3s^2$	$3p^6$	$4s^2$	$3d^2$											
42 Mo:	"	"	"	"	"	"	$3d^{10}$	$4p^6$	$5s$	$4d^5$								
64 Gd:	"	"	"	"	"	"	"	"	$5s^2$	$4d^{10}$	$5p^6$	$6s^2$	$4f^7$	$5d$				
74 W:	"	"	"	"	"	"	"	"	"	"	"	"	$4f^{14}$	$5d^4$				
94 Pu:	"	"	"	"	"	"	"	"	"	"	"	"	"	$5d^{10}$	$6p^6$	$7s^2$	$5f^5$	$6d$

Fig. 1.1. The periodic table. The electronic configurations of the atoms are indicated, with deviations from the regular order of build-up of the electron shell structure shown in the central boxes. The two columns on the left and six columns on the right are those referred to in the text as columns I through VIII of the periodic table. (*After R. B. Leighton*, "Principles of Modern Physics," *McGraw-Hill Book Company, Inc., New York*, 1959, *p.* 251.)

tions tend to take the completely closed-shell configuration. Thus, an atom such as Na, with one electron in the 3*s* shell, gives up this electron, with little persuasion, to a Cl atom, which lacks just one electron in its 3*p* shell. The net charge of the resulting Na *ion* is therefore one positive electronic charge while that of the resulting Cl *ion* is one negative electronic charge. Thus, the Na and Cl atoms ionize each other as they approach sufficiently closely, and the resulting positive and negative ions are then attracted by the ordinary Coulomb force of attraction. If, now, we have an assembly of 10^{24} Na atoms and 10^{24} Cl atoms in close enough proximity, they will all become ionized, and any given ion will thereby surround itself with ions of the opposite charge. We shall see later (Chap. 3), in a more detailed treatment, that a lattice of ions bonded by purely classical Coulomb forces is not a stable one. It turns out that the added repulsive force necessary to give stability to the ionic crystal arises by virtue of the Pauli exclusion principle. Let it suffice then, for the time being, to say that an ionic solid is one that is characterized by an array of positive and negative ions, bonded together by Coulomb forces.

Observations of the Ionic Bond

How does one verify that a particular solid is indeed characterized by an ionic bond? One very useful way of determining the ionic character of a solid is by examining the scattering of X rays from the constituent ions of the lattice. Since the scattering power depends on the number of electrons associated with the constituent ions, an X-ray analysis should be a very effective one.

Consider, for example, the potassium chloride salt. The scattering power of atomic potassium for X rays is higher than that of atomic chlorine, since K possesses 19 electrons while Cl has only 17 electrons. On the other hand, when KCl is bonded ionically, each ion has 18 electrons, and the scattering power for K^+ and Cl^- should be the same. This is found to be the case in experimental observations, thus revealing in a convincing way that KCl is characterized by an ionic bond. The extrapolation of this conclusion to the other alkali halides then follows, in accordance with the considerations of the similarity of electronic structure of the constituent atoms.

The Structure of an Ionic Solid

Since the Coulomb force depends only on the magnitude of the separation between ions but not on the direction of their lines of centers, any constituent positive (or negative) ion of a solid tends to gather as many negative (or positive) neighbors as would be allowed on the basis of the size of the ions and by the requirement of charge neutrality for the solid. Since the number of nearest neighbors of the positive ion must be equal to the number of nearest neighbors of the negative ion, this number (the coordination number) must equal the total number of nearest neighbors that the smaller of the two ions can accept (on geometrical grounds). Thus, a typical ionic crystal, NaCl, is characterized by a coordination number equal to 6—a number that is determined by the size of the smaller Na^+ ion and not by the larger Cl^- ion.

Besides the fact that each ion possesses the same number of neighbors, nature prefers to arrange this array of atoms so that the directions of the lines of centers of a given Na^+ ion with its six neighbors are not random; rather, the set of six angles is fixed and the same throughout the lattice, no matter at which one of the ions in the macroscopic solid one is looking.

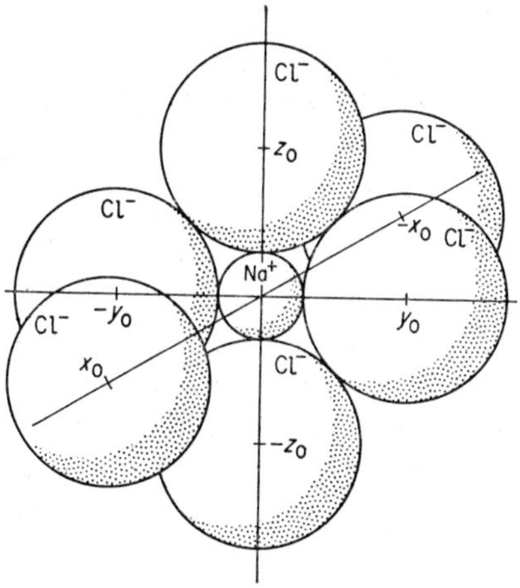

Fig. 1.2. Location of the line of centers of the nearest-neighbor Cl^- ions to a given Na^+ ion in the NaCl lattice.

(A more complete discussion of the structure of crystals is given in Chap. 2.)

Thus the geometrical mapping of the Na^+ and the Cl^- ions in the solid is characterized by an array of ions which are located in a perfectly ordered and periodic arrangement. In particular, each Na^+ ion has six Cl^- neighbors whose centers are at the locations ($x = \pm r_0$, $y = \pm r_0$, $z = \pm r_0$) with respect to the location of the Na^+ ion at (0,0,0) (see Fig. 1.2).

This ordered state of matter is called the *crystalline state.* The particular arrangement of ions described above is called the NaCl-type lattice and may be pictured as two interpenetrating face-centered-cubic crystals (see Chap. 2), one made up of Na^+ ions and the other of Cl^- ions with the vertex of a Na^+ cube at the body center of a Cl^- cube. All the alkali halides except CsCl, CsBr, and CsI have the NaCl-type structure. The CsCl-type structure is characterized by a coordination number 8 instead of 6. The reason for the larger number of nearest neighbors is the fact that the Cs^+ ion more nearly approximates the size of the halide ions.

Most solids that occur in nature are (independent of bonding mechanisms) in the crystalline state. Those that are not are called amorphous (discussed below). The crystalline state of matter is characterized by many distinct symmetry types (discussed in Chap. 2). As we shall see in the chapters that follow, the symmetry of a crystal lattice has an important effect on many of its physical properties. Also, there are some crystal lattices that can change their symmetry types at some critical temperature. An example is the important ferroelectric crystal $BaTiO_3$, in which the immediate surroundings of any Ti ion changes from cubic to tetragonal symmetry at 393°K. As the temperature is lowered further to 278°K, the surroundings change to trigonal symmetry. Finally, at 193°K the environment of the Ti ion changes to orthorhombic symmetry (see Chap. 2 for a definition of these symmetry types). Such substances are said to be *polymorphic*. The existence of a polymorphic substance indicates that the minimum internal energy of a crystal lattice does not change abruptly from one symmetry type to another.

How do we know that most solids are in the crystalline state? Once again, the techniques of X-ray diffraction provide a very sensitive tool for the establishment of this fact. The mechanism is as follows: When electromagnetic radiation impinges on an atom, the electronic constituents of the atom absorb the energy and then reemit it instantaneously, provided that the frequency of the radiation does not correspond to a resonant mode of the atomic system (i.e., the separation between atomic energy levels). Thus one observes that atoms scatter electromagnetic radiation. If, now, the atoms of the solid are arranged in a random fashion, there is no coherence in the radiation that is reflected by the different atoms. On the other hand, if the atoms are arranged in a periodic fashion and if the characteristic geometrical separation between the atoms is of the same order of magnitude as the wavelength of the radiation, the resulting radiation that is reflected from the solid is coherent and exhibits a diffraction pattern. The spacing between lattice planes in crystals is of the order of magnitude of the wavelength of X rays (~ 10 Å).

It is observed from Fig. 1.3 that the path of ray (2) is longer than the path of ray (1) by the amount $2r_0 \sin\theta$ when it is traced out from the initial wavefront (i) to the final wavefront (f). If this difference were equal to an integral number of wavelengths, the intensity of the reflected beam would indicate constructive interference. Thus, such a condition occurs when

$$n\lambda = 2r_0 \sin\theta \tag{1.1}$$

where λ is the wavelength of the radiation and n is the order of the diffraction pattern. This relationship is called the Bragg condition.

Thus, the observation of a diffraction pattern reveals the periodic arrangement of the crystal lattice, and at a fixed wavelength the variation of the direction of the X-ray beam with respect to different crystal orientations reveals the geometrical-spacing parameters for the different lattice planes. In an ionic crystal, the measured lattice parameter r_0 is the sum of the radii of adjacent ions. From this information, the radii of the individual ions are extracted (this is discussed later on in Chap. 3). The

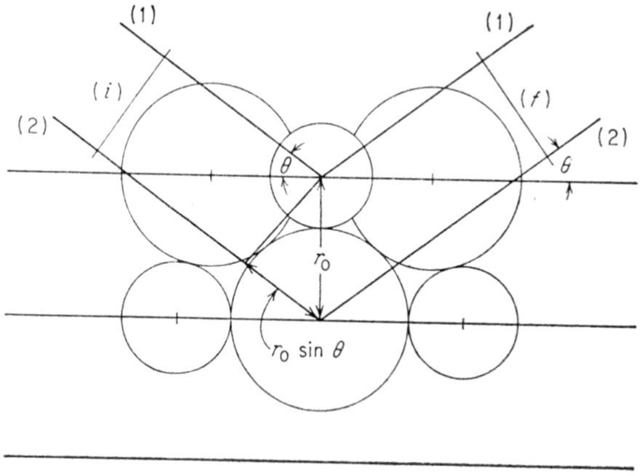

Fig. 1.3. The reflection of X rays from a crystal lattice.

model discussed here assumes a system of ions as a composite of hard spheres. The justification for this assumption will be given in Chap. 3.

A typical diffraction pattern is shown in Fig. 1.9.

1.2 The covalent-bonded crystal[1]

A very interesting property of crystals that are classified as covalent is the apparent lack of sensitivity of their physical properties to their bonding type. For example, carbon in the diamond structure is the hardest known solid material and has a very high melting point (near 3280°K). The hardness and melting point then decrease as we proceed to the other elements in column IV of the periodic table, from Si through Pb. Tin, for example, is very soft and has a low melting point. The variation in the electrical properties is also pronounced. Diamond is a very good electrical insulator, Si and Ge are well-known semiconductors, and Sn is a good conductor.

[1] For a complete discussion, see L. Pauling, "The Nature of the Chemical Bond," 3d ed., Cornell University Press, Ithaca, N.Y., 1960.

The covalent bond involves the mutual sharing of a pair of electrons (whose spins are oriented in opposite directions) between a pair of atoms. In contrast to the ionic bond, this one is highly directional.

Consider now some covalent-bonded substances. The Cl_2 molecule, for example, coming from group VII of the periodic table, forms via a covalent bond. An example from group VI of the periodic table is oxygen. The oxygen atom has the electronic configuration $1s^2 2s^2 2p^4$. Thus there are two electron vacancies in the $2p$ shell. The bonding of two oxygen atoms then entails the formation of two covalent bonds. Thus a box full of oxygen atoms could form into a large number of individual double-bonded molecules. However, in principle, a chain (i.e., a one-dimensional crystal) could also be formed if the environmental conditions were right (see Fig. 1.4).

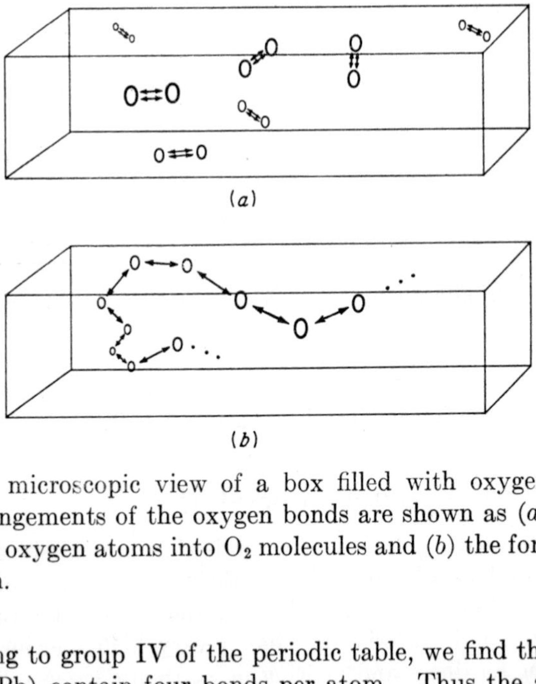

Fig. 1.4. A microscopic view of a box filled with oxygen. The two possible arrangements of the oxygen bonds are shown as (*a*) the pairing of individual oxygen atoms into O_2 molecules and (*b*) the formation of an oxygen chain.

Proceeding to group IV of the periodic table, we find that the atoms (C,Si,Ge,Sn,Pb) contain four bonds per atom. Thus the atoms in this column of the periodic table are capable of forming a three-dimensional covalent-bonded crystal. The directional properties of the bond are such that the maximum space in the crystal is not conserved (i.e., the atoms are not closely packed). An example is carbon in the diamond structure in which each carbon atom is surrounded by four carbon neighbors at the corners of a tetrahedron (see Fig. 1.5). As we see in Fig. 1.5, each carbon atom shares two of its four bonds with each of four other carbon atoms at the corners of the tetrahedron. The directional properties of the covalent bond arise essentially from the symmetry properties of the wave functions of the bonding electrons (e.g., *p*-state wave functions in the case of carbon).

Besides the elements of group IV of the periodic table, the covalent bond also characterizes the compounds belonging to columns around the central one. Thus, the III–V compound InSb, etc., are described most accurately in terms of a predominant covalent bond. In general, the ideally perfect crystal of one bonding type does not exist. Rather, one

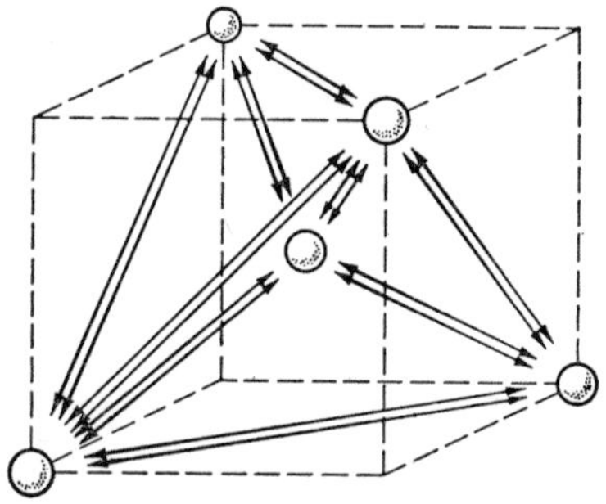

Fig. 1.5. The diamond structure. The atom at the center of the tetrahedron is the only one shown with all its bonds in use.

type of bonding mechanism usually predominates, with characteristics of other types of bonding mechanisms exhibited to a much smaller degree. The mixture of bonding types is discussed in great detail by Pauling.[1]

1.3 The metallic-bonded crystal

The physical properties of a metal are largely determined by the "almost"-free-electron gas, composed of the valence electrons of the constituent atoms (Chaps. 6 to 9). Such a system has high electrical and thermal conductivity, optical opacity, and reflecting power for electromagnetic radiation. The latter are observed from the measurements of photoelectric and thermionic emission. The mechanical properties of metals vary widely, once again indicating a lack of sensitivity to the metallic bond.

In the preceding paragraphs we have discussed solids that are bonded by virtue of the mutual sharing of electrons between nearest-neighbor atoms. Suppose now that a large number of identical atoms are brought together, which do not contain enough electrons per atom to effect a mutual sharing between neighbors. Under such conditions it is sometimes possible to bind the system by virtue of the mutual sharing of the outer electrons of the atoms, not between neighbors alone, but rather

[1] *Ibid.*

between all the constituent atoms of the solid. Such a substance, known as a metal, is therefore described in terms of a positive-ion lattice immersed in a sea of electrons. This free-electron model was first proposed by Drude (Chap. 6) and was later perfected in accordance with quantum mechanics by Sommerfeld, Bloch, and others (Chap. 7). The cohesive energy of a metal depends collectively on the interaction between all the ions with all the valence electrons of the constituent atoms. Typical metals are the solids that are made up of elements of groups I and II of the periodic table, as well as the transition elements.

Since there is no "local" requirement on the arrangement of the atoms in a metal due to the requirement of charge neutrality (as is the case for ionic crystals) and since the metallic bond has no directional properties, the constituent atoms tend to pack so as to use up as much space as possible. Thus, the coordination number in metals tends to be higher than in other types of solids. Two common metallic lattice structures are face-centered-cubic and hexagonal-close-packed (see Chap. 2) which have a coordination number 12. Another common metallic structure is the body-centered-cubic symmetry, with a coordination number equal to 8.

1.4 Imperfections in the crystalline state

Thus far in our discussion of the physical properties of crystals, it was tacitly assumed that, given the proper conditions of temperature and pressure, the solid state would be characterized by a perfectly ordered lattice; i.e., the environment of any given atom in the lattice is the same as that of any other like atom in the lattice in terms of the orientations and distances from all neighbors. This assumption is an ideal one since in nature the crystalline materials are characterized by several types of inherent imperfections.[1] These imperfections do indeed make a significant contribution to the physical properties of a crystal. Our purpose here is to give a concise qualitative description of the typical kinds of imperfections that are encountered in crystalline materials.[2]

The Crystal Surface

The first and most obvious deviation from the perfect crystalline state arises from the fact that any macroscopic crystal is finite in extent; i.e., it has surfaces that bound it in space. The constituent ions that

[1] See, for example, W. Shockley, "Imperfections in Nearly Perfect Crystals," John Wiley & Sons, Inc., New York, 1952.

[2] Very little will be said about this very important aspect of solid state theory throughout the remainder of the text. This represents a specialized topic that should be dealt with on its own merit, to follow a study such as the one presented here.

occupy locations at the surface of a macroscopic crystal do not have the same environment as the internal ions. We shall see later on that the perfect periodicity of the lattice (and therefore the periodicity of the electrostatic potential in the lattice) allows a simplification which effectively reduces the 10^{24}-body problem to the one-body problem (in the first approximation). The fact that the surface ions cannot be included in the rest of the perfectly periodic crystal represents a deviation from this simplifying approximation. The implications of perfect periodicity in the lattice potential are electronic energy levels that fall into distinct allowed and forbidden regions (see Chap. 7). These energy *bands* are indeed important in explaining many of the physical properties of crystals. On the other hand, the surface ions that destroy the perfect periodicity introduce discrete energy levels in the normally forbidden energy regions. These are the so-called *surface states* and are quite important in explaining phenomena involving the surfaces of solids. (Such a study is frequently referred to as "surface physics.") However, this type of imperfection is not important in explaining the gross features of solids. The reason is that the ratio of the number of ions on the surface to the number of interior ions is very small for a macroscopic crystal. If we have 1 g mole of substance, the ratio of surface ions to internal ions is

$$\frac{N^{2/3}}{N} \sim (10^{24})^{-1/3} = 10^{-8}$$

This number would indicate that, on an average, out of 10^8 electrons that contribute to the physical properties of the solid, only one would be found "trapped" in a surface state.

It should also be mentioned that one other type of imperfection having a similar effect on the properties of solids is the existence of internal cracks. Once again the effect is minor because of the relatively small number of ions to be found in the vicinity of the planes associated with these cracks.

Vacancies

A common type of imperfection occurring in solids is that of the ion vacancy. These vacancies occur at random throughout the lattice and generally do not appear until the temperature of the lattice is raised sufficiently to allow an observable number of bonds to be broken. One of the effects of ion vacancies is to allow the diffusion of ions through the solid by means of the motion of normal lattice ions into the vacancy, thereby leaving other vacancies behind (see Fig. 1.6).

Another important effect of the negative-ion vacancy is that of "trapping" an electron. The trapped electron then moves about in the vacancy, primarily under the influence of the nearest-neighbor ions, and has a set of discrete energy levels associated with its motion. These levels are (in ionic crystals) generally separated by energies that correspond to frequencies in the optical range and therefore allow the absorption of radiation in the optical spectrum. For this reason, such vacancies are called *color centers.*

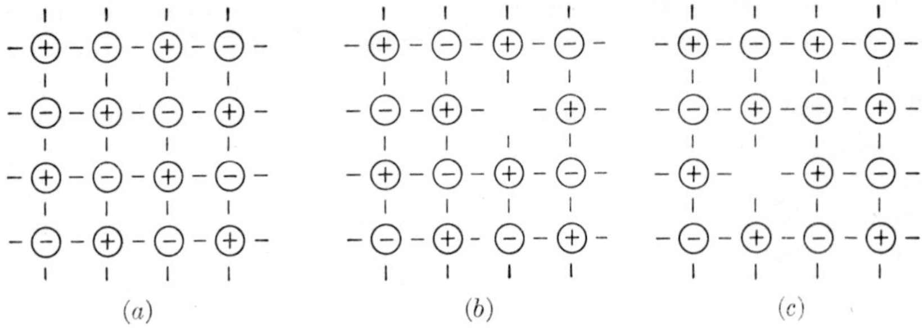

Fig. 1.6. Ion vacancies and migration. (*a*) A perfect lattice; (*b*) and (*c*), negative-ion migration from (*b*) to (*c*).

Stoichiometric Deviations

During the preparation of many types of chemical compounds in the solid state (either by nature or in the laboratory), there is a finite probability that the proper proportion of each type of element in the compound

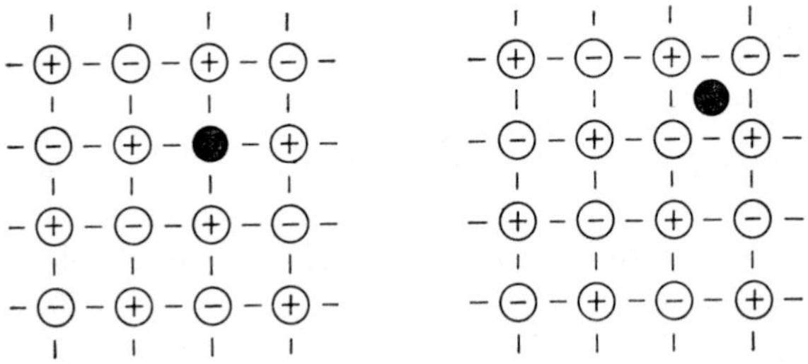

Fig. 1.7. Stoichiometric deviations. (*a*) A substitutional deviation and (*b*) an interstitial deviation.

will not be precisely maintained. Such deviations are called stoichiometric. A typical example is that of KCl with an excess of K atoms. The question that arises in connection with the atomic arrangement is: Where do these potassium atoms go? The answer is that they either go into an interstitial position (i.e., a position not at a regular lattice site) or may occupy a K^+ ion vacancy (if it is present). In both cases the perfect periodicity of the lattice is destroyed, and, again, the effect is to introduce extra electronic energy levels in the normally forbidden energy region.

We shall see later on, in a quantitative discussion of semiconductors (Chap. 9), that these discrete energy levels in the forbidden-energy gap can serve useful purposes, in influencing the electrical properties of these crystals. It is clear that a control of the amount and type of excess atoms in the lattice could result in a corresponding control of the electrical properties of the solid.

Foreign Impurities

Instead of like atoms, the presence of unlike atoms or ions in the lattice (either substitutionally or interstitially) also represents a type of imperfection that will always occur (to at least some small degree). Also, this type of imperfection can be controlled in order to produce a material with desired properties. A more quantitative discussion of this type of imperfection will be given in Chap. 7.

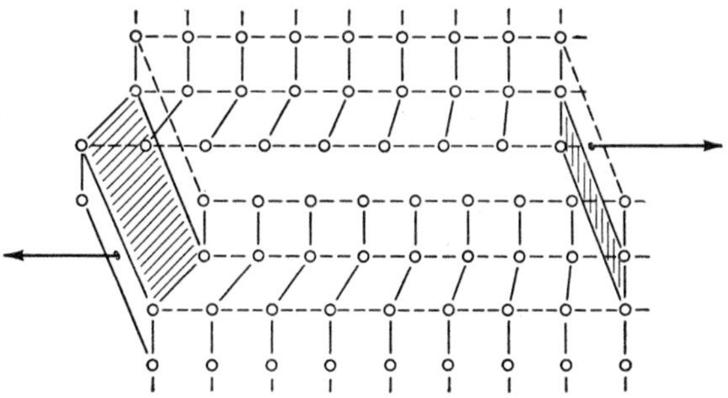

Fig. 1.8. An edge dislocation (the shaded area is the dislocation plane). (*See A. H. Cottrell,* "Progress in Metal Physics," *No.* 1, *Butterworth Scientific Publications, London,* 1949.) The arrows indicate the direction of the shear that produces the dislocation.

Dislocations

A type of imperfection in crystals that accounts for their plasticity is the relative displacement of macroscopic two-dimensional arrays of constituent atoms with respect to the rest of the lattice. Two of the important types are the *edge dislocation* (Fig. 1.8) and the *screw dislocation.* For an extensive treatment of this subject, the reader is referred to Read[1] and DeWitt.[2]

[1] W. T. Read, Jr., "Dislocations in Crystals," McGraw-Hill Book Company, Inc., New York, 1953.

[2] R. DeWitt, in F. Seitz and D. Turnbull (eds.), "Solid State Physics," vol. 10, Academic Press Inc., New York, 1960.

1.5 The amorphous state

The apparently rigid structure of an amorphous structure, such as glass, is formed by cooling the matter in its liquid state sufficiently rapidly so that there is not time enough for the constituent atoms to arrange themselves in an ordered fashion. Thus the formation of glass depends on the fact that the rate of crystallization of the corresponding liquid is slow, in comparison with the cooling time. It is believed that

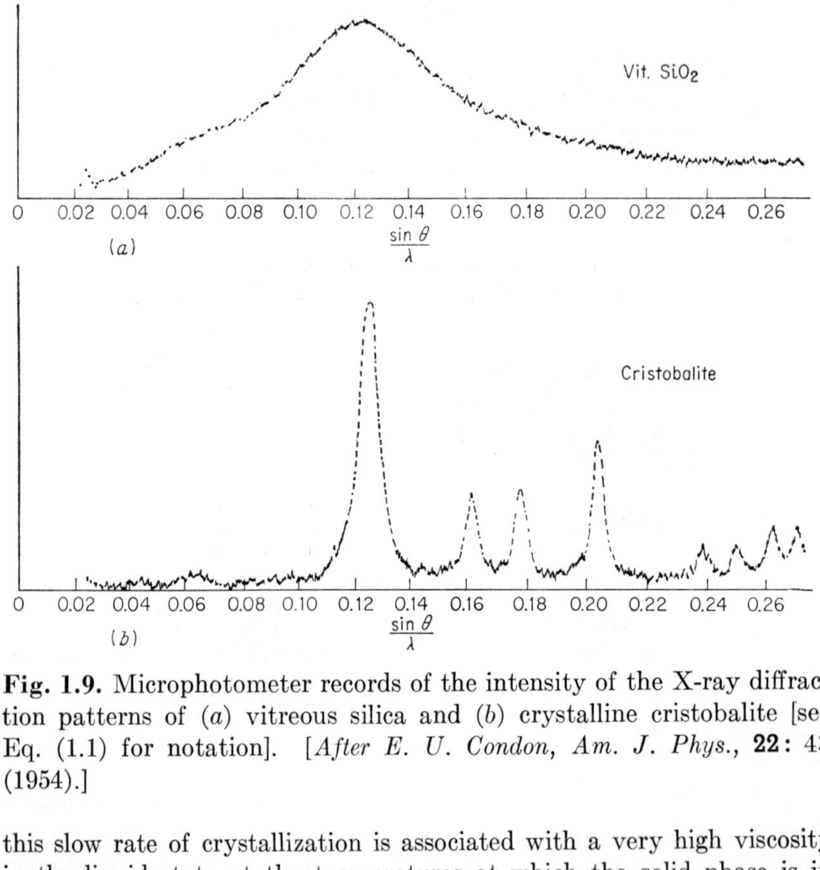

Fig. 1.9. Microphotometer records of the intensity of the X-ray diffraction patterns of (*a*) vitreous silica and (*b*) crystalline cristobalite [see Eq. (1.1) for notation]. [*After E. U. Condon, Am. J. Phys.*, **22**: 43 (1954).]

this slow rate of crystallization is associated with a very high viscosity in the liquid state at the temperatures at which the solid phase is in thermodynamic equilibrium with the liquid phase of the substance.[1] Thus it is possible, in principle, to bring any matter that solidifies into the amorphous state if it is cooled sufficiently rapidly. As an example of an amorphous substance, we shall consider glass.[1]

The composition of glass is primarily a combination of fused oxides, with silicon dioxide acting as a fundamental constituent. It is significant

[1] E. U. Condon, *Am. J. Phys.*, **22**: 43 (1954).

that SiO_2 is characterized by an incomplete *p* shell in its electronic configuration; this factor plays a primary role in the bonding of the glass. Other oxides that are important in the structure of glass and are also characterized by incomplete *p* shells are B_2O_3, Al_2O_3, and P_2O_5. Some of the oxides used in glassmaking that are characterized by incomplete *s* shells are Li_2O, Na_2O, K_2O, MgO, CaO, and BaO.

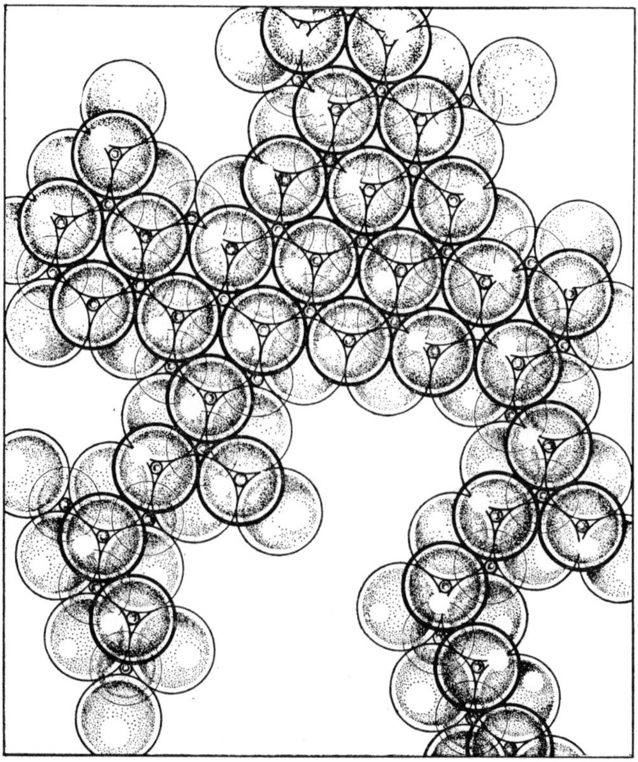

Fig. 1.10. Bonding of SiO_4 units in glass. [*From E. U. Condon, Physics of the Glassy State, Am. J. Phys.*, **22**: 43 (1954).]

The structure of amorphous material can be determined by an X-ray analysis. As we have seen earlier, the crystalline state is identified by an X-ray diffraction pattern with structure. Thus, an amorphous solid should reveal a typically smeared diffraction pattern (see Fig. 1.9*a*). This may be considered as a superposition of diffraction patterns from randomly oriented microcrystals. The existence of a maximum, however, enables one to estimate the average spacing between the constituent atoms. From a study of Fig. 1.9*a* it is deduced that the crystalline material has a periodicity with a lattice parameter of 8 to 25 Å, and, of course, the periodicity effects of the lattice are absent from the diffraction pattern of vitreous silica.

A more detailed analysis of the vitreous-silica curve indicates that the average Si-O spacing is 1.62 Å. It is also indicated from the X-ray pattern of the crystalline SiO that the average Si-O spacing is 1.60 Å. From the diffraction pattern in Fig. 1.9 it is deduced that the average number of oxygen atoms that surround each silicon atom is four (see the article by E. U. Condon referred to above).

Thus the structure indicated is a random arrangement of SiO_4 microcrystals, with each (tetrahedral) microcrystal interlocking with a neighboring microcrystal by means of the oxygen atoms belonging to adjacent SiO_4 tetrahedra. Such a structure is viewed as made up of Si^{4+} ions surrounded by four $O^{=}$ ions each (with each of the outer electrons of the $O^{=}$ ions filling the vacancy in the shells of the Si^{4+} ions of adjacent tetrahedra). The actual bonding, however, is not purely ionic; it is partly covalent and partly ionic.[1] A picture of such a structure is shown in Fig. 1.10.

We have attempted, in this chapter, to classify solids in terms of the various ways in which a large assembly of atoms bind, by virtue of their individual electronic structures. This type of classification is implied from other observed properties of solids and is in keeping with the fundamental approach to the understanding of the solid state that will be pursued in the rest of the text.

Solids may also be classified, initially, according to their observed gross physical properties. These are, for example, the electrical, magnetic, optical, thermal, and mechanical properties. Instead of doing this at the outset, however, we shall attempt to understand some of these properties throughout the remainder of the text from the microscopic point of view. The comparisons between the implications of physical models and experimental observations will be made where specific properties are discussed. Before commencing our discussion of the physical aspects of solids, however, the following chapter will be devoted to an essential preliminary study, that of the detailed symmetry properties of crystal lattices.

[1] See C. A. Coulson, "Valence," Oxford University Press, Fair Lawn, N.J., 1952.

2 the symmetry properties of crystal lattices

THROUGHOUT the ages, mankind, in its search for order in the universe, has been very keenly perceptive of the aspects of symmetry in nature, possibly motivated by its aesthetic appeal. The study of symmetry from the time of the geometricians of ancient Greece to the present day has revealed much of our current understanding of natural phenomena.

Among the developments in pure mathematics, an aspect of higher algebra, known as *group theory*, provides a very useful formalism for the description of the symmetry properties of physical systems. Thus, one of the most symmetrical structures exhibited in nature, a solid in its crystalline state, is readily adaptable to analysis by means of the theory of groups.

In this chapter, the concept of the group will be described in an introductory fashion, primarily in order to enlighten the reader as to its extreme usefulness in treating the symmetry properties of solid state structures. Next, the types of symmetry properties which define the crystal lattice will be discussed. The concept of the point group will be introduced, and the 32 different crystallographic point groups that appear in nature will be constructed by utilizing their group properties. These results will then be applied in Chap. 4 to a derivation of the functional form for the electrostatic potential (associated with the different point-group symmetries) at the site of any constituent ion of the crystal and then to a derivation of the splitting of the ionic energy levels in the crystal.

2.1 Elementary group theory[1]

The Concept of the Group

A group $\mathbf{G}(\alpha)$, of a particular type α, is defined as a (nonempty) set of elements $\{A_1, A_2, \ldots\}$ which are related to each other through the operation α, and which obey the following four rules.

1. *Rule of Combination.* If any two elements of the group, A_i and A_j, are combined according to the operation α of the group, then their product

$$(A_iA_j)_\alpha = A_k \tag{2.1}$$

is also a member of the group. Thus, if we are considering a multiplication group, the product $(A_iA_j)_\times = A_i \times A_j$ would refer to the multiplication of the two elements; for an addition group, the product

$$(A_iA_j)_+ = A_i + A_j$$

would refer to the addition of these elements; if we are considering a transformation group, $(A_iA_j)_t$ would refer to the successive application of the transformation A_j and then A_i (to some function). In each case, the result of taking the product would have to be equivalent to an element contained in the set, in order that this set be referred to as a group.

2. *Associative Law.* If A_i, A_j, A_k are any three elements of the group $\mathbf{G}(\alpha)$, then

$$[(A_iA_j)_\alpha A_k]_\alpha = [A_i(A_jA_k)_\alpha]_\alpha \tag{2.2}$$

3. *Existence of the Identity.* There exists at least one element in the group, called the *identity* (denoted by E), which is defined as

$$(A_iE)_\alpha = (EA_i)_\alpha = A_i \tag{2.3}$$

for any element A_i contained in the group.

4. *Existence of an Inverse.* If A_i is any element in $\mathbf{G}(\alpha)$, there exists at least one other element A_i^{-1} in the group, called the inverse of A_i, defined as follows:

$$(A_i^{-1}A_i)_\alpha = (A_iA_i^{-1})_\alpha = E \tag{2.4}$$

The order in which the product of any two elements is taken must be considered. If the product of any two elements do not commute, i.e., if

$$(A_iA_j)_\alpha \neq (A_jA_i)_\alpha \tag{2.5}$$

the group is said to be nonabelian. If *all* the constituent elements of the group commute with each other, then the group is abelian.

[1] See, for additional reading, E. P. Wigner, "Group Theory and Its Applications to the Quantum Mechanics of Atomic Spectra," chap. 7, Academic Press Inc., New York, 1959.

Examples of a Group

A multiplication group Let us consider the class of all rational numbers

$$\left\{0, \pm 1, \pm 2, \ldots, \pm\tfrac{1}{2}, \pm\tfrac{3}{2}, \ldots, \pm\frac{n}{m}, \ldots\right\}$$

(where n and m are integers) and ask whether such a set does indeed form a multiplication group.

1. *Rule of Combination.* It is clear that the multiplication of any two elements of the set is equal to another element of the set.

2. *Associative Law.* The validity of the associative law is also obvious.

3. *Existence of the Identity.* Since the product of the element +1 with all other elements A_i of the group gives

$$(A_i + 1)_\times = A_i \times 1 = A_i$$

we have for the identity $E = +1$.

4. *Existence of an Inverse.* For each element A_i (exept zero) there is an element $1/A_i$ in the set. Since

$$\left(A_i \frac{1}{A_i}\right)_\times = 1 = E$$

$1/A_i$ must be the inverse of A_i. However, *all* elements of the set must have an inverse, also contained in the set, in order that this set be called a group. Since the element 0 does not have an inverse in the set, the class of all rational numbers cannot form a multiplication group. On the other hand, if the zero element is left out of the set, a bona fide multiplication group

$$\left\{\pm 1, \pm 2, \ldots, \pm\tfrac{1}{2}, \pm\tfrac{3}{2}, \ldots, \pm\frac{n}{m}, \ldots\right\}$$

results, with $E = +1$ and $A_i^{-1} = 1/A_i$ for all elements of the group.

An addition group We now ask whether the class of all rational numbers (including zero) forms an addition group.

1. *Rule of Combination.* Once again it is clear that the addition of any two elements of the set results in another element of the set.

2. *Associative Law.* The validity of the associative law also follows.

3. *Existence of the Identity.* Since the addition of zero to any element of the group is equivalent to that element, i.e.,

$$(A_i\, 0)_+ = A_i + 0 = A_i$$

for all A_i, the zero element must be the identity.

4. *Existence of an Inverse for Each Element.* For each element of the set $\{A_i\}$ (except 0) there is a corresponding element $-A_i$. Since

$$(A_i - A_i)_+ = A_i - A_i = 0 = E$$

the element $-A_i$ must be the inverse of A_i. The identity element 0 is its own inverse, i.e.,

$$(0\ 0)_+ = 0 + 0 = 0$$

Thus, the set of all rational numbers does, indeed, form an addition group.

A transformation group We shall now consider a group which is made up of all the transformations that map a geometrical figure onto itself, while leaving a point in space unaltered. In particular, let us consider the transformation group which describes a cube (and leaves the geometric center of the cube unaltered). This particular example has been chosen in order to set the scene for the derivation of the different crystal symmetry groups, which is done later in this chapter.

Consider a cube, with vertices numbered from 1 through 8 (Fig. 2.1). The transformation group is constructed by first tabulating all rotations that map the cube onto itself and then taking the product of the rotation transformation elements with the inversion element (which is also clearly contained in the group). The inversion element, denoted by I, leads to the coordinate transformation

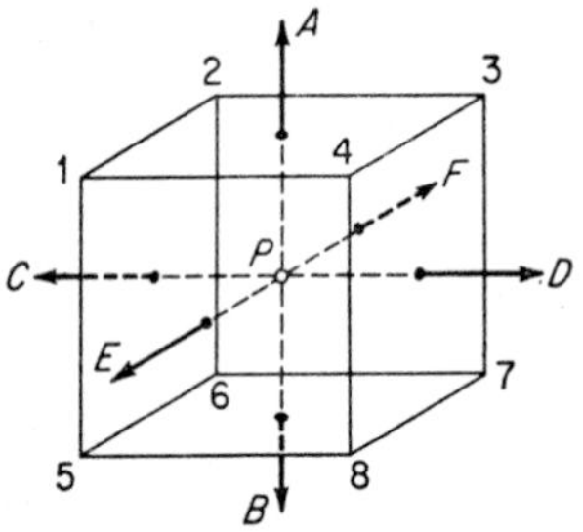

Fig. 2.1. The simple cube.

$$If(x,y,z) = f(-x,-y,-z) \qquad (2.6)$$

1. *Rotation Elements.* A rotation element may be denoted quite simply by an eight-column–two-row matrix in which the top row represents the initial points 1 to 8 and the bottom row, the final location of these points after the transformation has been carried out. For example, one rotation element of the group of the cube is a $+\pi$ rotation about the APB axis. This may then be represented symbolically as follows:

$$C_2 = \begin{pmatrix} 1 & 2 & 3 & 4 & 5 & 6 & 7 & 8 \\ 3 & 4 & 1 & 2 & 7 & 8 & 5 & 6 \end{pmatrix} \qquad (2.7)$$

It is clear that a rotation of $-\pi$ about the same axis also leads to C_2; thus $C_2(\pm\pi)$ is one element of the group. There are three such elements corresponding to $\pm\pi$ rotations about the three orthogonal axes APB, CPD, and EPF. These three elements are grouped together and denoted by $3C_2$. (The reason for this type of grouping into a three-element "class" will be discussed later in the chapter.)

Next, we consider $\pm\pi/2$ rotations about these same axes. The $+\pi/2$ and $-\pi/2$ rotations are not equivalent. This can be seen by considering $\pm\pi/2$ rotations about the APB axis.

$$C_4\left(\frac{+\pi}{2}\right) = \begin{pmatrix} 1 & 2 & 3 & 4 & 5 & 6 & 7 & 8 \\ 4 & 1 & 2 & 3 & 8 & 5 & 6 & 7 \end{pmatrix} \tag{2.8}$$

and

$$C_4\left(\frac{-\pi}{2}\right) = \begin{pmatrix} 1 & 2 & 3 & 4 & 5 & 6 & 7 & 8 \\ 2 & 3 & 4 & 1 & 6 & 7 & 8 & 5 \end{pmatrix} \tag{2.9}$$

Since the $\pm\pi/2$ rotations are not equivalent, there are six such elements for the three orthogonal axes. This grouping of six elements is called the class $6C_4$.

Continuing in this fashion, we find that a π rotation about each of the six axes that are parallel to the face diagonals (1–8, 4–5; 4–7, 3–8; 1–3, 2–4) (and containing the point P) map the cube onto itself. This class of six elements is denoted by $6C_2'$. Finally, the rotations of $\pm 2\pi/3$ about each of the body diagonals (1–7, 2–8, 3–5, 4–6) represent eight more elements of the group referred to as $8C_3$.

Thus far we have enumerated 24 rotation elements belonging to the transformation group of the simple cube, distributed among five classes, as follows:

$$E,\ 3C_2,\ 6C_4,\ 6C_2',\ 8C_3$$

If we now take the inversion element I and multiply it by each of the 24 rotation elements, 24 additional elements of the group are generated (in accordance with the first defining rule of a group), giving a 48-element group. The additional classes, denoted by

$$I,\ 3IC_2,\ 6IC_4,\ 6IC_2',\ 8IC_3$$

represent the following reflections and rotary reflections (i.e., elements made up of a simultaneous rotation and reflection).

I: Inversion; equivalent to a simultaneous π rotation about the x, y, or z directions and a reflection in the plane perpendicular to this axis

IC_2: Reflections in the planes perpendicular to the x, y, or z axes

IC_4: The simultaneous rotation of $\pm\pi/2$ about the x, y, or z axes and reflections in the planes perpendicular to these axes

IC_2': Reflections in the planes parallel to the face diagonals (1–8), (4–5), (4–7), (3–8), (1–3), and (2–4)

IC_3: The simultaneous $(\pm 2\pi/3)$ rotations about the body diagonals and reflection in a plane perpendicular to these axes

In order to demonstrate the equivalence of the elements above with reflections and rotary reflections, consider the element IC_4, where C_4 is a rotation about the APB axis. The inversion element I may be represented as follows:

$$I = \begin{pmatrix} 1 & 2 & 3 & 4 & 5 & 6 & 7 & 8 \\ 7 & 8 & 5 & 6 & 3 & 4 & 1 & 2 \end{pmatrix} \tag{2.10}$$

and C_4 is given above. The product is then[1]

$$IC_4\left(\frac{+\pi}{2}\right) = \downarrow\begin{pmatrix} 1 & 2 & 3 & 4 & 5 & 6 & 7 & 8 \\ 7 & 8 & 5 & 6 & 3 & 4 & 1 & 2 \end{pmatrix}\!\lrcorner\ \ulcorner\!\!\rightarrow\begin{pmatrix} 7 & 8 & 5 & 6 & 3 & 4 & 1 & 2 \\ 6 & 7 & 8 & 5 & 2 & 3 & 4 & 1 \end{pmatrix}$$

$$= \begin{pmatrix} 1 & 2 & 3 & 4 & 5 & 6 & 7 & 8 \\ 6 & 7 & 8 & 5 & 2 & 3 & 4 & 1 \end{pmatrix} \tag{2.11}$$

Thus this product is equivalent to a $-\pi/2$ rotation about APB and a simultaneous reflection through the plane perpendicular to this axis.

The group described above (called the $\mathbf{O}_h$ group) will be discussed later in the chapter. The elements of this group are summarized in Table 2.8. Such a group, which contains a finite number of elements, is called a *finite group*. It will be left as an exercise for the reader to show that the 48-element set described above does indeed obey the defining rules of a group and that this group is nonabelian.

The cyclic group One important type of group is the cyclic group. This is defined to be a set of elements which are formed by taking any one element A and successively raising this element to higher and higher integral powers[2] in order to generate the other members of the set until the maximum power is reached, giving the identity. Thus

$$\mathbf{G} = \{A, A^2, A^3, \ldots, A^n = E\} \tag{2.12}$$

Such a set does indeed obey the four defining rules for a group and it is clearly an abelian group.

A simple example of a cyclic group is the set of transformations which map an n-sided polygon onto itself while keeping the center fixed. These are the rotations about an axis (through the center and perpendicular to the polygon)

$$\{e^{2\pi i/n}, e^{2(2\pi i/n)}, \ldots, e^{n(2\pi i/n)} = 1\} \tag{2.13}$$

Further Properties of Groups

Classes of a group If A_1, A_2, A_3 are three elements of a group, and $A_1 = A_3A_2A_3^{-1}$, then A_1 is said to be a conjugate element to A_2.

[1] The product is obtained by taking the top row in the second element to be the bottom row in the first element and then performing the transformation. The top row of the first element is the initial configuration, and the bottom row of the second element is the final configuration.

[2] A^m means that A is applied m times in succession.

Theorem: If the element A_i is conjugate to A_j and if A_j is conjugate to A_k, then A_i is conjugate to A_k.

This can be seen as follows: If A_i is conjugate to A_j, then, there is a member A_m of the set such that

$$A_i = A_m A_j A_m^{-1} \tag{2.14}$$

and similarly, if A_j is conjugate to A_k,

$$A_j = A_n A_k A_n^{-1} \tag{2.15}$$

where A_m and A_n are elements of the group. Substituting (2.15) into (2.14),

$$A_i = (A_m A_n) A_k (A_n^{-1} A_m^{-1}) \tag{2.16}$$

Since $(A_m A_n)(A_n^{-1} A_m^{-1}) = A_m (A_n A_n^{-1}) A_m^{-1} = A_m^{-1} A_m = E$

and also $(A_m A_n)(A_m A_n)^{-1} = E$

we have $A_n^{-1} A_m^{-1} = (A_m A_n)^{-1}$

Thus

$$A_i = (A_m A_n) A_k (A_m A_n)^{-1} \tag{2.17}$$

Since $A_m A_n$ is also an element of the group, Eq. (2.17) says that A_i is conjugate to A_k, and the theorem is proved. Each set of conjugate elements of a group is called a *class* of the group. Thus, the class of the group, associated with any one element A_i, is constructed by forming the product

$$A_g A_i A_g^{-1}$$

where A_g is successively taken to be each element of the group. In this way the entire group may be broken up into classes. Clearly, the identity element E forms a class by itself, since

$$A_g E A_g^{-1} = A_g A_g^{-1} E = E^2 = E \tag{2.18}$$

for all elements A_g of the group. Further, if a group is abelian, each element forms a class by itself. This can be seen as follows: If the group is abelian, then for any two elements A_i, A_j

$$A_i A_j = A_j A_i \tag{2.19}$$

If each side of Eq. (2.19) is multiplied on the right by A_i^{-1}, we have

$$A_i A_j A_i^{-1} = A_j$$

thus proving that each element of the group is conjugate only to itself. Therefore, only in a nonabelian group can the classes contain more than one element. The division of the complete group into classes will become a very useful one in the description of the representations of transformation groups (Chap. 4). It will be left as an exercise for the reader to show that the subdivisions of the cubic group described in the example above are indeed the classes of the group.

Direct product Consider two different groups $\mathbf{G}_A = \{A_1, A_2, \ldots, A_n\}$ and $\mathbf{G}_B = \{B_1, B_2, \ldots, B_m\}$, where $\mathbf{G}_A$ is an n-element group and $\mathbf{G}_B$ is an m-element group. Assuming that each element of $\mathbf{G}_A$ commutes with each element of $\mathbf{G}_B$, we form the product of all elements in $\mathbf{G}_A$ with all elements in $\mathbf{G}_B$ to obtain a set of nm elements. (It will be left as an exercise for the reader to show that the resulting set also forms a group.) The resulting nm-element group is denoted by $\mathbf{G}_A \times \mathbf{G}_B$ and is called the direct product of the groups $\mathbf{G}_A$ and $\mathbf{G}_B$.

Isomorphism When a group is analyzed in the abstract sense, where the actual nature of the elements is not considered (they rather serve only to give structure to the group), the concept of isomorphism is introduced. Isomorphism is associated with a very important property of independent sets, called *one-to-one correspondence*. If we have two groups $\mathbf{G}_A$ and $\mathbf{G}_B$ and there is associated with each element A_i of $\mathbf{G}_A$ an element B_i of $\mathbf{G}_B$ in a one-to-one way such that

$$(A_iA_j) = A_k \rightleftarrows (B_iB_j) = B_k \tag{2.20}$$

the groups $\mathbf{G}_A$ and $\mathbf{G}_B$ are said to be isomorphic. We shall see later in the chapter that there is an isomorphism among transformation groups which describes the different crystal symmetries appearing in nature.

2.2 The crystalline structure

Let us now make use of the theory of groups in order to obtain a more detailed description of the symmetry types encountered in crystals. We begin our discussion with a description of all possible types of transformations of a crystal lattice.

The Transformations of the Crystal Lattice

There are three essential types of symmetry transformations which describe the geometrical pattern of the crystal lattice. These are (1) translational, (2) rotary, and (3) reflective transformation elements. There are also, in special cases, transformations which are made up of (4) a simultaneous reflection and rotation element (see the preceding discussion of the cube) and (5) simultaneous translation and rotation elements or translation and reflection elements. Let us now examine these symmetry transformations more carefully.

1. The translational symmetry transformations describe the spatial periodicity of the crystal lattice. According to this symmetry, if the vector $\mathbf{a}^{(i)} = (a_1^{(i)}, a_2^{(i)}, a_3^{(i)})$ picks out the ith point in the lattice, then the translational transformation of the type

$$T(\mathbf{a}^{(i)}) = \mathbf{a}^{(i)\prime} = \mathbf{a}^{(i)} + n_1\mathbf{b}_1 + n_2\mathbf{b}_2 + n_3\mathbf{b}_3 \tag{2.21}$$

for all atoms i of an infinite lattice will map the crystal lattice onto itself. Here,

$$(n_1,n_2,n_3) = \mathbf{n}$$

represents the set of all positive and negative integers, and zero and $(\mathbf{b}_1,\mathbf{b}_2,\mathbf{b}_3)$ (called basis vectors) are independent of the ith atom but characteristic of the lattice. It is seen, then, that each set of numbers (n_1,n_2,n_3) represents an element of the translation group. The identity element corresponds to (0,0,0), the inverse of the element (n_1,n_2,n_3) is $(-n_1,-n_2,-n_3)$, and the rule of combination and the associative law clearly hold. Thus the set of translations defined by (2.21) constitute a group (of infinite order for an infinite crystal). The translational symmetry will be discussed below in our consideration of the Bravais lattice.

2. The rotational symmetry transformations apply to the invariance of the crystal lattice under definite rotations about specified axes in the lattice. For instance, the example of the simple cube in the preceding section indicates that 24 out of the 48 elements of the simple-cubic group correspond to rotations about axes which are perpendicular to the faces and parallel to the face and body diagonals of the cube.

3. The reflection symmetry transformations refer to the invariance of the crystal lattice with respect to reflections through specified planes in the lattice. For instance, the elements contained in the classes $3IC_2$ and $6IC_2'$ of the simple-cubic group describe reflections in the planes perpendicular to the cube edges and parallel to the face diagonals, respectively.

4. The combination of rotation and reflection (rotary reflection) symmetry transformations have also been indicated in our example of the simple cube. Here, the classes $6IC_4$ and $8IC_3$ describe such transformations.

It is noted that the axes of rotation and the reflection planes for the types of transformations 2, 3, and 4 described above all contain one common point in the description of the cube (the center of the cube). The group of such a set of transformations is called a *point group*. We shall see below that there are a total of 32 different point groups to describe natural crystal symmetries.

5. A symmetry element which cannot be contained in a point group is one which describes simultaneous rotations (or reflections) and translation transformations. It can be seen that, if the translation is perpendicular to the rotation axis, the combination of the rotation and translation is equivalent to a simple rotation about an axis parallel to the original one. However, if the translation is parallel to the rotation axis, then a new symmetry element is obtained. The axis associated with such a transformation is called a *screw axis*. Clearly, if the lattice

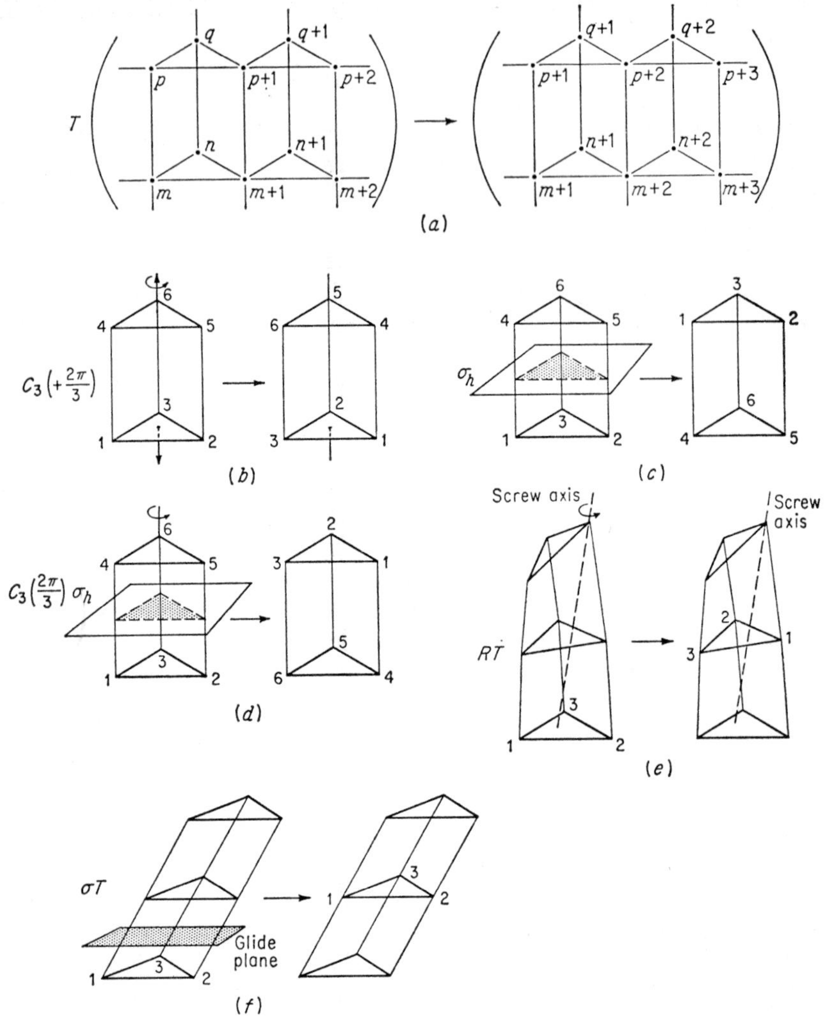

Fig. 2.2. Symmetry transformations of crystal lattices. (*a*) An element of the translation group corresponding to a translation in the x direction by one lattice dimension. (*b*) A rotation transformation of $+2\pi/3$. (*c*) A horizontal-reflection transformation. (*d*) A rotary-reflection transformation. (*e*) A rotary-translation transformation. The screw axis is indicated in the z direction. (*f*) A reflection-translation transformation. The glide plane is indicated in the horizontal plane.

maps onto itself after a rotation of $2\pi/n$ about the screw axis with the simultaneous displacement of d along that axis, then a rotation through $2\pi/n$, n times, will translate the axis a distance nd.

From an argument similar to the one above, it is seen that only if a reflection plane contains the direction of the translation will a combination translation-reflection transformation lead to a new symmetry element. Analogous to the screw axis, such a plane is referred to as a *glide reflection plane.* A double reflection in such a plane results in a simple displacement.

Simple illustrations of the transformation types described above are shown in Fig. 2.2.

The Bravais Lattice[1]

The periodic translational symmetry of crystal lattices may be described in terms of three noncoplanar basis vectors $\mathbf{b}_1$, $\mathbf{b}_2$, $\mathbf{b}_3$ defined in such a way that any lattice point $\mathbf{a}(n_1,n_2,n_3)$ can be obtained from any other lattice point $\mathbf{a}(0,0,0)$ by the simple transformation

$$\mathbf{a}(n_1,n_2,n_3) = \mathbf{a}(0,0,0) + n_1\mathbf{b}_1 + n_2\mathbf{b}_2 + n_3\mathbf{b}_3 \qquad n_1, n_2, n_3 = 0, 1, 2, \ldots \tag{2.22}$$

The lattice generated by such a transformation is called the simple *Bravais lattice*, and the parallelepiped spanned by the three basis vectors $(\mathbf{b}_1,\mathbf{b}_2,\mathbf{b}_3)$ is called the *unit cell.* Not all lattices may be obtained by displacements from one lattice point (as above). If it is necessary to displace two or more atoms in order to generate the entire lattice, it is also necessary to give the positions of these lattice points. There are a total of 14 Bravais lattices of which only seven are simple (i.e., they can be described by displacements which start at one lattice point). In the other seven, it is convenient to consider that the unit cell contains a sufficient number of points to be able to generate the entire lattice. Examples of lattices which contain more than one point per cell are the face-centered-cubic (four points per cell), body-centered-cubic (two points per cell), and the hexagonal-close-packed (two points per cell) lattices. These are shown in Fig. 2.3.

Symmetry types of Bravais lattices Let us now go on to consider all the possible symmetry types which would be encountered in the construction of Bravais lattices.

In order to define the symmetry of the lattice with respect to rotations and reflections, we consider those lattices in which the rotation axes and reflection planes all have one point in common (i.e., the point that remains stationary under the rotations and reflections which map the lattice onto itself).

[1] See, for additional reading, L. Landau and E. Lifshitz, "Statistical Physics," p. 415, Addison-Wesley Publishing Company, Inc., Reading, Mass., 1958.

The Bravais lattices are constructed by considering the symmetry elements associated with the axes of rotation. First, we define an n-fold rotation axis such that rotations of $2\pi/n$ about this axis map the lattice onto itself. Elementary geometrical considerations lead to the result that a crystal (i.e., a lattice with translational symmetry) can have

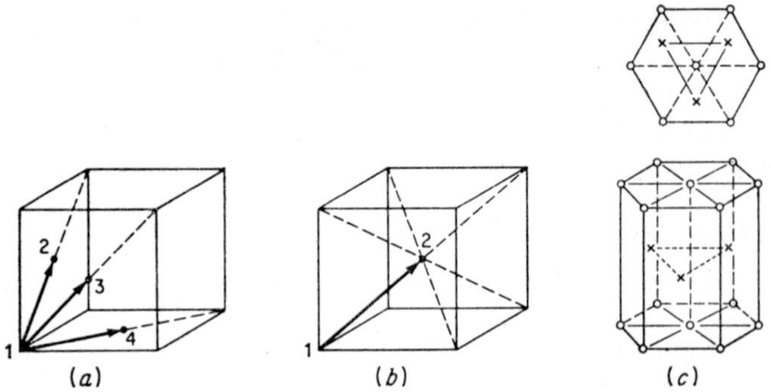

Fig. 2.3. Lattices with more than one atom per cell. (*a*) Face-centered-cubic lattice. (*b*) Body-centered-cubic lattice. (*c*) Hexagonal-close-packed lattice.

n-fold axes of rotation with $n = 1, 2, 3, 4$, and 6 only. A proof of this result[1] is as follows: We construct the Bravais lattice by first applying a translation $\mathbf{b}$ to the lattice point $\mathbf{a}_0$. Thus we generate the point $\mathbf{a}_1$ (Fig. 2.4), that is, $\mathbf{a}_1 = \mathbf{a}_0 + \mathbf{b}$, where $|\mathbf{b}|$ is defined to be the shortest possible lattice vector which, when added vectorially to $\mathbf{a}_0$, will generate another lattice point $\mathbf{a}_1$. The coordinate system is defined so that the vector $\mathbf{b}$ is parallel to the y axis. Consider now an n-fold axis of rotation to pass through the point $\mathbf{a}_0$ parallel to the x axis. By definition, a rotation of $\pm 2\pi/n$ about this axis will move one lattice vector into another lattice vector. Thus the rotation of $-2\pi/n$ will transform the lattice vector $\mathbf{a}_1$ into the lattice vector $\mathbf{a}_1'$. Since $\mathbf{a}_1$ is a lattice point, it must be defined by the same symmetry elements as is $\mathbf{a}_0$. Thus the same n-fold axis of rotation discussed above belongs to the point at $\mathbf{a}_1$. A rotation of $2\pi/n$ about this axis rotates the lattice vector $\mathbf{a}_0$ into the lattice vector $\mathbf{a}_0'$.

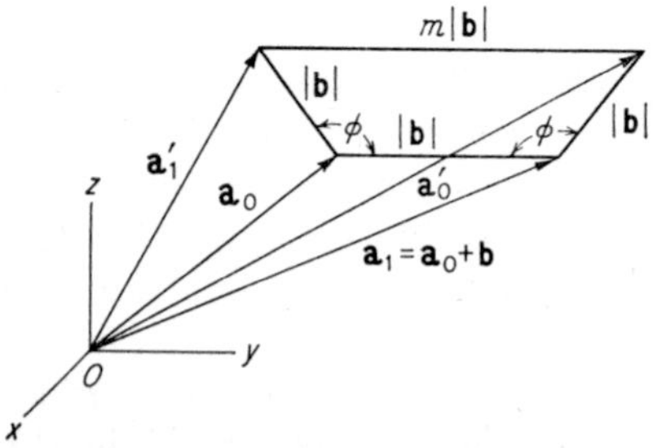

Fig. 2.4. Rotation operations of the Bravais lattice.

Since $\mathbf{a}_1'$ and $\mathbf{a}_0'$ define points in the Bravais lattice, they must also be

[1] *Ibid.*, p. 416.

related by a translation, i.e.,

$$\mathbf{a}_1' = \mathbf{a}_0' + m\mathbf{b} \tag{2.23}$$

where m is an integer. From Fig. 2.4 and Eq. (2.23), we see that

$$m|\mathbf{b}| = |\mathbf{b}| + 2|\mathbf{b}| \sin\left(\phi - \frac{\pi}{2}\right) = |\mathbf{b}| - 2|\mathbf{b}| \cos\phi \tag{2.24}$$

or

$$|\cos\phi| = \left|\frac{1-m}{2}\right| \leq 1 \tag{2.25}$$

Equation (2.25) can be valid only for $m = 3, 2, 1, 0, -1$.

Correspondingly

$$\phi = \cos^{-1}\frac{1-m}{2} = \pm\left(\frac{2\pi}{2}, \frac{2\pi}{3}, \frac{2\pi}{4}, \frac{2\pi}{6}, \frac{2\pi}{1}\right) \tag{2.26}$$

Thus the rotation axes in a Bravais lattice can be only 1-fold (the identity), 2-fold, 3-fold, 4-fold, or 6-fold. It is interesting to note the absence of the 5-fold symmetry axis in crystal lattices.

We are now in a position to classify the different symmetry types of Bravais lattices in terms of their corresponding n-fold rotation axes and reflection symmetries. We consider, then, each point in the Bravais lattice as a center of symmetry with its associated set of symmetry elements (comprising the symmetry group). The types will be described in the order of increasing symmetry.

1. *Triclinic Symmetry.* The least symmetric of all symmetry types is characterized by the absence of any rotation or reflection symmetry in the Bravais lattice. One cell of such a lattice may be described by a parallelepiped with edges of unequal lengths ($a \neq b \neq c$) and at unequal angles ($\alpha \neq \beta \neq \gamma$) with respect to each other (see Fig. 2.5). Such a system is characterized by a 1-fold axis of symmetry and no reflection planes.

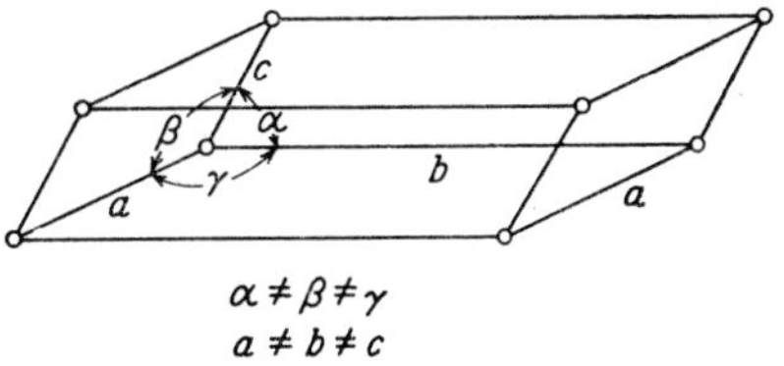

Fig. 2.5. The triclinic cell.

2. *Monoclinic Symmetry.* The elements of the monoclinic system are next in order of degree of symmetry and are described by one 2-fold axis of symmetry and a reflection plane which is perpendicular to this axis. This symmetry may be described by a unit cell in which the three edges are unequal in length but in which one edge is perpendicular to the 2-fold symmetry axis. The Bravais lattice for such a system may be constructed in two ways. First, we may consider the points of the lattice to be situated at the vertices of the parallelepiped described above (Fig. 2-6a). Second, in addition to points at the vertices of the

parallelepiped, the horizontal reflection symmetry also allows the construction of a Bravais lattice from a cell with points at the centers of the faces (which are parallel to the reflection plane) as well as the vertices (Fig. 2.6*b*). The former is called a simple-monoclinic lattice while the latter is the base-centered lattice.

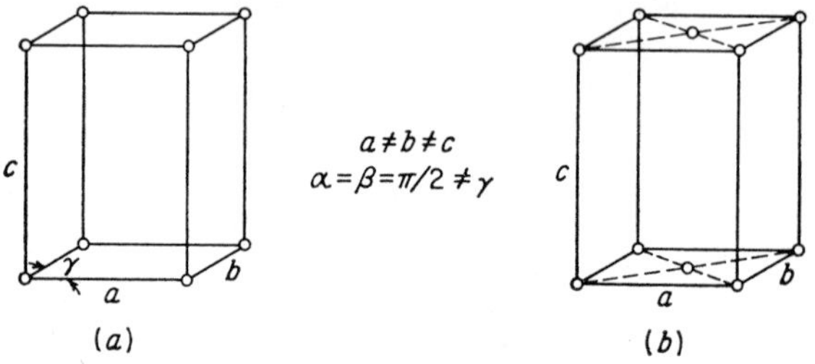

Fig. 2.6. (*a*) The simple monoclinic cell. (*b*) The base-centered monoclinic cell.

3. *Orthorhombic Symmetry.* Orthorhombic symmetry refers to two mutually orthogonal 2-fold axes of rotation and a reflection plane perpendicular to one of the 2-fold axes. This symmetry can thus be considered as an increase in the symmetry of the monoclinic lattice by the addition of another 2-fold rotation axis, perpendicular to the original one. Since the edges of the orthorhombic cell are mutually orthogonal,

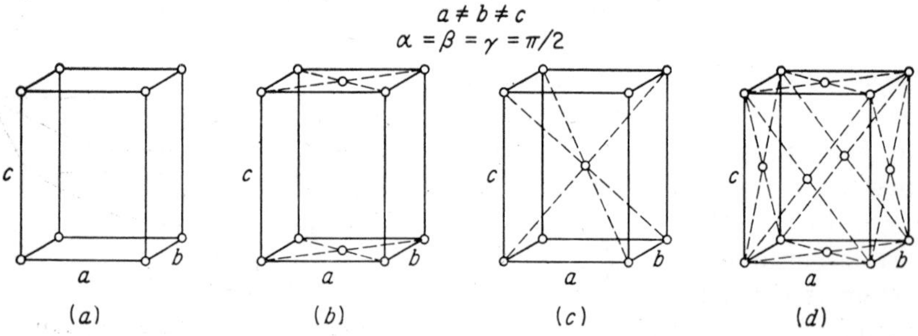

Fig. 2.7. (*a*) The simple orthorhombic cell. (*b*) The base-centered orthorhombic cell. (*c*) The body-centered orthorhombic cell. (*d*) The face-centered orthorhombic cell.

Bravais lattices may be constructed not only from a simple and a base-centered lattice (Figs. 2.7*a*,*b*) (of the symmetrized monoclinic system) but also from a simple orthorhombic system in which a lattice point is at the intersection of the body diagonals (body-centered lattice) (Fig. 2.7*c*) and from the simple system in which lattice points occur at the intersection of all face diagonals (face-centered lattice) (Fig. 2.7*d*). Thus there are four orthorhombic Bravais lattices.

4. *Tetragonal Symmetry.* This symmetry type is generated from the orthorhombic symmetry by adding a 4-fold rotation axis along one of the original 2-fold rotation axes. If we call the latter direction z, tetragonal symmetry may then be characterized by an orthorhombic symmetry in which the x and y directions are equivalent. Because of this equivalence, it becomes impossible to construct a Bravais lattice from base-centered

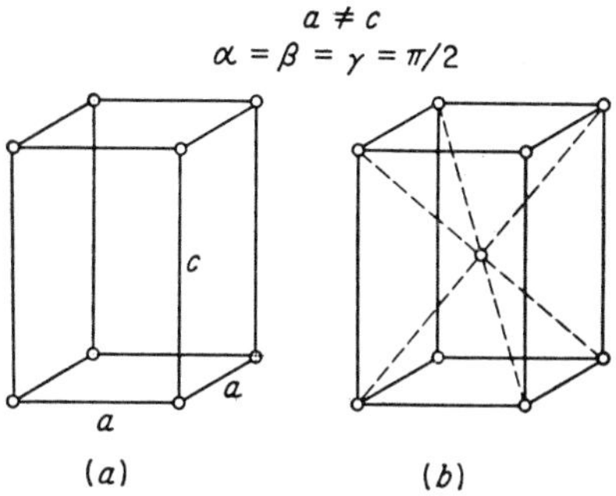

Fig. 2.8. (*a*) The simple tetragonal cell. (*b*) The body-centered tetragonal cell.

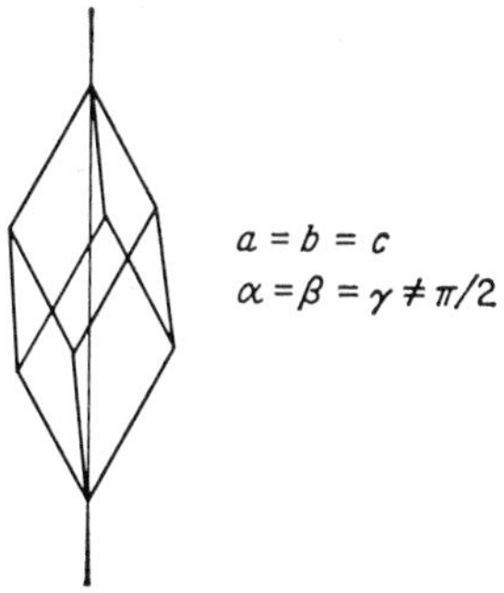

Fig. 2.9. The trigonal cell.

or face-centered lattices. The proof of this statement will be left as an exercise for the reader. There then remain two tetragonal Bravais lattices, the simple tetragonal lattice and the body-centered tetragonal lattice (Fig. 2.8).

5. *Trigonal Symmetry.* Thus far we have described symmetry types with 1-fold, 2-fold, and 4-fold rotation axes. Trigonal symmetry is characterized by a 3-fold axis of rotation. The Bravais lattice for such a symmetry type is obtained from a unit cell which is constructed by stretching a simple-cubic lattice along one of its body diagonals (called the trigonal axis). The lattice thus generated (called a rhombohedron) contains a 3-fold rotation axis (along the trigonal axis), three 2-fold rotation axes (perpendicular to the trigonal axis), the inversion, two rotary reflection elements (made up of a simultaneous $2\pi/6$ rotation about the trigonal axis and a reflection in the plane perpendicular to this axis), and three reflection planes containing the trigonal axis. (The totality of symmetry elements for each of the point groups will be discussed in greater detail later on.) The Bravais lattice for trigonal symmetry can be generated only from the rhombohedron described above (Fig. 2.9).

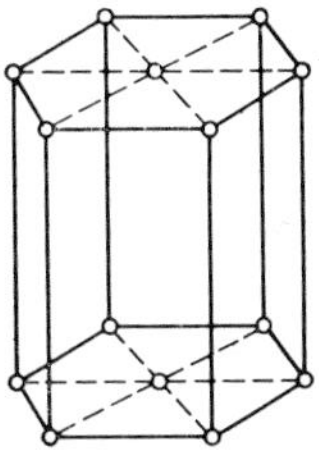

Fig. 2.10. The hexagonal cell.

6. *Hexagonal Symmetry.* The Bravais lattice for this symmetry is constructed from a unit cell in which lattice points are at the 12 vertices of a right hexagonal prism and there is a lattice point in the center of the two faces perpendicular to the 6-fold axis (the hexagonal axis) (Fig. 2.10).

Such a cell clearly contains 6-fold, 3-fold, and 2-fold rotation axes (along the hexagonal axis) and 2-fold rotation axes perpendicular to the hexagonal axis. Also, the inversion symmetry element is present.

7. *Cubic Symmetry.* The symmetry elements in the cubic point groups have been completely described in the preceding section as an example of a transformation group. The cubic system is a further symmetrization of the orthorhombic system in which all three mutually orthogonal rotation axes are made equivalent (i.e., the x, y, and z axes may not be distinguished from each other). Thus, the base-centered cell (Fig. 2.7*b*) cannot be present since it distinguishes one of the mutually orthogonal rotation axes. Consequently, the Bravais lattice for cubic symmetry may be constructed from three types of cubic cells: *simple-cubic, body-centered-cubic,* and *face-centered-cubic* (Fig. 2.11). This symmetry type, being the most symmetric, contains 2-fold, 3-fold, and 4-fold rotation axes.

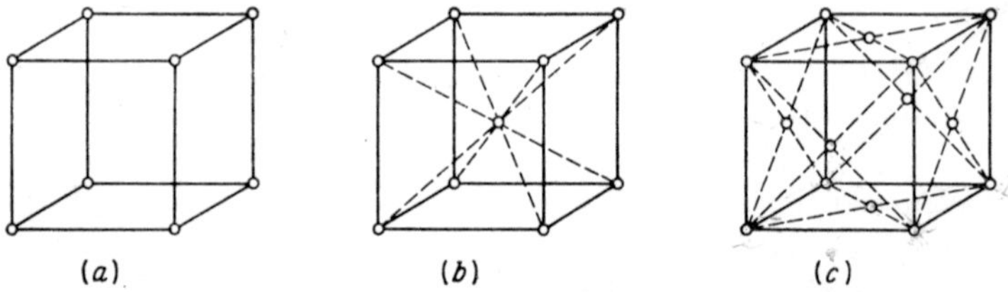

Fig. 2.11. The three cubic Bravais lattices: (*a*) the simple-cubic cell, (*b*) the body-centered-cubic cell, and (*c*) the face-centered-cubic cell.

We have seen that there are 14 different Bravais lattices, divided among the seven symmetry types: triclinic, monoclinic, orthorhombic, tetragonal, trigonal, hexagonal, and cubic. These 14 Bravais lattices are all that are needed in order to describe the translational symmetry of any crystal lattice. The description of any particular lattice in terms of a modification of any of the 14 Bravais lattices above will always result once again in an equivalence with one of these 14 lattices.

As mentioned earlier, the Bravais lattice does not describe the totality of invariance properties of the crystal with respect to rotations and reflections. There are indeed for each of the simple cells above several symmetry groups characterized by a set of rotations and reflections of the lattice about a single point (one of the vertices of the simple lattice). The other lattices above (as described earlier) do not contain one lattice point per cell.

It is frequently convenient to describe these lattices in terms of an interpenetration of several simple unit cells. For example, the face-centered-cubic lattice is described in terms of four interpenetrating simple cubes (with the origin of each at 1, 2, 3, and 4, in Fig. 2.3*a*) and the body-centered cube in terms of two interpenetrating simple cubes (with the origin of each at 1 and 2, in Fig. 2.3*b*). In this way, any crystal lattice may be described in terms of simple unit cells. Therefore, in the remainder of this chapter we need consider only the properties associated with the symmetries of the simple unit cells.

2.3 Point groups[1]

Let us now divide the seven simple Bravais-lattice symmetry types, discussed in the preceding section, into their constituent point groups. According to the definition previously given, a point group is a finite group, made up of the set of rotation and reflection transformations that map a lattice onto itself and in which all rotation axes and reflection planes have at least one point in common.

Each of the simple Bravais cells is represented by a point group which contains the maximum number of elements of all the point groups of that symmetry type. The remaining point groups, which we now wish to derive, generally contain fewer symmetry elements. We shall find that there is a total of 32 point groups of which 2 are triclinic, 3 are monoclinic, 3 are orthorhombic, 7 are tetragonal, 5 are trigonal, 7 are hexagonal, and 5 are cubic.

Classes of Point Groups

Before describing in detail the 32 crystallographic point groups, let us see how the elements of these groups may be divided into classes. The class is, as defined in Sec. 2.1, that set of symmetry elements of the group which are conjugate to each other; i.e., any two elements A_i and A_j are conjugate to each other if

$$A_j = A_k A_i A_k^{-1}$$

where A_k is another element of the group.

Suppose now that A_i is that element of the group which represents a rotation through the angle ϕ about an axis OP. If A_k is another element of the group that rotates the axis OP into OP', then the element

$$A_j = A_k A_i A_k^{-1}$$

corresponds to a rotation about OP' through the same angle ϕ. This is seen pictorially in Fig. 2.12.

The conjugate element A_j leaves the OP' axis fixed, so that A_j represents a rotation of ϕ about this axis. Thus, if there is in the group a transformation which takes one rotation axis into another, the two rotations about each of these axes belong to the same class. Similarly, two

[1] See, for additional reading, G. F. Koster, in F. Seitz and D. Turnbull (eds.), "Solid State Physics," vol. 4, Academic Press Inc., New York, 1957.

reflections belong to the same class if there exists in the group a transformation that takes one reflection plane into the other. (These rotation axes or reflection planes are said to be *equivalent.*)

Applying the above rule, we see that, if the group contains a π rotation about an axis perpendicular to an n-fold rotation axis, the elements describing the rotations $\phi = +(2\pi/n)m$ $(m \leq n)$ and $\phi = -(2\pi/n)m$ belong to the same class. This is clear since the π rotation reverses the direction of the rotation axis. On the other hand, the absence of the π rotation but the existence of a reflection plane perpendicular to the rotation axes (a horizontal reflection plane) does not give the same result since the reflection not only reverses the direction of the

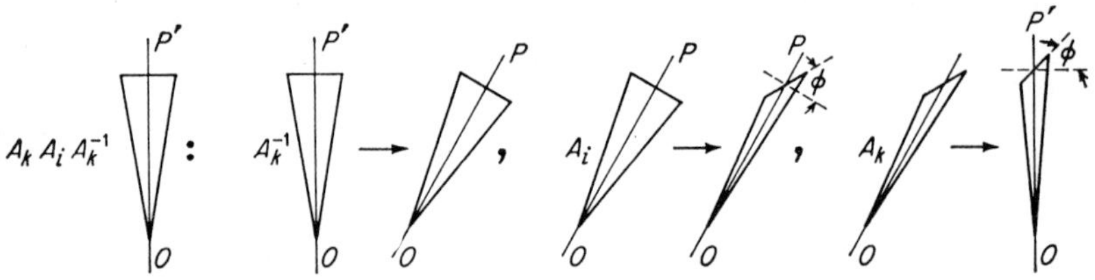

Fig. 2.12. Demonstration of the operation $A_k A_i A_k^{-1}$.

rotation axis but also changes the direction of rotation. However, a reflection plane parallel to the rotation axis (a vertical reflection plane) does not change the direction of the rotation axis but it does change the direction of rotation. Summarizing, two elements of a group which correspond to $\phi = \pm(2\pi/n)m$ belong to the same class if (1) the group also contains a π rotation about an axis perpendicular to the n-fold rotation axis and/or (2) the group contains a vertical reflection plane. (Rotations of $\pm 2\pi m/n$ which belong to the same class are called *bilateral.*) The reason for the grouping of the plus and minus rotations into classes in the example of the cube (see Sec. 2.1) now becomes clear.

Point-group Transformations

The types of transformations which make up a point group are rotations, reflections, and rotary reflections. These transformations have already been illustrated in our study of the simple cube (see Sec. 2.1). The notation which is commonly used is as follows:

1. *Rotations* about a specified axis, through an angle $2\pi/n$, that map a lattice onto itself are denoted by C_n. If C_n is an element of a group, the successive repetition of this transformation m times $(m \leq n)$ introduces the element $C_n^m = C_{n/m}$ which clearly also maps the lattice onto itself and is contained in the group. In particular, when

$$m = n, \qquad C_n^n = C_1 = E$$

corresponds to a rotation (about the C axis) of 2π. This is equivalent to the identity (or no rotation at all). Thus, a group containing only rotations $C_n, C_n^2, \ldots, C_n^n$ is a cyclic group.

In 27 of the 32 crystallographic point groups there is a preferred axis of rotation, called the C axis (chosen to lie along the z direction). The cubic groups do not distinguish between the mutually orthogonal directions x, y, and z. Among the 27 noncubic point groups, there are some which contain a 2-fold axis of symmetry perpendicular to the C axis (i.e., in the xy plane). These elements will be referred to as U_2, and the groups which contain them are called **D** groups. The transformations described above are illustrated in Fig. 2.13.

2. *Reflections* through a specified plane which map the lattice onto itself are denoted by σ. Just as the successive rotation (about a C axis) of

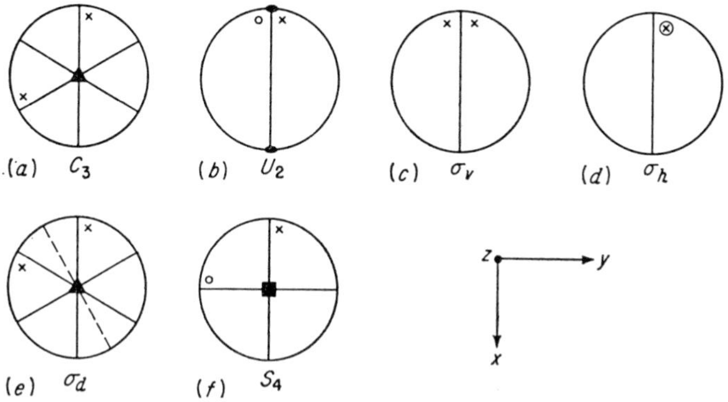

Fig. 2.13. Point-group transformations. (*a*) The rotation C_3, (*b*) a 2-fold rotation U_2, (*c*) a vertical reflection σ_v, (*d*) a horizontal reflection σ_h, (*e*) a diagonal reflection σ_d, (*f*) a rotary reflection S_4. The z axis is pointing out of the page, × represents a point above the page, and ∘ represents a point below the page.

$2\pi/n$, taken n times, is equivalent to the identity, so the successive reflection, taken twice, is equivalent to the identity (that is, $\sigma^2 = E$). When a preferred axis of rotation (the C axis) is specified, the orientation of the reflection planes is defined with respect to this axis. When the reflection plane contains the C axis, the (vertical) reflection element of the group is denoted by σ_v. When the reflection plane is perpendicular to the C axis, the (horizontal) reflection element is denoted by σ_h. Finally, when the reflection plane contains the C axis and also bisects each rotation π/n, the corresponding (diagonal) reflection element is denoted by σ_d. Thus there are three types of reflection elements which occur in point groups: σ_v, σ_h, and σ_d.

3. *Rotary reflections* refer to the simultaneous rotation about a C axis and a reflection through the plane perpendicular to this axis. When the

rotation taken is $2\pi/n$, the symbol for the rotary reflection is S_n. Thus, by definition, $S_n = C_n\sigma_h$ $(= \sigma_h C_n)$. An important particular case of a rotary reflection is $S_2 = \sigma_h C_2$, which is equivalent to an inversion. Examples of rotary reflections have been illustrated in the group of the simple cube (Sec. 2.1). Here, the rotary reflections which are contained in the group are (1) the inversion, (2) IC_4, and (3) IC_3. The cyclic group of transformations S_n occurs only for even n. If n were odd, then an n-fold repetition of S_n would be equivalent to a rotation of 2π (i.e., no rotation at all) and a reflection in the horizontal plane. Thus, $S_n^n = \sigma_h \neq E$ if n is odd but $S_n^n = E$ if n is even.

The transformations described above may be illustrated with the help of stereograms[1] (Fig. 2.13). The symbols are interpreted as follows: The figure in the center of the circle with n vertices represents an n-fold rotation axis. The × denotes a point above the plane of the paper and the ∘ a point below the plane of the paper. (The lack of a point on both sides of a line indicates no vertical reflection symmetry.)

Construction of the Point Groups

Now that we have classified the types of transformations to be encountered in point groups, we are in a position to describe systematically all possible point groups. The groups will be denoted with bold type.

1. $\mathbf{C}_n$ *groups* The elements of the $\mathbf{C}_n$ groups contain only rotations of multiples of $2\pi/n$ about a fixed axis (the C axis). It has been pointed out earlier that this is a cyclic group, that is,

$$\mathbf{C}_n \equiv \{C_n, C_n^2, \ldots, C_n^n = E\}$$

thus it is an abelian group, and each constituent element forms its own class. According to the discussion of the possible Bravais lattices, n can

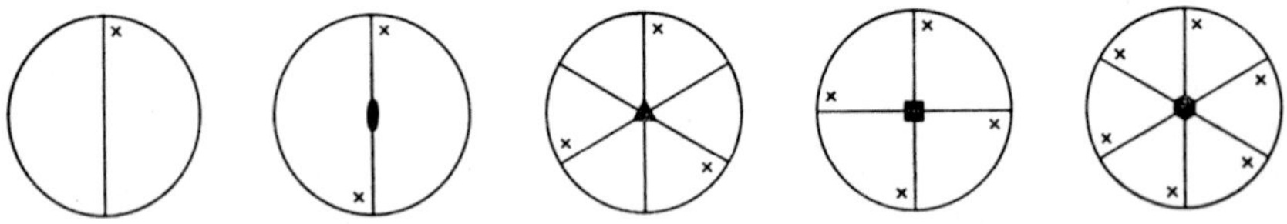

$\mathbf{C}_1$ $\mathbf{C}_2$ $\mathbf{C}_3$ $\mathbf{C}_4$ $\mathbf{C}_6$

Fig. 2.14. Stereograms for the $\mathbf{C}_n$ groups.

take only the values 1, 2, 3, 4, and 6. Thus there are five $\mathbf{C}_n$ groups: $\mathbf{C}_1$, $\mathbf{C}_2$, $\mathbf{C}_3$, $\mathbf{C}_4$, and $\mathbf{C}_6$. The elements contained in these groups are given in Table 2.1, and their corresponding stereograms are shown in Fig. 2.14.

[1] A stereogram is a stereographic projection diagram. This is a mapping of the points on a sphere onto a plane which is tangent to the sphere at the south pole. Points are projected by extrapolating the line connecting the north pole and the point in question to the plane.

TABLE 2.1 *Classes of the* $\mathbf{C}_n$ *Groups*

Group	$\mathbf{C}_1$(T)	$\mathbf{C}_2$(M)	$\mathbf{C}_3$(Tr)	$\mathbf{C}_4$(Te)
Classes	E	E, C_2	E, C_3, C_3^2	$E, C_4, C_4^2 = C_2, C_4^3$

Group	$\mathbf{C}_6$(H)
Classes	$E, C_6, C_6^2 = C_3, C_6^3 = C_2, C_6^4, C_6^5$

The symmetry types, denoted by T, M, O, Te, Tr, H, and C, stand, respectively, for triclinic, monoclinic, orthorhombic, tetragonal, trigonal, hexagonal, and cubic.

2. $\mathbf{S}_{2n}$ ***groups*** The elements of $\mathbf{S}_{2n}$ groups also form a cyclic group and therefore form classes by themselves. The number of elements in the $\mathbf{S}_{2n}$ group is $2n$, and there are three allowed point groups, $\mathbf{S}_2$, $\mathbf{S}_4$, and $\mathbf{S}_6$. As we have seen earlier, the element $S_2 = I$, where I is an inversion. The $\mathbf{S}_4$ group does not contain the inversion, but the $\mathbf{S}_6$ group does (see Fig. 2.15). The point group, $\mathbf{S}_6$, is the direct product of the inversion with another group. Inspection of Fig. 2.15 indicates that the other group is $\mathbf{C}_3$, that is,

$$\mathbf{S}_6 = \mathbf{C}_3 \times \mathbf{I}$$

Consequently, the elements of $\mathbf{S}_6$ may be obtained by taking the products of the elements of $\mathbf{C}_3$ with the inversion $\mathbf{I}$. (We recall that this was the

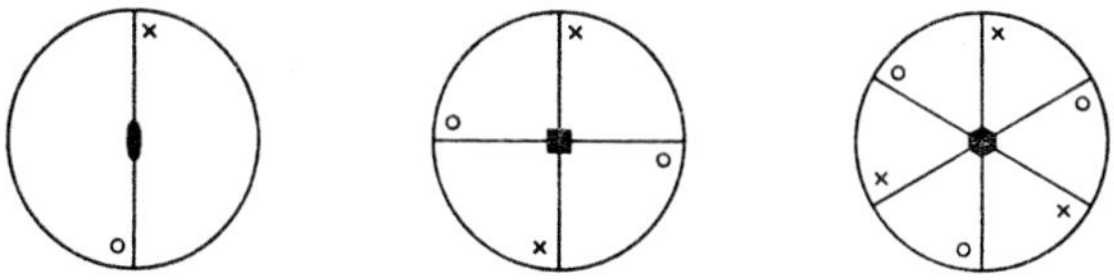

$\mathbf{S}_2 \equiv \mathbf{I}$ $\mathbf{S}_4$ $\mathbf{S}_6$

Fig. 2.15. Stereograms for the $\mathbf{S}_{2n}$ groups.

method of obtaining 24 of the 48 elements belonging to the group of the simple cube.) The classes of the $\mathbf{S}_{2n}$ groups are given in Table 2.2, and

TABLE 2.2 *Classes of the* $\mathbf{S}_{2n}$ *Groups*

Group	$\mathbf{S}_2 = \mathbf{I}$(T)	$\mathbf{S}_4$(Te)	$\mathbf{S}_6$(Tr) $= \mathbf{C}_3 \times \mathbf{I}$
Classes	E, I	$E, S_4, S_4^2 = C_2, S_4^3$	$E, C_3, C_3^2, I, IC_3, IC_3^2$

the stereograms are shown in Fig. 2.15.

3. $\mathbf{C}_{nh}$ ***groups*** The $\mathbf{C}_{nh}$ group is formed by adding to the rotation axis of the $\mathbf{C}_n$ group a reflection in the horizontal plane (i.e., the plane perpendicular to the C axis). Since the element σ_h is present in $\mathbf{C}_{nh}$ and all the elements of $\mathbf{C}_n$ must also be present, the remaining elements of the group $\mathbf{C}_{nh}$ are determined by taking the direct product of the elements of $\mathbf{C}_n$ with $\boldsymbol{\sigma}_h$. Thus the group $\mathbf{C}_{nh}$ contains $2n$ elements: n rotations

$$(C_n, C_n^2, \ldots, C_n^n = E)$$

and n rotary reflections $(\sigma_h C_n, \sigma_h C_n^2, \ldots, \sigma_h C_n^n = \sigma_h)$. The possible $\mathbf{C}_{nh}$ groups are $\mathbf{C}_{1h} = \boldsymbol{\sigma}_h$, $\mathbf{C}_{2h}$, $\mathbf{C}_{3h} = \mathbf{C}_3 \times \boldsymbol{\sigma}_h$, $\mathbf{C}_{4h} = \mathbf{C}_4 \times \mathbf{I}$, $\mathbf{C}_{6h} = \mathbf{C}_6 \times \mathbf{I}$. Although the $\mathbf{C}_{nh}$ groups are not cyclic, they are abelian. Thus each

TABLE 2.3 *Classes of the* $\mathbf{C}_{nh}$ *Groups*

Group	$\mathbf{C}_{1h}$(M) $= \boldsymbol{\sigma}_h$	$\mathbf{C}_{2h}$(M)	$\mathbf{C}_{3h}$(H)
Classes	E, σ_h	E, C_2, σ_h, I	$E, C_3, C_3^2, S_3, S_3^2, \sigma_h$

Group	$\mathbf{C}_{4h}$(T) $= \mathbf{C}_4 \times \mathbf{I}$
Classes	$E, C_4, C_4^3, C_4^2, I, IC_4, IC_4^2, IC_4^3$

Group	$\mathbf{C}_{6h}$(H) $= \mathbf{C}_6 \times \mathbf{I}$
Classes	$E, C_6, C_6^2 = C_3, C_6^3 = C_2, C_6^4, C_6^5, I, IC_6, IC_3, IC_2, IC_6^4, IC_6^5$

element of these groups forms a class by itself. The classes of the $\mathbf{C}_{nh}$ groups are given in Table 2.3, and the stereograms are shown in Fig. 2.16.

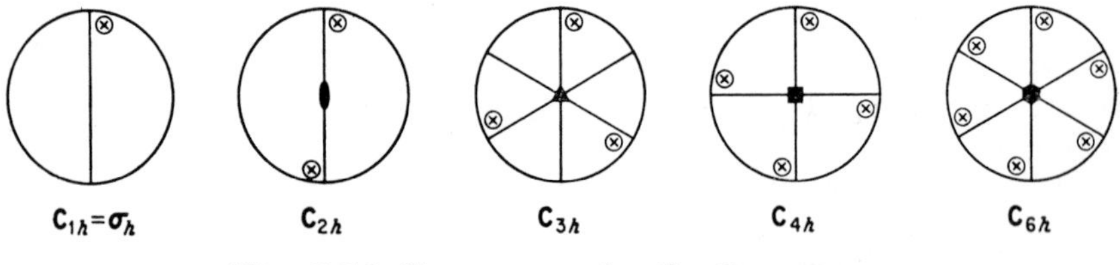

Fig. 2.16. Stereograms for the $\mathbf{C}_{nh}$ groups.

4. $\mathbf{C}_{nv}$ ***groups*** The $\mathbf{C}_{nv}$ groups are formed by adding to the rotation axis of the $\mathbf{C}_n$ group a (vertical) reflection plane, containing the C axis. It is easily verified that the introduction of one vertical reflection plane automatically introduces $n - 1$ additional vertical reflection planes, at angles of π/n. Thus the group $\mathbf{C}_{nv}$ contains $2n$ elements: n rotations of the $\mathbf{C}_n$ group and n reflections in vertical planes.

We have seen earlier that the element σ_v in the group makes the rotations $\pm\phi$ bilateral (i.e., they belong to the same class).

The distribution of the $2n$ elements among the classes of this group depends on the evenness or oddness of n. If n is odd, the rotations C_n take each of the n reflection planes into each other; the reflection planes are therefore equivalent and therefore belong to the same class. Another way of saying this is as follows: If $\sigma_v^{(i)}$ and $\sigma_v^{(j)}$ denote two of the n vertical reflections, then if n is odd

$$\sigma_v^{(i)} = C_n^m \sigma_v^{(j)} (C_n^m)^{-1}$$

for all i, j, and C_n^m of the group (see Fig. 2.17). Thus all vertical reflections are conjugate to each other and therefore form one class.

On the other hand, if n is even, then

$$\sigma_v^{(i)} = C_n^m \sigma_v^{(j)} (C_n^m)^{-1}$$

only for every other reflection plane (that is, $j = i + 2k$); therefore one-half of the reflection planes forms one class and the other half another class. These remarks are illustrated in Fig. 2.17.

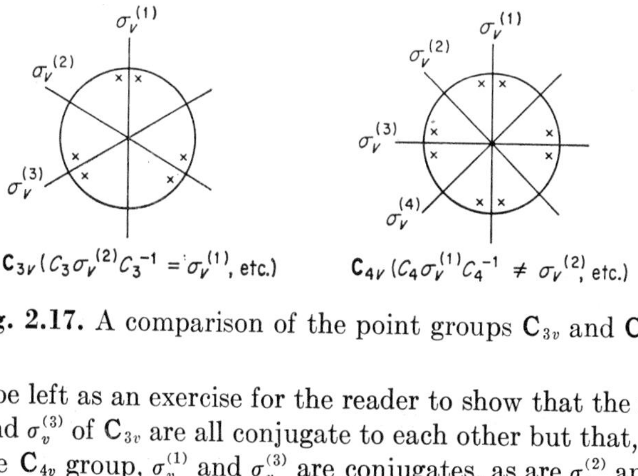

C_{3v} ($C_3\sigma_v^{(2)}C_3^{-1} = \sigma_v^{(1)}$, etc.) C_{4v} ($C_4\sigma_v^{(1)}C_4^{-1} \neq \sigma_v^{(2)}$, etc.)

Fig. 2.17. A comparison of the point groups $\mathbf{C}_{3v}$ and $\mathbf{C}_{4v}$.

It will be left as an exercise for the reader to show that the reflections $\sigma_v^{(1)}$, $\sigma_v^{(2)}$, and $\sigma_v^{(3)}$ of $\mathbf{C}_{3v}$ are all conjugate to each other but that, for reflections in the $\mathbf{C}_{4v}$ group, $\sigma_v^{(1)}$ and $\sigma_v^{(3)}$ are conjugates, as are $\sigma_v^{(2)}$ and $\sigma_v^{(4)}$, but that $\sigma_v^{(1)}$, $\sigma_v^{(3)}$ are not conjugate to $\sigma_v^{(2)}$, $\sigma_v^{(4)}$.

Thus, if n is odd, the $\mathbf{C}_{nv}$ group contains $1/2(n - 1)$ classes, representing the pairs of elements $C_n^{\pm m}$, one class for the vertical reflection planes and one for the identity E, thereby giving a total of $1/2(n + 3)$ classes. If n is even, the element $C_n^{n/2} = C_2$ forms a class by itself, there are $n/2 - 1$ remaining pairs of rotations $C_n^{\pm m \pm n/2}$, there are two classes corresponding to the two sets of $n/2$ equivalent reflection planes, and there is the identity. Thus for n even the $\mathbf{C}_{nv}$ group contains a total of $n/2 + 3$ classes. The possible $\mathbf{C}_{nv}$ groups are $\mathbf{C}_{2v}$, $\mathbf{C}_{3v}$, $\mathbf{C}_{4v}$, and $\mathbf{C}_{6v}$. Since the triclinic-symmetry type does not single out any particular direction, the group $\mathbf{C}_{1v}$ is equivalent to $\mathbf{C}_{1h}$ (i.e., without a preferred axis, there is no difference between a vertical and a horizontal reflection plane).

The classes of the $\mathbf{C}_{nv}$ groups are given in Table 2.4, and the stereograms are shown in Fig. 2.18. The numbers preceding the symbols for

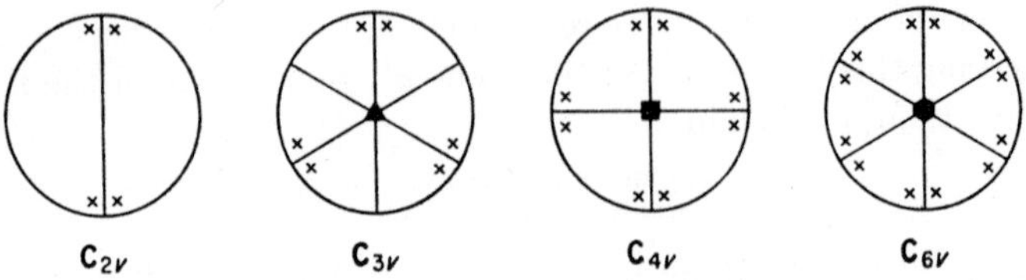

Fig. 2.18. Stereograms for the $\mathbf{C}_{nv}$ groups.

the transformations represent, as before, the number of elements in the class, i.e., in $\mathbf{C}_{3v}$, $2C_3$ refers to the two rotations $\pm 2\pi/3$ and $3\sigma_v$ refers to the three equivalent vertical reflections.

TABLE 2.4 *Classes of the* $\mathbf{C}_{nv}$ *Groups*

Group	$\mathbf{C}_{2v}$(O)	$\mathbf{C}_{3v}$(Tr)	$\mathbf{C}_{4v}$(Te)
Classes	$E, C_2, \sigma_v, \sigma_v'$	$E, 2C_3, 3\sigma_v$	$E, C_2, 2C_4, 2\sigma_v, 2\sigma_v'$
Group	$\mathbf{C}_{6v}$(H)		
Classes	$E, C_2, 2C_3, 2C_6, 3\sigma_v, 3\sigma_v'$		

5. $\mathbf{D}_n$ ***groups*** The $\mathbf{D}_n$ groups are formed by adding to the n-fold $\mathbf{C}_n$ rotation group a rotation of π about an axis that is perpendicular to the C axis. The introduction of this perpendicular axis introduces $n - 1$ additional axes separated by an angle of π/n. Thus the $\mathbf{D}_n$ group contains $2n$ elements: n rotations about the C axis and n rotations of π about n perpendicular axes. The element for these π rotations is called U_2 (or sometimes C_2^x and C_2^y corresponding to π rotations about the x or y axis).

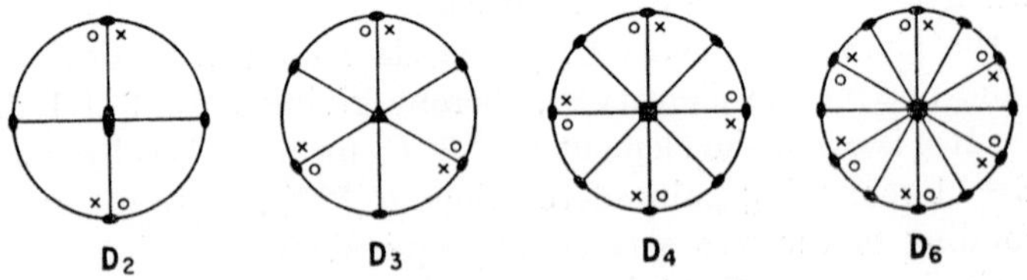

Fig. 2.19. Stereograms for the $\mathbf{D}_n$ groups.

Using the same method that was applied to the $\mathbf{C}_{nv}$ groups, it can be shown that the elements of the $\mathbf{D}_n$ group are bilateral and that, if n is even, the group contains $n/2 + 3$ classes and if n is odd, $1/2(n + 3)$

classes. Here, of course, the elements U_2 play the role of the elements σ_v in the $\mathbf{C}_{nv}$ group. The possible $\mathbf{D}_n$ groups are $\mathbf{D}_2$, $\mathbf{D}_3$, $\mathbf{D}_4$, and $\mathbf{D}_6$. Their classes are given in Table 2.5, and the corresponding stereograms are shown in Fig. 2.19.

6. **$\mathbf{D}_{nh}$ groups** The $\mathbf{D}_{nh}$ groups are formed by adding to the $\mathbf{D}_n$ group a horizontal reflection plane. It is clear from a comparison of the stereograms of the $\mathbf{D}_{nh}$ groups (Fig. 2.20) and the $\mathbf{D}_n$ groups that the presence

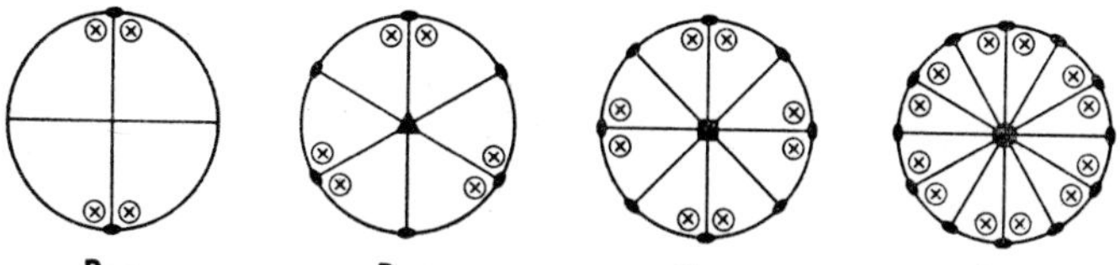

$\mathbf{D}_{2h}$ $\mathbf{D}_{3h}$ $\mathbf{D}_{4h}$ $\mathbf{D}_{6h}$

Fig. 2.20. Stereograms for the $\mathbf{D}_{nh}$ groups.

of the horizontal reflection plane is equivalent to the introduction of n vertical reflection planes. Thus, the $\mathbf{D}_{nh}$ group contains $4n$ elements: the $2n$ elements of $\mathbf{D}_n$, plus the product of each of these $2n$ elements with σ_h. (The latter is equivalent to n reflections σ_v and n rotary reflections $\sigma_h C_n^k$.) The reflections σ_v all belong to the same class if n is odd; they form two classes if n is even (for the reasons given in the discussion of

TABLE 2.5 *Classes of the* $\mathbf{D}_n$ *Groups*

Group	$\mathbf{D}_2$(O)	$\mathbf{D}_3$(Tr)	$\mathbf{D}_4$(Te)
Classes	$E, C_2^z, C_2^x, C_2^y,$	$E, 2C_3, 3U_2,$	$E, C_2, 2C_4, 2U_2, 2U_2'$
Group	$\mathbf{D}_6$(H)		
Classes	$E, C_2, 2C_3, 2C_6, 3U_2, 3U_2'$		

TABLE 2.6 *Classes of the* $\mathbf{D}_{nh}$ *Groups*

Group	$\mathbf{D}_{2h}(\mathrm{O}) = \mathbf{D}_2 \times \mathbf{I}$	$\mathbf{D}_{3h}$(H)
Classes	$E, C_2^z, C_2^x, C_2^y, I, \sigma_h, IC_2^x, IC_2^y$	$E, \sigma_h, 2C_3, 2S_3, 3U_2, 3\sigma_v$
Group	$\mathbf{D}_{4h}(\mathrm{Te}) = \mathbf{D}_4 \times \mathbf{I}$	
Classes	$E, C_2, 2C_4, 2U_2, 2U_2', I, \sigma_h, 2IC_4, 2IU_2, 2IU_2'$	
Group	$\mathbf{D}_{6h} = \mathbf{D}_6 \times \mathbf{I}$	
Classes	$E, C_2, 2C_3, 2C_6, 3U_2, 3U_2', I, \sigma_h, 2IC_3, 2IC_6, 3IU_2, 3IU_2'$	

the $\mathbf{C}_{nv}$ groups). The classes of the $\mathbf{D}_{nh}$ groups are given in Table 2.6, and the stereograms are shown in Fig. 2.20. The possible groups are $\mathbf{D}_{2h} = \mathbf{D}_2 \times \mathbf{I}$, $\mathbf{D}_{3h}$, $\mathbf{D}_{4h} = \mathbf{D}_4 \times \mathbf{I}$, $\mathbf{D}_{6h} = \mathbf{D}_6 \times \mathbf{I}$.

7. $\mathbf{D}_{nd}$ ***groups*** The $\mathbf{D}_{nd}$ groups are formed by adding to the $\mathbf{D}_n$ group the vertical reflection planes σ_d which bisect the angles between the 2-fold rotation axes U_2. There are n such planes in a $\mathbf{D}_{nd}$ symmetry. The group contains $4n$ elements: $2n$ elements of $\mathbf{D}_n$, n reflections σ_d in the vertical planes, and n transformations obtained from the product $\sigma_d U_2$. The latter is equivalent to a rotary reflection S_{2n}^k. (This may be seen from an inspection of the stereograms in Fig. 2.21.)

The diagonal reflection planes interchange two horizontal 2-fold axes; thus adjacent axes (for both even and odd n) are equivalent. Consequently, all the 2-fold axes U_2 are equivalent. If n is even, then $\mathbf{D}_{nd}$ contains $n + 3$ classes: the identity E, the rotation C_2, $n/2 - 1$ remaining conjugate rotation elements $C_n^{\pm k}$, one class for the n rotations U_2, one class for the n reflections σ_d, and $n/2$ classes corresponding to the conjugate rotary reflections $S_{2n}^{\pm k}$. If n is odd, $\mathbf{D}_{nd}$ contains the inversion class and $\mathbf{D}_{nd} = \mathbf{D}_n \times \mathbf{I}$. Since $\mathbf{D}_n$ (for odd n) contains $1/2(n + 3)$ classes, $\mathbf{D}_{nd}$ must therefore contain $n + 3$ classes; one-half of the classes are obtained by multiplying the elements of $\mathbf{D}_n$ by the inversion $\mathbf{I}$.

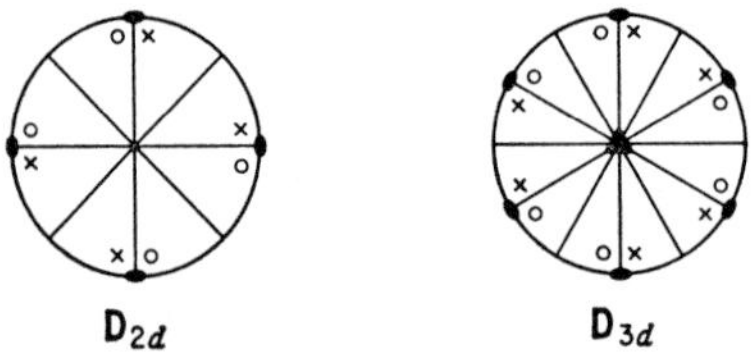

Fig. 2.21. Stereograms for the $\mathbf{D}_{nd}$ groups.

The groups $\mathbf{D}_{4d}$ and $\mathbf{D}_{6d}$ would contain in their rotary reflections $S_8 = C_8\sigma_h$ and $S_{12} = C_{12}\sigma_h$, respectively. According to our discussion of the translation symmetry of the lattice, the presence of such elements would not allow the construction of a Bravais lattice. Consequently, these groups are not permissible crystallographic point groups. The possible groups $\mathbf{D}_{nd}$ which describe crystals are $\mathbf{D}_{2d}$ and $\mathbf{D}_{3d}$. Their corresponding classes are given in Table 2.7, and the stereograms are shown in Fig. 2.21.

TABLE 2.7 *Classes of the* $\mathbf{D}_{nd}$ *Groups*

Group	$\mathbf{D}_{2d}$(Te)	$\mathbf{D}_{3d}$(Tr) $= \mathbf{D}_3 \times \mathbf{I}$
Classes	$E, C_2, 2S_4, 2U_2, 2\sigma_d$	$E, 2C_3, 3U_2, I, 2IC_3, 3IU_2$

8. ***Cubic groups*** The cubic groups differ from those discussed thus far in so far as they do not single out a preferred axis of symmetry but rather contain equivalent orthogonal axes. There are five point groups that are classified as cubic.

(*a*) *The* $\mathbf{O}_h$ *Group.* The first of the cubic groups represents the set of transformations that map a simple cube onto itself. This group is called $\mathbf{O}_h$ and has been discussed earlier as an example of a transformation group. It was found that the $\mathbf{O}_h$ group contains 48 elements which are distributed among 10 classes. These classes are defined in Table 2.8. The single C axis of the other 27 point groups makes it possible to picture these groups very simply with stereograms. Unfortunately, such a diagram does not clarify the geometry of the cubic groups. Consequently, we shall describe the symmetry properties of the cubic groups by considering their relation to the symmetry of the simple cube. The classes of the $\mathbf{O}_h$ group given in Table 2.8 may be pictured with the aid of Fig. 2.1.

TABLE 2.8 *Classes of the* $\mathbf{O}_h$ *Group*

Class	*Meaning*
E	Identity (i.e., no rotations or reflections)
$3C_2$	Rotations of π about the three axes parallel to the cube edges
$6C_4$	Rotations of $\pm\pi/2$ about the three axes parallel to the cube edges
$6C_2'$	Rotations of π about the six axes parallel to the face diagonals
$8C_3$	Rotations of $\pm 2\pi/3$ about the four body diagonals
I	Inversion $(x,y,z) \rightarrow (-x, -y, -z)$ [or $(\theta,\phi) \rightarrow (\pi - \theta, \phi + \pi)$]
$3IC_2$	Reflections through the planes perpendicular to the cube edges
$6IC_4$	Rotary reflections made up of simultaneous rotations of $\pm\pi/2$ about the axes parallel to the cube edges, with reflections in the planes perpendicular to these axes
$6IC_2'$	Reflections through the planes parallel to the six face diagonals
$8IC_3$	Rotary reflections made up of the simultaneous rotations about the body diagonals of $\pm 2\pi/3$ and reflections in the planes perpendicular to these axes

(*b*) *The* $\mathbf{O}$ *Group.* The $\mathbf{O}$ (or octahedral) group is made up of the pure rotations of the simple cube. Therefore this group contains 24 elements distributed among the five classes E, $3C_2$, $6C_4$, $6C_2'$, and $8C_3$ of the $\mathbf{O}_h$ group. Clearly $\mathbf{O}$ is a subgroup of the $\mathbf{O}_h$ group, i.e.,

$$\mathbf{O}_h = \mathbf{O} \times \mathbf{I}$$

(*c*) *The* $\mathbf{T}_d$ *Group.* The $\mathbf{T}_d$ group is made up of the transformations that map a regular tetrahedron onto itself. A convenient way to observe the symmetry properties of this figure is to construct it inside a cube. This is done by making its edges the oppositely oriented diagonals of opposing faces of the cube (see Fig. 2.22). An inspection of Fig. 2.22 shows that the following classes of $\mathbf{O}_h$ make up the $\mathbf{T}_d$ group: E, $3C_2$, $8C_3$, $6IC_4$, $6IC_2'$. Thus $\mathbf{T}_d$ contains 24 elements distributed among 5 classes.

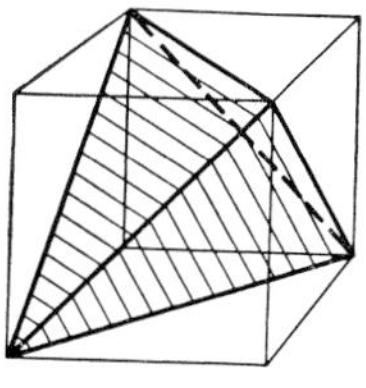

Fig. 2.22. The regular tetrahedron ($\mathbf{T}_d$).

(*d*) *The* $\mathbf{T}$ *Group.* The $\mathbf{T}$ (or tetrahedral) group is made up of the pure rotations of the regular tetrahedron (i.e., of the $\mathbf{T}_d$ group). Thus, the **T** group contains 12 elements distributed among the classes E, $3C_2$, and $8C_3$.

(*e*) *The* $\mathbf{T}_h$ *Group.* The $\mathbf{T}_h$ group is formed by adding an inversion to the **T** group, that is, $\mathbf{T}_h = \mathbf{T} \times \mathbf{I}$. The resulting group contains 24 elements distributed among the following classes of the simple cube: E, $3C_2$, $8C_3$, I, $3IC_2$, $8IC_3$.

The totality of crystallographic point groups is summarized in Table 2.9 where each of them is categorized according to its symmetry type. Those point groups that correspond to the simple Bravais lattices are marked with an asterisk. These point groups contain the maximum number of classes of all groups of a common symmetry type.

TABLE 2.9 *The Crystallographic Point Groups*

Symmetry type	*Point groups*
Triclinic	$\mathbf{C}_1$, $\mathbf{I}^*$
Monoclinic	σ_h, $\mathbf{C}_2$, $\mathbf{C}_{2h}^*$
Orthorhombic	$\mathbf{C}_{2v}$, $\mathbf{D}_2$, $\mathbf{D}_{2h}^*$
Tetragonal	$\mathbf{S}_4$, $\mathbf{D}_{2d}$, $\mathbf{C}_4$, $\mathbf{C}_{4h}$, $\mathbf{C}_{4v}$, $\mathbf{D}_4$, $\mathbf{D}_{4h}^*$
Trigonal	$\mathbf{C}_3$, $\mathbf{S}_6$, $\mathbf{C}_{3v}$, $\mathbf{D}_3$, $\mathbf{D}_{3d}^*$
Hexagonal	$\mathbf{C}_{3h}$, $\mathbf{D}_{3h}$, $\mathbf{C}_6$, $\mathbf{C}_{6h}$, $\mathbf{C}_{6v}$, $\mathbf{D}_6$, $\mathbf{D}_{6h}^*$
Cubic	$\mathbf{T}$, $\mathbf{T}_h$, $\mathbf{T}_d$, $\mathbf{O}$ $\mathbf{O}_h^*$

* Point groups marked with an asterisk correspond to the simple Bravais lattices.

In this chapter, we have introduced the concepts of group theory in order to build up a systematic description of all possible symmetry types (and their constituent point groups) which would be compatible with the crystalline structure of solids. We have described the mappings of the crystalline state of solids for the same reasons that an astronomer would construct a scheme for mapping the heavenly bodies. Just as the astronomer's next step would be to investigate the physical properties of the geometrical configuration that he observes, so we must now look into some of the physical properties of the variety of symmetry types of crystals. At this point, we do not ask why a specific crystal assumes, let us say, a $\mathbf{D}_{3h}$ symmetry while another assumes the $\mathbf{O}_h$ symmetry. We shall merely assume that one of the 32 symmetry types which must exist does so by virtue of the consideration of the minimum energy required to assemble the crystal.

In the chapters which follow, we shall depart from the *geometrical* discussion given here and look into effects that the different symmetry types have on the physical properties of a crystal.

3 the ionic crystal

ONE PURPOSE of discussing the properties of the ionic crystal before those of other types of solids is twofold. First, the physical properties of ionic crystals may be attributed to interactions of a much simpler nature than those of other crystals. Second, it is possible to gain some insight, from a very physical point of view, into the *raison d'être* for electronic energy bands and their associated symmetry properties in general types of crystals from an analysis of the properties of ionic crystals. We have discussed the differences between the different types of crystal bonding mechanisms in Chap. 1. We shall discover in this chapter, after a more detailed quantitative analysis of the electronic-energy-level structure of a presupposed "pure ionic crystal," that in reality the bonding of any crystal has the features of all types of crystalline bonds, although one type of bond always predominates over the others. Our aim in this chapter is not to calculate the properties of ionic crystals to a high degree of precision; rather it is to discuss the physical nature of an ionic crystal in terms of natural properties of the crystal, such as its internal energy, temperature, cell dimensions and symmetry, and the important interactions which are experienced by its constituent ions. We shall assume that we are dealing with a static lattice.

3.1 General properties of ionic crystals

An atom that belongs to group I of the periodic table is characterized by a single electron in its outermost orbital shell. An example is the alkali atom sodium which has the electronic configuration $1s^22s^22p^63s^1$. Similarly, an atom that belongs to group VII of the periodic table is characterized by one electron vacancy in its outermost orbital shell. An example is the halogen atom chlorine, which has the electronic configuration $1s^22s^22p^63s^23p^5$. As a single sodium atom is brought into very close proximity with a single chlorine atom, the affinity of the chlorine atom for one extra electron to complete its $3p$ shell becomes large enough to ionize the sodium atom and transfer the $3s$ electron of Na to its own $3p$ shell, resulting in a bonding of the ionized sodium atom Na^+ (with the closed-shell configuration $1s^22s^22p^6$) and the ionized chlorine atom Cl^- (with the closed-shell configuration $1s^22s^22p^63s^23p^6$). The coupling of the two ions is called an ionic bond and is due to the electrostatic attraction of the positively charged sodium ion and the negatively charged chlorine ion. The resulting system of two ions is the sodium chloride molecule NaCl.

Suppose that, instead of a single sodium atom and a single chlorine atom, we choose to bring 10^{23} sodium atoms and 10^{23} chlorine atoms into very close proximity. Will each sodium atom and chlorine atom pair off to form 10^{23} individual NaCl molecules or will the entire group of atoms form a crystalline structure? We know from our elementary chemistry that, under the standard conditions of temperature and pressure, the latter will be the case. The resulting structure is verified by X-ray analysis to be characterized by an ionic bond and is called an ionic crystal. Such a crystal is made up of a periodic array of positively and negatively charged ions, arranged in such a way that each positive (or negative) ion has nearest-neighbor negative (or positive) ions.

The electron affinity of an atom with a partially filled electron shell decreases as the number of electron vacancies in the shell increases. Also, the ionization potential of an atom with one electron in its outer shell increases as the number of electrons in the outer shell is increased. Consequently, we should expect that among the most frequently occurring ionic crystals would be the alkali halides. Also, this result indicates that crystals which are made up of group III–V compounds and group IV elements should exhibit a much weaker ionic character. This is indeed the case, with the crystals made up of the III–V compounds and the group IV elements frequently exhibiting a predominant covalent character. In general, the III–V compounds possess a small amount of ionic character.

In this chapter we shall confine ourselves to the properties of an ideally purely ionic NaCl-type crystal. We shall start by calculating the electrostatic binding energy of the ionic crystal. We shall then proceed to investigate the effect of the entire crystal on the system of electronic energy levels of a constituent anion and a constituent cation of the lattice and thereby develop the one-electron-energy-level scheme for the entire crystal. We shall then indicate how the electronic energy levels broaden into bands as the atoms approach each other. The effect of defects in the crystal lattice on the electronic-energy-level scheme will not be discussed (see Chap. 1). We assume throughout this chapter that the anion and cation nuclei are fixed in their lattice positions. Although the nuclei are in reality oscillating about their fixed lattice positions with amplitudes dependent upon the crystal temperature, the assumption of a rigid lattice will not materially alter the general results which we shall obtain.

The symmetry of the NaCl crystal may be described by the interpenetration of two face-centered-cubic crystals, one for each type of ion, Na^+ and Cl^-. Figure 3.1*a* shows a representative section of a face of the NaCl-type structure. Each positive (or negative) ion has six nearest-neighbor negative (or positive) ions at a distance r_0. The entire lattice may then be viewed as an interpenetration of a face-centered-cubic cation lattice and a face-centered-cubic anion lattice (see Fig. 3.1*a*). The constant r_0 is referred to as the lattice constant, and the ions' positions are labeled according to Fig. 3.1*b*. The spherical symmetry implied by the closed-shell configuration of the constituent ions would permit a maximum

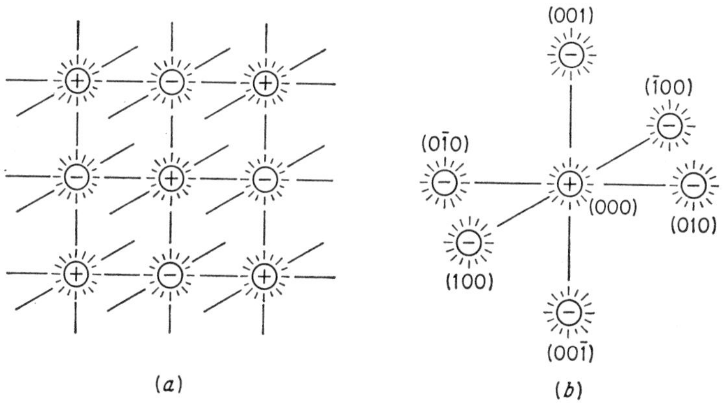

Fig. 3.1. The NaCl structure. (*a*) A representative section of the lattice. (*b*) Notation for locating ions in the lattice.

number of ions to be packed into the entire crystal. However, the number of nearest neighbors to any given constituent ion (the coordination number) is restricted by the necessity of charge neutrality. For example, let us consider the LiI crystal. From a geometrical point of view, a large ion such as I^- (ionic radii are given in Table 3.1) may be able to accommodate many small ions such as Li^+ around its surface. However, in order to maintain charge neutrality each of the Li^+ ions would have to accommodate the same number of nearest-neighbor I^- ions. Because of the differences in the physical sizes of Li^+ and I^-, this is impossible, and the number of nearest neighbors is necessarily restricted by the requirement of charge neutrality.

Stability of Ionic Crystals

Suppose that we have 10^{23} sodium ions and 10^{23} chlorine ions arranged on a NaCl-type lattice in which the ions are an infinite distance apart.

Let us consider the energy that is required to bring these ions together, while maintaining the NaCl-lattice structure, to form a stable crystal lattice. This energy is defined as the cohesive (or binding) energy of the crystal.

As we bring the ions in from infinity, while maintaining the static lattice structure, we gain energy, because of the electrostatic attraction between all pairs of positive and negative ions. Let us now suppose that the only forces present are those due to the classical electrostatic interactions between the array of charged ions, and let us determine the magnitude of the interionic spacing at equilibrium. Since the Coulomb force acting between any pair of ions is inversely proportional to the distance between the ions, it is clear that, because of the lack of a minimum value for the electrostatic potential as a function of the interionic spacing, the supposition of the existence of electrostatic forces alone leads to the result that there will be no equilibrium value for the interionic spacing and that the entire crystal will collapse in toward the origin.

There is one other effect which also implies that an ionic crystal cannot be stable under the action of electrostatic forces alone. This is the effect of the deviation of the lattice ions from the equilibrium lattice positions, because of their random oscillating motion about these positions. The amplitude of oscillation of the constituent ions of a crystal depends on the temperature and, even at $T = 0°K$, there still remains a residual *zero-point* oscillation. If we assume that the ion at (0,0,0) (see Fig. 3.1) moves to the position $(\delta,0,0)$ while all other ions remain fixed in their lattice positions, the Coulomb attraction between this ion and its neighbor at (1,0,0) would become greater than the attraction between the ions at (1,0,0) and (2,0,0) and the attraction between the ion at $(\delta,0,0)$ and its neighbor at $(\bar{1},0,0)$. In order to compensate for this effect, the ions at (2,0,0) and $(\bar{1},0,0)$ would move in toward the ion at $(\delta,0,0)$, thereby changing the distance from their own nearest neighbors. Thus, in a short period of time, the entire crystal would collapse in toward the misbehaving ion which was originally at (0,0,0).

It is seen from these arguments that it would be impossible to maintain a stable ionic crystal under the action of electrostatic forces alone. There must, therefore, exist a repulsive force (which has an origin other than the classical electrostatic field) that compensates for the effects of the singular Coulomb force and deviations of ions from their equilibrium positions, in order to have the effect of establishing a stable crystalline structure. The repulsive potential required must necessarily be short-range and have a magnitude of sufficient strength to compensate for the attractive electrostatic potential, thereby producing a minimum in the total potential at the equilibrium interionic spacing. The shape of the total potential necessary to maintain a stable crystal is shown in Fig. 3.2.

The need for a repulsive potential in order to maintain a stable crystal was recognized long before the discovery of quantum mechanics, and in order to facilitate the computation of the cohesive energy of ionic crystals, many of the early workers adopted an empirical repulsive potential of the form $b|\mathbf{r}_{ij}|^{-n}$, where b and n were taken as constants to be determined by the condition of thermodynamic equilibrium of the crystal lattice.[1] However, the source of a repulsive potential was not discovered until the advent of quantum mechanics and the requirement of the Pauli exclusion principle. We recall that the Pauli principle forbids the simultaneous occurrence of two electrons in the same state of motion and at the same location in space. As adjacent atoms approach each other, their electronic clouds tend to overlap. The Pauli principle would then predict that the only way that an electron associated with one ion may occupy the location in space occupied by an equivalent electron of the adjacent ion would be to excite that electron to a higher energy state. On the other hand, the energy that is required to excite the neighboring ion is generally much greater in magnitude than is available to the considered ion. Consequently, the outermost electronic clouds of adjacent ions tend to repel their further motion toward each other after they have come into very close proximity. Since the atomic binding energy is greatest for electrons in closed shells and decreases for partially full shells, the strength of the repulsive potential should be greatest for ionic crystals whose constituent ions have the rare-gas configuration (such as NaCl).

The repulsive potential, which is due to the Pauli exclusion principle, is sometimes referred to as the overlap potential since it depends quantitatively on the amount of overlap of the wave functions of the valence electrons of the interacting adjacent ions. The repulsive potential between a pair of ions in a crystal is represented by the following approximate analytical form:

$$v_{ij}^{(r)} = \lambda_{ij} e^{-|\mathbf{r}_{ij}|/\rho}$$

where $|\mathbf{r}_{ij}|$ is the magnitude of the distance between any two ions i and j in the crystal and where the terms λ_{ij} and ρ depend, in general, on the nature of the ions i and j but are independent of the distance between them. This potential, originally introduced by Born and Mayer,[2] is discussed by Seitz.[3]

The total potential which any one ion experiences in the crystal may then be given by a sum of the Coulomb attractive and the overlap

[1] M. Born, "Handbuch der Physik," vol. 26, no. 2, Springer-Verlag OHG, Berlin, 1933; F. Seitz, "The Modern Theory of Solids," chap. II, McGraw-Hill Book Company, Inc., New York, 1940.

[2] M. Born and J. E. Mayer, *Z. Physik*, **75**: 1 (1932); J. E. Mayer, *J. Chem. Phys.*, **1**: 270 (1933); J. E. Mayer and M. G. Mayer, *Phys. Rev.*, **43**: 605 (1933).

[3] *Op. cit.*

repulsive potentials. The minimum in the total potential ($-U_0$) occurs at the equilibrium interionic spacing (see Fig. 3.2). It is observed from the shape of the total potential shown in Fig. 3.2 that the constituent ions of an ionic crystal behave in a way not unlike the behavior of rigid spheres which have been packed into a box in such a way as to use up the maximum amount of free space. It is interesting to note that, were it not for the presence of the Pauli exclusion principle, neither complex nuclei, complex atoms, nor crystals could exist as stable structures.

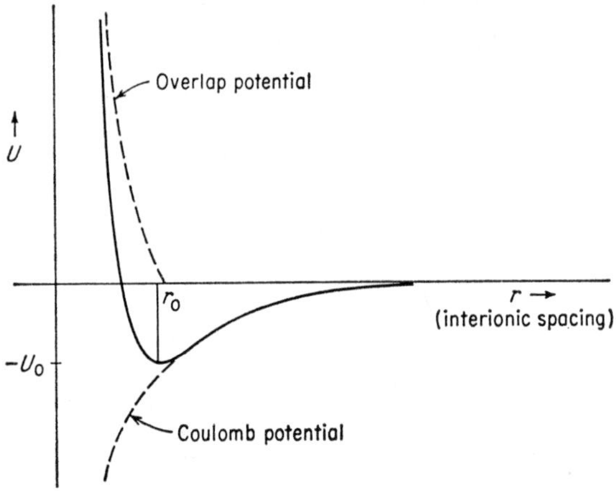

Fig. 3.2. Potential energy of a pair of ions in an ionic crystal.

In the following text, we shall treat the qualitative ideas expressed above in a more quantitative way. We shall first consider the radii of ions in crystals. Then we shall calculate the cohesive energy of an ionic crystal in terms of an attractive electrostatic potential and a repulsive Pauli overlap potential. Finally, we shall investigate the nature of electronic energy levels of ionic crystals.

Ionic Radii in Crystals

The cohesive energy of an ionic crystal is very sensitive to the average extent of the charge clouds of the constituent ions in the crystal. This quantity is referred to as the *crystal ionic radius*, as distinguished from the *free-ion radius*. The ionic radius is defined in terms of the extent of the ion's influence on its surroundings.

In view of this definition, we must distinguish between the radius of a free ion and the radius of an ion that is a constituent part of an ionic crystal. In free space, a test charge brought into the vicinity of an ion will experience a potential which depends on $|\mathbf{R} - \mathbf{r}|$, where $\mathbf{r}$ is the radius of the free ion and $\mathbf{R}$ is the vector from the origin (the nucleus of the ion) to the point of observation. The radius of the ion could then be described, quantum-mechanically, in terms of the radius at which the absolute value of the square of the wave function for the outermost electronic-orbital state has its maximum value. This wave function is in turn a solution of the Schroedinger wave equation, in which the hamiltonian depends on the ordinary Coulomb potential and is subject to the boundary condition that its magnitude and derivative vanish at infinity. On the other hand, the hamiltonian for an ion in a crystal depends on a potential such as the one described previously (Fig. 3.2), and the corresponding wave function must satisfy the boundary condition that its magnitude and derivative vanish at the boundary of the ion itself. (This is equivalent to the statement that the binding electron remains with its parent ion.) When we speak of the radii of free ions and the crystal ionic radii, we are referring to two different concepts, and consequently we should expect them to differ in magnitude.

The calculation of the radii of ions may be carried out by solving the one-electron Schroedinger equation by the Hartree-Fock self-consistent field method. In the free-ion case, the solution must be made self-consistent with the field of the constituent ionic electrons, whereas in the crystal case, the solution must be made self-consistent with the field of the constituent electrons plus the electronic clouds of the surrounding ions.[1]

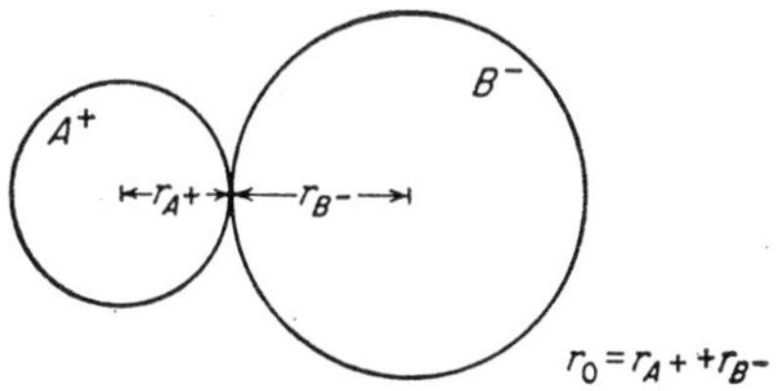

Fig. 3.3. The lattice constant in terms of ionic radii.

Semiempirical methods of calculating the radii of ions in crystals have been proposed by several authors. The form of the potential (Fig. 3.2) indicates that the distance between neighboring ions in the crystal (which is referred to as the lattice constant r_0) should be approximately equal to the sum of the radii of the neighboring ions. This is referred to as the additivity rule (Fig. 3.3).

The lattice constants of crystals are measured by X-ray techniques, and thus it remains merely to determine the ratio of the radii of the two ions A^+ and B^- in order to determine the radii of all other ions which occur in crystals with the ions A^+ or B^-. Wasastjerna[2] measured the ratio of molar refractions of ions and, assuming them to be proportional to the volumes of spherical ions, deduced the ratio of the radii of several ions. Goldschmidt[3] then took Wasastjerna's results and, com-

[1] A discussion of self-consistent field calculations is given in Chap. 10 and is outlined extensively by J. C. Slater, "Quantum Theory of Atomic Structure," vols. I and II, McGraw-Hill Book Company, Inc., New York, 1960.

[2] J. A. Wasastjerna, *Soc. Sci. Fennica, Commentationes Phys.-Math.*, **38**: 1 (1923).

[3] V. M. Goldschmidt, *Skrifter Norske Videnskaps Akad.* no. 2: (1926); no. 8: (1927).

bining them with the measured lattice constants and the assumption of the additivity rule, calculated the radii of many ions in ionic crystals. These radii are referred to as Goldschmidt radii; some of them are tabulated in Table 3.1.

Pauling has also demonstrated a method of calculating ionic radii, and he obtains results which are in general agreement with the values of the Goldschmidt radii. Pauling's method depends on the assumption that groups of isoelectronic ions (i.e., those ions which contain equal numbers of electrons, such as N^{3-}, O^- F^-, Ne, Na^+, Mg^{++}, etc., and have spherical symmetry) have corresponding wave functions for the outermost electrons which are all inversely proportional to $Z - S$, where Z is the valence of the considered ion and S is the screening constant.[1] Pauling chooses the constant of proportionality in such a way that the additivity rule reproduces the empirical lattice constant of the alkali halide lattice, formed from the ions in the isoelectronic series. The empirical lattice constant was taken as that of the crystals made up of univalent ions. These results were then modified to take into account the correct valency of the ions that were investigated. Some of the Pauling radii are also tabulated in Table 3.1.

TABLE 3.1 *Ionic Radii in Crystals (in Angstrom Units)*

Ion	Li^+	Be^{++}	$O^=$	F^-	Na^+	Mg^{++}	Al^{3+}	Si^{4+}	$S^=$
Goldschmidt	0.78	0.34	1.32	1.33	0.98	0.78	0.57	0.39	1.74
Pauling	0.60	0.31	1.40	1.36	0.95	0.65	0.50	0.41	1.84
Ion	Cl^-	K^+	Ca^{++}	Sc^{3+}	Ti^{4+}	$Se^=$	Br^-	Rb^+	Sr^{++}
Goldschmidt	1.81	1.33	1.06	0.83	0.64	1.91	1.96	1.49	1.27
Pauling	1.81	1.33	0.99	0.81	0.68	1.98	1.95	1.48	1.13
Ion	Y^{3+}	Zr^{4+}	$Te^=$	I^-	Cs^+	Ba^{++}	La^{3+}	Ce^{4+}	
Goldschmidt	1.06	0.87	2.11	2.20	1.65	1.43	1.22	1.02	
Pauling	0.93	0.80	2.21	2.16	1.69	1.35	1.15	1.01	

3.2 The electrostatic potential[2]

The Classical Coulomb Potential

Let us consider a NaCl crystal which is made up of N Na^+ ions and N Cl^- ions (where N is Avogadro's number). The total number of

[1] All the ions in the isoelectronic series have the same principal quantum number, and the corresponding effective charge is $Z - S$, where Z changes by unity from one ion to the next in the series. For spherical symmetry, the wave functions for the outermost electrons are then proportional to $(Z - S)^{-1}$. See L. Pauling, "The Nature of the Chemical Bond," 2d ed., p. 343, Cornell University Press, Ithaca, N.Y., 1948.

[2] See E. Madelung, *Physik. Z.*, **11**: 898 (1910); M. Born, *op. cit.*

ions is $2N$, and the *electrostatic potential* (neglecting for the moment the overlap potential) felt by one of the constituent ions in the presence of the remaining ions is

$$U_i = \sum_{j=1}^{2N-1} v_{ij} \tag{3.1}$$

where

$$v_{ij} = \pm \frac{e^2}{|\mathbf{r}_{ij}|} \qquad \mathbf{r}_{ij} = \mathbf{r}_i - \mathbf{r}_j \tag{3.2}$$

is the electrostatic potential between any two ions in the lattice. The total electrostatic potential energy of the lattice is

$$U_? = NU_i \tag{3.3}$$

where N is the total number of ion pairs in the crystal.

Let us take the origin of our coordinate system to be at one of the positive ions. All other ions in the lattice may now be located in terms of three integers (n_1,n_2,n_3), signifying the number of lattice constants that the given ion is from the origin in the x, y, and z directions, respectively. Thus

$$\mathbf{r}_{ij} = (\hat{\mathbf{i}}n_1 + \hat{\mathbf{j}}n_2 + \hat{\mathbf{k}}n_3)r_0 \tag{3.4}$$

and

$$|\mathbf{r}_{ij}| = (n_1^2 + n_2^2 + n_3^2)^{1/2} r_0$$

With a positive ion at the origin, any negative ion will be at a location $(n_1,n_2,n_3)r_0$ when the sum $(n_1 + n_2 + n_3)$ is an odd integer and any positive ion will be at a location $(n_1,n_2,n_3)r_0$ when the sum $(n_1 + n_2 + n_3)$ is an even integer. Thus the electrostatic energy between the ion at the origin and any other given ion at $\mathbf{r}_j$ may be expressed in the form

$$v_{ij} = \frac{(-1)^{n_1+n_2+n_3}}{(n_1^2 + n_2^2 + n_3^2)^{1/2}} \frac{e^2}{r_0} \tag{3.5}$$

The total potential energy which acts on the ion at the origin is

$$U_i = \frac{Me^2}{r_0} \tag{3.6}$$

where the constant

$$M = \sum_{\substack{n_1=0 \\ (n_1,n_2,n_3) \neq (0,0,0)}}^{2N-1} \sum_{n_2=0}^{2N-1} \sum_{n_3=0}^{2N-1} (-1)^{n_1+n_2+n_3}(n_1^2 + n_2^2 + n_3^2)^{-1/2} \tag{3.7}$$

is called the Madelung constant. In the general case, the potential acting on a given ion of an ionic crystal in which Z_1 and Z_2 are the valences of the two types of ion which make up the crystal is

$$U_i = \frac{Z_1 Z_2 M e^2}{r_0} \tag{3.7'}$$

and M depends on the type of lattice structure considered. The first term in the Madelung series (3.7) arises from the six nearest neighbors which are one lattice parameter away from the origin and are located at (1,0,0), $(\bar{1},0,0)$, (0,1,0), $(0,\bar{1},0)$, (0,0,1), and $(0,0,\bar{1})$. The contribution of this "shell" to the Madelung constant is $-6/\sqrt{1}$. Similarly, the next contribution comes from 12 next-nearest neighbors which are $\sqrt{2}\, r_0$ units away from the origin and are located at $(\pm 1, \pm 1, 0)$, $(\pm 1, 0, \pm 1)$, and $(0, \pm 1, \pm 1)$. This contribution to M is equal to $+12/\sqrt{2}$. Following this procedure, we express M as the series

$$M = \sum_n \frac{C_n}{n} \qquad n \equiv (n_1^2 + n_2^2 + n_3^2)^{1/2} \tag{3.7''}$$

with the coefficients C_n given in Table 3.2 as a function of the distance from the origin.

TABLE 3.2 *Coefficients* C_n [Eq. (3.7″)]

n_1	n_2	n_3	$n = r/r_0$	C_n
1	0	0	$\sqrt{1}$	−6
1	1	0	$\sqrt{2}$	12
1	1	1	$\sqrt{3}$	−8
2	0	0	$\sqrt{4}$	6
2	1	0	$\sqrt{5}$	−24
2	1	1	$\sqrt{6}$	24
2	2	0	$\sqrt{8}$	12
2	2	1	$\sqrt{9}$	−30
3	0	0		
3	1	0	$\sqrt{10}$	24
3	1	1	$\sqrt{11}$	−24
2	2	2	$\sqrt{12}$	8
3	2	0	$\sqrt{13}$	−24
3	2	1	$\sqrt{14}$	48

The series (3.7″) is an alternating series with very slow convergence properties. In order to evaluate M it is necessary to employ somewhat sophisticated mathematical techniques. Let it suffice at this point to say that it is possible to evaluate the series with the use of the properties of the theta function. This method is discussed in great detail by Born and Huang.[1] The value which is obtained for M for NaCl structures is -1.7476. The Madelung constants for other typical ionic crystals are tabulated in Table 3.3. One way of estimating the sum of the series is to consider a basic cell with charge $+e$ in the center (0,0,0) and $-e$ around it. To distribute the latter, we assume that at the six equivalent positions (100) there are $\frac{1}{2}e$ inside and $\frac{1}{2}e$ outside the cell. At the 12

[1] M. Born and K. Huang, "Dynamical Theory of Crystal Lattices," Oxford University Press, Fair Lawn, N.J., 1954.

equivalent positions (110) there are $\frac{1}{4}e$ inside and $\frac{3}{4}e$ outside; at the 8 positions (111) there are $\frac{1}{8}e$ inside and $\frac{7}{8}e$ outside, etc. Thus the net charge in the cube is (to this approximation)

$$+e - \tfrac{6}{2}e + \tfrac{12}{4}e - \tfrac{8}{8}e = 0$$

The Madelung constant for the cube is then

$$M = -\frac{6}{2\sqrt{1}} + \frac{12}{4\sqrt{2}} - \frac{8}{8\sqrt{3}} = -1.457$$

compared with the correct value -1.7476.

TABLE 3.3 *Madelung Constants for Typical Ionic Crystals**

Lattice type	$-M$
Sodium chloride	1.7476
Cesium chloride	1.7627
Zinc blende (ZnS)	1.6381
Wurtzite (ZnS)	1.641
Fluorite (CuF_2)	5.0388
Cuprite (CuO_2)	4.1155
Rutile (TiO_2)	4.816
Aratose (TiO_2)	4.800
Corundum (Al_2O_3)	25.0312

* For diagrams of some of these different lattice types, see A. J. Dekker, "Solid State Physics," p. 123, Prentice-Hall, Inc., Englewood Cliffs, N.J., 1957.

Using the value just obtained for the Madelung constant for NaCl, we have

$$U_i = \frac{-1.7476e^2}{r_0} \tag{3.8}$$

and the total electrostatic energy becomes

$$U_e = NU_i = \frac{-1.7476e^2N}{r_0} \tag{3.9}$$

The Repulsive Overlap Potential

The repulsive potential which arises through the action of the Pauli exclusion principle has been described above to have the form

$$v_{ij}^{(r)} = \lambda_{ij}e^{-|\mathbf{r}_{ij}|/\rho}$$

where ρ is a measure of the falloff of the repulsive potential and depends on the pair of ions considered.

The net potential energy that acts between an ion at $\mathbf{r}_i$ and an ion at $\mathbf{r}_j$ (which is represented schematically in Fig. 3.2) is the sum of the attractive potential energy v_{ij} and the repulsive potential energy $v_{ij}^{(r)}$, that is,

$$v_{ij}^{(t)} = \frac{-e^2}{|\mathbf{r}_{ij}|} + \lambda_{ij} e^{-|\mathbf{r}_{ij}|/\rho}$$

The total potential energy is then given the general expression

$$U = N\left(\frac{-MZ_iZ_je^2}{r_0} + 6\lambda_{+-}e^{-\sqrt{1}r_0/\rho} + 12\lambda_{++}e^{-\sqrt{2}r_0/\rho} + 8\lambda_{+-}e^{-\sqrt{3}r_0/\rho} + \cdots\right) \tag{3.10}$$

where the separate subscripts on the coefficient λ indicate that this coefficient is not the same when referring to the interaction of like and of unlike charged ions.

The cohesive energy of the NaCl lattice is obtained by determining the value of the potential U at the equilibrium lattice spacing r_0. There are many unknowns which appear in the expression for U; thus it is necessary, in principle, to have just as many restraints on U in order to determine these parameters. Because of the exponential dependence of the repulsive energy, we shall assume for simplicity that the series may be cut off after the first exponential term without losing too much accuracy. This gives for NaCl

$$U = N\left(\frac{-|M|e^2}{r_0} + 6\lambda_{+-}e^{-r_0/\rho}\right) \tag{3.11}$$

We are now left with two unknowns to determine; these are the values of λ and ρ at the equilibrium interionic separation r_0. In the following section, the two relations necessary to evaluate these parameters will be obtained from thermodynamic considerations.

3.3 Thermodynamics and the cohesive energy of the crystal lattice[1]

We shall now use the first and second laws of thermodynamics in order to obtain two conditions on the potential which will allow us to calculate the cohesive energy of the NaCl lattice. Combining the first law of thermodynamics

$$dQ = dU + p\,dV \tag{3.12}$$

with the second law of thermodynamics

$$dS = \frac{dQ}{T} \tag{3.13}$$

[1] For additional reading see Born and Mayer, *op. cit.;* Born and Huang, *op. cit.*, chap. I; R. A. Hutner and E. S. Rittner, *Philips Res. Repts.* 25, 1949.

we have
$$dS = \frac{dU}{T} + \frac{p}{T}\,dV \tag{3.14}$$

where S = entropy, U = internal energy, Q = injected energy from the outside of the crystal, p = pressure (exerted by the crystal on the outside), and V = molar volume of the crystal.

Substituting the expressions

$$\begin{aligned} dU(V,T) &= \left(\frac{\partial U}{\partial T}\right)_V dT + \left(\frac{\partial U}{\partial V}\right)_T dV \\ dS(V,T) &= \left(\frac{\partial S}{\partial T}\right)_V dT + \left(\frac{\partial S}{\partial V}\right)_T dV \end{aligned} \tag{3.15}$$

into Eq. (3.14), we have, after equating the coefficients of dV and of dT, the following equalities:

$$\left(\frac{\partial S}{\partial T}\right)_V = \frac{1}{T}\left(\frac{\partial U}{\partial T}\right)_V \tag{3.16}$$

$$\left(\frac{\partial S}{\partial V}\right)_T = \frac{1}{T}\left(\frac{\partial U}{\partial V}\right)_T + \frac{p}{T} \tag{3.17}$$

Using the relation

$$\frac{\partial}{\partial V}\left(\frac{\partial S}{\partial T}\right)_V = \frac{\partial}{\partial T}\left(\frac{\partial S}{\partial V}\right)_T \tag{3.18}$$

together with Eqs. (3.16) and (3.17), we find that

$$\left(\frac{\partial U}{\partial V}\right)_T = T\left(\frac{\partial p}{\partial T}\right)_V - p \tag{3.19}$$

The quantity $(\partial p/\partial T)_V$ may be expressed in terms of measurable properties of the crystal lattice. At constant pressure, we have

$$dp(V,T) = \left(\frac{\partial p}{\partial V}\right)_T dV + \left(\frac{\partial p}{\partial T}\right)_V dT = 0$$

giving the following relation:

$$\left(\frac{\partial p}{\partial T}\right)_V = -\left(\frac{\partial p}{\partial V}\right)_T\left(\frac{\partial V}{\partial T}\right)_p = \frac{(1/V)(\partial V/\partial T)_p}{-(1/V)(\partial V/\partial p)_T} = \frac{\alpha}{\beta} \tag{3.20}$$

where $\alpha = \dfrac{1}{V}\left(\dfrac{\partial V}{\partial T}\right)_p \equiv$ volume coefficient of expansion of the crystal

$\beta = -\dfrac{1}{V}\left(\dfrac{\partial V}{\partial p}\right)_T \equiv$ coefficient of compressibility of the crystal

Substituting Eq. (3.20) into Eq. (3.19), we have the first required thermodynamic relation

$$\left(\frac{\partial U}{\partial V}\right)_T = T\frac{\alpha}{\beta} - p \tag{3.21}$$

The second thermodynamic relation is obtained by determining the second derivative $(\partial^2 U/\partial V^2)_T$ in terms of measurable quantities. If we differentiate Eq. (3.19) with respect to volume, we obtain

$$\begin{aligned}\left(\frac{\partial^2 U}{\partial V^2}\right)_T &= T\frac{\partial}{\partial V}\left(\frac{\partial p}{\partial T}\right)_V - \left(\frac{\partial p}{\partial V}\right)_T \\ &= \frac{T}{V}\frac{\partial}{\partial T}\left(V\frac{\partial p}{\partial V}\right)_T + \frac{1}{V\beta} \\ &= \frac{T}{V\beta^2}\left(\frac{\partial \beta}{\partial T}\right)_V + \frac{1}{V\beta}\end{aligned} \tag{3.22}$$

We now differentiate $\beta(p,T)$ with respect to temperature at constant volume and obtain

$$\left(\frac{\partial \beta}{\partial T}\right)_V = \left(\frac{\partial \beta}{\partial p}\right)_T\left(\frac{\partial p}{\partial T}\right)_V + \left(\frac{\partial \beta}{\partial T}\right)_p \tag{3.23}$$

or

$$\left(\frac{\partial \beta}{\partial T}\right)_V = \frac{\alpha}{\beta}\left(\frac{\partial \beta}{\partial p}\right)_T + \left(\frac{\partial \beta}{\partial T}\right)_p \tag{3.24}$$

Combining Eq. (3.24) with Eq. (3.22), we finally have

$$\left(\frac{\partial^2 U}{\partial V^2}\right)_T = \frac{1}{V\beta}\left[1 + T\frac{\alpha}{\beta^2}\left(\frac{\partial \beta}{\partial p}\right)_T + \frac{T}{\beta}\left(\frac{\partial \beta}{\partial T}\right)_p\right] \tag{3.25}$$

The first and second derivatives of the internal energy U with respect to the volume [Eqs. (3.21) and (3.25)] are the desired expressions that will enable us to calculate the two unknowns λ and ρ and thereby obtain the cohesive energy U.

It will be convenient to express our results in terms of the lattice constant r_0 instead of the molar volume V. Since in the NaCl structure we have $N/4$ cells per mole (i.e., there are four ion pairs per unit cell; see Fig. 3.1) and since the volume per cell is just $(2r_0)^3$, the volume per mole is

$$V = (2r_0)^3\frac{N}{4} = 2Nr_0^3 \tag{3.26}$$

Combining Eq. (3.26) with Eqs. (3.21) and (3.25), we have

$$\left(\frac{\partial U}{\partial r_0}\right)_T = 6Nr_0^2\left(T\frac{\alpha}{\beta} - p\right) \tag{3.21$'$}$$

$$\left(\frac{\partial^2 U}{\partial r_0^2}\right)_T = \frac{18Nr_0}{\beta}\left[1 + \frac{2\beta}{3}\left(T\frac{\alpha}{\beta} - p\right) + T\frac{\alpha}{\beta^2}\left(\frac{\partial \beta}{\partial p}\right)_T + \frac{T}{\beta}\left(\frac{\partial \beta}{\partial T}\right)_p\right] \tag{3.25$'$}$$

In the case where we have static equilibrium, $p = 0$ and

$$\left(\frac{\partial U}{\partial r_0}\right)_T = 6Nr_0^2T\frac{\alpha}{\beta} \tag{3.21''}$$

$$\left(\frac{\partial^2 U}{\partial r_0^2}\right)_T = \frac{18Nr_0}{\beta}\left\{1 + T\alpha\left[\frac{2}{3} + \frac{1}{\beta^2}\left(\frac{\partial\beta}{\partial p}\right)_T\right] + \frac{T}{\beta}\left(\frac{\partial\beta}{\partial T}\right)_p\right\} \tag{3.25''}$$

If we now impose conditions (3.21) and (3.25) at $T = 0°\text{K}$, we have [combining Eqs. (3.21″), (3.25), and (3.11)] the following relations:

$$\left(\frac{\partial U}{\partial r_0}\right)_{\substack{T=0\\p=0}} = 0 = N\left(\frac{|M|e^2}{r_0^2} - \frac{6\lambda_{+-}e^{-r_0/\rho}}{\rho}\right) \tag{3.27}$$

$$\left(\frac{\partial^2 U}{\partial r_0^2}\right)_{\substack{T=0\\p=0}} = \frac{18Nr_0}{\beta_0} = N\left(-\frac{2|M|e^2}{r_0^3} + \frac{6\lambda_{+-}e^{-r_0/\rho}}{\rho^2}\right) \tag{3.28}$$

where β_0 is the value of the compressibility at $T = 0°\text{K}$. We may now solve Eqs. (3.27) and (3.28) for ρ and λ_{+-} (at $T = 0°\text{K}$).

$$\rho^{(0)} = \frac{|M|e^2\beta_0 r_0}{2|M|e^2\beta_0 + 18r_0^4} \tag{3.29}$$

$$\lambda_{+-}^{(0)} = \frac{|M|e^2\rho}{6r_0^2}e^{r_0/\rho^{(0)}} \tag{3.30}$$

The cohesive energy is given by the following expression:

$$U_0 = N\left(-\frac{|M|e^2}{r_0} + 6\lambda_{+-}^{(0)}e^{-r_0/\rho^{(0)}}\right) \tag{3.31}$$

Substituting the lattice constant $r_0 = 2.814$ Å, the compressibility $\beta_0 = 4.26 \times 10^{-12}$ cm²/dyne, and $|M| = 1.7476$ into Eqs. (3.27), (3.30), and (3.31), we find that the cohesive energy of NaCl is $U_0 = 182$ kcal/mole. The experimental value is $U_0 = 184.7$ kcal/mole. The calculated and measured values for the cohesive energies of the alkali halides are given (in kilocalories per mole) in Table 3.4.

An error introduced in the calculation of the cohesive energies results from the use of the value of the compressibility at room temperature whereas the theoretical expression (3.31) was derived for β at $T = 0°\text{K}$. There is also some error introduced in the neglect of higher terms in the repulsive potential (3.10). This error should be significant only in the cases of those alkali halides in which one type of ion is very small and the other type of ion is very large. In such a case there would be an appreciable overlap of the electron clouds of a given ion and its next-nearest neighbors as well as its nearest neighbors. The repulsive

TABLE 3.4 *Cohesive Energies of the Alkali Halides*

Substance	r_0, Å	β (*at room temp.*), $cm^2/dyne \times 10^{-12}$	*Cohesive energy, kcal/mole* Eq. (3.31)	*Exper.*
LiF	2.010	1.17	254	
LiCl	2.572	3.41	196	201.5
LiBr	2.745	4.31	184	191.5
LiI	3.000	6.01	169	180.0
NaF	2.310	2.11	220	
NaCl	2.814	4.26	182	184.7
NaBr	2.981	5.08	173	175.9
NaI	3.231	7.07	159	166.3
KF	2.665	3.30	193	
KCl	3.639	5.63	166	167.8
KBr	3.293	6.70	158	161.2
KI	3.526	8.54	148	152.8
RbF	2.815	4.10	183	
RbCl	3.270	6.65	159	163.3
RbBr	3.427	7.94	152	158.0
RbI	3.663	9.57	143	149.7
CsF	3.004	4.25	175	
CsCl	3.559	5.95	150	157.8
CsBr	3.713	7.6	143	152.3
CsI	3.95	8.57	135	145.4

potential for a crystal such as LiI should then include at least the first two terms of the total expansion, giving

$$v_{ij}^{(r)} = 6\lambda_{+-}e^{-r_0/\rho_{+-}} + 12\lambda_{++}e^{-\sqrt{2}r_0/\rho_{++}} \tag{3.32}$$

There is also some error introduced in our assumption that the lattice is at static equilibrium ($p = 0$) since even at $T = 0°K$ the crystal lattice is oscillating in its zero-point mode.

One of the striking differences between ionic crystals and other types of bonded crystals is the great difference in the magnitudes of their respective cohesive energies. For example, the cohesive energy of the NaCl crystal is 184 kcal/mole, whereas the cohesive energy of Na metal is only 26 kcal/mole. The tighter binding of the ionic crystal is due to the fact that the electrons that participate in the bonding mechanism spend much more time in the bound states of the interacting ions than they do out of the bound states. These electrons may be described by wave functions made up of a linear combination of a very small number of atomic-orbital states and are therefore more localized in the immediate vicinity of the interacting ions than elsewhere in the crystal. (The tight-binding approximation will be discussed in more detail in Chap. 8.) On the other hand, the electrons that participate in the bonding of metals must be shared over the entire lattice without very much preference for any particular location in the crystal. This result is obvious from the high electrical conductivity in metals. As a first approximation, one can consider the valence electron in the metal to be free and thus it may be described by a wave function which has the form of a plane wave. (For the purpose of comparison with the small number of atomic orbitals which describe the bonding electron in the ionic crystal, note that the plane wave may be expressed as an infinite sum of orbital waves.[1]) The plane-wave description of the electron implies an equal probability for the occurrence of the electron at any location in the crystal. The free-electron model of metals will be discussed in detail in Chap. 6.

3.4 Electronic properties of ionic crystals

It is recalled from elementary atomic physics that, as the charge of the nucleus is built up, electrons must be added to the system in order to maintain the charge neutrality of the atom. These electrons fall into discrete energy levels, characterized by three quantum numbers (n, l, s), which are characteristic of the charge distribution in the atom. The binding energy of the electrons in the atom is strongest for those electrons closest to the nucleus (i.e., the electrons in the energy states characterized by the minimum principal quantum number n). The binding energy of electrons in states with increasing orbital radii then decreases until we reach the outermost electron in the energy state which is characterized by the maximum principal quantum number and orbital-momentum quantum number. These are the most loosely bound electrons and are referred to as the valence electrons. Let us now carry the analysis of the electronic-energy-level structure of atoms one step further by considering the influence that the lattice of an ionic crystal would have on the electronic energy levels of any constituent ion. Once again, let us imagine that we have N anions and N cations, arranged on a typical lattice structure but in which the ions are initially an infinite distance apart.

Electronic Energy Levels of Ionic Crystals

Let us assume that we have a perfect ionic NaCl crystal, which is in static equilibrium, has no surface (i.e., it is infinite in extent), and has no imperfections such as ion vacancies, interstitial or substitutional foreign impurities, cracks, etc. We shall calculate the energy-level scheme of this crystal in a fashion which is not precise but does indicate the behavior of the constituent electrons in the crystal.

[1] See L. I. Schiff, "Quantum Mechanics," chap. 5, sec. 19, McGraw-Hill Book Company, Inc., New York, 1955.

Let us consider a crystal made up of Na^+ anions, with the electronic configuration $1s^22s^22p^6$ and Cl^- cations with the electronic configuration $1s^22s^22p^63s^23p^6$. We shall neglect the distorting effect of the cubic crystalline field on the spherical symmetry of the ground states of the Na^+ and Cl^- ions and shall assume that they are in their normal *free-ion* S states. Since all but the outermost electrons are electrostatically shielded from the crystalline field, we shall assume that the low-lying free-ion energy levels of the inner electrons of the Na^+ and Cl^- ions are unperturbed. Our calculation will deal only with the electrons down to the $2p$ shell of Na and the $3p$ shell of Cl.

In our calculation of the energy-level structure of NaCl, we are concerned with the energy required to transfer an electron from the electronic configuration of one ion to the electronic configuration of another ion (which may be either far from or close to the original ion).[1] We shall assume initially that the energy levels of the ions are discrete and equal for each ion in the crystal, so that a given energy level of the NaCl crystal is simply the energy that corresponds to a state of one of the crystalline ions (Na^+ or Cl^-) multiplied by the number of (Na^+ or Cl^-) ions in the crystal. We shall consider two types of electron transfer. The first process deals with the transfer of an electron from one ion to another ion which is an infinite distance away from it. This process will be referred to as a *conduction* process. The second process deals with the transfer of an electron from one ion to a neighboring ion (i.e., an ion which is close enough to be influenced by the original ion). This process will be referred to as an *exciton* process. The reason for these nomenclatures will become clear in the following discussion.

The excitation $Cl^-(3p) \rightarrow Na(3s)$ Let us first determine the approximate energy ($h\nu$) for the conduction process in which an electron is transferred from the $3p$ state of Cl^- to the $3s$ state of a Na^+ ion which is an infinite distance away. To do this we use the Born-Haber-cycle method. Thus,

$$Cl^-(3p^6) + Na^+(2p^6) \rightarrow Cl(3p^5) + Na(2p^63s) + h\nu \qquad (3.33)$$

We may calculate $h\nu$ by considering the following cycle:

1. The energy $\epsilon(Cl^-)$ required to remove a Cl^- ion from the crystal
2. The energy $\epsilon(Na^+)$ required to remove from the crystal a Na^+ ion which is an infinite distance away from the Cl^- vacancy
3. The energy $A_{3p}(Cl^-)$ required to remove an electron from the $3p$ shell of the isolated Cl^- ion ($Cl^- \rightarrow Cl$)

[1] In the discussion that follows, use is made of the calculational procedure (introduced originally by M. Born) known as the Born-Haber cycle. A discussion similar to the one that follows is given by Hutner and Rittner, *op. cit.*

4. The energy $-I_{3s}(\mathrm{Na}^+)$ gained when this electron is transferred to the 3s state of the Na^+ ion ($\mathrm{Na}^+ \rightarrow \mathrm{Na}$)

5. The energy $-\epsilon(\mathrm{Cl})$ gained when replacing the Cl atom in the site vacated by the original Cl^- ion

6. The energy $-\epsilon(\mathrm{Na})$ gained when replacing the Na atom in the original site vacated by the Na^+ ion

The energy required to transfer the electron from the 3p state of Cl^- to the 3s state of Na (in the NaCl crystal) is given simply by the sum of the energies required for processes 1 through 6.

$$h\nu[\mathrm{Cl}^-(3p) \rightarrow \mathrm{Na}(3s)] = \epsilon(\mathrm{Cl}^-) + \epsilon(\mathrm{Na}^+) + A_{3p}(\mathrm{Cl}^-) - I_{3s}(\mathrm{Na}^+) - \epsilon(\mathrm{Cl}) - \epsilon(\mathrm{Na}) \qquad (3.34)$$

The electron affinity $A_{3p}(\mathrm{Cl}^-)$ and the ionization potential $I_{3s}(\mathrm{Na}^+)$ are known experimentally to have the approximate values

$$A_{3p}(\mathrm{Cl}^-) \simeq 3.72 \text{ ev} \qquad (3.35)$$

$$I_{3s}(\mathrm{Na}^+) \simeq 5.12 \text{ ev} \qquad (3.36)$$

The energies $\epsilon(\mathrm{Cl})$ and $\epsilon(\mathrm{Na})$ are given, according to Eq. (3.10), by the approximate expressions

$$\begin{aligned}\epsilon(\mathrm{Cl}) &= \frac{MZ(Z-1)e^2}{r_0} - 6\lambda_{+\mathrm{Cl}}e^{-r_0/\rho_{+\mathrm{Cl}}} \\ &= -6\lambda_{+\mathrm{Cl}}e^{-r_0/\rho_{+\mathrm{Cl}}} \qquad (Z = 1) \qquad (3.37)\\ \epsilon(\mathrm{Na}) &\simeq -6\lambda_{-\mathrm{Na}}e^{-r_0/\rho_{-\mathrm{Na}}} \qquad (3.38)\end{aligned}$$

The energies $\epsilon(\mathrm{Cl}^-)$ and $\epsilon(\mathrm{Na}^+)$ are somewhat more complicated to determine than $\epsilon(\mathrm{Cl})$ and $\epsilon(\mathrm{Na})$ because of the presence of a polarization energy which must be gained when an ion is removed from an ionic crystal. The required energies are given by the expressions

$$\epsilon(\mathrm{Cl}^-) = \frac{|M|e^2}{r_0} - 6\lambda_{+-}e^{-r_0/\rho_{+-}} - \epsilon(\mathrm{pol}-) \qquad (3.39)$$

$$\epsilon(\mathrm{Na}^+) = \frac{|M|e^2}{r_0} - 6\lambda_{+-}e^{-r_0/\rho_{+-}} - \epsilon(\mathrm{pol}+) \qquad (3.40)$$

Thus the energy required for this process is

$$h\nu = \frac{2|M|e^2}{r_0} - [\epsilon(\mathrm{pol}+) + \epsilon(\mathrm{pol}-)] + A_{3p}(\mathrm{Cl}^-) - I_{3s}(\mathrm{Na}^+) - 6e^{-r_0/\rho}[(\lambda_{+-} - \lambda_{+\mathrm{Cl}}) + (\lambda_{+-} - \lambda_{-\mathrm{Na}})] \qquad (3.41)$$

Since the radius of the Cl^- ion is slightly larger than the radius of the chlorine atom, we should expect that the magnitude of the repulsive overlap potential should be larger for the ion than it is for the atom;

hence $(\lambda_{+-} - \lambda_{+\text{Cl}}) > 0$. Similarly, the radius of the Na^+ ion is smaller than the radius of the Na atom and we should expect the quantity $(\lambda_{+-} - \lambda_{-\text{Na}}) < 0$. Thus, the two parts of the last bracketed term in Eq. (3.41) tend to cancel each other. Using this argument as a justification, we shall assume, for the purpose of simplicity, that an exact cancellation occurs. Taking the values

$$|M| = 1.7476 \qquad r_0 = 2.813 \times 10^{-8} \text{ cm}$$

and the values for $I_{3s}(\text{Na}^+)$ and $A_{3p}(\text{Cl}^-)$ given in Eqs. (3.35) and (3.36), the desired energy may be reduced to the form

$$h\nu[\text{Cl}^-(3p) \rightarrow \text{Na}(3s)] = 16.35 - [\epsilon(\text{pol}+) + \epsilon(\text{pol}-)] \quad \text{ev} \qquad (3.42)$$

Energy required to polarize an ionic crystal It is clear from the arrangement of the anions and cations in an ionic crystal (Fig. 3.1) that one may view this crystal as an assembly of electric dipoles arranged on a lattice. The electric field associated with each dipole is exactly canceled out by the electric field of an equal and oppositely oriented electric dipole in the lattice. Thus there is no polarization effect in the perfect lattice. The removal of one constituent ion [let us say the ion at (000)] would electrostatically unbalance the entire lattice and produce a net polarization. The removal of this ion would result in the pulling in of the (100) ion by the (200) ion [or a displacement of the ion at (100) away from the (000) location would occur], and the subsequent displacement of all the ions in the lattice would also occur. If φ_i represents the electrostatic potential due to a single electric dipole, then the total potential $\varphi = \sum_i \varphi_i$ is the potential due to all the electric dipoles in the lattice. As we have just illustrated, the removal of a negative ion at (000) produces a vacancy which acts like a positive charge; i.e., it tends to repel the neighboring ions. Thus there is a gain in energy due to the polarization of the lattice when an ion is removed from an ionic crystal.

There are two types of polarization produced in an ionic crystal. These are caused by (1) a displacement of the electronic charge cloud with respect to its parent nucleus and (2) a displacement of a given ion with respect to the remaining ions in the lattice, respectively. For the solution of our particular problem, we shall consider only the latter type of polarization. The energy required to polarize the lattice is, according to Maxwell's equations,

$$\epsilon(\text{pol}) = \frac{1}{8\pi} \int_{\substack{\text{crystal}\\ \text{volume}}} \mathbf{E} \cdot \mathbf{D} \, dV \qquad (3.43)$$

where

$$\mathbf{E} = -\nabla \sum_i \varphi_i \qquad (3.44)$$

and φ_i is the electrostatic potential due to the electric dipole at the site of the ion i.

If we consider the vacancy left by the removal of the charged ion to be surrounded by a conducting spherical shell, with the following boundary conditions on the surface of the spherical shell

$$\rho = 0 \qquad \varphi = \text{const} \tag{3.45}$$

the combination of (3.43) to (3.45) gives for the polarization energy[1]

$$\epsilon(\text{pol}) = -\frac{1}{2} e \sum_i \varphi_i = -\frac{1}{2} e \sum_i \frac{\mu_i}{r_i^2} \tag{3.46}$$

where μ_i is the electric dipole moment of a constituent ion. There are two ions with dipole moments μ_1 and μ_2 in a volume $2r_0^3$ in our lattice. Thus the dipole moment per unit volume (i.e., the polarization) is[2]

$$\mathbf{P} = \frac{\boldsymbol{\mu}_1 + \boldsymbol{\mu}_2}{2r_0^3} \tag{3.47}$$

Also, from Maxwell's equations we have

$$\mathbf{D} = \mathbf{E} + 4\pi\mathbf{P} = \hat{\mathbf{r}}\frac{e}{r^2} = \kappa_0\mathbf{E} \tag{3.48}$$

where κ_0 is the static dielectric constant of the crystal. From (3.48) and (3.47), the polarization may be expressed in the form

$$|\mathbf{P}| = \frac{e}{4\pi r^2}\left(1 - \frac{1}{\kappa_0}\right) = \frac{|\boldsymbol{\mu}_1 + \boldsymbol{\mu}_2|}{2r_0^3} \tag{3.49}$$

giving, with $\boldsymbol{\mu}_1$ parallel to $\boldsymbol{\mu}_2$

$$|\boldsymbol{\mu}_1| = 2r_0^3 \frac{\mu_1}{\mu_1 + \mu_2} \frac{1}{4\pi}\left(1 - \frac{1}{\kappa_0}\right)\frac{e}{r^2} \tag{3.50}$$

$$|\boldsymbol{\mu}_2| = 2r_0^3 \frac{\mu_2}{\mu_1 + \mu_2} \frac{1}{4\pi}\left(1 - \frac{1}{\kappa_0}\right)\frac{e}{r^2} \tag{3.51}$$

The electric dipole moment μ_i which is induced in the ith ion is proportional to the electric field intensity at the site of that ion (i.e., the local field $\mathbf{E}_i^{(loc)}$):

$$\boldsymbol{\mu}_i = \alpha_i \mathbf{E}_i^{(loc)}$$

where α_i is called the polarizability of the ion. If we are allowed to make the assumption that the local electric field intensity is the same at all

[1] See, for example, J. A. Stratton, "Electromagnetic Theory," sec. 2.7, McGraw-Hill Book Company, Inc., 1941.

[2] See N. F. Mott and M. J. Littleton, *Trans. Faraday Soc.*, **34:** 485 (1938).

ion sites in the lattice, we have the equality

$$\frac{\mu_i}{\mu_1 + \mu_2} = \frac{\alpha_i}{\alpha_1 + \alpha_2} \qquad i = 1, 2 \tag{3.52}$$

The polarizability of an ion is measured by spectroscopic means, and it may be calculated by the methods of quantum mechanics. Let us assume that the polarizabilities of ions are known quantities; then the electric dipole moment of the ith ion may be expressed in the following form:

$$\mu_i = \xi_i r_0^3 \frac{e}{r_i^2} \tag{3.53}$$

where

$$\xi_i = \frac{2\alpha_i}{\alpha_1 + \alpha_2} \frac{1}{4\pi} \left(1 - \frac{1}{\kappa_0}\right) \tag{3.54}$$

Combining Eqs. (3.53) and (3.54) with Eq. (3.46), we have

$$\begin{aligned} \epsilon(\text{pol}) &= \frac{e^2 r_0^3}{2} \sum_{i=1}^{2} \frac{\xi_i}{r_i^4} \\ &= \frac{e^2}{2r_0} \left\{ \xi_1 \left[\frac{6}{(\sqrt{1})^4} + \frac{8}{(\sqrt{3})^4} + \cdots \right] \right. \\ &\qquad \left. + \xi_2 \left[\frac{12}{(\sqrt{2})^4} + \frac{6}{(\sqrt{4})^4} + \cdots \right] \right\} \end{aligned} \tag{3.55}$$

The first bracketed sum on the right-hand side of Eq. (3.55) represents the sum over the contributions to the polarization energy from the electric dipole moments of oppositely charged ions at the odd-neighbored sites from the ion which has been removed [at (000)] (i.e., nearest neighbor, next to the next-nearest neighbor, etc.). Similarly, the second sum represents the contribution from the electric dipole moments of equally charged ions at the even-neighbored sites from (000). These sums may be evaluated by the method outlined by Born and Huang.[1] The result obtained is as follows:

$$\epsilon(\text{pol}) = \frac{e^2}{r_0} (5.0988\xi_1 + 3.1673\xi_2) \tag{3.55'}$$

Thus the polarization energies required for the calculation of the NaCl energy-level structure are

$$\epsilon(\text{pol}+) = \frac{e^2}{r_0} [5.0988\xi(\text{Na}^+) + 3.1673\xi(\text{Cl}^-)] \tag{3.56}$$

$$\epsilon(\text{pol}-) = \frac{e^2}{r_0} [5.0988\xi(\text{Cl}^-) + 3.1673\xi(\text{Na}^+)] \tag{3.57}$$

[1] *Op. cit.*

Using the polarizabilities given by Shockley,[1]

$$\alpha(Na^+) = 0.28 \times 10^{-24}\ cm^3 \qquad \alpha(Cl^-) = 2.92 \times 10^{-24}\ cm^3$$

the dielectric constant which is associated with the polarization due to ionic displacement (Born and Huang) as

$$\kappa_0 = 2.25$$

and the lattice parameter $r_0 = 2.813 \times 10^{-8}$ cm, we obtain

$$\epsilon(\text{pol}+) = 1.49 \text{ ev} \qquad \epsilon(\text{pol}-) = 2.25 \text{ ev} \tag{3.58}$$

Combining Eqs. (3.58) and (3.42), the energy-level separation between the $Cl^-(3p)$ level and the $Na(3s)$ level becomes

$$h\nu[Cl^-(3p) \rightarrow Na(3s)] = 12.61 \text{ ev} \tag{3.59}$$

The excitation $Cl^-(3p) \rightarrow Na(3p)$ Let us now consider the energy required to excite an electron from the $3p$ shell of Cl^- to the $3p$ shell of a Na^+ ion which is an infinite distance away. The reaction considered is

$$Cl^-(3p^6) + Na^+(2p^6) \rightarrow Cl(3p^5) + Na(2p^6 3p) + h\nu \tag{3.60}$$

This calculation duplicates the previous calculation for the transition (3.33) except that the ionization energy which is gained when bringing the electron into the electronic configuration of sodium is less when we transfer it to the $3p$ shell instead of the $3s$ shell of that atom. The difference in the energies required to ionize an electron from the $3s$ state of Na and the $3p$ state of Na is 2.09 ev. Thus we have

$$h\nu[Cl^-(3p) \rightarrow Na(3p)] = 12.61 + 2.09 = 14.70 \text{ ev} \tag{3.61}$$

The excitation $Na^+(2p^6) \rightarrow Na(2p^6 3s)$ Following the same procedure as that in the preceding subsection, we consider the following cycle:

1. Remove a Na^+ ion from the crystal.
2. Remove another Na^+ ion, which is an infinite distance from the Na^+ ion vacancy left by the first ion, from the crystal.
3. Remove a $3s$ electron from one of the Na^+ ions.

$$(Na^+ \rightarrow Na^{++} + e)$$

4. Transfer this electron to the $3s$ state of the other Na^+ ion.

$$(Na^+ + e \rightarrow Na)$$

5. Replace the Na^{++} ion in one of the Na^+ vacancies.
6. Replace the Na atom in the other Na^+ vacancy.

[1] W. Shockley, *Phys. Rev.*, **70**: 105 (1946).

The excitation energy is

$$
\begin{aligned}
h\nu &= 2\epsilon(\mathrm{Na}^+) + I_{3s}(\mathrm{Na}^+ \rightarrow \mathrm{Na}^{++}) - I_{3s}(\mathrm{Na} \rightarrow \mathrm{Na}^+) \\
&\quad - \epsilon(\mathrm{Na}^{++}) - \epsilon(\mathrm{Na}) \\
&= \frac{2Me^2}{r_0} - 2\epsilon(\mathrm{pol}+) + I(\mathrm{Na}^+ \rightarrow \mathrm{Na}^{++}) - I(\mathrm{Na} \rightarrow \mathrm{Na}^+) \\
&\quad - \frac{2Me^2}{r_0} + \epsilon(\mathrm{pol}\ 2+)
\end{aligned}
\tag{3.62}
$$

Taking $\epsilon(\mathrm{pol}\ 2+) = 2\epsilon(\mathrm{pol}+)$ and using the values

$$
\begin{aligned}
I(\mathrm{Na}^+ \rightarrow \mathrm{Na}^{++}) &= 47.10 \text{ ev} \\
I(\mathrm{Na} \rightarrow \mathrm{Na}^+) &= 5.12 \text{ ev}
\end{aligned}
$$

we have

$$
h\nu[\mathrm{Na}^+(2p^6) \rightarrow \mathrm{Na}(2p^63s)] = 41.98 \text{ ev} \tag{3.63}
$$

The excitation $\mathrm{Na}^+(2p^63s) \rightarrow (\mathrm{Na}^+)^*(2p^63p)$ The energy cycle here is as follows:

1. Remove a Na^+ ion from the crystal.
2. Excite this Na^+ ion so that the $3s$ electron is promoted to the $3p$ state.
3. Replace the excited $(\mathrm{Na}^+)^*$ ion in the Na^+ ion vacancy.

The energy consumed in going through this process is

$$
\begin{aligned}
h\nu[\mathrm{Na}^+(2p^63s) \rightarrow (\mathrm{Na}^+)^*(2p^63p)] &\simeq \frac{Me^2}{r_0} - 6\lambda_{+-}e^{-r_0/\rho} \\
&\quad - \epsilon(\mathrm{pol}+) + \epsilon_{exc} - \frac{Me^2}{r_0} + 6\lambda_{+-}^*e^{-r_0/\rho^*} + \epsilon(\mathrm{pol}+) \\
&\simeq \epsilon_{exc} = 32.7 \text{ ev}
\end{aligned}
\tag{3.64}
$$

This result is obtained by assuming that the repulsive overlap potential is the same for a Na^+ ion and an excited $(\mathrm{Na}^+)^*$ ion. Actually, the radius of the excited ion is slightly larger than the radius of the unexcited ion, so that the overlap potential is greater for the excited than for the unexcited ion. This effect would result in the actual level lying somewhat higher than the ordinary ionic excitation energy ϵ_{exc}. As a $2p$ electron of Na^+ is promoted to higher and higher excited states, neglecting the difference in the overlap potential terms introduces successively larger errors.

Exciton[1] states of Cl^- The energy of an exciton state of an ion in a crystal refers to the energy required to transfer an electron from a constituent ion to an electron shell of a neighboring ion so that this electron still remains under the influence of the parent ion. Let us first consider

[1] The concept of the exciton was originally introduced by J. Frenkel, *Phys. Rev.*, **37**: 17 (1931); **37**: 1276 (1931).

the energy that is required to transfer an electron from the $3p$ state of Cl^- to the $3s$ state of a nearest-neighbor Na^+ ion. We shall refer to this energy as the first exciton state of Cl^-. The energy process involved in calculating this energy is the same as the case of a transfer of an electron to the $3s$ shell of a distant Na^+ ion except that, once the Cl^- ion is removed the energy required to remove a Na^+ ion adjacent to the Cl^- cavity is different from that in the former case. Denoting this energy by $\epsilon'(Na^+)$, we have

$$h\nu[Cl^-(3p) \rightarrow Na(3s)_{nn}] = \epsilon(Cl^-) + \epsilon'(Na^+) + A_{3p}(Cl^-) - I_{3s}(Na^+) - \epsilon(Cl) - \epsilon(Na) \quad (3.65)$$

where all terms are the same as in Eq. (3.34) except $\epsilon'(Na^+)$:

$$\epsilon'(Na^+) = \frac{(M-1)e^2}{r_0} - \epsilon'(pol+) - 6\lambda'_{+-}e^{-r_0/\rho} \quad (3.66)$$

As before, we shall assume that the overlap repulsive potential is canceled by the similar terms in the other parts of (3.65). If we now calculate $\epsilon'(pol+) + \epsilon(pol-)$ by assuming that both the Cl^- and the neighboring Na^+ ions are removed from the lattice simultaneously, the result obtained is

$$\epsilon'(pol+) + \epsilon(pol-) = \frac{2.025}{2\pi r_0}\left(1 - \frac{1}{\kappa_0}\right) = 0.93 \text{ ev} \quad (3.67)$$

Thus,

$$h\nu[Cl^-(3p) \rightarrow Na(3s)_{nn}] = \frac{Me^2}{r_0} + \frac{(M-1)e^2}{r_0} - [\epsilon'(pol+) + \epsilon(pol-)] + A_{3p}(Cl^-) - I_{3s}(Na^+) = 10.3 \text{ ev} \quad (3.68)$$

The second exciton state is obtained by calculating the energy required to transfer a $3p$ electron from the Cl^- ion to a $3s$ shell of a Na^+ ion which is a distance $\sqrt{3}\, r_0$ away. The Madelung energy in this case is $(M - 1/\sqrt{3})e^2/r_0$. The exciton states differ from each other in energy by the Madelung terms

$$\frac{e^2}{r_0}\left[(M-1), \left(M - \frac{1}{\sqrt{3}}\right), \left(M - \frac{1}{\sqrt{5}}\right), \ldots, \left(M - \frac{1}{\sqrt{2n+1}}\right), \ldots\right]$$

As n increases to large values, it becomes less meaningful to refer to the states as *exciton states*, since the electron is getting so far from its original parent ion that it no longer feels its influence to any great extent. In the limit, as n approaches infinity, the exciton state approaches the conduction state $Na(3s)$. These states are shown schematically in Fig. 3.4.

The excitation $(Na)_1 + (Na^+)_2 \rightarrow (Na^+)_1 + (Na)_2$ Let us first calculate the energy required to transfer an electron from the $3s$ state of a sodium atom in the lattice to the $3s$ state of another sodium ion which is an infinite distance from the first sodium ion. We consider the following energy process:

1. Remove a Na atom from the lattice.
2. Remove from the lattice a Na^+ ion which is an infinite distance from the Na atom vacancy.
3. Ionize the Na atom.
4. Add this electron to the Na^+ ion to form a sodium atom.

$$(Na^+)_2(2p^6) + e \rightarrow (Na)_2(2p^63s)$$

5. Replace the Na^+ ion in the Na atom vacancy.
6. Replace the Na atom in the Na^+ ion vacancy.

The energy required to go through this cycle is

$$\begin{aligned} h\nu[(Na)_1(3s) + (Na^+)_2(2p^6) \rightarrow (Na^+)_1(2p^6) + (Na)_2(3s)] \\ = \epsilon(Na) + \epsilon(Na^+) + I_{3s}(Na) - I_{3s}(Na) - \epsilon(Na) - \epsilon(Na^+) = 0 \end{aligned}$$

Under the simplifying assumptions that we have made, it appears that any one $3s$ electron which belongs to a given parent sodium atom may move about among all the other Na^+ ions, transforming them into atoms and leaving Na^+ ions in its wake, without expending any energy. This is a case of perfect electrical conduction since the lattice seems to offer no resistance to the flow of this electronic charge. The application of an external electric field would tend to accelerate these charges in a preferred direction and give rise to electrical current, undeterred by the lattice. In Chap. 7 we shall study the behavior of a free-electron gas in the periodic potential of a crystal lattice. We shall discover there that the rigorous quantum-mechanical description of the scattering of conduction electrons by a static periodic lattice also leads to a vanishing of the resistivity which the lattice offers to the flow of electrons. The detailed study of the behavior of free electrons in a crystal and under the influence of an external electric field does, however, lead to the result that the inertial mass with which the electrons resist the force due to the applied field is not necessarily the same as the free-electron mass, and it is, in general, velocity-dependent. In fact, it is not possible, in the most general case, to ascribe a mass to the electron in the crystal. When simplifying assumptions permit a mass to be defined, it is referred to as the effective mass.

The excitation $(Cl)_1 + (Cl^-)_2 \rightarrow (Cl^-)_1 + (Cl)_2$ Following the same procedure as described in the preceding discussion, it is seen that there is no energy required for the transfer of an electron vacancy from the $3p$ shell of one Cl atom to any Cl^- ion in the lattice. Such a process is referred to as "hole conduction," since the passage in one direction of an electron from the closed $3p$ shell of a Cl^- ion to fill the $3p$ shell of some Cl atom in the lattice (forming Cl^- and leaving a Cl atom behind) is equivalent to the passage in the opposite direction of the electron vacancy, or "hole," from one $3p$ shell to the other of the chlorine ions. The inertial mass with which the hole resists a force caused by an external electric field is not necessarily the same as the inertial mass of an electron. Thus, it is necessary, in general, to treat hole conductivity and electron conductivity separately and the electron effective mass and the hole effective mass separately.

It is interesting to note that predictions of this model, a model depending on electrons which are rather tightly bound to their parent ions, display features similar to predictions of the free-electron model, in which it is assumed that electrons may not be associated with any particular constituent ion of the lattice (Chap. 6).

Energy bands It has been tacitly assumed in this section that the electronic clouds of constituent ions of an ionic crystal are not interacting with each other. Under this assumption, the relative locations of the energy levels that we have calculated for the states of the ions are equivalent to the relative locations of the energy levels of the entire crystal, and the locations of the crystal energy levels are obtained by multiplying the magnitudes of the energy of the level of a single ion by the number of ions in the lattice. Thus, each energy level of the crystal is, under these simplifying assumptions, N-fold degenerate. As soon as we allow interaction to take place between the ions in the crystal, the energies of the valence electrons of neighboring ions become slightly different, with some valence electrons gaining energy and some valence electrons losing energy. The result is that the N-fold degeneracy is lifted, and the discrete levels of our previous model broaden into energy bands, in which the energy levels may be considered to be in a quasi continuum. The width of the energy band for a given state in the crystal depends on the relative magnitude of the interaction between the valence electron and the surrounding crystal, and the binding energy of this electron to its parent ion. Thus, the looser the binding of the electron to its parent ion, the broader will be the band in which this electron is found. On the basis of this analysis, we should expect the $Na^+(2p)$ band to be quite narrow, the $Cl^-(3p)$ band to be broader, and the $Na(3s)$ and the $Na(3p)$ bands to be quite broad [in fact, the $Na(3s)$ and $Na(3p)$ bands actually overlap]. The exciton energy bands should be very narrow, since they arise from the interaction between a very small number of ions. The results of the previous discussion are shown schematically in Fig. 3.4. Note that the uppermost band describes conduction electrons having the symmetry properties of a charge distribution which is made up of a mixture of both "s-like" electrons ($l = 0$) and "p-like" electrons ($l = 1$).

Many of the electrical and optical properties of an ionic crystal such as NaCl are determined by the electronic-energy-level structure, such as the one shown in Fig. 3.4. It is clear from this diagram that NaCl will absorb radiation very strongly in the ultraviolet region of the light spectrum ($h\nu > 10$ ev) but that it will not absorb radiation in the visible part of the spectrum ($h\nu \sim 1$ ev). Thus, single crystals of NaCl should be transparent to visible light but strongly absorbent in the ultraviolet end of the spectrum. The electrons that absorb ultraviolet

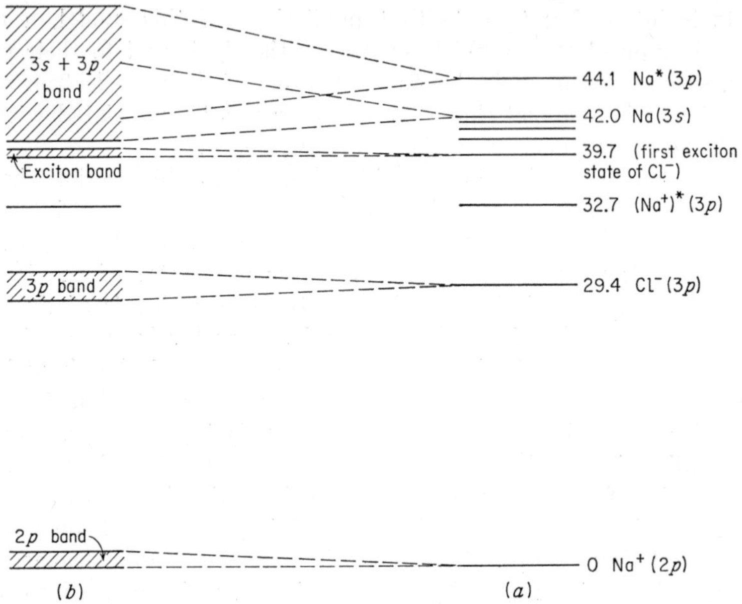

Fig. 3.4. (*a*) Discrete energy levels of the NaCl crystal. (*b*) Typical broadening into energy bands when the interactions between the ions are taken into account. The ordinate is in units of electron volts. The abscissa represents the distance between the ions, with (*b*) occurring at the equilibrium separation r_0.

light and are excited up to the $3s + 3p$ conduction band of NaCl should be very mobile (i.e., the electrical conductivity of NaCl should increase when the proper frequency of radiation impinges on the crystal), whereas electrons that are excited into exciton bands would still be tightly bound and the electrical conductivity should remain very low. These predictions of the energy-band model are borne out by experimental evidence. In fact, the experimental evidence of a large "dark" electrical resistivity and a small "light" electrical resistivity[1] of NaCl appeared strange indeed until the energy-band picture was able to give meaning to it.

[1] The term "dark" (or "light") electrical resistivity refers to the electrical resistivity of a substance when electromagnetic radiation is not (or is) impinging on that substance.

The symmetry properties of electron distributions in the various bands in the crystal may be investigated by means of an observation of the effects of the absorption of polarized radiation. For example, the excitation of a $Cl^-(3p)$ electron to the $(Na^+)^*(3p)$ level by the absorption of electric dipole radiation is forbidden, whereas the excitation of a $Cl^-(3p)$ electron to the first exciton band of $Cl^-(3s)$ by electric dipole radiation is allowed. This selection rule may be considered equivalent to the principle of the conservation of angular momentum. In the first case, the initial and final states of the electron are both associated with p-state symmetry; this is equivalent to saying that the electron in each state has one unit of angular momentum. Electric dipole radiation carries with it one unit of angular momentum. Thus, if an electron has initially one unit of angular momentum and if it absorbs one unit of angular momentum, it must in the final state have two units of angular momentum (D-state symmetry) or no angular momentum (S-state symmetry), depending on whether its initial state of angular momentum was parallel or antiparallel to the angular momentum of the absorbed radiation. Thus there is a threshold value for the excitation of an electron in the $Cl^-(3p)$ band to the exciton band $Cl^-(3s)$. This value is the magnitude of the forbidden-energy gap between the two bands.

In situations in which the crystal does not have cubic symmetry but rather has a preferred axis associated with its symmetry, there would generally be separate threshold values for the absorption of electric dipole radiation which is (1) polarized parallel to the crystal axis (C axis) and (2) polarized perpendicular to the crystal axis. Thus the absorption of polarized radiation provides a powerful tool for the study of the properties of energy bands of crystals. In Chap. 9 we shall discuss in more detail the nature of the interaction between the quasi-free-electron gas which characterizes a metal or a semiconductor and polarized monochromatic electromagnetic radiation.

In conclusion, we should note that, although the ionic crystal differs from the covalent and metallic types of crystals in their initially assumed bonding mechanisms, there is a great similarity in the electronic properties of the different bonded types of crystals. Since the electronic behavior plays a vital role in the bonding mechanism itself, it appears that the actual binding energy of ionic as well as covalent and metallic crystals is never purely of those types but in general has properties with the features of all the types of bonding mechanisms that are encountered in crystals.

The discussion presented in this chapter was semiclassical. The macroscopic details, the thermodynamics, and classical electrical forces were emphasized. The purpose was, however, to show why it was absolutely necessary to introduce some nonclassical notions to explain macroscopic properties. Thus, the overlap potential resulting from the required imposition of the Pauli exclusion principle was found to be necessary to ensure the stability of an ionic crystal. Next, the introduction of the details of the electronic configuration was necessary in order to derive the energy-band structure, which in turn provided the first reasonable explanation for electronic processes in ionic crystals.

In the chapter that follows, we explore further the influence of symmetry on the energy-level structure of ionic crystals. For this, it becomes necessary to go more extensively into the quantum-mechanical nature of the system and to exploit further the group-theory methods developed in the preceding chapter.

4 crystal field theory

IN THIS chapter we wish to derive some of the important physical effects which point-group symmetry can have on crystals. The approach adopted here is to consider the properties of a single constituent ion of a crystal to be subjected to an average electrostatic field that is due to all the other ions of the lattice. This approach (called the Heitler-London approximation) is extremely useful in considerations of ionic crystals. For example, the methods and results to be developed here are useful in interpreting the properties of those ionic crystals which are paramagnetic (see Chap. 5).

The Heitler-London approach is, then, to ask the question: What is the effect of the surrounding crystal lattice on the energy levels and the corresponding eigenfunctions of an (otherwise) free ion? The answer is obtained from the solutions of the Schroedinger wave equation

$$(\mathcal{H}_0 - E)\psi = e\varphi_c\psi \tag{4.1}$$

The free-ion hamiltonian is

$$\mathcal{H}_0 = \sum_{i=1}^{n} \left(-\frac{\hbar^2}{2m_i} \nabla_i^2 - e\varphi_0 + \lambda \mathbf{s}_i \cdot \mathbf{l}_i \right) \tag{4.2}$$

where the three terms in (4.2) correspond, respectively, to (1) the kinetic energy, (2) the Coulomb potential acting on each constituent atomic electron due to the parent nucleus and sister electrons, and (3) the spin-orbit interaction. The added term $e\varphi_c$ is the electrostatic potential energy which is due to the entire lattice, excluding the considered ion, at the site of that ion.

Before examining the properties of the wave equation (4.1), we must first consider the actual functional form of the crystalline electrostatic potential φ_c (which would be compatible with each of the 32 crystallographic point-group symmetries discussed in Chap. 2). We shall then introduce further properties of the point groups which will enable us to determine the effect of the potential φ_c on the degeneracy of the free-ion energy levels. It will be seen that the crystal potential φ_c, being of a lower degree of symmetry than the free-ion potential φ_0, must necessarily lift some of the degeneracy of the free-ion system by splitting the free-ion energy levels.[1]

4.1 The crystalline potential

According to Maxwell's equations, the electrostatic potential at the site of an ion vacancy (in the absence of that ion) is a solution of Laplace's equation

$$\nabla^2 \varphi_c = 0 \tag{4.3}$$

The crystalline potential φ_c is considered to act on each of the constituent electrons of the ion in question; thus the total potential energy experienced by the electrons of the ion is

$$-\sum_{i=1}^{n} e\varphi_c(r_i,\theta_i,\phi_i)$$

where n is the number of electrons belonging to the given ion and (r,θ,ϕ) are the spherical coordinates of the electrons (taking the ionic nucleus to be at the origin). Henceforth, the summation over electrons and the subscript i will be implied.

The most general solution of Laplace's equation (4.3) is given by the multipole expansion[2]

$$\varphi_c = \sum_{\lambda=0}^{\infty} \sum_{\mu=-\lambda}^{\lambda} \Lambda_{\lambda\mu} r^\lambda Y_\lambda^\mu(\theta,\phi) \tag{4.4}$$

where

$$\Lambda_{\lambda\mu} = \Lambda_{\lambda\mu}^{(r)} + i\Lambda_{\lambda\mu}^{(i)} \tag{4.5}$$

is an arbitrary (complex) coefficient (independent of the electron coordinates), associated with the λ, μ moment of the potential. Y_λ^μ is the spherical harmonic

$$Y_\lambda^\mu(\theta,\phi) = N_{\lambda\mu}^{-1/2} P_\lambda^\mu(\cos\theta) e^{i\mu\phi} = N_{\lambda\mu}^{-1/2} y_\lambda^\mu \tag{4.6}$$

[1] For further discussion of the splitting of atomic energy levels by a crystalline field, see the article by H. A. Bethe, *Ann. Physik*, **3**: 133 (1929). Also, there is some discussion on this topic in the text by W. Low, "Paramagnetic Resonance in Solids," Academic Press Inc., New York, 1960.

[2] The discussion in this section is contained in an article by M. Sachs, *J. Phys. Chem. Solids*, **15**: 291 (1960).

y_λ^μ is the unnormalized spherical harmonic,

$$N_{\lambda\mu} = (-1)^{2\mu} \frac{4\pi(\lambda + \mu)!}{(2\lambda + 1)(\lambda - \mu)!}$$

and
$$P_\lambda^\mu(\cos\theta) = (-1)^\mu \frac{(\lambda + \mu)!}{(\lambda - \mu)!} P_\lambda^{-\mu}(\cos\theta) \tag{4.7}$$

is the associated Legendre polynomial, defined as follows:

$$P_\lambda^\mu(x) = \frac{(1 - x^2)^{\mu/2}}{2^\lambda \lambda!} \frac{d^{(\lambda+\mu)}}{dx^{(\lambda+\mu)}} (x^2 - 1)^\lambda \tag{4.8}$$

The electrostatic potential (4.4) is restricted by the following two conditions:

1. The potential must be real in order to represent a physically observable effect.
2. The symmetry of φ_c must be compatible with each of the symmetry elements contained in the point group that characterizes this potential.

In accordance with condition 1, φ_c may be reexpressed in the following functional form:

$$\varphi_c = \sum_{\lambda=0}^{\infty} \sum_{\mu=0}^{\lambda} [\varphi_{\lambda\mu}(r,\theta,\phi) + \bar{\varphi}_{\lambda\mu}(r,\theta,\phi)] \tag{4.9}$$

where the moments of the potential are

$$\varphi_{\lambda\mu} = A_{\lambda\mu}^{(r)} r^\lambda [Y_\lambda^\mu + (-1)^\mu Y_\lambda^{-\mu}] = 2A_{\lambda\mu}^{(r)} r^\lambda P_\lambda^\mu \cos\mu\phi \tag{4.10a}$$
$$\bar{\varphi}_{\lambda\mu} = iA_{\lambda\mu}^{(i)} r^\lambda [Y_\lambda^\mu + (-1)^{\mu+1} Y_\lambda^{-\mu}] = 2A_{\lambda\mu}^{(i)} r^\lambda P_\lambda^\mu \sin\mu\phi \tag{4.10b}$$

Imposing now the further condition 2 that φ_c be invariant under the transformations of the point group that characterizes the ion site, the particular moments (4.10*a*) and (4.10*b*) that will actually appear are determined by considering their invariance with respect to the various transformation elements of the group. Let us now consider the method for calculating which of these moments are indeed present.

Since the symmetry elements of the point groups leave the length of the radius vector unaltered, we need consider only what happens to the angular functions $[Y_\lambda^\mu(\theta,\phi) + (-1)^\mu Y_\lambda^{-\mu}(\theta,\phi)]$ and $[Y_\lambda^\mu(\theta,\phi) + (-1)^{\mu+1} Y_\lambda^{-\mu}(\theta,\phi)]$ after the various symmetry transformations have been applied. The types of transformations which appear in the point groups have been described in Chap. 2. These are given in Table 4.1 together with the corresponding transformations of (θ,ϕ), the moments $\varphi_{\lambda\mu}(r,\theta,\phi)$ and $\bar{\varphi}_{\lambda\mu}(r,\theta,\phi)$ of the crystalline electrostatic potential, and the corresponding

TABLE 4.1 *Point-group Transformations and Invariance Requirements for the Electrostatic Potential Moments* ($m = 0, 1, 2, \ldots$)

	Point-group transformations						
	E	C_n	σ_h	σ_v	$\sigma_d(n)$*	$U_2(n)$*	S_n
$(\theta,\phi) \rightarrow$	(θ,ϕ)	$(\theta,\ \phi + 2\pi/n)$	$(\pi - \theta,\ \phi)$	$(\theta,\ -\phi)$	$(\theta,\ -\phi + \pi/n)$	$\left(\pi - \theta,\ -\phi + \frac{2\pi}{n}\right)$	$\left(\pi - \theta,\ \phi + \frac{2\pi}{n}\right)$
$\varphi_{\lambda\mu} \rightarrow$	$\varphi_{\lambda\mu}$	$(-1)^{2\mu/n}\varphi_{\lambda\mu}$	$(-1)^{\lambda+\mu}\varphi_{\lambda\mu}$	$\varphi_{\lambda\mu}$	$(-1)^{\mu/n}\varphi_{\lambda\mu}$	$(-1)^{\lambda+2\mu/n+\mu}\varphi_{\lambda\mu}$	$(-1)^{\lambda+\mu+2\mu/n}\varphi_{\lambda\mu}$
Invariance requirement	None	$\mu = nm$	$\lambda + \mu = 2m$	None	$\mu = 2nm$	$\lambda + \frac{2\mu}{n} + \mu = 2m$	$\lambda + \mu + \frac{2\mu}{n} = 2m$
$\bar{\varphi}_{\lambda\mu} \rightarrow$	$\bar{\varphi}_{\lambda\mu}$	$(-1)^{2\mu/n}\bar{\varphi}_{\lambda\mu}$	$(-1)^{\lambda+\mu}\bar{\varphi}_{\lambda\mu}$	$-\bar{\varphi}_{\lambda\mu}$	$(-1)^{\mu/n+1}\bar{\varphi}_{\lambda\mu}$	$(-1)^{\lambda+2\mu/n+1+\mu}\bar{\varphi}_{\lambda\mu}$	$(-1)^{\lambda+\mu+2\mu/n}\bar{\varphi}_{\lambda\mu}$
Invariance requirement	None	$\mu = nm$	$\lambda + \mu = 2m$	$\bar{\varphi}_{\lambda\mu} = 0$	$\mu = n(2m - 1)$	$\lambda + \frac{2\mu}{n} + \mu = 2m - 1$	$\lambda + \mu + \frac{2\mu}{n} = 2m$

* The index n refers here to the maximum n-fold rotation about the C axis which is a member of the same group as is σ_d or U_2.

invariance requirements. In the derivation of the results in Table 4.1 use was made of the following identities:

$$\bar{P}_\lambda^{-\mu}(\cos\theta) = (-1)^\mu \bar{P}_\lambda^\mu(\cos\theta) \qquad \bar{P}_\lambda^\mu = (-1)^\mu N_{\lambda\mu}^{-1/2} P_\lambda^\mu$$
$$P_\lambda^\mu(-\cos\theta) = (-1)^{\mu+\lambda} P_\lambda^\mu(\cos\theta)$$
$$e^{2\pi i\mu/n} = (-1)^{2\mu/n}$$

The formulation of the functional form of the electrostatic potential as a function of the point group in question is now carried out by combining the invariance requirements given in Table 4.1 with the particular set of transformations which make up the point group in question (i.e., the transformations indicated in Tables 2.1 to 2.8).

It should be noted that, while this method of evaluating the moments $\varphi_{\lambda\mu}$ and $\bar{\varphi}_{\lambda\mu}$ is quite useful for the 27 noncubic point groups, it is not particularly useful for the five cubic groups (which are described by the transformations in Table 2.8). This is because the singled-out axis (i.e., the C axis) of the noncubic symmetries uniquely defines the angular coordinates (θ,ϕ). On the other hand, the three coordinates (x,y,z) are equivalent in the cubic symmetries. It is for this reason that we shall treat the potentials for the cubic and the noncubic symmetries separately.

For the purposes of illustrating the method of determining the moments associated with the point groups, let us consider the trigonal point groups $\mathbf{C}_3$, $\mathbf{S}_6$, $\mathbf{C}_{3v}$, $\mathbf{D}_3$, and $\mathbf{D}_{3d}$.

The* $\mathbf{C}_3$ *point group According to Tables 2.1 and 4.1, this group contains only rotations about the C axis (and the identity); the moments are therefore prescribed by the requirement on $\varphi_{\lambda\mu}$ and $\bar{\varphi}_{\lambda\mu}$ that

$$\mu = 3m = 0, 3, 6, \ldots$$

There is no restriction on the integer λ (that is, $\lambda = 0, 1, 2, 3, \ldots$). Thus, since μ is summed from 0 to λ, φ_c is given by the following multipole expansion:

$$\varphi_c(\mathbf{C}_3) = \varphi_{00} + \varphi_{10} + \varphi_{20} + \varphi_{30} + \varphi_{33} + \bar{\varphi}_{33} + \varphi_{40} + \varphi_{43} + \bar{\varphi}_{43} + \varphi_{50} + \varphi_{53} + \bar{\varphi}_{53} + \cdots \tag{4.11}$$

The* $\mathbf{C}_{3v}$ *point group According to Table 2.4, the $\mathbf{C}_{3v}$ point group contains, in addition to the 3-fold axis, the vertical reflection plane σ_v. From Table 4.1, this indicates that the potential is identical to (4.11), with the absence of all terms $\bar{\varphi}_{\lambda\mu}$; that is,

$$\varphi_c(\mathbf{C}_{3v}) = \varphi_{00} + \varphi_{10} + \varphi_{20} + \varphi_{30} + \varphi_{33} + \varphi_{40} + \varphi_{43} + \varphi_{50} + \varphi_{53} + \varphi_{60} + \varphi_{63} + \varphi_{66} + \cdots \tag{4.12}$$

The* $\mathbf{S}_6$ *point group In addition to the elements of C_3, this group contains the inversion ($I = S_2$) (Table 2.2). From Table 4.1, we see that the requirement due to the presence of the class C_3 is $\mu = 3m$, and the added requirement $\lambda + \mu + \mu = 2m$ (due to the presence of S_2) leads to the result that λ must be even. Thus, the potential for the $\mathbf{S}_6$ point group is

$$\varphi_c(\mathbf{S}_6) = \varphi_{00} + \varphi_{20} + \varphi_{40} + \varphi_{43} + \bar{\varphi}_{43} + \varphi_{60} + \varphi_{63} + \bar{\varphi}_{63} + \varphi_{66} + \cdots \qquad (4.13)$$

The* $\mathbf{D}_3$ *point group This group contains the classes C_3, U_2, and the identity. Once again, the presence of the element C_3 indicates that $\mu = 3m$. According to Table 4.1, the additional restriction due to the presence of the elements contained in the U_2 class leads to the following requirement:

$$\varphi_{\lambda\mu}: \qquad \lambda + \frac{2\mu}{3} + \mu = 2m \qquad \text{or} \qquad \begin{cases} \lambda \text{ even, } \mu = 6m \\ \lambda \text{ odd, } \mu = 6m - 3 \end{cases} \qquad (4.14a)$$

and

$$\bar{\varphi}_{\lambda\mu}: \qquad \lambda + \frac{2\mu}{3} + \mu + 1 = 2m \qquad \text{or} \qquad \begin{cases} \lambda \text{ odd, } \mu = 6m \\ \lambda \text{ even, } \mu = 6m - 3 \end{cases} \qquad (4.14b)$$

This leads to the following crystalline potential:

$$\varphi_c(\mathbf{D}_3) = \varphi_{00} + \varphi_{20} + \varphi_{40} + \varphi_{53} + \varphi_{60} + \varphi_{66} + \varphi_{33} + \bar{\varphi}_{43} + \bar{\varphi}_{63} + \cdots \qquad (4.15)$$

The* $\mathbf{D}_{3d}$ *point group This group is the direct product of the $\mathbf{D}_3$ point group and the inversion ($I = S_2$). The condition for inversion symmetry (Table 4.1)

$$\lambda + 2\mu = 2m$$

that λ shall be even restricts the moments of $\mathbf{D}_{3d}$ to those terms in $\mathbf{D}_3$ with λ even. Thus, we have, from (4.15),

$$\varphi_c(\mathbf{D}_{3d}) = \varphi_{00} + \varphi_{20} + \varphi_{40} + \bar{\varphi}_{43} + \varphi_{60} + \bar{\varphi}_{63} + \varphi_{66} + \cdots \qquad (4.16)$$

The potential moments for all 27 noncubic point groups are given in Table 4.2 in terms of their allowed values of λ and μ. The verification of the functional forms of the potentials for the remaining point-group symmetries will be left as an exercise for the reader.

The cubic point groups The cubic point groups $\mathbf{T}$, $\mathbf{T}_d$, $\mathbf{T}_h$, $\mathbf{O}$, and $\mathbf{O}_h$ cannot be described by potentials which are made up of the individual moments $\varphi_{\lambda\mu}$ and $\bar{\varphi}_{\lambda\mu}$. In the case of the cubic groups, it is much more convenient to derive the potential from the series

$$\varphi_c = \sum_{i,j,k} a_{ijk}[x^i y^j z^k + f(r^{i+j+k})] \qquad (4.17)$$

where $f(r^{i+j+k})$ is a function of the radial coordinate which is chosen so as to make the $(i + j + k)$-th moment of φ_c a solution of Laplace's equation.

TABLE 4.2 *Crystalline Potentials for Noncubic Point Groups*

$$\varphi_c = \sum_{\lambda=0}^{\infty} \sum_{\mu=0}^{\lambda} (\varphi_{\lambda\mu} + \bar{\varphi}_{\lambda\mu}), \quad \varphi_{\lambda\mu} = \Lambda_{\lambda\mu}^{(r)} r^{\lambda}[Y_{\lambda}^{\mu}(\theta,\phi) + (-1)^{\mu} Y^{-\mu}(\theta,\phi)],$$

$$\bar{\varphi}_{\lambda\mu} = i\Lambda_{\lambda\mu}^{(i)} r^{\lambda}[Y_{\lambda}^{\mu}(\theta,\phi) + (-1)^{\mu+1} Y_{\lambda}^{-\mu}(\theta,\phi)] \qquad n,\ m \text{ integers}$$

Symmetry group	$\varphi_{\lambda\mu}$		$\bar{\varphi}_{\lambda\mu}$	
	λ	μ	λ	μ
Triclinic				
*C_1	n	m	n	m
I	$2n$	m	$2n$	m
Monoclinic				
*σ_h	$\{2n+1$	$2m+1\}$	$\{2n+1$	$2m+1\}$
	$\{2n$	$2m\}$	$\{2n$	$2m\}$
*C_2	n	$2m$	n	$2m$
C_{2h}	$2n$	$2m$	$2n$	$2m$
Orthorhombic				
*C_{2v}	n	$2m$	0	
*D_2	$2n$	$2m$	$2n+1$	$2m$
D_{2h}	$2n$	$2m$	0	
Tetragonal				
*S_4	$\{2n$	$4m\}$	$\{2n$	$4m\}$
	$\{2n+1$	$4m-2\}$	$\{2n+1$	$4m-2\}$
*D_{2d}	$2n$	$4m$	$2n+1$	$4m-2$
*C_4	n	$4m$	n	$4m$
C_{4h}	$2n$	$4m$	$2n$	$4m$
*C_{4v}	n	$4m$	0	
*D_4	$2n$	$4m$	$2n+1$	$4m$
D_{4h}	$2n$	$4m$	0	
Trigonal				
*C_3	n	$3m$	n	$3m$
S_6	$2n$	$3m$	$2n$	$3m$
*C_{3v}	n	$3m$	0	
*D_3	$\{2n$	$6m\}$	$\{2n+1$	$6m\}$
	$\{2n+1$	$6m-3\}$	$\{2n$	$6m-3\}$
D_{3d}	$2n$	$6m$	$2n$	$6m-3$
Hexagonal				
*C_{3h}	$\{2n$	$6m\}$	$\{2n$	$6m\}$
	$\{2n+1$	$6m-3\}$	$\{2n+1$	$6m-3\}$
*D_{3h}	$\{2n$	$6m\}$	0	
	$\{2n+1$	$6m-3\}$		
*C_6	n	$6m$	n	$6m$
C_{6h}	$2n$	$6m$	$2n$	$6m$
*C_{6v}	n	$6m$	0	
*D_6	$2n$	$6m$	$2n+1$	$6m$
D_{6h}	$2n$	$6m$	0	

* The potentials determined by these groups lack an inversion center.

The potentials are then determined by requiring the invariance of φ_c with respect to the classes of the particular cubic group in question. Following this procedure, it is seen that the leading term in the potential for all cubic symmetries takes the form

$$\varphi_c(\text{cubic}) = a_0 + a_4(x^4 + y^4 + z^4 - \tfrac{3}{5}r^4) + \cdots \tag{4.18}$$

This may be expressed in terms of spherical harmonics as follows:

$$\varphi_c(\text{cubic}) = a_0 + \frac{a_4 r^4}{5} [2y_4^0 - \tfrac{1}{168}(y_4^4 - y_4^{-4})] + \cdots \tag{4.19}$$

4.2 Energy-level splitting in a crystal field

In this section, we shall further explore the properties of groups in order to find a systematic method of predicting the degree of degeneracy of a free-ion (or atom) energy level which is lifted by the crystalline field. This will be done in terms of the so-called *representations* of the space groups.

Before following this formal procedure, it would be instructive to illustrate, in a more physical way, that a crystal field would indeed split a normally degenerate free-ion level. For this purpose, let us consider the effect of squashing a free ion, which is normally in a D state, into the electrostatic field of a (nonmagnetic) crystal which has cubic symmetry.

The free-ion wave function is expressed as a product of a function dependent only on the electron spatial coordinates and a function dependent only on the electron-spin coordinates. Since there is no evidence to date that an electric field interacts directly with the spin of an electron, the crystal potential can affect only the degeneracy which is inherent in the parts of the electron wave functions which depend on spatial coordinates.[1] Henceforth in this section, when discussing the degeneracy of a state of the ion, we shall refer only to the portion of the wave functions that depends on spatial coordinates.

The D state of the free ion is 5-fold degenerate. Thus, there are five orthonormal wave functions which describe this energy state. These functions are

$$\psi_{nlm_l} = R_{nl}(r) Y_l^{m_l}(\theta,\phi) \tag{4.20}$$

with $m_l = 2, 1, 0, -1, -2$; $l = 2$, and where $R_{nl}(r)$ is the normalized radial wave function and $Y_l^{m_l}$ is the spherical harmonic, defined according to Eq. (4.6). The explicit functional form for each of the angular func-

[1] There is, of course, an indirect coupling of the electron spin to the crystal field through the intermediary of the spin-orbit interaction. Also, if there are magnetic ions in the neighborhood of this ion, an electric field effect exhibits itself in terms of the exchange interaction (see Chap. 5).

tions is as follows:

$$\left.\begin{aligned}\psi_{n2\pm2} &= \frac{3}{4}\sqrt{\frac{5}{6\pi}}\sin^2\theta e^{\pm 2i\phi}\\ \psi_{n2\pm1} &= \pm\frac{3}{2}\sqrt{\frac{5}{6\pi}}\sin\theta\cos\theta e^{\pm i\phi}\\ \psi_{n20} &= \frac{1}{2}\sqrt{\frac{5}{4\pi}}(3\cos^2\theta - 1)\end{aligned}\right\} R_{n2}(r) \tag{4.21}$$

The existence of the 5-fold degeneracy of the D state is interpreted, according to quantum mechanics, as five equally probable charge distributions, given by the functions

$$|\psi_{n22}|^2 \qquad |\psi_{n21}|^2 \qquad |\psi_{n20}|^2 \qquad |\psi_{n2-1}|^2 \qquad |\psi_{n2-2}|^2$$

The wave functions for the states $l_z = +m_l$ and $l_z = -m_l$ are the so-called *time-reversed states.* Since the electric field of the crystal is a representation of a *static* source of charge distributions, the time-reversed states of the ion in the crystal must represent charge distributions which occur with equal probability. Thus, instead of representing the wave function in terms of the complex functions $e^{im_l\phi}$ and $e^{-im_l\phi}$, they may be represented in terms of the real functions $\cos m_l\phi$ and $\sin m_l\phi$. This is done by introducing the functions

$$\begin{aligned}\Upsilon_{nlm_l} &= \frac{1}{2}[\psi_{nlm_l} + (-1)^{m_l}\psi_{nl-m_l}]\left(\frac{r^2}{R_{n2}(r)}\right)\\ \bar{\Upsilon}_{nlm_l} &= \frac{1}{2i}[\psi_{nlm_l} + (-1)^{m_l+1}\psi_{nl-m_l}]\left(\frac{r^2}{R_{n2}(r)}\right)\end{aligned} \tag{4.22}$$

which become in our particular case (in terms of x, y, z)

$$\begin{aligned}\Upsilon_{n22} &= \frac{3}{4}\sqrt{\frac{5}{6\pi}}(x^2 - y^2) \qquad & \bar{\Upsilon}_{n21} &= \frac{3}{2}\sqrt{\frac{5}{6\pi}}yz\\ \bar{\Upsilon}_{n22} &= \frac{3}{2}\sqrt{\frac{5}{6\pi}}xy & &\\ \Upsilon_{n21} &= \frac{3}{2}\sqrt{\frac{5}{6\pi}}xz & \Upsilon_{n20} &= Y_2^0 = \frac{1}{2}\sqrt{\frac{5}{4\pi}}(3z^2 - r^2)\end{aligned} \tag{4.23}$$

Thus, in view of the time-reversal invariance of the crystalline electrostatic field interaction,[1] we look at the unperturbed states of the free ion in the D state in terms of the five equally probable charge distributions

$$|\Upsilon_{n22}|^2 \qquad |\bar{\Upsilon}_{n22}|^2 \qquad |\Upsilon_{n21}|^2 \qquad |\bar{\Upsilon}_{n21}|^2 \qquad |\Upsilon_{n20}|^2$$

Our object is now to investigate the effect of different symmetry potential fields on the degeneracy of the states of the ion. Let us recall

[1] The implications of time-reversal noninvariance and parity nonconservation in electromagnetic interactions are discussed by M. Sachs, *Ann. Phys.* (*N.Y.*), **6:** 244 (1959), and M. Sachs and S. L. Schwebel, *Ann. Phys.* (*N.Y.*), **8:** 475 (1959).

once more the properties of a degenerate state.[1] We say that a state is n-fold degenerate if there exist n orthogonal wave functions which all correspond to the same energy eigenvalue of the system. Such an energy level may consequently be described by any linear combination of the n orthogonal functions. This statement then implies that, under the transformations which characterize the symmetry of the D state, each one of the orthogonal wave functions $(\Upsilon_{n2m_l}, \bar{\Upsilon}_{n2m_l})$ (or ψ_{n2m_l}) must transform into linear combinations of all five degenerate wave functions.[2]

Consider now the ion which was originally in a D state to be at the center of symmetry of an electrostatic field with cubic ($\mathbf{O}_h$) symmetry. The potential field is now lowered from the free-ion symmetry to one in which we can say only that the x, y, and z axes are indistinguishable. Since the cubic symmetry is lower in degree than was the symmetry of the free ion, we should expect that part of the 5-fold degeneracy of the state characterized by the angular momentum $l = 2$ could, in general, be lifted. The actual degeneracy that is lifted may be determined by considering which of the functions Υ_{nlm_l} now transform into one another under the transformations of the cube.

Consider a transformation element (of the class $8C_3$) of the cubic group, which transforms the coordinates as follows: $(x \rightarrow y,\ y \rightarrow z,\ z \rightarrow x)$. Under this transformation the functions Υ_{n2m_l} [Eq. (4.23)] transform into each other as follows:

$$^3\Gamma_4 \begin{cases} \bar{\Upsilon}_{n22} \rightarrow \bar{\Upsilon}_{n21} \\ \Upsilon_{n21} \rightarrow \bar{\Upsilon}_{n22} \\ \bar{\Upsilon}_{n21} \rightarrow \Upsilon_{n21} \end{cases} \qquad ^2\Gamma_3 \begin{cases} \Upsilon_{n20} \rightarrow -\frac{1}{2}\Upsilon_{n20} + \sqrt{\frac{3}{2}}\,\Upsilon_{n22} \\ \Upsilon_{n22} \rightarrow -\frac{1}{2}\Upsilon_{n22} - \frac{1}{2}\sqrt{\frac{3}{2}}\,\Upsilon_{n20} \end{cases} \tag{4.24}$$

Thus we see that, under the transformations of the cube, the wave functions do not all transform into one another. Rather, the wave functions $\bar{\Upsilon}_{n22}$, $\bar{\Upsilon}_{n21}$, and Υ_{n21} transform among each other as do Υ_{n20} and Υ_{n22}. The original 5-fold degenerate level is therefore split into one 3-fold degenerate level (denoted by $^3\Gamma_4$) and one 2-fold degenerate level (denoted by $^2\Gamma_3$). (The symmetry properties of the crystal field do not tell us anything about the ordering of these energy levels.)

Let us now carry this analysis one step further by considering the cubic crystal to be stretched along one of the cube axes (let us say the z axis). The resultant electrostatic field at the site of the considered ion is no longer cubic; rather it is characterized by tetragonal ($\mathbf{D}_{4h}$) symmetry. This new field has less symmetry than the original cubic field since there is now one preferred axis of symmetry. Thus we should expect that a further splitting of the energy levels can occur. This is

[1] See, for example, L. I. Schiff, "Quantum Mechanics," McGraw-Hill Book Company, Inc., New York, 1955.

[2] This follows from invariance of the Schroedinger wave equation (for the free atom) under arbitrary rotations of the coordinate system.

indeed the case. Since only the x and y axes are now equivalent, it is clear that the only wave functions which transform into one another under the transformation (C_4) $x \rightarrow y$, $y \rightarrow x$, $z \rightarrow z$ are Υ_{n21} and $\bar{\Upsilon}_{n21}$, while the remaining three wave functions transform only into themselves. Thus we see that the tetragonal symmetry field further splits the energy

Electronic energy levels, cubic symmetry	Angular distribution of electronic charge density	Electronic energy levels, tetragonal symmetry
$E\,({}^2\Gamma_3{}^{(1)})$	$e(3\cos^2\theta - 1)^2$	$E\,({}^1\Gamma_7{}^{(1)})$
	$e(\sin^2\theta\,\cos^2\theta\,\sin^2\phi)$	$E\,({}^2\Gamma_7{}^{(2)})$
$E\,({}^3\Gamma_4{}^{(2)})$	$e(\sin^2\theta\,\cos^2\theta\,\cos^2\phi)$	
	$e(\sin^4\theta\,\sin^2 2\phi)$	$E\,({}^1\Gamma_7{}^{(3)})$
	$e(\sin^4\theta\,\cos^2 2\phi)$	$E\,({}^1\Gamma_7{}^{(4)})$

Fig. 4.1. Combinations of charge distributions for a D-state ion in a crystalline field of cubic and tetragonal symmetry.

levels of the cubic field by lifting the double degeneracy of the E (${}^2\Gamma_3$) energy level and splitting the triplet $E({}^3\Gamma_4)$ into a singlet and a doublet (causing the two energy levels of the atom in a cubic field to split into the four energy levels of the atom in a tetragonal field).

These results are illustrated in Figs. 4.1 and 4.2.

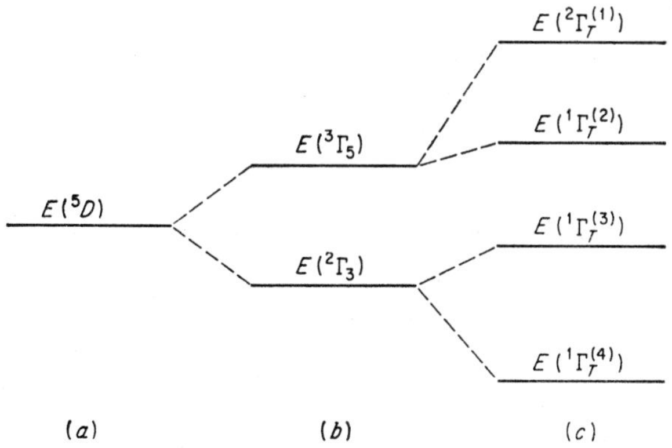

Fig. 4.2. Schematic diagram for the energy levels of (a) a free ion in a D state, when subjected to (b) a cubic crystalline field, and (c) a tetragonal crystalline field. The degeneracy of the energy levels is given by the upper left-hand superscript on the crystal quantum numbers Γ. The ordering and spacing of the energy levels have been drawn arbitrarily.

Problem

Determine the effect of a cubic and tetragonal electrostatic field on an ion which, when free, is in an F state. Assume that the mixing of higher orbital-momentum states by the crystal field is negligibly small.

The foregoing example was given for illustrative purposes. The assumption was made that while the crystalline field destroyed the operator l_z as a constant of the motion (and replaced it with the "crystal quantum numbers" Γ) it did not affect the total orbital-momentum quantum number l. This assumption is a good one only if the levels corresponding to the other orbital-momentum states of the free ion are far removed in energy in comparison with the magnitude of the interaction between the ion and the crystalline field. In actuality, the presence of the crystalline field does indeed mix the different orbital-momentum states together and l is not, in general, a constant of the motion. Instead, the actual energy levels of the ion in the crystal [i.e., the exact eigenvalues of the wave equation (4.1)] may be described by wave functions which are made up of some definite linear combination of atomic-orbital wave functions. Thus one may think of the state of the ion in the crystal in terms of some definite probabilities of finding the ionic charge distribution in any of a variety of orbital distributions at any given time. It is clear that, if the binding energy of the electronic cloud to the parent ion is large compared with the crystalline potential, one particular orbital state would be preferred most of the time, whereas if these energies were comparable in magnitude there would be comparable probabilities for several of the orbital states. The expansion in terms of atomic-orbital states becomes meaningless in the limit when the number of orbitals becomes large (they must be replaced by a new angular-momentum operator Γ, which commutes with the total hamiltonian $\mathcal{H}_0 - e\varphi_c$). The latter phenomenon is known as orbital-momentum quenching.

Let us now proceed to describe, in a more rigorous fashion, the actual wave functions that are associated with the different point-group symmetries.

The Representations of Groups[1]

The degeneracy of a particular energy level of an atom in a crystal has been described in the preceding discussion in terms of the number of linearly independent wave functions which transform into linear

[1] For a complete and rigorous treatment of this topic see E. P. Wigner, "Group Theory and Its Application to the Quantum Mechanics of Atomic Spectra," Academic Press Inc., New York, 1959; J. S. Lomont, "Applications of Finite Groups," Academic Press Inc., New York, 1959; M. Hamermesh, "Group Theory," Addison-Wesley Publishing Company, Inc., Reading, Mass., 1962.

combinations of each other under the transformations of the point group. Thus, if $A^{(i)}$ is a constituent transformation element of a point group, then one eigensolution of the wave equation for the atom *in the crystal* would have the form

$$\psi'_\lambda = A^{(i)}\psi_\lambda = \sum_{\mu=1}^{n} A^{(i)}_{\lambda\mu}\psi_\mu \tag{4.25}$$

Consider, for example, the effect of an $8C_3$ element of the cubic group on the degenerate eigenfunctions belonging to the D state of a free atom. The transformation of these functions, given in Eq. (4.24), may be expressed in the following compact matrix form:

$$\begin{pmatrix} \Upsilon'_{n22} \\ \bar{\Upsilon}'_{n22} \\ \Upsilon'_{n21} \\ \bar{\Upsilon}'_{n21} \\ \Upsilon'_{n20} \end{pmatrix} = A^{(8C_3)} \begin{pmatrix} \Upsilon_{n22} \\ \bar{\Upsilon}_{n22} \\ \Upsilon_{n21} \\ \bar{\Upsilon}_{n21} \\ \Upsilon_{n20} \end{pmatrix} = \begin{pmatrix} -\frac{1}{2} & 0 & 0 & 0 & -\frac{1}{2}\sqrt{\frac{3}{2}} \\ 0 & 0 & 0 & 1 & 0 \\ 0 & 1 & 0 & 0 & 0 \\ 0 & 0 & 1 & 0 & 0 \\ \sqrt{\frac{3}{2}} & 0 & 0 & 0 & -\frac{1}{2} \end{pmatrix} \begin{pmatrix} \Upsilon_{n22} \\ \bar{\Upsilon}_{n22} \\ \Upsilon_{n21} \\ \bar{\Upsilon}_{n21} \\ \Upsilon_{n20} \end{pmatrix} \tag{4.24'}$$

The set of five algebraic equations (4.24′) may obviously be arranged in any desired order. Let us rearrange the order of the equations as follows:

$$\begin{pmatrix} \bar{\Upsilon}'_{n22} \\ \Upsilon'_{n21} \\ \bar{\Upsilon}'_{n21} \\ \Upsilon'_{n22} \\ \Upsilon'_{n20} \end{pmatrix} = \left(\begin{array}{ccc:cc} 0 & 0 & 1 & 0 & 0 \\ 1 & 0 & 0 & 0 & 0 \\ 0 & 1 & 0 & 0 & 0 \\ \hdashline 0 & 0 & 0 & -\frac{1}{2} & -\frac{1}{2}\sqrt{\frac{3}{2}} \\ 0 & 0 & 0 & \sqrt{\frac{3}{2}} & -\frac{1}{2} \end{array}\right) \begin{pmatrix} \bar{\Upsilon}_{n22} \\ \Upsilon_{n21} \\ \bar{\Upsilon}_{n21} \\ \Upsilon_{n22} \\ \Upsilon_{n20} \end{pmatrix} \tag{4.24''}$$

The matrix $(A^{(8C_3)}_{\lambda\mu})$ of the transformation $8C_3$, represented by

$$\begin{pmatrix} -\frac{1}{2} & 0 & 0 & 0 & -\frac{1}{2}\sqrt{\frac{3}{2}} \\ 0 & 0 & 0 & 1 & 0 \\ 0 & 1 & 0 & 0 & 0 \\ 0 & 0 & 1 & 0 & 0 \\ \sqrt{\frac{3}{2}} & 0 & 0 & 0 & -\frac{1}{2} \end{pmatrix}$$

can be rearranged in $5! - 1$ other ways, representing $5! - 1$ other arrangements of the five algebraic equations. If at least one of the $5!$ arrangements corresponds to a matrix which is box diagonal [Eq. (4.24″)], then $A^{(i)}$ is said to be a reducible matrix. The matrix given by Eq. (4.24″) is the irreducible form of $(A^{(8C_3)}_{\lambda\mu})$, *if each box can be reduced no further.* The irreducible form (4.24″) indicates which of the five functions transform into each other and therefore how the atomic energy level is split. In our particular case, we see that the matrix $(A^{(8C_3)}_{\lambda\mu})$ is reduced to a 3×3 matrix, giving the 3-fold degenerate state ${}^3\Gamma_4$, and a 2×2 matrix, giving the 2-fold degenerate state ${}^2\Gamma_3$.

When there is a true 5-fold degeneracy, the matrix is not reducible (thus indicating that each of the five functions transforms into a linear combination of all five functions, as in the case of the free atom). On the other hand, a nondegenerate system must correspond to a matrix which is completely diagonal.

To each element $A^{(i)}$ of the group there corresponds a matrix $(A^{(i)}_{\lambda\mu})$. The set of matrices $\{A^{(1)}_{\lambda\mu}, \ldots, A^{(n)}_{\lambda\mu}\}$ for all n elements of the group is called the *representation* of the group. We have seen above that the matrices $(A^{(i)})$ may be reducible to box-diagonal form. When this is the case there must exist a transformation matrix S which reshuffles the matrix elements as follows:[1]

$$S(A^{(i)}_{\lambda\mu})S^{-1} = (A^{(i)}_{\lambda\mu})' = \begin{pmatrix} \boxed{\Gamma^{(i)}_1} & & & \\ & \boxed{\Gamma^{(i)}_2} & & \\ & & \boxed{\Gamma^{(i)}_\kappa} & \\ & & & \ddots \end{pmatrix} \tag{4.26}$$

where $\Gamma^{(i)}_\kappa$ is an irreducible matrix of order n_κ. [The transformation (4.26) is called a similarity transformation.] The set of matrices (for all classes i) $\Gamma_\kappa = \{\Gamma^{(1)}_\kappa, \Gamma^{(2)}_\kappa, \ldots, \Gamma^{(n)}_\kappa\}$ is called an irreducible representation of the group. It will be seen below that the number of irreducible representations is just equal to the number of classes in the group. The functions ψ_μ, with which the irreducible representations are defined (e.g., the functions Υ_{nlm_l} in the above example), are called the *basis* of the representation.

The character of a representation The trace of an irreducible matrix [that is, $\sum_\mu (\Gamma^{(i)}_\kappa)_{\mu\mu}$] is referred to as its *character* and is denoted by $\chi^{(i)}_\kappa$. The properties of the characters of the irreducible representations allow a simple method for treating the group properties of symmetrical systems.

The characters of all elements that belong to the same class are equal. This may be seen as follows: According to our definition of a class (Sec. 2.3), two elements $A^{(i)}$ and $A^{(j)}$ of a group belong to the same class if they are conjugate to each other, i.e., if

$$A^{(i)} = (A^{(k)})^{-1}A^{(j)}A^{(k)}$$

where $A^{(k)}$ is another element of the group. Thus, if $\Gamma^{(i)}_\kappa$, $\Gamma^{(j)}_\kappa$, and Γ^k_κ are irreducible matrices associated with the symmetry elements $A^{(i)}$, $A^{(j)}$, $A^{(k)}$, then, according to the rule for matrix multiplication, we have

$$\chi^{(i)}_\kappa \equiv \sum_\lambda (\Gamma^{(i)}_\kappa)_{\lambda\lambda} = \sum_{\lambda\mu\nu} [(\Gamma^{(k)}_\kappa)^{-1}]_{\lambda\mu}(\Gamma^{(j)}_\kappa)_{\mu\nu}(\Gamma^{(k)}_\kappa)_{\nu\lambda}$$
$$= \sum_{\mu\nu} (\Gamma^{(j)}_\kappa)_{\mu\nu}\delta_{\mu\nu} = \sum_\mu (\Gamma^{(j)}_\kappa)_{\mu\mu} = \chi^{(j)}_\kappa \tag{4.27}$$

[1] See, for example, E. Wigner, *op cit.*, p. 20.

The third step in Eq. (4.27) follows from the definition of the inverse matrix $(\Gamma^{(k)})^{-1}$, that is,

$$\Gamma^{(k)}(\Gamma^{(k)})^{-1} = (1) \equiv \begin{pmatrix} 1 & 0 & \cdots & 0 \\ 0 & 1 & & \\ \cdot & & \cdot & \\ \cdot & & & \cdot \\ \cdot & & & \cdot \\ 0 & & & 1 \end{pmatrix}$$

The wave functions associated with the irreducible representations of a point group may then be conveniently described in terms of the characters of these representations. This is done by constructing a character table in which the columns are labeled by the classes of the group (i) and the rows by the particular irreducible representation κ. In order to construct and use these tables, let us now investigate some of the further properties of the characters of the group.

The following orthogonality relation holds for the matrices of the irreducible representations of the group:[1]

$$\sum_{i=1}^{n} (\Gamma_{\kappa}^{(i)})_{\lambda\mu}(\Gamma_{\kappa'}^{(i)})^{*}_{\lambda'\mu'} = \frac{n}{(n_{\kappa}n_{\kappa'})^{1/2}} \delta_{\kappa\kappa'}\delta_{\lambda\lambda'}\delta_{\mu\mu'} \tag{4.28}$$

where the sum is taken over the elements of the group, n is the order of the group (i.e., the number of elements in the group), and n_{κ} and $n_{\kappa'}$ are the dimensionalities of the irreducible matrices Γ_{κ} and $\Gamma_{\kappa'}$, respectively.

If we now sum both sides of Eq. (4.28) over λ, $\mu = \lambda$, and λ', $\mu' = \lambda'$, the following orthogonality relation for the characters is obtained:

$$\sum_{i=1}^{n} \chi_{\kappa}^{(i)}(\chi_{\kappa'}^{(i)})^{*} = n\delta_{\kappa\kappa'} \tag{4.29}$$

Since the characters of all elements in a given class are the same, the summation over elements may be replaced by a summation over classes as follows:

$$\sum_{c=1}^{n_c} \nu_c\chi_{\kappa}^{(c)}(\chi_{\kappa'}^{(c)})^{*} = n\delta_{\kappa\kappa'} \tag{4.30}$$

where n_c is the number of classes in the group and ν_c is the number of elements in the cth class. If we define $\xi_{\kappa}^{(c)}$ as

$$\xi_{\kappa}^{(c)} = \sqrt{\frac{\nu_c}{n}}\,\chi_{\kappa}^{(c)}$$

[1] For the proof of Eq. (4.28), see, for example, H. Weyl, "The Theory of Groups and Quantum Mechanics," p. 157, Dover Publications, Inc., New York, 1931; M. Hamermesh, *op. cit.*, p. 101.

then Eq. (4.30) takes the form of the scalar product of orthonormal vectors

$$\sum_{c=1}^{n_c} \xi_\kappa^{(c)}(\xi_{\kappa'}^{(c)})^* = \delta_{\kappa\kappa'} \tag{4.31}$$

Thus, $\xi_\kappa^{(c)}$ may be regarded as a component of a vector in an n_c-dimensional space. The number of independent vectors (i.e., the number of characters) is then equal to the number of classes n_c. Consequently, *the number of independent irreducible representations must be equal to the number of classes in the group.*

Suppose that A is a (reducible) matrix of order n. The similarity transformation (4.26) groups A into box-diagonal form, and the character is some linear combination of the characters of the component irreducible representations $(\chi_\kappa^{(i)})$. Thus,

$$\chi^{(i)}(A) = \sum_\kappa a_\kappa \chi_\kappa^{(i)} \tag{4.32}$$

Multiplying both sides of (4.32) by $(\chi_{\kappa'}^{(i)})^*$ and summing over all elements (i), we have [according to Eq. (4.29)]

$$\sum_i \chi^{(i)}(A)(\chi_{\kappa'}^{(i)})^* = \sum_i \sum_\kappa a_\kappa \chi_\kappa^{(i)}(\chi_{\kappa'}^{(i)})^* = n \sum_\kappa a_\kappa \delta_{\kappa\kappa'} = n a_{\kappa'}$$

Thus,

$$a_{\kappa'} = \frac{1}{n} \sum_{i=1}^{n} \chi^{(i)}(A)(\chi_{\kappa'}^{(i)})^* = \frac{1}{n} \sum_{c=1}^{n_c} \nu_c \chi^{(c)}(\chi_{\kappa'}^{(c)})^* \tag{4.33}$$

This equation provides a powerful method for decomposing reducible matrices into their irreducible parts. However, it is useful only if the characters of the reducible matrix and of the irreducible matrices are already known.

Consider the representation of order n which describes a group of transformations $\{G_n\}$ such that their operation on any member of the set of basis functions of equal order $(\psi_1, \psi_2, \ldots, \psi_n)$ generates all the n linearly independent basis functions. Such a representation is called *regular* if described by matrices which do not contain any diagonal elements, except for the matrix associated with the identity, i.e.,

$$\begin{aligned} \chi(E) &= \sum_1^n 1 = n \\ \chi(A^{(i)} \neq E) &= 0 \end{aligned} \tag{4.34}$$

Combining (4.34) with (4.33), we have

$$a_{\kappa'} = \frac{1}{n} \cdot n[\chi_{\kappa'}(E)]^* = [\chi_{\kappa'}(E)]^* = n_{\kappa'}$$

Since, according to Eq. (4.32)

$$\chi(E) = \sum_{\kappa} a_\kappa \chi_\kappa(E)$$

we have

$$n = \sum_{\kappa} n_\kappa^2 \qquad (4.35)$$

Thus the sum of the squares of the dimensionalities of the irreducible representations is equal to the order of the group. This relation may be used to determine the dimensionalities of the different irreducible representations of the group.

Consider, for example, the octahedral group **O** (discussed in Chap. 2). This group, which is made up of the rotation transformations of the cube, was found in Chap. 2 to contain 24 elements distributed among 5 classes. According to Eq. (4.35),

$$n_1^2 + n_2^2 + n_3^2 + n_4^2 + n_5^2 = 24 \qquad (4.36)$$

The only way of picking the five integers n_κ which will satisfy Eq. (4.36) is as follows:

$$3^2 + 3^2 + 2^2 + 1^2 + 1^2 = 24$$

Thus, the **O** group is described by two three-dimensional, one two-dimensional, and two one-dimensional irreducible representations (see Table 4.3).

Characters of the irreducible representations of the point groups Because of the one-to-one correspondence between the irreducible representations of the point groups and their corresponding characters and also because of the orthogonality properties of the characters, the symmetry properties of the wave functions which diagonalize the crystal potential may be exhibited in the appropriate character tables. We can now proceed to construct the character tables for the 32 crystallographic point groups. Consider a few examples of the construction of these character tables.

The $\mathbf{C}_n$ groups As we have seen in Chap. 2, the $\mathbf{C}_n$ groups are abelian, and consequently each of their constituent elements forms a class by itself. Since the number of classes and therefore the number of irreducible representations are equal to the order of the group, Eq. (4.35) can be satisfied only if the irreducible representations are all one-dimensional, i.e.,

$$\sum_{1}^{n} 1^2 = n$$

Among the irreducible representations of any group there is always one (called the unit representation ${}^1\Gamma_1$) which corresponds to a basis function that is invariant under all the transformations of the group. Thus, each character for this representation is unity.

The character tables for the $\mathbf{C}_n$ groups are obtained as follows: The classes of the $\mathbf{C}_n$ group are $C_n, C_n^2, C_n^3, \ldots, C_n^n = E$. These correspond to the transformations: $(2\pi/n)$, $2(2\pi/n)$, . . . , $n(2\pi/n)$ rotations about the C axis; the corresponding transformed wave functions are

$$\psi' = e^{2\pi i/n}\psi, \; e^{2(2\pi i/n)}\psi, \; \ldots$$

Thus, in addition to ${}^1\Gamma_1$, one of the irreducible representations of $\mathbf{C}_n$ has the characters

$$\chi(C_n) = e^{2\pi i/n} \equiv \epsilon_n, \; \chi(C_n^2) = \epsilon_n^2, \; \ldots, \; \chi(C_n^n) = \epsilon_n^n = 1 \tag{4.37}$$

The characters for the remaining $n - 2$ representations are obtained by using the orthogonality relation (4.30). For example, consider the $\mathbf{C}_3$ group. Two of the representations are given by the known characters, and we wish to derive the characters a, b, c of the third irreducible representation

	E	C_3	C_3^2
${}^1\Gamma_1$:	1	1	1
${}^1\Gamma_2$:	1	ϵ_3	ϵ_3^2
${}^1\Gamma_3$:	a	b	c

The characters of the third representation ${}^1\Gamma_3$ are obtained from the orthogonality relation (4.30) which gives three linear algebraic equations:

$$\sum_{i=1}^{3} (\chi_1^{(i)})^*\chi_3^{(i)} = a + b + c = 0$$

$$\sum_{i=1}^{3} (\chi_2^{(i)})^*\chi_3^{(i)} = a + b\epsilon_3^* + c(\epsilon_3^2)^* = 0$$

$$\sum_{i=1}^{3} |\chi_3^{(i)}|^2 = |a|^2 + |b|^2 + |c|^2 = 3$$

Noting that

$$\epsilon_3^* = e^{-2\pi i/3} = e^{4\pi i/3} = \epsilon_3^2$$
$$(\epsilon_3^*)^2 = e^{-4\pi i/3} = e^{2\pi i/3} = \epsilon_3$$

we find the solution

$$a = 1 \qquad b = \epsilon_3^2 \qquad c = \epsilon_3$$

By this procedure, the character tables for all five of the $\mathbf{C}_n$ groups are constructed (Table 4.3).

The $\mathbf{C}_{nh}$ and $\mathbf{C}_{nv}$ groups Once again, the $\mathbf{C}_{nh}$ groups are abelian, and the irreducible representations are all one-dimensional. Consider the group $\mathbf{C}_{2h}$. The classes are E, C_2, σ_h, and I; thus there are four irreducible representations. The first is the unit representation ${}^1\Gamma_1$. The second is obtained, as before, by considering the rotations about the C axis which correspond to the classes. Thus,

$$\Gamma_2\colon\ \chi(E) = 1 \quad \chi(C_2) = e^{i\pi} = -1 \quad \chi(\sigma_h) = e^0 = 1 \quad \chi(I) = e^{i\pi} = -1$$

Once again, using the orthogonality relations (4.30), the characters for the other two representations are determined. The groups ($\mathbf{C}_{3h}$, $\mathbf{C}_{4h}$, and $\mathbf{C}_{6h}$) are determined in the same way. [The $\mathbf{C}_{1h} = \boldsymbol{\sigma}_h$ group is a two-element group; since ${}^1\Gamma_1 = (\chi(E) = 1,\ \chi(\sigma_h) = 1)$, the other representation must correspond to $\chi(E) = 1$, $\chi(\sigma_h) = -1$ in order to satisfy the orthogonality condition.]

The groups $\mathbf{C}_{nv}$ have, in addition to the n-fold rotation axis, the vertical reflections. These groups are not abelian. Consider, for example, the $\mathbf{C}_{3v}$ group. There are six elements and three irreducible representations (three classes) associated with this group. The decomposition into irreducible representations is, according to Eq. (4.35),

$$2^2 + 1^2 + 1^2 = 6$$

Thus, we have one two-dimensional and two one-dimensional representations.

$$\begin{array}{llll} {}^1\Gamma_1: & \chi(E) = 1 & \chi(2C_3) = 1 & \chi(3\sigma_v) = 1 \\ {}^2\Gamma_2: & \chi(E) = 2 & \chi(2C_3) = a & \chi(3\sigma_v) = b \\ {}^1\Gamma_3: & \chi(E) = 1 & \chi(2C_3) = c & \chi(3\sigma_v) = d \end{array}$$

According to Eq. (4.30), we find

$$a = -1 \qquad b = 0 \qquad c = 1 \qquad d = -1$$

By this procedure the character tables for all the point groups are determined. They are given in Table 4.3. Note that many of the different point groups are isomorphous (i.e., their irreducible representations are in one-to-one correspondence through the corresponding characters).

Applications to the Spectra of Crystalline Atoms

The reader may wonder why we have gone into so much detail in describing the wave functions in terms of the mathematical properties of the different crystallographic point groups. The answer to this question will be given in this subsection where the one-to-one correspondence between the characters and the irreducible representations of the point groups and the orthogonality properties of the characters will

TABLE 4.3 *(a) Character Tables for the Point Groups of Single-valued Group Representations*

1. $\mathbf{C}_1$	E
$^1\Gamma_1$	1

2.	$\mathbf{I}$			E	I
3.		$\mathbf{C}_2$		E	C_2
4.			σ_h	E	σ_h
	$^1\Gamma_1$	$^1\Gamma_1$; (z)	$^1\Gamma_1$; (x,y)	1	1
	$^1\Gamma_2$; (x,y,z)	$^1\Gamma_2$; (x,y)	$^1\Gamma_2$; (z)	1	-1

5. $\mathbf{C}_3$	E	C_3	C_3^2
$^1\Gamma_1$; (z)	1	1	1
(a) { $^1\Gamma_2$; $(x+iy)$	1	ϵ	ϵ^*
$^1\Gamma_3$; $(x-iy)$	1	ϵ^*	ϵ

$\epsilon \equiv e^{2\pi i/3}$

6. $\mathbf{C}_{3h} = \mathbf{C}_3 \times \sigma_h$

(b) 7. $\mathbf{S}_6 = \mathbf{C}_3 \times \mathbf{I}$

8.	$\mathbf{C}_4$		E	C_4	C_4^2	C_4^3
9.		$\mathbf{S}_4$	E	S_4	C_2	S_4^3
	$^1\Gamma_1$; (z)	$^1\Gamma_1$	1	1	1	1
	$^1\Gamma_2$	$^1\Gamma_2$; (z)	1	-1	1	-1
	{ $^1\Gamma_3$; $(x+iy)$	$^1\Gamma_3$; $(x+iy)$	1	i	-1	$-i$
	$^1\Gamma_4$; $(x-iy)$	$^1\Gamma_4$; $(x-iy)$	1	$-i$	-1	i

10. $\mathbf{C}_{4h} = \mathbf{C}_4 \times \mathbf{I}$

11. $\mathbf{C}_6$	E	C_6	C_6^2	C_6^3	C_6^4	C_6^5
$^1\Gamma_1$; (z)	1	1	1	1	1	1
$^1\Gamma_2$	1	-1	1	-1	1	-1
{ $^1\Gamma_3$	1	$-\omega^*$	$-\omega$	1	$-\omega^*$	$-\omega$
$^1\Gamma_4$	1	$-\omega$	$-\omega^*$	1	$-\omega$	$-\omega^*$
{ $^1\Gamma_5$; $(x+iy)$	1	ω	$-\omega^*$	-1	$-\omega$	ω^*
$^1\Gamma_6$; $(x-iy)$	1	ω^*	$-\omega$	-1	$-\omega^*$	ω

$\omega \equiv e^{\pi i/3}$

12. $\mathbf{C}_{6h} = \mathbf{C}_6 \times \mathbf{I}$

13.	$\mathbf{C}_{2h}$			E	C_2	σ_h	I
14.		$\mathbf{C}_{2v}$		E	C_2	σ_v	σ_v'
15.			$\mathbf{D}_2$	E	C_2^z	C_2^y	C_2^x
	$^1\Gamma_1$	$^1\Gamma_1$; (z)	$^1\Gamma_1$	1	1	1	1
	$^1\Gamma_2$	$^1\Gamma_2$; (y)	$^1\Gamma_2$; (x)	1	-1	-1	1
	$^1\Gamma_3$; (z)	$^1\Gamma_3$	$^1\Gamma_3$; (z)	1	1	-1	-1
	$^1\Gamma_4$; (x,y)	$^1\Gamma_4$; (x)	$^1\Gamma_4$; (y)	1	-1	1	-1

16. $\mathbf{D}_{2h} = \mathbf{D}_2 \times \mathbf{I}$

17.	$\mathbf{C}_{3v}$		E	$2C_3$	$3\sigma_v$
18.		$\mathbf{D}_3$	E	$2C_3$	$3U_2$
	$^1\Gamma_1$; (z)	$^1\Gamma_1$	1	1	1
	$^1\Gamma_2$	$^1\Gamma_2$; (z)	1	1	-1
	$^2\Gamma_3$; (x,y)	$^2\Gamma_3$; (x,y)	2	-1	0

19. $\mathbf{D}_{3d} = \mathbf{D}_3 \times \mathbf{I}$

TABLE 4.3 *(a) Character Tables for the Point Groups of Single-valued Group Representations (Continued)*

20.	$\mathbf{C}_{4v}$			E	C_2	$2C_4$	$2\sigma_v$	$2\sigma_v'$
21.		$\mathbf{D}_4$		E	C_2	$2C_4$	$2U_2$	$2U_2'$
22.			$\mathbf{D}_{2d}$	E	C_2	$2S_4$	$2U_2$	$2\sigma_d$
	${}^1\Gamma_1$; (z)	${}^1\Gamma_1$	${}^1\Gamma_1$	1	1	1	1	1
	${}^1\Gamma_2$	${}^1\Gamma_2$; z	${}^1\Gamma_2$	1	1	1	−1	−1
	${}^1\Gamma_3$	${}^1\Gamma_3$	${}^1\Gamma_3$	1	1	−1	1	−1
	${}^1\Gamma_4$	${}^1\Gamma_4$	${}^1\Gamma_4$; (z)	1	1	−1	−1	1
	${}^2\Gamma_5$; (x,y)	${}^2\Gamma_5$; (x,y)	${}^2\Gamma_5$; (x,y)	2	−2	0	0	0

23. $\mathbf{D}_{4h} = \mathbf{D}_4 \times \mathbf{I}$

24.	$\mathbf{D}_6$			E	C_2	$2C_3$	$2C_6$	$3U_2$	$3U_2'$
25.		$\mathbf{C}_{6v}$		E	C_2	$2C_3$	$2C_6$	$3\sigma_v$	$3\sigma_v'$
26.			$\mathbf{D}_{3h}$	E	σ_h	$2C_3$	$2S_3$	$3U_2$	$3\sigma_v'$
	${}^1\Gamma_1$	${}^1\Gamma_1$; (z)	${}^1\Gamma_1$	1	1	1	1	1	1
	${}^1\Gamma_2$; (z)	${}^1\Gamma_2$	${}^1\Gamma_2$	1	1	1	1	−1	−1
	${}^1\Gamma_3$	${}^1\Gamma_3$	${}^1\Gamma_3$	1	−1	1	−1	1	−1
	${}^1\Gamma_4$	${}^1\Gamma_4$	${}^1\Gamma_4$; (z)	1	−1	1	−1	−1	1
	${}^2\Gamma_5$	${}^2\Gamma_5$	${}^2\Gamma_5$; (x,y)	2	2	−1	−1	0	0
	${}^2\Gamma_6$; (x,y)	${}^2\Gamma_6$; (x,y)	${}^2\Gamma_6$	2	−2	−1	1	0	0

27. $\mathbf{D}_{6h} = \mathbf{D}_6 \times \mathbf{I}$

28.	$\mathbf{T}$	E	$3C_2$	$4C_3$	$4C_3^2$
	${}^1\Gamma_1$	1	1	1	1
	{ ${}^1\Gamma_2$	1	1	ϵ	ϵ^*
	{ ${}^1\Gamma_3$	1	1	ϵ^*	ϵ
	${}^3\Gamma_4$; (x,y,z)	3	−1	0	0

$\epsilon \equiv e^{2\pi i/3}$

29. $\mathbf{T}_h = \mathbf{T} \times \mathbf{I}$

30.	$\mathbf{O}$		E	$8C_3$	$3C_2$	$6C_2'$	$6C_4$
31.		$\mathbf{T}_d$	E	$8C_3$	$3C_2$	$6\sigma_d$	$6S_4$
	${}^1\Gamma_1$	${}^1\Gamma_1$	1	1	1	1	1
	${}^1\Gamma_2$	${}^1\Gamma_2$	1	1	1	−1	−1
	${}^2\Gamma_3$	${}^2\Gamma_3$	2	−1	2	0	0
	${}^3\Gamma_4$	${}^3\Gamma_4$; (x,y,z)	3	0	−1	1	−1
	${}^3\Gamma_5$; (x,y,z)	${}^3\Gamma_5$	3	0	−1	−1	1

32. $\mathbf{O}_h = \mathbf{O} \times \mathbf{I}$

NOTES. (*a*) The pairs of irreducible representations in the braces represent eigenfunctions that are degenerate due to the time-reversal invariance of the hamiltonian. The correspondence of the irreducible representations with the spatial coordinates (x,y,z) is indicated.
(*b*) For each representation Γ_κ of a group **G**, there are two representations Γ_κ^+ and Γ_κ^- of the group $\mathbf{G} \times \mathbf{I}$. These correspond to states of opposite parity.

be exploited in order to determine the splitting of atomic energy levels and the selection rules for the absorption (or emission) of radiation by atoms subjected to a crystalline electric field.

The energy-level splitting by a crystalline field has already been described in the preceding subsection for the special case in which the ion was originally in a D state and the crystalline field had cubic symmetry. The purpose of that discussion was to indicate the physical reasons for the energy-level splitting. On the other hand, the method used there would, in general, become quite cumbersome when applied to most physical problems. The properties of the characters of the point groups provide a very powerful method with which the energy-level splitting may be determined quite readily. This method will now be described.

Energy-level splittings of crystalline atoms Let us consider, for simplicity, an ion that contains one unpaired orbital electron. The energy levels E_n of this ion may be determined to a high degree of accuracy by the one-electron Schroedinger eigenvalue equation[1]

$$\nabla^2\psi_n + \frac{2m}{\hbar^2}(E_n + e\varphi_0)\psi_n = 0$$

Although the example refers to the one-electron atom, the arguments presented are sensitive only to the symmetry character of the hamiltonian and therefore also apply to the general case of the many-electron atom.

The potential energy $e\varphi_0$ which binds the unpaired electron to the atom is invariant under any (infinitesimal) rotation of the coordinate system and to an inversion through the origin (located at the nucleus). The symmetry properties of such a hamiltonian may thus be described by a group which is made up of a continuous set of infinitesimal rotations. Such a group is called the *rotation group of the sphere,* and, in distinction from the *finite groups* discussed previously, it contains an infinite number of elements (it is called a *continuous group*). Without proof, we shall assert that the rotation group of the sphere always contains within it an irreducible representation of order $2l + 1$ (where $l = 0, 1, 2, \ldots$).[2] This irreducible representation describes an angular function which transforms like the spherical harmonic

$$Y_l^{m_l}(\theta,\phi) \propto P_l^{m_l}(\cos\theta)e^{im_l\phi} \qquad m_l = -l, -l+1, \ldots, l$$

Since the atomic-orbital wave functions also transform like $Y_l^{m_l}$, we

[1] For a review of the properties of the many-electron atom see, for example, J. C. Slater, "Quantum Theory of Atomic Structure," vol. I, McGraw-Hill Book Company, Inc., New York, 1960.

[2] E. P. Wigner, *Z. Physik,* **43**: 624 (1927).

may associate this irreducible representation with the angular part of the wave function which is associated with a particular atomic orbital $\hbar l$.

The assertion made above is verified experimentally by the fact that we observe "free" atoms to be in distinct states which are characterized by different orbital–angular-momentum quantum numbers.

Suppose now that this atom is placed in a crystal. The eigenvalue equation for this situation represents a reduction of symmetry from the sphericity of the free atom to the lower symmetry described by one of the crystallographic point groups. The reduction of symmetry means that each $(2l + 1)$-dimensional irreducible representation of the free-atom rotation group is reduced further into a combination of irreducible representations of the crystal group (in special cases it may not reduce at all). Since *each* irreducible representation describes a set of eigenfunctions which uniquely transform into a linear combination of each other under the elements of the group, the reduction of the $(2l + 1)$-order representation into n $(n \leq 2l + 1)$ irreducible representations of the crystal group describes a splitting of an atomic-orbital level $E(l)$ into n energy levels. Each of the n newly formed irreducible representations clearly forms a subgroup of the original rotation group.

In order to decompose the $(2l + 1)$-dimensional representation of the rotation group into irreducible representations of the crystal symmetry group, we make use of the following uniqueness theorem of group theory (which will also be stated without proof):

Theorem: Every reducible representation of a group can be decomposed in only one way into its irreducible components.

According to this theorem, then, the character of each element of the reducible rotation group is (uniquely) equal to the sum of the characters of the constituent irreducible representations for the corresponding crystal group elements. Denoting the characters of the $(2l + 1)$-dimensional continuous group by $\chi_l(\phi_i)$, the above statement is represented mathematically as follows:

$$\chi_l(\phi_i) = \Sigma a_\kappa \chi_\kappa^{(i)} \tag{4.38}$$

where a_κ is the number of times that the irreducible representation Γ_κ of the crystal group is contained in the $(2l + 1)$-dimensional representation of the rotation group. ϕ_i is the angle ϕ corresponding to the particular rotation transformation i of the crystal group, and $\chi_\kappa^{(i)}$ is the character for the class belonging to the irreducible representation Γ_κ [tabulated in the character tables (Tables 4.3)].

The task then remains to determine the functional form of $\chi_l(\phi_i)$. This is done by noting that the most general rotation is one about an arbitrary axis by some angle ϕ. Under this transformation, the spherical harmonic (defined in terms of this arbitrary axis) transforms to

$$P_l^{m_l}(\cos\theta)e^{im\phi'} = P_l^{m_l}(\cos\theta)e^{im(\phi+\phi_i)}$$

Since $m_l = -l, -l+1, \ldots, l$, the $(2l+1)$-dimensional representation of the rotation group is given by the diagonal matrix

$$R_l(\phi_i) = \begin{pmatrix} e^{-il\phi_i} & 0 & \cdots & 0 \\ 0 & e^{-i(l-1)\phi_i} & & \vdots \\ \vdots & & \ddots & \vdots \\ 0 & 0 & & e^{il\phi_i} \end{pmatrix} \tag{4.39}$$

with the character

$$\chi_l(\phi_i) = \mathrm{Tr}\,[R_l(\phi_i)] = \frac{\sin(l+\frac{1}{2})\phi_i}{\sin\phi_i/2} \tag{4.40}$$

We now replace ϕ_i by the particular ϕ_i for each class of the group and determine the corresponding character from Eq. (4.40). Combining these results with Eq. (4.38) leads to a determination of the decomposition of the continuous rotation group into its irreducible components of the crystal group.

Consider, for example, the splitting of atomic orbitals in a crystal field which is characterized by the cubic point group **O** (Table 4.3). The angles ϕ_i associated with the classes of the **O** group are as follows:

$$\begin{aligned} &\phi_E = 0 \qquad \phi_{8C_3} = \frac{\pm 2\pi}{3} \qquad \phi_{3C_2} = \pi \\ &\phi_{6C_2'} = \pi \qquad \phi_{6C_4} = \frac{\pm\pi}{2} \end{aligned} \tag{4.41}$$

The corresponding characters are, according to Eq. (4.40),

$$\begin{aligned} \chi(\phi_E) &= 2l+1 \qquad \chi(\phi_{8C_3}) = \frac{\sin(l+\frac{1}{2})2\pi/3}{\sin\pi/3} \\ \chi(\phi_{3C_2}) &= \frac{\sin(l+\frac{1}{2})\pi}{\sin\pi/2} = (-1)^l = \chi(\phi_{6C_2'}) \\ \chi(\phi_{6C_4}) &= \frac{\sin(l+\frac{1}{2})\pi/2}{\sin\pi/4} = \cos\frac{l\pi}{2} + \sin\frac{l\pi}{2} \end{aligned} \tag{4.42}$$

Substituting into Eq. (4.42), the characters for $l = 0, 1, 2, 3, 4, 5, 6$ are evaluated and are given in Table 4.4.

Combining each row of Table 4.4 with Eq. (4.38) and the character table for the **O** group (Table 4.3), we have for each value of l a set of five simultaneous algebraic equations, with the solutions giving the coefficients of the composite irreducible representations. Let us now consider specific orbital splittings.[1]

TABLE 4.4 *Characters of the Classes of the* **O** *Group in the* $(2l + 1)$*-dimensional Representation of the Rotation Group*

l	*Class*				
	$\chi(E)$	$\chi(8C_3)$	$\chi(3C_2)$	$\chi(6C_4)$	$\chi(6C_2')$
0	1	1	1	1	1
1	3	0	−1	1	−1
2	5	−1	1	−1	1
3	7	1	−1	−1	−1
4	9	0	1	1	1
5	11	−1	−1	1	−1
6	13	1	1	−1	1

The ^3P ***state*** $(l = 1)$ According to Eq. (4.38) and Tables 4.3 and 4.4, we have the following equations:

$$\begin{aligned}
\chi_1(E) &= 3 = a_1 + a_2 + 2a_3 + 3a_4 + 3a_5 \\
\chi_1(\phi_{8C_3}) &= 0 = a_1 + a_2 - a_3 \\
\chi_1(\phi_{3C_2}) &= -1 = a_1 + a_2 + 2a_3 - a_4 - a_5 \\
\chi_1(\phi_{6C_{2'}}) &= -1 = a_1 - a_2 + a_4 - a_5 \\
\chi_1(\phi_{6C_4}) &= 1 = a_1 - a_2 - a_4 + a_5
\end{aligned} \tag{4.43}$$

The solution of Eq. (4.43) is

$$a_5 = 1 \qquad a_1 = a_2 = a_3 = a_4 = 0$$

Thus

$$^3R_1 = {}^3\Gamma_5 \tag{4.44}$$

This result relates to the fact that an ion, which was originally in the (3-fold degenerate) ^3P state, does not have any of its degeneracy removed by a cubic **O** crystalline field. (The new state is denoted by $^3\Gamma_5$ rather than ^3P.)

The ^5D ***state*** $(l = 2)$ From Eq. (4.38) and Tables 4.3 and 4.4, we have

$$\begin{aligned}
\chi_2(E) &= 5 = a_1 + a_2 + 2a_3 + 3a_4 + 3a_5 \\
\chi_2(\phi_{8C_3}) &= -1 = a_1 + a_2 - a_3 \\
\chi_2(\phi_{3C_2}) &= 1 = a_1 + a_2 + 2a_3 - a_4 - a_5 \\
\chi_2(\phi_{6C_{2'}}) &= +1 = a_1 - a_2 + a_4 - a_5 \\
\chi_2(\phi_{6C_4}) &= -1 = a_1 - a_2 - a_4 + a_5
\end{aligned} \tag{4.45}$$

[1] For the S state (that is, $l = 0$), $\chi_0(^1R_0) = \chi(^1\Gamma_1)$; thus $^1R_0 \equiv {}^1\Gamma_1$. This follows from the uniqueness theorem stated above. The S state is unaffected by a crystal field since it is initially nondegenerate (in terms of the spatial dependence of the wave function).

The solution of Eq. (4.45) is

$$a_3 = a_4 = 1 \qquad a_1 = a_2 = a_5 = 0$$

Thus[1]

$$^5R_2 = {}^2\Gamma_3 + {}^3\Gamma_4 \tag{4.46}$$

We see in this case that the 5-fold degenerate ^5D level is split by the octahedral crystalline field into a 2-fold degenerate energy level and a 3-fold degenerate energy level, described, respectively, by the representations $^2\Gamma_3$ and $^3\Gamma_4$ of the **O** group. We have seen earlier that the symmetry of the simple cube is described by the $\mathbf{O}_h$ point group and also that the $\mathbf{O}_h$ group is made up of the direct product of the **O** group with the inversion group. Since the symmetry character of the ^5D state (and any even atomic-orbital state) is invariant under an inversion of spatial coordinates, the presence of the inversion cannot affect the splitting already obtained. Thus, the same orbital splitting is obtained for the $\mathbf{O}_h$ group as for the **O** group. The result for the $\mathbf{O}_h$ group was obtained earlier [Eq. (4.24)] by the non-group-theory technique.

Continuing in this fashion, we may determine the splittings of any atomic-orbital state in a crystalline field of any symmetry type. The results for the **O** group for $l = 0$ through 6 and, for comparison, the results for the hexagonal $\mathbf{D}_6$ group are given in Table 4.5. Note that the splittings of all atomic states after the S state (that is, $l = 0$) are greater in the case of the hexagonal $\mathbf{D}_6$ symmetry group than in the cubic **O** symmetry group. This is a result of a general property of quantum-mechanical systems that the amount of degeneracy is proportional to the symmetry of the system.

Problem

Using the techniques demonstrated above, determine the energy-level splitting of an ion, originally in an F state, subjected to a crystalline field that is characterized by the (trigonal) $\mathbf{C}_{3v}$ symmetry.

The components of the atomic-orbital states which are associated with the irreducible representations of the groups are determined by expressing them as a function of (x,y,z) and then associating the coordinates (x,y,z) with the characters belonging to the irreducible representations of the group. Consider, for example, the $\mathbf{C}_{2v}$ point group (Table 4.3). The classes are E, C_2, σ_v, and σ_v'. The coordinate z is unaffected by any of these transformations; thus z is associated with the identity representation $^1\Gamma_1$. On the other hand, the coordinate x changes sign under the transformations C_2 and one of the reflections σ_v' while y changes

[1] Note that the superscript integer on the left-hand side of the equation must always be equal to the sum of the superscript integers on the terms on the right-hand side of the equation.

TABLE 4.5 *Atomic-orbital Splitting in a Crystalline Field with Cubic* (**O**) *and Hexagonal* ($\mathbf{D}_6$) *Symmetry*
The notation used is $\Gamma(\mathbf{O}) \equiv A$, $\Gamma(\mathbf{D}_6) \equiv B$

State	*L*	*Point Group*	*Decomposition*	*Number of terms*
^1S	0	**O**	$^1A_1$	1
		$\mathbf{D}_6$	$^1B_1$	1
^3P	1	**O**	$^3A_5$	1
		$\mathbf{D}_6$	$^1B_2 + {}^2B_6$	2
^5D	2	**O**	$^2A_3 + {}^3A_4$	2
		$\mathbf{D}_6$	$^1B_1 + {}^2B_5 + {}^2B_6$	3
^7F	3	**O**	$^1A_2 + {}^3A_4 + {}^3A_5$	3
		$\mathbf{D}_6$	$^1B_2 + {}^1B_3 + {}^1B_4 + {}^2B_5 + {}^2B_6$	5
^9G	4	**O**	$^1A_1 + {}^2A_3 + {}^3A_4 + {}^3A_5$	4
		$\mathbf{D}_6$	$^1B_1 + {}^1B_3 + {}^1B_4 + 2{}^2B_5 + {}^2B_6$	6
^{11}H	5	**O**	$^2A_3 + 2{}^3A_5 + {}^3A_4$	4
		$\mathbf{D}_6$	$^1B_2 + {}^1B_3 + {}^1B_4 + 2{}^2B_5 + 2{}^2B_6$	7
^{13}I	6	**O**	$^1A_1 + {}^1A_2 + {}^2A_3 + {}^3A_5 + 2{}^3A_4$	6
		$\mathbf{D}_6$	$2{}^1B_1 + {}^1B_2 + {}^1B_3 + {}^1B_4 + 2{}^2B_5 + 2{}^2B_6$	9

sign under the transformations C_2 and the other reflection σ_v. Thus x and y are associated with the irreducible representations $^1\Gamma_4(\mathbf{C}_{2v})$ and $^1\Gamma_2(\mathbf{C}_{2v})$, respectively. [The coordinate transformations are indicated in the character tables (Tables 4.3).] Thus, the three components of the ^3P state, i.e., the first-order polynomials

$$\frac{z}{r} \propto Y_1^0 \qquad \frac{x}{r} \propto Y_1^1 + Y_1^{-1} \qquad \frac{y}{r} \propto Y_1^1 - Y_1^{-1}$$

are associated with $^1\Gamma_1(\mathbf{C}_{2v})$, $^1\Gamma_4(\mathbf{C}_{2v})$, and $^1\Gamma_2(\mathbf{C}_{2v})$, respectively. The same procedure may be followed in determining the associations of the irreducible representations with the higher-order polynomials which transform as the atomic wave functions. Just as we did previously, the different irreducible representations may thus be interpreted in terms of the orientations of the charge distributions associated with the components of angular momenta.

Orientation of Half-integral Angular Momenta in a Crystal; Double-valued Representations

Up to this point we have discussed the splitting of atomic-orbital states by making use of the fact that the corresponding wave functions transform precisely like the irreducible representations of the rotation group. Thus, it has not yet been necessary to resort to any techniques involving the effects of small perturbations. If we now consider the fact that electrons possess an intrinsic spin, account must be taken of the interaction that couples the atomic-orbital momentum to the net spin of the electron cloud. This coupling gives rise to a further splitting of the atomic orbitals into energy levels that are characterized by different relative orientations between the orbital momenta and the spin of the atom.

When the spin-orbit interaction energy is small compared with the configuration interaction $\left(\sum_{i<j} e^2/r_{ij}\right)$ (i.e., the interaction that separates the different atomic-orbital levels), the resulting states are characterized by the quantum numbers[1]

$$J = L + S, L + S - 1, \ . \ . \ . \ , L - S$$

with

$$L = \Sigma l_i \qquad S = \Sigma s_i$$

and where the sums are taken over all the atomic electrons. (This is the Russell-Saunders coupling scheme.)

When the spin-orbit interaction is large compared with $\sum_{i<j} e^2/r_{ij}$, the spin and orbital momenta of individual electrons prefer to couple separately to form a net momentum (for each electron) $j_i = l_i + s_i$; the resulting atomic states are characterized by the quantum numbers

$$J = j_1 + j_2 + \cdot \cdot \cdot + j_n, j_1 - j_2 + j_3 + \cdot \cdot \cdot + j_n, \ . \ . \ .$$

(This is the j-j coupling scheme.)

In any case, when the number of atomic electrons is even, S, and therefore J, is an integer. The resulting wave functions then still transform under rotations like the ordinary representations of the rotation group, and our previous considerations of atomic orbitals may be applied. On the other hand, if the number of electrons is odd, the angular momentum J is a half-integer. If the crystalline potential energy is small compared with the splitting between the different J levels (that is, $\langle e\varphi_c \rangle \ll \langle \lambda L \cdot S \rangle$), then we must consider how these

[1] The summations refer to the possible combinations $l_1 + l_2 + \cdot \cdot \cdot + l_n, l_1 - l_2 + l_3 + \cdot \cdot \cdot + l_n$, etc., and $s_1 + s_2 + \cdot \cdot \cdot + s_n, s_1 - s_2 + s_3 + \cdot \cdot \cdot + s_n$, etc.

individual levels [which are initially $(2J + 1)$-fold degenerate] are split by the crystalline field.

The electron spin is represented by a function which has two degrees of freedom (i.e., a spinor), corresponding physically to the two orientations of the electron spin along some chosen axis that is singled out in an interaction (i.e., the axis of quantization). Thus, the spin is described, in group-theory terms, by a two-dimensional irreducible representation $\Gamma_{1/2}$. The irreducible representations of the rotation group, associated with a given value of J, are then obtained by taking the direct product of $\Gamma_{1/2}$ with the spatial representations. This results in a *double-valued* representation of the rotation group.

Just as we found earlier [Eq. (4.40)], the character associated with a rotation ϕ about an arbitrary axis is

$$\chi_J(\phi) = \frac{\sin (J + \frac{1}{2})\phi}{\sin \phi/2} \tag{4.47}$$

However, if $J + \frac{1}{2}$ is integral,

$$\chi_J(\phi + 2\pi) = \frac{\sin [(J + \frac{1}{2})(\phi + 2\pi)]}{\sin [(\phi + 2\pi)/2]} = -\frac{\sin (J + \frac{1}{2})\phi}{\sin (\phi/2)} = -\chi_J(\phi)$$

while previously, with $l + \frac{1}{2}$ a half integer,

$$\chi_l(\phi + 2\pi) = \frac{\sin [(l + \frac{1}{2})(\phi + 2\pi)]}{\sin [(\phi + 2\pi)/2]} = +\frac{\sin (l + \frac{1}{2})\phi}{\sin (\phi/2)} = \chi_l(\phi) \tag{4.48}$$

Since the characters χ_J change sign after rotations of 2π, they are double-valued. Also, the character of the identity representation is double-valued, i.e.,

$$\begin{aligned} \chi_E(0) &= 2J + 1 \\ \chi_E(2\pi) &= -(2J + 1) \end{aligned} \tag{4.49}$$

However, the rotation of π about an arbitrary axis gives a single-valued character

$$\chi(\pi) = \chi(3\pi) = 0$$

and, in general,

$$\chi(\phi) = \chi(4\pi - \phi) \tag{4.50}$$

It is clear that a double-valued representation of the continuous rotation group must contain double-valued representations of the crystal group. In order to obtain these representations, the fictitious assumption is made that the crystal lattice does not map onto itself after a 2π rotation but rather does so only after a rotation of 4π has been completed. A new element (R) of the group is defined, different from the identity, which describes a 2π rotation of the lattice (about some arbitrary axis). The remaining elements of the group are then obtained by multiplying all the elements of the original group by the element R.

Thus the double-valued group has twice as many elements as does the corresponding single-valued group. On the other hand, the double-valued group does not generally contain twice as many classes as the original group. This is due to the property of the characters of the double group, given by Eq. (4.50). This result implies that each class of the single- and double-valued groups which contains π rotations corresponds to one class of the double-valued group, while others correspond to two classes of the double-valued group.

The characters for the original representations of the single-valued group are the same for the classes C and RC of the double-valued group. The characters of the additional irreducible representations of the double-valued point groups are given in Table 4.3*b*.[1]

The splitting of atomic energy levels that are associated with the different half-integer J values is determined in exactly the same way as was done previously, except that the character tables of the double-valued groups must now be used. The decomposition of energy levels (characterized by $J = \frac{1}{2}$ through $J = \frac{11}{2}$) by $\mathbf{O}$ and $\mathbf{D}_6$ symmetry potentials is shown in Table 4.6.

Problem

Determine the splitting of the ground state of the Ce^{3+} ion ($J = \frac{5}{2}$) when subjected to (hexagonal) $\mathbf{D}_{3h}$ crystal symmetry.

Once again, we note from Table 4.6 that, as expected, for all energy levels with $J > \frac{1}{2}$, the (lower-symmetry) $\mathbf{D}_6$ group lifts more degeneracy than does the (higher-symmetry) $\mathbf{O}$ group. The failure of the crystalline field to lift the double degeneracy which is associated with the $J = \frac{1}{2}$ level, or more than an even-fold degeneracy of any of the irreducible representations of the double-valued group, is a consequence of the fact that there is no assumed direct spin coupling to the electrostatic field of the crystal. Under this assumption (which is based on the more general assumption that electromagnetic interactions are invariant under time reversal and space reflection), Kramers has shown that, when J is a a half-integer angular-momentum quantum number, there must always remain at least a residual 2-fold degeneracy in the energy levels of the system. This is a statement of *Kramers' theorem*.[2] The remaining 2-fold degeneracy is associated with the two oppositely oriented components $\pm J_z$ of the angular-momentum vector $\mathbf{J}$. A proof of this theorem is given in Appendix A.

[1] For further discussion on the determination of the character tables for the double-valued groups, see M. Hamermesh, *op. cit.*, p. 357.

[2] H. A. Kramers, *Proc. Acad. Sci. Amsterdam*, **33**: 959 (1930). Also see L. Landau and E. Lifshitz, "Quantum Mechanics, Nonrelativistic Theory," p. 202, Addison-Wesley Publishing Company, Inc., Reading, Mass., 1958.

TABLE 4.3 (*b*) *Additional Characters for the Irreducible Representations of the Double-valued Groups*

1.

$^2C_1$	E	R
$^1\Gamma_2$	1	-1

2.

^2I	E	I	R	RI
$^1\Gamma_3$	1	1	-1	-1
$^1\Gamma_4$	1	-1	-1	1

3. / **4.**

$^2C_2$		E	C_2	R	RC_2
	$^2\sigma_h$	E	σ_h	R	$R\sigma_h$
{ $^1\Gamma_3$	$^1\Gamma_3$	1	i	-1	$-i$
{ $^1\Gamma_4$	$^1\Gamma_4$	1	$-i$	-1	i

5.

$^2C_3$	E	C_3	C_3^2	R	RC_3	RC_3^2
{ $^1\Gamma_4$	1	ω	$-\omega^*$	-1	$-\omega$	ω^*
{ $^1\Gamma_5$	1	ω^*	$-\omega$	-1	$-\omega^*$	ω
$^1\Gamma_6$	1	-1	1	-1	1	-1

$(\omega \equiv e^{i\pi/3})$

6. $^2C_{3h} = {}^2C_3 \times \sigma_h$

7. $^2S_6 = {}^2C_3 \times I$

8. / **9.**

$^2C_4$		E	C_4	C_4^2	C_4^3	R	RC_4	RC_4^2	RC_4^3
	$^2S_4$	E	S_4	C_2	S_4^3	R	RS_4	RC_2	RS_4^3
{ $^1\Gamma_5$		1	δ	i	$-\delta^*$	-1	$-\delta$	$-i$	δ^*
{ $^1\Gamma_6$		1	δ^*	$-i$	$-\delta$	-1	$-\delta^*$	i	δ
{ $^1\Gamma_7$		1	$-\delta$	i	δ^*	-1	δ	$-i$	$-\delta^*$
{ $^1\Gamma_8$		1	$-\delta^*$	$-i$	δ	-1	δ^*	i	$-\delta$

$(\delta \equiv e^{i\pi/4})$

10. $^2C_{4h} = {}^2C_4 \times I$

11.

$^2C_6$	E	C_6	C_3	C_2	C_6^4	C_6^5	R	RC_6	RC_3	RC_2	RC_6^4	RC_6^5
{ $^1\Gamma_7$	1	γ	γ^2	γ^3	$-(\gamma^2)^*$	$-\gamma^*$	-1	$-\gamma$	$-\gamma^2$	$-\gamma^3$	$(\gamma^2)^*$	γ^*
{ $^1\Gamma_8$	1	γ^*	$(\gamma^2)^*$	$(\gamma^3)^*$	$-\gamma^2$	$-\gamma$	-1	$-\gamma^*$	$-(\gamma^2)^*$	$-(\gamma^3)^*$	γ^2	γ
{ $^1\Gamma_9$	1	i	-1	$-i$	1	i	-1	$-i$	1	i	-1	$-i$
{ $^1\Gamma_{10}$	1	$-i$	-1	i	1	$-i$	-1	i	1	$-i$	-1	i
{ $^1\Gamma_{11}$	1	$-\gamma$	γ^2	$-\gamma^3$	$-(\gamma^2)^*$	γ^*	-1	γ	$-\gamma^2$	γ^3	$(\gamma^2)^*$	$-\gamma^*$
{ $^1\Gamma_{12}$	1	$-\gamma^*$	$(\gamma^2)^*$	$-(\gamma^3)^*$	$-\gamma^2$	γ	-1	γ^*	$-(\gamma^2)^*$	$(\gamma^3)^*$	γ^2	$-\gamma$

12. $^2C_{6h} = {}^2C_6 \times I$ $\gamma \equiv e^{i\pi/6}$

13.

$^2C_{2h}$	E	C_2	σ_h	I	R	RC_2	$R\sigma_h$	RI
{ $^1\Gamma_5$	1	i	i	1	-1	$-i$	$-i$	-1
{ $^1\Gamma_6$	1	$-i$	$-i$	1	-1	i	i	-1
{ $^1\Gamma_7$	1	i	$-i$	-1	-1	$-i$	i	1
{ $^1\Gamma_8$	1	$-i$	i	-1	-1	i	$-i$	1

14. / **15.**

$^2C_{2v}$		E	C_2	σ_v	σ_v'	R	RC_2	$R\sigma_v$	$R\sigma_v'$
	$^2D_2$	E	C_2	U_2	U_2'	R	RC_2	RU_2	RU_2'
$^2\Gamma_5$	$^2\Gamma_5$	2	0	0	0	-2	0	0	0

16. $^2D_{2h} = {}^2D_2 \times I$

TABLE 4.3 (*b*) *Additional Characters for the Irreducible Representations of the Double-valued Groups (Continued)*

17.	$^2\mathbf{C}_{3v}$		E	$2C_3$	$3\sigma_v$	R	$2RC_3$	$3R\sigma_v$
18.		$^2\mathbf{D}_3$	E	$2C_3$	$3U_2$	R	$2RC_3$	$3RU_2$
	$^2\Gamma_5$	$^2\Gamma_5$	2	1	0	-2	-1	0
	$\{\ ^1\Gamma_6$	$^1\Gamma_6$	1	-1	i	-1	1	$-i$
	$\ \ ^1\Gamma_7$	$^1\Gamma_7$	1	-1	$-i$	-1	1	i

19. $^2\mathbf{D}_{3d} = {}^2\mathbf{D}_3 \times \mathbf{I}$

20.	$^2\mathbf{C}_{4v}$			E	$2C_4$	C_2	$2\sigma_v$	$2\sigma_d$	R	$2RC_4$	RC_2	$2R\sigma_v$	$2R\sigma_d$
21.		$^2\mathbf{D}_4$		E	$2C_4$	C_2	$2U_2$	$2U_2'$	R	$2RC_4$	RC_2	$2RU_2$	$2RU_2'$
22.			$^2\mathbf{D}_{2d}$	E	$2S_4$	C_2	$2U_2$	$2\sigma_d$	R	$2RS_4$	RC_2	$2RU_2$	$2R\sigma_d$
	$^2\Gamma_6$	$^2\Gamma_6$	$^2\Gamma_6$	2	$\sqrt{2}$	0	0	0	-2	$-\sqrt{2}$	0	0	0
	$^2\Gamma_7$	$^2\Gamma_7$	$^2\Gamma_7$	2	$-\sqrt{2}$	0	0	0	-2	$\sqrt{2}$	0	0	0

23. $^2\mathbf{D}_{4h} = {}^2\mathbf{D}_4 \times \mathbf{I}$

24.	$^2\mathbf{D}_6$			E	R	C_2	RC_2	$2C_3$	$2RC_3$	$2C_6$	$2RC_6$	$3U_2$	$3RU_2$	$3U_2'$	$3RU_2'$
25.		$^2\mathbf{C}_{6v}$		E	R	C_2	RC_2	$2C_3$	$2RC_3$	$2C_6$	$2RC_6$	$3\sigma_v$	$3R\sigma_v$	$3\sigma_v'$	$3R\sigma_v'$
26.			$^2\mathbf{D}_{3h}$	E	R	C_2	R	$2C_3$	$2RC_3$	$2S_3$	$2RS_3$	$3U_2$	$3RU_2$	$3\sigma_v'$	$3R\sigma_v'$
	$^2\Gamma_7$	$^2\Gamma_7$	$^2\Gamma_7$	2	-2	0	0	1	-1	$\sqrt{3}$	$-\sqrt{3}$	0	0	0	0
	$^2\Gamma_8$	$^2\Gamma_8$	$^2\Gamma_8$	2	-2	0	0	1	-1	$-\sqrt{3}$	$\sqrt{3}$	0	0	0	0
	$^2\Gamma_9$	$^2\Gamma_9$	$^2\Gamma_9$	2	-2	0	0	-2	2	0	0	0	0	0	0

27. $^2\mathbf{D}_{6h} = {}^2\mathbf{D}_6 \times \mathbf{I}$

28.	$^2\mathbf{T}$	E	R	$3C_2$	$3RC_2$	$4C_3$	$4RC_3$	$4C_3^2$	$4RC_3^2$
	$^2\Gamma_5$	2	-2	0	0	1	-1	1	-1
	$\{\ ^2\Gamma_6$	2	-2	0	0	ω	$-\omega$	$-\omega^*$	ω^*
	$\ \ ^2\Gamma_7$	2	-2	0	0	ω^*	$-\omega^*$	$-\omega$	ω

$(\omega \equiv e^{i\pi/3})$

29. $^2\mathbf{T}_h = {}^2\mathbf{T} \times \mathbf{I}$

30.	$^2\mathbf{O}$		E	R	$8C_3$	$8RC_3$	$3C_2$	$3RC_2$	$6C_2'$	$6RC_2'$	$6C_4$	$6RC_4$
31.		$^2\mathbf{T}_d$	E	R	$8C_3$	$8RC_5$	$3C_2$	$3RC_2$	$6\sigma_d$	$6R\sigma_d$	$6S_4$	$6RS_4$
	$^2\Gamma_6$	$^2\Gamma_6$	2	-2	1	-1	0	0	0	0	$\sqrt{2}$	$-\sqrt{2}$
	$^2\Gamma_7$	$^2\Gamma_7$	2	-2	1	-1	0	0	0	0	$-\sqrt{2}$	$\sqrt{2}$
	$^4\Gamma_8$	$^4\Gamma_8$	4	-4	-1	1	0	0	0	0	0	0

32. $^2\mathbf{O}_h = {}^2\mathbf{O} \times \mathbf{I}$

TABLE 4.6 *Splitting of Half-integer Angular-momentum Energy Levels in a Crystalline Field with Cubic* (**O**) *and Hexagonal* ($\mathbf{D}_6$) *Symmetry.* (*L stands for the orbital momentum associated with the angular momentum J.*)
The notation used is $\Gamma(\mathbf{O}) = A$, $\Gamma(\mathbf{D}_6) = B$

State	*Point group*	*Decomposition*	*Number of terms*
$^2L_{1/2}$	**O**	$^2A_6$	1
	$\mathbf{D}_6$	$^2B_7$	1
$^4L_{3/2}$	**O**	$^4A_8$	1
	$\mathbf{D}_6$	$^2B_7 + {^2B_9}$	2
$^6L_{5/2}$	**O**	$^2A_7 + {^4A_8}$	2
	$\mathbf{D}_6$	$^2B_7 + {^2B_8} + {^2B_9}$	3
$^8L_{7/2}$	**O**	$^2A_6 + {^2A_7} + {^4A_8}$	3
	$\mathbf{D}_6$	$^2B_7 + 2{^2B_8} + {^2B_9}$	4
$^{10}L_{9/2}$	**O**	$^2A_6 + 2{^4A_8}$	3
	$\mathbf{D}_6$	$^2B_7 + 2{^2B_8} + 2{^2B_9}$	5
$^{12}L_{11/2}$	**O**	$^2A_6 + {^2A_7} + 2{^4A_8}$	4
	$\mathbf{D}_6$	$2{^2B_7} + 2{^2B_8} + 2{^2B_9}$	6

4.3 Selection rules for the absorption (or emission) of radiation

Let us now briefly review the standard treatment of the absorption (or emission) of electromagnetic radiation by atoms, and then consider the case of crystalline atoms.

The probability for the occurrence of a transition between two unperturbed states ψ_i and ψ_f as caused by the interaction of an electromagnetic radiation field and a crystal is dependent on the matrix element:[1]

$$\int \psi_f^* \mathcal{H}_{int} \psi_i \, d\tau \tag{4.51}$$

The interaction hamiltonian operator, derived from the classical form $(e/c)\mathbf{p} \cdot \mathbf{A}$, has the well-known form

$$\mathcal{H}_{int} = \frac{e\hbar}{imc} \mathbf{A} \cdot \nabla \tag{4.52}$$

[1] See, for example, Schiff, *op. cit.*, p. 193.

The vector potential **A** of the radiation field has the plane wave form

$$\mathbf{A} = \hat{\mathbf{n}}|\mathbf{A}_0|e^{i(\mathbf{q}\cdot\mathbf{r}-\omega t)} \tag{4.53}$$

where $\hat{\mathbf{n}}$ is a unit vector in the direction of polarization (i.e., in the direction of the oscillating electric field vector),

$$\mathbf{q} = \frac{2\pi}{\lambda}\hat{\mathbf{q}} \tag{4.54}$$

is the field wave vector, $\hat{\mathbf{q}}$ is a unit vector in the direction of propagation of the radiation, and λ is the wavelength of the radiation field.

The common procedure is now to expand the spatial part of the vector potential in a power series, giving[1]

$$\mathcal{H}_{int} = \sum_{s=0}^{\infty} \mathcal{H}_{int}^{(s)} \tag{4.55a}$$

with

$$\mathcal{H}_{int}^{(s)} \propto (\mathbf{q}\cdot\mathbf{r})^s(\hat{\mathbf{n}}\cdot\nabla) \tag{4.55b}$$

Such an expansion leads to a power series for the matrix element (4.51) (and therefore for the probability of the corresponding transition). Such an expansion converges quite rapidly when the ratio r_0/λ is small, where r_0 is of the order of the atomic radius.

The interaction moment with $s = 0$ corresponds to electric dipole radiation ($E1$). The terms with $s = 1$ are expressed as the sum of a symmetric and antisymmetric operator, giving the electric quadrupole ($E2$) and magnetic dipole ($M1$) radiation terms, respectively. In general, the multipole terms associated with s ($s > 0$) describe electric 2^{s+1}-pole and magnetic 2^s-pole radiation. [Multipole radiation emission or absorption (from atoms) with $s > 1$ is extremely difficult to observe because of the very small probability that such transitions will occur.]

Consider now the transitions between the states of an atom (which is in a crystalline field) as caused by the electromagnetic radiation field. In this case, the initial and final states of the atom are characterized by irreducible representations of the point group of the crystal field. Also, the interaction operator $\mathcal{H}_{int}^{(s)}$ must transform like one of the irreducible representations of the group. If we call the representations which correspond to the initial and final states of the transition and to the multipole radiation of order s, Γ_i, Γ_f, and $\Gamma_R^{(s)}$, respectively, then the integrand indicated in Eq. (4.51) transforms under rotations like the triple direct product

$$\Gamma_f \times \Gamma_R^{(s)} \times \Gamma_i \tag{4.56}$$

[1] W. Heitler, "Quantum Theory of Radiation," 3d ed., chap. V, Oxford University Press, Fair Lawn, N.J., 1953.

Thus the selection rules are computed by determining which triple direct products (4.56) of the representations of the group in question do not vanish. With $\Gamma_R^{(s)}$ fixed, the choices of Γ_i and Γ_f for which (4.51) does not vanish correspond to allowed transitions $\psi_i \rightarrow \psi_f$. The remaining transitions are forbidden.

In practice, the following procedure is carried out in order to determine the selection rules.

1. $\Gamma_R^{(s)}$, for the multipole moment in question, is associated with one of the irreducible representations of the group in question.

2. The coefficients a_κ of the direct product $\Gamma_R^{(s)} \times \Gamma_i = \Sigma a_\kappa \Gamma_\kappa$ are calculated. These are determined from the one-to-one correspondence with the scalar product of the corresponding characters.
Thus, for each class (j) of the group,

$$\Gamma_R^{(s)} \times \Gamma_i \leftrightarrow \chi^{(j)}(\Gamma_R^{(s)} \times \Gamma_i) = \chi^{(j)}(\Gamma_R^{(s)})\chi^{(j)}(\Gamma_i) \tag{4.57}$$

and, according to Eq. (4.32),

$$\chi^{(j)}(\Gamma_R^{(s)} \times \Gamma_i) = \sum_\kappa a_\kappa \chi_k^{(j)} \tag{4.58}$$

for each irreducible representation Γ_κ of the group. Combining (4.57) and (4.58), we have for each class

$$\chi^{(j)}(\Gamma_R^{(s)})\chi^{(j)}(\Gamma_i) = \Sigma a_\kappa \chi_k^{(j)} \tag{4.59}$$

and

$$\Gamma_R^{(s)} \times \Gamma_i = \Sigma a_\kappa \Gamma_\kappa \tag{4.59$'$}$$

Because of the orthogonality properties of the irreducible representations of the group and of the corresponding characters [Eq. (4.31)], the triple direct product (4.56) will not vanish only if one of the characters in the summation on the right-hand side of Eq. (4.59) is the character of the irreducible representation Γ_f of the final state. The proof of this statement will be left as an exercise for the reader.

Let us now illustrate this method by considering the selection rules for ($E1$) and ($M1$) radiation absorption by an atom in a hexagonal crystalline field. Assume that the states of the atom are characterized by integral angular-momentum quantum numbers (so that we need use only the single-valued representations).

Polarized Electric Dipole Radiation Absorption

The interaction operator for $E1$ radiation transforms like x, y, or z (depending on the polarization direction). According to the character table (Table 4.3a) for $\mathbf{D}_{3h}$, both x and y belong to the irreducible representation ${}^2\Gamma_5(\mathbf{D}_{3h})$ and z belongs to ${}^1\Gamma_4$. (Remember that z is defined to be along the C axis of the crystal.) Thus, if the radiation is polarized parallel to the C axis (this is called π radiation)

$$\Gamma_R^{(0)}(\pi) \equiv {}^1\Gamma_4$$

and if the polarization is perpendicular to the C axis (this is called σ radiation)

$$\Gamma_R^{(0)}(\sigma) = {}^2\Gamma_5$$

Forming the direct product of ${}^1\Gamma_4$ with each of the representations of the $\mathbf{D}_{3h}$ group [according to Eq. (4.59)], we can determine the selection rules for $E1$ π-radiation emission or absorption. We have, for example, for ${}^1\Gamma_4 \times {}^1\Gamma_2$

$$\begin{aligned}
\chi^{(E)}({}^1\Gamma_4)\chi^{(E)}({}^1\Gamma_2) &= 1 = a_1 + a_2 + a_3 + a_4 + 2a_5 + 2a_6 \\
\chi^{(C_3)}({}^1\Gamma_4)\chi^{(C_3)}({}^1\Gamma_2) &= 1 = a_1 + a_2 + a_3 + a_4 - a_5 - a_6 \\
\chi^{(U_2)}({}^1\Gamma_4)\chi^{(U_2)}({}^1\Gamma_2) &= 1 = a_1 - a_2 + a_3 - a_4 \\
\chi^{(\sigma_h)}({}^1\Gamma_4)\chi^{(\sigma_h)}({}^1\Gamma_2) &= -1 = a_1 + a_2 - a_3 - a_4 + 2a_5 - 2a_6 \\
\chi^{(\sigma_v)}({}^1\Gamma_4)\chi^{(\sigma_v)}({}^1\Gamma_2) &= -1 = a_1 - a_2 - a_3 + a_4 \\
\chi^{(S_3)}({}^1\Gamma_4)\chi^{(S_3)}({}^1\Gamma_2) &= -1 = a_1 + a_2 - a_3 - a_4 - a_5 + a_6
\end{aligned} \tag{4.60}$$

The solution of Eqs. (4.60) is

$$a_3 = 1 \qquad a_1 = a_2 = a_4 = a_5 = a_6 = 0$$

and therefore

$$^1\Gamma_4 \times {}^1\Gamma_2 = {}^1\Gamma_3$$

Thus, $E1$ radiation polarized along the direction of the C axis (π_E radiation), if absorbed by an atom in the state ${}^1\Gamma_2$, can cause a transition only to the state ${}^1\Gamma_3$. All other transitions are forbidden for this type of radiation absorption.

Polarized Magnetic Dipole Radiation Absorption

The interaction operator for magnetic dipole radiation transforms like $\mathbf{L} \propto (\mathbf{r} \times \nabla)$. Thus, if the magnetic vector of the radiation field is parallel to the C axis of the crystal (σ_M radiation),[1]

$$\mathcal{H}^{(2)}(M1) \propto L_z = -i\hbar\left(x\frac{\partial}{\partial y} - y\frac{\partial}{\partial x}\right)$$

According to the character table for $\mathbf{D}_{3h}$, this operator belongs to the irreducible representation ${}^1\Gamma_2$. Following the same procedure as above, we find that, if the atom is originally in a state described by the representation ${}^1\Gamma_2$, then

$$^1\Gamma_2 \times {}^1\Gamma_2 = {}^1\Gamma_1$$

or, if the initial state is characterized by ${}^1\Gamma_2$, magnetic dipole σ_M transitions are allowed only to the state which is characterized by ${}^1\Gamma_1$.

[1] $\mathcal{H}^{(2)}(M1)\alpha L_z$ is denoted by σ_M since it means that the magnetic vector, being perpendicular to the E vector, is perpendicular to the polarization direction.

If this procedure is carried out for each of the states of the atom which is in a $\mathbf{D}_{3h}$ symmetry crystal, the complete set of selection rules for the absorption or emission of $E1$ and $M1$ radiation is obtained and is given in Table 4.7. The notation used is that only the symbol which appears is an allowed transition.

TABLE 4.7 *Selection Rules for Electric and Magnetic Dipole Radiation Absorption by Atoms in a Crystalline Field with* $\mathbf{D}_{3h}$ *Symmetry*

Initial state	*Final state*					
	$^1\Gamma_1$	$^1\Gamma_2$	$^1\Gamma_3$	$^1\Gamma_4$	$^2\Gamma_5$	$^2\Gamma_6$
$^1\Gamma_1$		σM		πE	σE	πM
$^1\Gamma_2$	σM		πE		σE	πM
$^1\Gamma_3$		πE		σM	πM	σE
$^1\Gamma_4$	πE		σM		πM	σE
$^2\Gamma_5$	σE	σE	πM	πM	σE, σM	πE, πM
$^2\Gamma_6$	πM	πM	σE	σE	πE, πM	σE, σM

In this way, the selection rules may be determined for the absorption or emission of polarized electromagnetic radiation by atoms in the electrostatic potential of any of the 32 crystal symmetry groups.[1,2]

Problem

Determine the selection rules for electric quadrupole transitions between the states of an atom subjected to a crystalline field with $\mathbf{D}_6$ symmetry and the tetragonal $\mathbf{D}_{4h}$ symmetry. Consider the three cases in which (*a*) the radiation is directed along the x axis with the electric field vector parallel to the y axis; (*b*) the radiation is propagated in the x direction with $\mathbf{E}_{rad} \| z$, and (*c*) radiation is propagated along the y direction with $\mathbf{E}_{rad} \| z$. (The z axis is taken to coincide with the crystallographic C axis.)

4.4 Conclusions

We have, in this chapter, exploited the symmetry properties of crystal lattices in order to derive their effects on the energy levels of the constituent atoms. It should be stressed once again that the approach taken assumes that the energy levels of the crystal, as a whole, may be derived from the individual atomic energy levels. This is the Heitler-

[1] A discussion of these selection rules applied to mobile electrons in crystals is given by M. Sachs, *Phys. Rev.*, **107**: 437 (1957). Much of the formalism discussed there is identical with the problem discussed above.

[2] As an example of the application of these selection rules to optical absorption by crystals, see the article by R. A. Satten, *J. Chem. Phys.*, **21**: 637 (1953).

London approach and is quite applicable to nonmetallic solids. On the other hand, many of the group properties which have been used in describing ionic wave functions will be found quite useful later, in our discussion of the electron wave functions in (three-dimensional) metals. It will be seen that associated with each point **k** in the wave-vector space of the free electrons of a metal is an appropriate symmetry group (in **k** space) which must characterize the "free"-electron wave functions. Thus, in much the same way as we have done here, selection rules can be derived for transitions between allowed zones in a metal.

Much of the discussion in this chapter is necessary in order to understand many of the properties of paramagnetic crystals. An illustration of experimental observation of the symmetry properties discussed here will be given in the part of the following chapter devoted to paramagnetism.

5 the magnetic properties of crystals

IN ACCORDANCE with the approach to the study of solids in terms of the mutual interactions between the constituent atoms, let us now investigate the magnetic properties of those crystals made up (at least in part) of atoms which, when free, possess a permanent magnetic moment. Examples of ions which normally possess a magnetic moment in solid compounds are the elements of the transition group ($Z = 21$ to 29), the rare-earth group ($Z = 58$ to 71), and the transuranic group ($Z = 90$ to 103). The transition-group elements are magnetic because of unpaired electrons in the $3d$ shell, the rare-earth group is magnetic because of unpaired electrons in the $4f$ shell, and the transuranic group is magnetic because of unpaired electrons in the $5f$ and/or $6d$ shells. As we have remarked earlier, the purely ionic crystal contains no conduction electrons (i.e., it is a perfect insulator) while the pure metallic crystal is bonded solely by "free" electrons. Of course, the word "pure" refers to a mathematical limit in the description of the crystalline bond which is not actually realized in nature. In this chapter, in our consideration of the magnetic properties of purely ionic crystals, the contribution of the inherent magnetic moments of the free conduction electrons will be neglected. The contribution of the free-electron magnetic moments to the magnetic properties of metals will be discussed later in the book (Chap. 6).

We observe in nature that there are solids which do not exhibit any spontaneous magnetization but become magnetic when subjected to an external magnetic field intensity. Also, there are solids which are magnetized, independent of any external magnetic field. The former type of material is called *paramagnetic* and the latter *ferromagnetic*. We also observe that the magnetic properties of a crystal depend on the temperature. There are substances which are paramagnetic at high temperature but become ferromagnetic when the temperature is lowered to some critical value T_C (called the Curie temperature). There are paramagnetic crystals which effectively become nonmagnetic at some Curie temperature; the state of such a material below this temperature is called *antiferromagnetic.* There also exist materials, made up of a variety of different species of magnetic atoms, each possessing different characteristic magnetic moments, whose magnetization may be increased (or decreased) by a change in the concentration of one type of magnetic atom or the other. Such materials are called *ferrimagnetic* (this situation commonly occurs in the *ferrites* which may possess, for example, one concentration of Fe^{++} ions and another concentration of Fe^{3+} ions).

It is the purpose of this chapter to discuss some of the fundamental properties of crystals which exhibit these different types of magnetism. The discussion contained here should not be regarded by the reader as a complete treatise on the subject of magnetism but rather as an outline of the physical models, based on the quantum theory and statistical mechanics, which are currently evoked in explaining the magnetic properties of crystals.

5.1 Paramagnetism in the solid state

Let us now consider an ionic crystal in which only a small fraction of the constituent ions possess a permanent magnetic moment. Further, we shall assume that the magnitude of the electric and magnetic interactions mutual to the magnetic ions may be neglected when compared with the interactions that couple the magnetic ions with their immediate (nonmagnetic) environments. Such a crystal is said to be *paramagnetic* since it is equivalent to a large number of magnetically uncoupled magnets which orient themselves *parallel* to the local field intensity that is set up by an externally applied magnetic field. When the interaction energy between a given magnetic ion and its immediate crystalline environment is small in comparison with its interaction with an externally applied magnetic field, the magnetic properties of the crystal may be derived by assuming the crystal to be a rarefied gas made up of magnetic ions. (This is the Langevin-Debye approximation and will be considered in more detail later on.) This condition does not hold at lower temperatures, and the crystalline field interaction (which is the same for each magnetic ion) must then be taken into account. The crystalline field has the effect of splitting the energy levels of the magnetic ion (in the manner discussed in Chap. 4), thus giving rise to a preferential orientation of the ionic charge distribution with respect to the crystal axes. Such a situation (which becomes important at low temperatures) increases the order (decreases the entropy) of the macroscopic crystal since, in this case, the ionic magnetic moments can no longer be considered to be randomly oriented.

A typical example of a paramagnetic crystal is the salt cerium ethylsulfate $[Ce(C_2H_5SO_4)_3 \cdot 9H_2O]$. The magnetic properties of this salt are due to the constituent Ce^{3+} ions (which are magnetic by virtue of the single electron in the $4f$ shell). The nearest neighbors to any given Ce^{3+} ion are the nine water molecules (waters of hydration). The major part of the crystalline electrostatic potential at the Ce^{3+} site arises from the electric dipole moments of the water molecules. The symmetry of the immediate surroundings of each Ce^{3+} ion is characterized by the (hexagonal) $\mathbf{C}_{3h}$ point group.

The limitations of the assumptions made above, that the crystalline electrostatic potential is characterized by one of the point-group symmetries and that the mutual interactions between magnetic ions may be neglected, are especially pronounced in this crystal. A detailed study of the magnetic properties of this crystal has been carried out by Elliott and Stevens.[1] They find that, in order to explain the experimental data, it becomes necessary to assume that in addition to the (hexagonal) $\mathbf{C}_{3h}$ crystal field there is a small admixture of a (trigonal) $\mathbf{C}_{3v}$ field. Also, Finkelstein and Mencher[2] found that, in order to explain the anomalous properties of this crystal at low temperatures ($T \sim 1°K$), it became necessary to take account of the electric quadrupole-quadrupole interactions between the Ce^{3+} ions themselves.

A detailed discussion of the magnetic properties of salts containing transition elements, rare-earth elements, and the transuranic elements has been given by Bleaney and Stevens[3] and by Bowers and Owen.[4] A general treatment of paramagnetism is given by Van Vleck.[5]

Magnetic Energy Levels of a Paramagnetic Salt

For the purposes of illustration, let us consider the simplified model of a (purely) paramagnetic salt (i.e., one which does not behave anomalously at any temperature). Let us assume that we have a cerium salt in which each Ce^{3+} ion is characterized by precisely the same cylindrical ($\mathbf{C}_\infty$) symmetry field. The statistical properties of such a system may be considered in the same way as we consider the statistical properties of the rarefied gas in the classical (Maxwell-Boltzmann) approximation.[6] Here, the constituent systems of the statistical ensemble are the individual Ce^{3+} ions (each one immersed in an identical $\mathbf{C}_\infty$ electrostatic

[1] R. J. Elliott and K. W. H. Stevens, *Proc. Roy. Soc. (London), Ser. A*, **215**: 437 (1952).

[2] R. J. Finkelstein and A. Mencher, *J. Chem. Phys.*, **21**: 472 (1953).

[3] B. Bleaney and K. W. H. Stevens, *Rept. Progr. Phys.*, **16**: 108 (1953).

[4] K. D. Bowers and J. Owen, *Rept. Progr. Phys.*, **18**: 304 (1955).

[5] J. H. van Vleck, "The Theory of Electric and Magnetic Susceptibilities," Oxford University Press, London, 1932.

[6] See, for example, L. Landau and E. Lifshitz, "Statistical Physics," Addison-Wesley Publishing Company, Inc., Reading, Mass., 1958.

field). Since the magnetic ions do not interact with each other (according to this model), the energy levels of the crystal are given merely by the energy levels of a single ion multiplied by the number of magnetic ions that have this energy. (Recall that the mean energy of the ensemble is determined by making use of the statistical distribution function, and the temperature of the crystal is defined in terms of the populations of the various energy levels of the magnetic crystal.) We shall first consider the energy levels of a single constituent cerium ion and then go

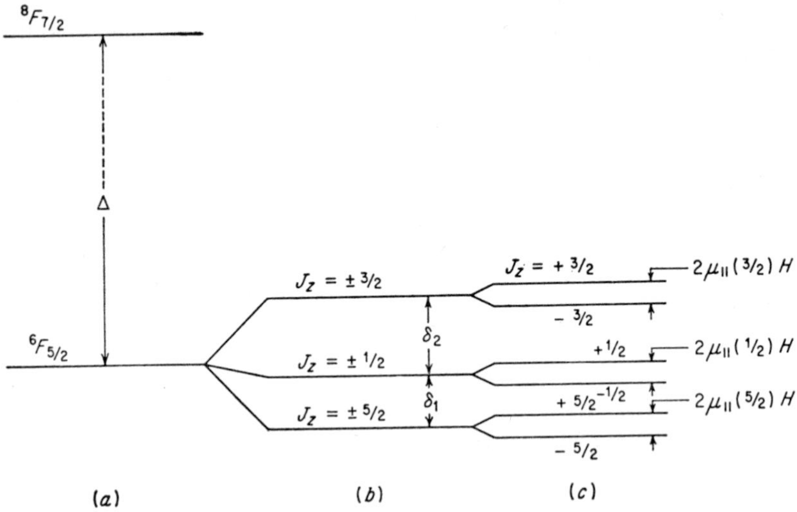

Fig. 5.1. (*a*) Energy levels of the ground state ($F_{5/2}$) of a Ce^{3+} ion, (*b*) in a hexagonal ($\mathbf{C}_{3h}$) crystalline field, and (*c*) with an added constant external magnetic field. The separation $\Delta/k = [\epsilon(F_{7/2}) - \epsilon(F_{5/2})]k^{-1} \sim$ 2000°K. Typical values for the other separations are δ_1/k, $\delta_2/k \sim$ 100°K, $<\mu_{\parallel}\mathbf{H}>/k \sim 0.1$°K (for $\mathbf{H} = 3000$ gauss). The order and magnitude of the energy-level spacings are arbitrarily assigned.

on to determine the macroscopic properties of the crystal according to the classical approximation of statistical mechanics.

The Ce^{3+} ion has one unpaired electron in the $4f$ shell. This electron is electrostatically shielded from the crystal environment by its (closed) $5s$ and $5p$ shells. The ground state of the free Ce^{3+} ion is $^6F_{5/2}$ and is therefore 6-fold degenerate [i.e., the six orthonormal wave functions which characterize the states $J = \frac{5}{2}$, ($J_z = \pm\frac{5}{2}$, $J_z = \pm\frac{3}{2}$, $J_z = \pm\frac{1}{2}$) all correspond to the same energy level $\epsilon(^6F_{5/2})$]. As soon as the free ion is immersed in the crystalline field, the magnetic $4f$ electron shell becomes distorted, because of its interaction with the charge distribution of the ($5s5p$) electrons which is distorted by the crystalline environment. Following the arguments of Chap. 4, it is readily verified that such a distortion, due to purely axial $\mathbf{C}_\infty$ symmetry, leads to the result that the states with $J_z = \pm\frac{5}{2}$, $J_z = \pm\frac{3}{2}$, and $J_z = \pm\frac{1}{2}$ are no longer energetically equivalent (see Sec. 4.2).[1] Thus, the free-ion energy level $\epsilon(^6F_{5/2})$ splits into three doublets, $\epsilon_c(\pm\frac{5}{2})$, $\epsilon_c(\pm\frac{3}{2})$, and $\epsilon_c(\pm\frac{1}{2})$ (see Fig. 5.1*b*). The remaining degeneracy is predicted by Kramers' theorem which is, in turn, based on the assumption that electromagnetic interactions are

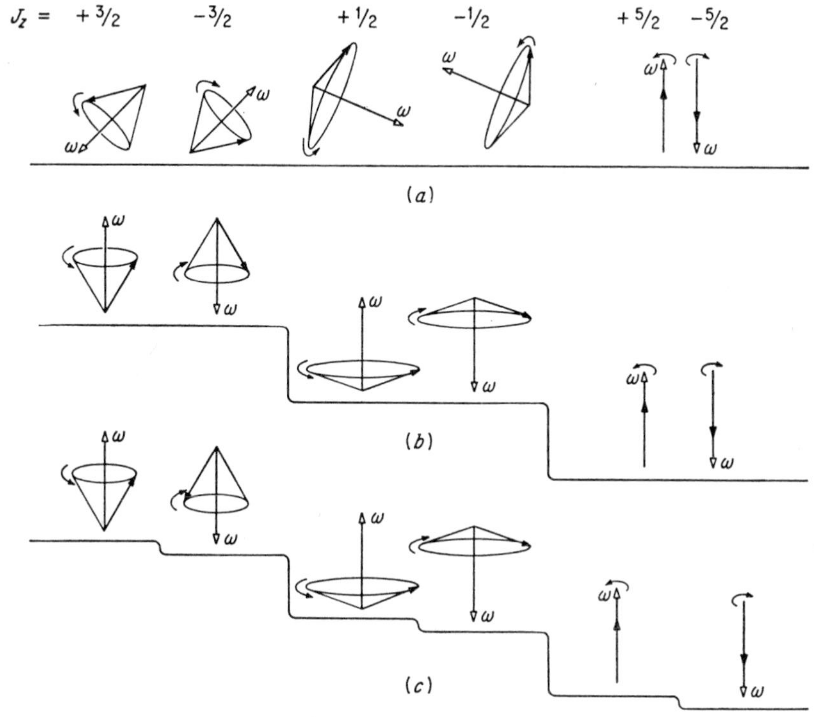

Fig. 5.2. Pictorial diagram of the energy states of a magnetic ion with total angular momentum $J = \frac{5}{2}$ (*a*) in free space, (*b*) in a crystal with a C axis, and (*c*) in a crystal plus a magnetic field.

invariant under time reversal (see Sec. 4.2 and Appendix A). As we have seen in Chap. 4, the z axis (i.e., the axis of quantization) is in the direction of the C axis of the crystal.

Suppose now that an external constant magnetic field $\mathbf{H}$ is applied to the crystal in a direction parallel to its C axis. We know from classical electromagnetic theory that the magnetic moments (associated with the individual magnetic ions) will then precess about the direction of the

[1] The crystalline field moments (Chap. 4) that are compatible with $\mathbf{C}_\infty$ symmetry have $\mu = 0$. The diagonal matrix elements of φ_c then relate to the integrals $\int \psi^*(J,J_z) Y_\lambda^0 \psi(J,J_z)\, dV$ with λ even, which in turn depend on powers of J_z^2.

magnetic field with the Larmor frequency ($e|\mathbf{H}|/2mc$) and an energy $-\boldsymbol{\mu} \cdot \mathbf{H}$. Further, the moments will precess according to the quantum theory in such a way that only the specific components

$$\mu_z = \beta J_z \qquad \left(\beta = \frac{e\hbar}{mc}\right)$$

of the magnetic moment $\boldsymbol{\mu}$ will be energetically coupled to the external magnetic field. Thus, the six states corresponding to $J_z = \pm\frac{5}{2}, \pm\frac{3}{2}, \pm\frac{1}{2}$ will all be energetically different. This is illustrated in Fig. 5.1*c* where the three (crystalline) doublets have split into six nondegenerate energy levels. It should be noted that, in general, the magnetic energy $|\boldsymbol{\mu} \cdot \mathbf{H}|$ is much smaller than the electrostatic splitting (for normally accessible magnetic fields) and that the relative splittings shown in Fig. 5.1*c* are greatly exaggerated. The effects described in terms of the energy-level scheme in Fig. 5.1 are illustrated pictorially in Fig. 5.2.

In the discussions of the physical properties of a crystal which follow, we shall neglect the next-higher energy level corresponding to the $^2F_{7/2}$ state, since, in accordance with the Boltzmann distribution function $e^{-\epsilon/kT}$, its very low population at all but very high temperatures would contribute very little to the macroscopic properties of the crystal.

Paramagnetic Susceptibility

Using the *density-matrix* method, we show in Appendix B that, for a system of quantum-mechanical *distinguishable* particles, an observed quantity Q_{obs} (averaged over a "canonical ensemble") takes the form

$$Q_{obs} = \frac{\sum_n Q_{nn} e^{-\epsilon_n/kT}}{\sum_n e^{-\epsilon_n/kT}} \tag{5.1}$$

where ϵ_n denotes an energy level of the *entire crystal* and Q_{nn} is the diagonal matrix element

$$Q_{nn} = \int \psi_n^* \hat{Q} \psi_n \, dV$$

with $\hat{Q}$ the quantum-mechanical operator associated with the observable quantity.

The susceptibility is defined as $\chi = \partial|\mathbf{M}|/\partial|\mathbf{H}|$, where $\mathbf{M}$ is the observed macroscopic magnetic moment (i.e., the magnetization) of the crystal and, according to (5.1), is given by the expression

$$\mathbf{M} = \frac{\sum_n \mu_{nn} e^{-\epsilon_n/kT}}{\sum_n e^{-\epsilon_n/kT}} \tag{5.2}$$

where μ_{nn} is the diagonal element of the atomic magnetic-moment operator $\hat{\boldsymbol{\mu}} = (e\hbar/mc)\mathbf{J}$. It should be emphasized that in (5.2) ϵ_n refers to an energy level of the entire crystal.

As an example, we now consider the cerium crystal described above. When the magnetic ions are assumed uncoupled, the magnetic energy levels of the crystal are just the sum of energies of the individual Ce^{3+} ions. Thus, in a magnetic field, the *i*th Ce^{3+} ion is characterized by the low-lying levels (see Fig. 5.2).

$$\epsilon(J_z) = \epsilon_0(F_{5/2}) + \epsilon_c(\pm J_z) + \boldsymbol{\mu} \cdot \mathbf{H}(J,J_z) \tag{5.3}$$

where ϵ_0 is the ground-state energy level of the *free atom* and ϵ_c refers to the atomic energy level in the crystal (with purely axial $\mathbf{C}_\infty$ symmetry). In the last term the wave functions $\psi(J,J_z)$ refer to solutions of the wave equation

$$(\mathcal{H}_0 + \mathcal{H}_c)\psi(J,J_z) = (\epsilon_0 + \epsilon_c)\psi(J,J_z) \tag{5.4}$$

where $\mathcal{H}_0 + \mathcal{H}_c$ is the hamiltonian operator for the ion in the crystal. Note that the z direction refers to the C axis of the crystal.

It is readily demonstrated that the matrix elements of the magnetic term have the form[1]

$$\boldsymbol{\mu} \cdot \mathbf{H}(J,J_z) = g(J,J_z)\beta H J_z \tag{5.5}$$

where $\beta = e\hbar/mc$,

$$\hat{\mathbf{k}}'g = \hat{\mathbf{i}}g_x \sin\theta \cos\phi + \hat{\mathbf{j}}g_y \sin\theta \sin\phi + \hat{\mathbf{k}}g_z \cos\theta \tag{5.6}$$

and (θ,ϕ) is the solid angle subtended by the $\mathbf{H}$ vector with respect to the optic axis of the crystal (the primed coordinate system refers to $\mathbf{H}$ and the unprimed system refers to the crystal axes). In our special case of axial symmetry, we can express g in terms of a component parallel to the optic axis[2] ($g_\parallel$) and a component perpendicular to the optic axis ($g_\perp$), giving

$$g^2 = g_\parallel^2 \cos^2\theta + g_\perp^2 \sin^2\theta \tag{5.6$'$}$$

For the purposes of simplicity, we consider the case in which $\mathbf{H}$ is directed along the axis of the crystal, giving for Ce^{3+} (in its ground state)

$$\epsilon(J_z) = \epsilon_0(F_{5/2}) + \epsilon_c(\pm J_z) + g_\parallel(\tfrac{5}{2})\beta H J_z \tag{5.3$'$}$$

The corresponding value of the paramagnetic susceptibility to be derived below will refer then to its value when $\mathbf{H}$ is parallel to the optic axis of the crystal and will be denoted by $\chi_\parallel$.

[1] See, for example, M. Sachs, *J. Phys. Chem. Solids*, **15**: 291 (1960). In this reference, the notation for β refers to $\frac{1}{2}$ of the value defined here.

[2] Optic axis refers to C axis.

Using the expression for $\mathbf{M}_{\parallel}$ according to (5.2), we have

$$<M_{\parallel}> = \frac{\displaystyle\sum_{J_z(1)=-J}^{J} \cdots \sum_{J_z(n)=-J}^{J} \Big[\sum_i \mu_{\parallel}[J_z(i)]\Big] e^{-\sum_i \epsilon[J_z(i)]/kT}}{\displaystyle\sum_{J_z(1)=-J}^{J} \cdots \sum_{J_z(n)=-J}^{J} e^{-\sum_i \epsilon[J_z(i)]/kT}} \tag{5.7}$$

Since all Ce^{3+} ions in the crystal are identical and energetically uncoupled, Eq. (5.7) factors into a product of n identical functions for each of the Ce^{3+} ions. Thus [inserting Eq. (5.6) for the ionic energy levels, and $\mu_{\parallel} = g_{\parallel}\beta J_z$], the susceptibility $\chi_{\parallel}$ takes the form

$$\chi_{\parallel} = \frac{<M_{\parallel}>}{H} = \frac{n\beta e^{-\epsilon_0(F_{5/2})/kT} \displaystyle\sum_{J_z=-J}^{J} J_z g_{\parallel}(J_z) e^{-[\epsilon_c(\pm J_z)+J_z g_{\parallel}(J_z)\beta H]/kT}}{He^{-\epsilon_0(F_{5/2})/kT} \displaystyle\sum_{J_z=-J}^{J} e^{-[\epsilon_c(\pm J_z)+J_z g_{\parallel}(J_z)\beta H]/kT}} \tag{5.8}$$

The expression (5.8) can be simplified if one assumes that $|\boldsymbol{\mu} \cdot \mathbf{H}| \ll kT$. (For $\mathbf{H} \sim 3000$ gauss, $\mu H/k \sim 0.1°\text{K}$; thus this assumption is certainly valid at temperatures greater than or equal to $\sim 1°\text{K}$.) With this assumption, the part of the exponential term containing the magnetic field may be expanded in powers of $\mu H/kT$. Since $g_{\parallel}(J_z) = +g_{\parallel}(-J_z)$, the leading nonvanishing term then becomes

$$\chi_{\parallel} \cong \frac{<M_{\parallel}>}{H} \cong \frac{n\beta^2}{kT} \frac{\displaystyle\sum_{J_z=-J}^{J} J_z^2 g_{\parallel}^2(J_z) e^{-\epsilon_c(\pm J_z)/kT}}{\displaystyle\sum_{J_z=-J}^{J} e^{-\epsilon_c(\pm J_z)/kT}} \tag{5.9}$$

If we now apply (5.9) to the Ce^{3+} paramagnetic crystal and assume the ordering of the energy levels shown in Fig. 5.1, we obtain the following expression (which may readily be compared with experimental observations):

$$\nu_{\parallel} = \frac{\chi_{\parallel} kT}{n\beta^2} = \frac{25g_{\parallel}^2(\frac{5}{2}) + g_{\parallel}^2(\frac{1}{2})e^{-\delta_1/T} + 9g_{\parallel}^2(\frac{3}{2})e^{-\delta_2/T}}{4(1 + e^{-\delta_1/T} + e^{-\delta_2/T})} \tag{5.10}$$

with $k\delta_1 = \epsilon_c(\frac{1}{2}) - \epsilon_c(\frac{5}{2})$, $k\delta_2 = \epsilon_c(\frac{3}{2}) - \epsilon_c(\frac{5}{2})$. The (dimensionless) quantity $\nu_{\parallel}$ is the parallel component of the so-called *effective Bohr magneton*. (A procedure similar to that shown above may be followed in order to calculate $\nu_{\perp}$. Such an expression would necessarily involve the off-diagonal matrix elements of the magnetic-moment operator.) A typical plot of $\nu_\parallel$ vs T is shown in Fig. 5.3, with typical values for $g_\parallel^2(J_z)$ and δ_1, δ_2. Such behavior of $\nu_\parallel$ with T was observed experimentally by Becquerel et al.[1]

Problem

Determine the expression for the perpendicular Bohr magneton number applied to the case of a cerium salt discussed above. Plot $\nu_\perp$ vs T for the parameters shown in Fig. 5.3.

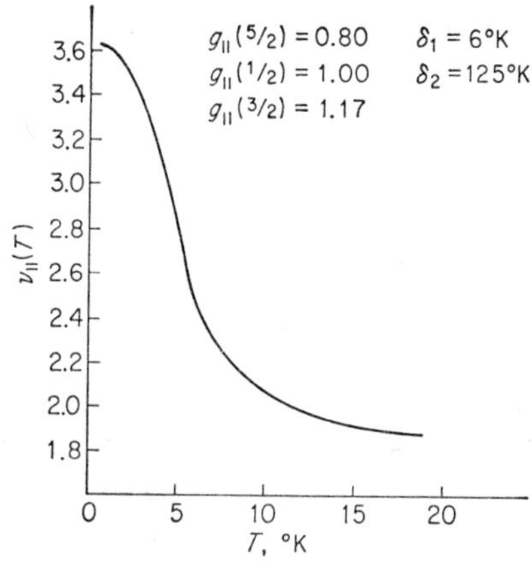

Fig. 5.3. Effective Bohr magneton number $\nu_\parallel$ as a function of temperature for a cerium ion in a crystalline field with axial symmetry. Typical g values and energy-level splittings are indicated on the figure.

If we can assume that (1) the crystalline-field hamiltonian has a negligible effect on mixing in states with angular momenta $J' \neq \frac{5}{2}$ with the ground state, (2) the temperature is sufficiently high that $e^{-\epsilon_c(J,J_z)/kT}$ can be assumed independent of J_z, and (3) the g factor can be taken independent of J_z, then the following expression is obtained for the parallel susceptibility:

$$\chi_\parallel(\text{free}) = \frac{n\beta^2 g^2}{kT} \frac{\sum_{J_z=-J}^{J} J_z^2}{\sum_{J_z=-J}^{J} 1} \tag{5.11}$$

Since

$$\sum_{-J}^{J} J_z^2 = (\tfrac{1}{3})(2J+1)J(J+1)$$

and

$$\sum_{-J}^{J} 1 = 2J + 1 \tag{5.12}$$

we have

$$\chi_\parallel(\text{free}) = \frac{n\beta^2 g^2}{3kT} J(J+1) = \frac{n}{3kT} <\mu>_J^2 \tag{5.13}$$

which is the quantum-mechanical analogue of the classical Langevin-Debye formula for the paramagnetic susceptibility of a system of n free magnetic moments per unit volume (in the limit where $|\boldsymbol{\mu} \cdot \mathbf{H}| \ll kT$).[2]

[1] J. Becquerel, W. J. de Haas, and J. van den Handel, *Physica*, **5**: 864 (1938).
[2] Van Vleck, *op. cit.*

The Entropy of a Paramagnetic Crystal

The expression for the entropy of a quantum-mechanical ensemble is shown in Appendix B to have the form

$$S = -k \operatorname{Tr} (\rho \ln \rho) = -k \sum_n \omega_n \ln \omega_n \tag{5.14}$$

where ρ is the density matrix and

$$\rho_{nn} \equiv \omega_n = \frac{e^{-\epsilon_n/kT}}{\sum_n e^{-\epsilon_n/kT}} \tag{5.15}$$

is the classical approximation to the distribution function (that is, ω_n is of the Maxwell-Boltzmann form). The denominator of (5.15) is called the partition function, denoted by Z.

Consider, for example, the entropy of the "free" system of magnetic moments which has been discussed above. We once again consider a Ce salt and neglect the states $\epsilon(J')$, which are higher than the ground-state energy $\epsilon(J)$, on the grounds that they are relatively unpopulated at the normal temperatures [recalling that ω_n may be interpreted in terms of the population of the energy level ϵ_n (Appendix B)]. On the other hand, the assumption will be made initially that $kT \gg \delta_1, \delta_2$ (see Fig. 5.1) so that the states $\epsilon_c(\pm J_z)$ for all J_z may be considered to be equally populated (i.e., crystalline field effects can be neglected).

In view of the fact that the magnetic ions are uncoupled, the partition function for this system in an externally applied magnetic field takes the form[1]

$$Z \cong \Big(\sum_{J_z=-J}^{J} e^{g\beta H J_z/kT} \Big)^N \equiv Z_\mu^N \tag{5.16}$$

It is observed that the function Z_μ represents the sum of $2J + 1$ terms of a geometric series of which the first term is $e^{-g\beta HJ/kT}$ and the common ratio is $e^{g\beta H/kT}$. The sum of this series is then

$$Z_\mu = e^{-g\beta HJ/kT} \frac{1 - e^{(2J+1)g\beta H/kT}}{1 - e^{g\beta H/kT}} = \frac{\sinh [(J + \frac{1}{2})g\beta H/kT]}{\sinh (g\beta H/2kT)} \tag{5.17}$$

Thus, under the simplifying assumptions used above, we obtain the following expression for the entropy of the crystal in a magnetic field:

$$\begin{aligned} S(H,T) &= k \frac{\partial}{\partial T} (T \ln Z) = Nk \frac{\partial}{\partial T} \left[T \ln \frac{\sinh [(2J+1)x/T]}{\sinh (x/T)} \right] \\ &= Nk \bigg(\ln \frac{\sinh [(2J+1)x/T]}{\sinh (x/T)} - \frac{x}{T} [(2J+1) \coth (2J+1)x/T \\ &\qquad - \coth (x/T)] \bigg) \end{aligned} \tag{5.18}$$

[1] The factors in Z not dependent on magnetic quantum numbers are dropped here because they will cancel out in all of the calculations to follow.

where
$$x = \frac{g\beta H}{2k} \qquad {}^\circ\mathrm{K} \tag{5.19}$$

Clearly, a change (dS) in the entropy of the system may be introduced by arbitrarily changing the magnitude of the applied magnetic field **H** or by changing the temperature of the system. Thus

$$\begin{aligned} dS(H,T) &= \left(\frac{\partial S}{\partial H}\right)_{T,V} dH + \left(\frac{\partial S}{\partial T}\right)_{H,V} dT \\ &= \left(\frac{\partial S}{\partial H}\right)_{T,V} dH + \frac{C_V}{T}\, dT \end{aligned} \tag{5.20}$$

The second part of Eq. (5.20) follows from the definition of specific heat, $C_V = \langle d\epsilon/dT \rangle_V$.

According to Eq. (5.18), the derivative $(\partial S/\partial H)_{T,V}$ takes the form

$$\left(\frac{\partial S}{\partial H}\right)_{T,V} = \frac{Nkx^2}{HT^2}\left[(2J+1)\operatorname{csch}^2\frac{(2J+1)x}{T} - \operatorname{csch}^2\frac{x}{T}\right] \tag{5.21}$$

It is observed that, for $J \neq 0$, the derivative $(\partial S/\partial H)_{T,V}$ is negative for all values of x. This decrease in entropy with increasing magnetic field is due to the increase in the order of the system which is introduced as the increasing magnetic field increases the number of magnetic moments which line up along its direction (i.e., parallel or antiparallel to **H**). Thus,

$$S(H,T) < S(0,T) \tag{5.22}$$

for all values of H.

The entropy $S(0,T)$, which represents the limiting value of $S(H,T)$ as the magnetic field tends toward zero, is [according to Eq. (5.18)]

$$S(0,T) = Nk \ln (2J+1) \tag{5.23}$$

Thus, the entropy in zero magnetic field is related to the a priori number of ways of orienting the atomic magnetic moment, where the atomic ground state is specified by an angular momentum $J\hbar$, and under the assumption that all the $2J+1$ states are equally populated.

In a fashion similar to the derivation of $S(H,T)$, the specific heat is found to have the following form:

$$\begin{aligned} C_V(H,T) = T\left[\frac{\partial S(H,T)}{\partial T}\right]_{V,H} &= Nk\left(\frac{x}{T}\right)^2 \left\{\operatorname{csch}^2\left(\frac{x}{T}\right)\right. \\ &\quad \left. - (2J+1)^2 \operatorname{csch}^2\left[(2J+1)\frac{x}{T}\right]\right\} > 0 \end{aligned} \tag{5.24}$$

Also, in the limit of zero magnetic field, the ground state of each atom is a degenerate (occupied) state; therefore the system cannot accept energy, and we should expect C_V to be zero. It is readily verified that

$$\lim_{H\to 0} C_V(H,T) = C_V(0,T) = 0 \tag{5.25}$$

Note that the thermodynamic functions $S(\mathbf{H},T)$ and $C_V(\mathbf{H},T)$ have been derived under the assumption of a model in which the internal energy of the system is equal only to the internal energy of the magnetic ions in the system. There is also, in general, a contribution to the internal energy of a paramagnetic crystal which is due to the lattice vibrations of the crystal and to the system of free (conduction) electrons, which may be available to absorb energy from the outside (Chap. 6). The latter contribution is very small in paramagnetic salts because the bonding in the types of crystals discussed here is primarily ionic and so the number of conduction electrons available to absorb energy

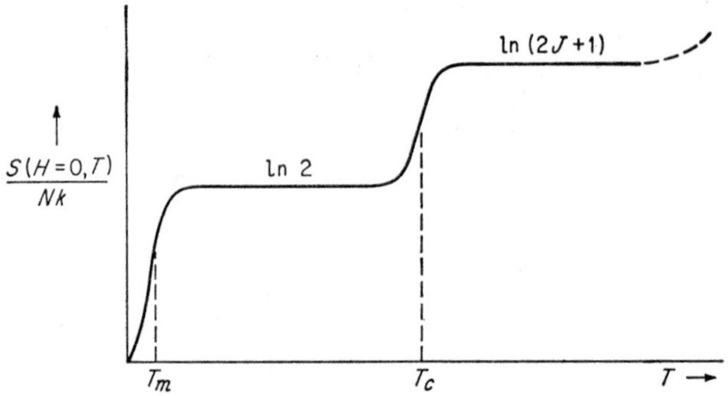

Fig. 5.4. Entropy vs temperature for a paramagnetic crystal in which the ground state of the constituent magnetic ions is $\hbar J$, J being a one-half integer number. $T_C \sim \delta_2/k$, $T_M \sim |\mu|^2 \langle \mathbf{r}^3 \rangle k \sim 0.01°\mathrm{K}$.

is extremely small. Both effects mentioned become totally negligible at low temperatures.

Let us now consider the situation in which the temperature of the Ce^{3+} salt is lowered sufficiently so that the population of the states $\epsilon_c(\pm\frac{3}{2})$ and $\epsilon_c(\pm\frac{1}{2})$ can also be neglected [so that we need consider only the contribution of the ground state $\epsilon_c(\pm\frac{5}{2})$ to the physical properties of the crystal]. This is the case when $kT \ll \delta_1, \delta_2$ (Fig. 5.1). As the temperature is lowered from the range in which $\delta_2 < kT < \delta_1$ to the range in which $kT < \delta_2$, the states $\epsilon_c(\pm\frac{3}{2})$ and $\epsilon_c(\pm\frac{1}{2})$ become unpopulated (see Appendix B) and the entropy (at zero magnetic field) drops (in an exponential way) from its constant value $Nk \ln(2J+1)$ to the constant value $Nk \ln 2$. In general, a plot of S vs T will appear as a series of plateaus, with each drop-off corresponding to the depopulation of particular discrete states (see Fig. 5.4).

In accordance with the Nernst theorem (i.e., the third law of thermodynamics), the entropy must approach its minimum value as $T \to 0$.[1] In the case of a paramagnetic crystal, there are inherent magnetic fields,

[1] See, for example, D. ter Haar, "Elements of Statistical Mechanics," App. III, Holt, Rinehart and Winston, Inc., New York, 1954.

due to the presence of magnetic moments, which tend to lift all the degeneracy of the system. (These interactions have thus far been neglected because of their small magnitude.) The two-body magnetic dipole-dipole interactions are described by the following additional interaction term in the hamiltonian operator for the crystal:

$$\sum_{i<j=1}^{N} \mathcal{H}_{ij} = \sum_{i<j=1}^{N} \frac{3(\boldsymbol{\mu}_i \cdot \mathbf{r}_{ij})(\boldsymbol{\mu}_j \cdot \mathbf{r}_{ij}) - \boldsymbol{\mu}_i \cdot \boldsymbol{\mu}_j |\mathbf{r}_{ij}|^2}{|\mathbf{r}_{ij}|^5} \tag{5.26}$$

where $|\mathbf{r}_{ij}|$ is the distance between two magnetic ions i and j. The presence of this term in the hamiltonian gives rise to a partition function that cannot be factored as we have done above [Eq. (5.16)]. The magnitude of the interaction is, however, very small, because of the great distance between neighboring magnetic ions in a paramagnetic crystal. Its magnitude is typically of the order $k(10^{-4}$ to $10^{-2}°\text{K})$ and thus does not effectively contribute to the physical properties of the crystal until temperatures in the range of $10^{-2}°$K are reached. Then (in the cerium salt under study), the entropy plateau drops from its value $Nk \ln 2$ toward zero (Fig. 5.4).[1] The minimum entropy of the system is zero since the ground state of the system corresponds to a total removal of degeneracy.

Note that the plateau at $Nk \ln 2$ appears as a consequence of the Kramers degeneracy of a one-half-integer spin system. For magnetic ions in which the ground-state angular momentum is an integral number of units $\hbar$, the electrostatic field of the crystal could, in principle, lift all the degeneracy of this state, causing the plateau at $Nk \ln (2J + 1)$ to drop to zero at some critical temperature T_C.

Cooling by Adiabatic Demagnetization

The behavior of entropy as a function of the temperature of a paramagnetic salt is utilized in cooling these salts to very low temperatures. The process of cooling is illustrated in Fig. 5.5.[2] The first step in this process is to cool the crystal as far as possible by conventional methods. Cooling to 4°K (liquid He temperature) is usually sufficient. This stage represents the initial point $A_1(T \sim 4°\text{K}, \mathbf{H} = 0)$ on our diagram. The next step in the process is to increase the intensity of the externally applied magnetic field from zero to some value H_A, while maintaining a constant temperature T_i. During this isothermal process, increased order is introduced into the system by virtue of the alignment of the

[1] Cerium ethylsulfate behaves anomalously in this respect. Its entropy appears to drop toward zero near 1°K. Finkelstein and Mencher, *loc. cit.*, have attributed this effect to an electric quadrupole-quadrupole interaction between the constituent cerium ions.

[2] For an experimental demonstration of this behavior of entropy vs T, see D. de Klerk, M. J. Steenland, and C. J. Gorter, *Physica*, **15**: 649 (1949).

constituent magnetic moments along the direction of the applied magnetic field. The entropy is thereby reduced to the point $A_2(T_i,H_A)$ which lies on the entropy curve $S(T_i,H_A)$, in accordance with the expression given by Eq. (5.18). Finally, the sample is demagnetized in an adiabatic fashion ($dS = 0$), and as the magnetic field approaches zero, the entropy once again approaches the zero-field-entropy curve, at A_3, where the final temperature T_f is reached. It is clear from Fig. 5.5 that larger values of the applied magnetic field would result in corresponding final temperatures which are lower (i.e., compare the $A_1 \rightarrow A_2 \rightarrow A_3$ process with the $B_1 \rightarrow B_2 \rightarrow B_3$ process).

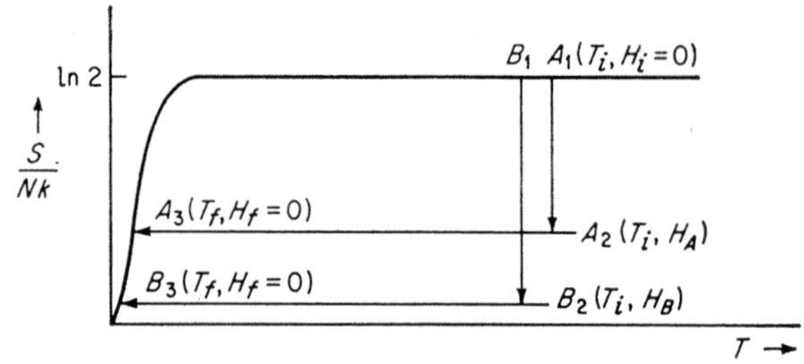

Fig. 5.5. Cooling by adiabatic demagnetization, T_i is an initial and T_f a final temperature. $A_1 \rightarrow A_2 \rightarrow A_3$ and $B_1 \rightarrow B_2 \rightarrow B_3$ represent two different runs.

Quantitatively, the final temperature T_f may be calculated (in principle) from the relation which defines the adiabatic process $A_2 \rightarrow A_3$, or $B_2 \rightarrow B_3$, that is,

$$S(H,T_i) = S(0,T_f) \tag{5.27}$$

However, the exact solution of Eq. (5.27) for $T_f(T_i,H)$ is generally very difficult to obtain in practice, since $S(0,T_f)$ depends in a sensitive way on the partition function which involves the two-body interactions of the type given by Eq. (5.26). The difficulties involved in evaluating this function arise from the nonfactorizability of the partition function because of the presence of the two-body interaction (5.26).

A *crude* estimate of the final temperature reached after the adiabatic demagnetization may be made if one assumes that the partition function may be replaced by the product of partition functions for each individual magnetic ion. In this case, since the entropy is invariant and is represented by the same function of magnetic field/temperature at both the initial temperature T_i and at the final temperature T_f, we may equate the ratio H_{eff}/T at both points. At the initial temperature, the effective magnetic field acting as a given magnetic ion is

$$H_{eff} \sim H_A + \frac{<\mu>}{r^3} \simeq H_A \tag{5.28}$$

where r is the mean distance between magnetic ions. At the final temperature, the external magnetic field is zero, and the residual effective magnetic field is of the order $<\mu>/r^3$. Thus, an approximation for the temperature may be determined from the formula

$$\frac{H_A}{T_i} \sim \frac{H_f}{T_f} \tag{5.29}$$

where $H_f \sim <\mu>/r^3$. The magnitude of $<\mu>/r^3$ in paramagnetic crystals is typically of the order of 100 gauss. Thus

$$T_f \sim \frac{10^2 T_i}{H_A}$$

If one starts with an initial temperature of 4°K and a maximum external magnetic field of the order of 10^4 gauss, the final temperature reached will be of the order of 0.04°K. It should be emphasized, however, that Eq. (5.29) is crude and is used here only for the purpose of estimating the order of magnitude of the final temperature reached in an adiabatic-demagnetization experiment.

5.2 Ferromagnetism

Thus far we have considered the magnetic properties of a paramagnetic crystal described as a statistical ensemble of atomic moments which are magnetically uncoupled but each with an identical nonmagnetic environment. It is, of course, wrong to assume perfect paramagnetism, since, as mentioned above, the magnetic dipole-dipole interactions are always present, even though they are unimportant at normal temperatures.

Let us now consider the exact opposite of pure paramagnetism, i.e., the ferromagnetic crystal in which all the neighbors of a given magnetic ion of a lattice are also magnetic (this results in a spontaneous magnetization). The magnetic properties of such a crystal may not be analyzed in terms of a "rarefied-gas model" since they are due to the cooperative behavior of all (10^{24}) magnetic ions which make up the macroscopic crystal. The metals of the transition group (Fe, Ni, Co) and of the rare-earth group (Gd and Dy) exhibit this spontaneous magnetization. Also, there are many ferromagnetic alloys (which contain, in part, elements of the transition group).

Let us now consider the *observed* magnetic properties of a crystal which is called ferromagnetic. As mentioned above, the essential property of the ferromagnet is the lack of proportionality between the magnetization of the crystal and an applied magnetic field. Also, a very large magnetization may be produced in the crystal by applying a very small external magnetic field. This magnetization will then remain after the (small) external field is removed, so long as the temperature maintains values at which the crystal remains ferromagnetic.

Consider a ferromagnet at a fixed temperature T. If an externally applied magnetic field H_e is slowly increased from zero, the magnetic moments lining up with this field will line up each other because of their proximity. Thus, the net magnetization of the crystal builds up very rapidly until the magnetization M reaches a maximum value where a further increase in H_e has very little effect on its value (Fig. 5.6*a*, $1 \rightarrow 2$). This maximum magnetization is called saturation and is denoted by the value M_s. Because of the fact that part of the work done on the metal is used up in heat, a reversal of the direction of H_e will not retrace the original path $1 \rightarrow 2$ (i.e., the process described is an irreversible one).

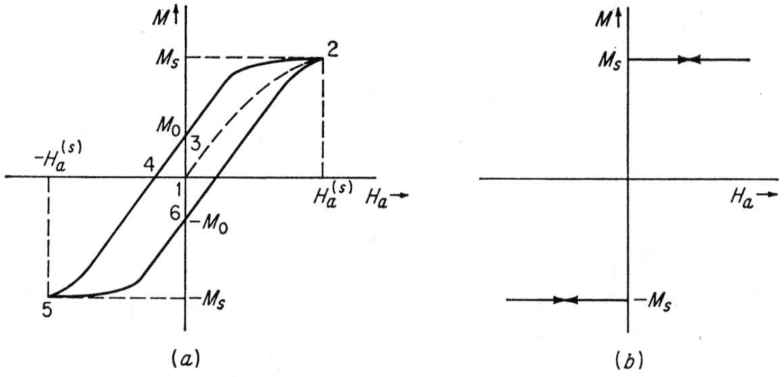

Fig. 5.6. (*a*) A typical hysteresis loop and (*b*) the limiting form of hysteresis loop for maximum magnetic purity in the crystal. M is the magnetization of the crystal, M_s is its saturation value, and H_a is the magnitude of the applied magnetic field intensity.

A reduction of H_e to zero then leads to the residual magnetization M_0 (at point 3 in Fig. 5.6). If the applied field is then reversed in direction and gradually increased in magnitude, the residual magnetizations M_0 will eventually be canceled (at point 4), and a further increase in the magnitude of H_e will bring the magnetization to the saturation value (M_s) but with a negative sign (point 5). If now H_e is diminished in magnitude, the irreversibility of the process again will not allow a retracing of the path $2 \rightarrow 5$; instead, the magnetization will reach the value $-M_0$ at $H_e = 0$ (point 6), and an increase of H_e (with a positive sign again) will take the magnetization to the original saturated magnetization (at point 2). From elementary electromagnetic theory[1] the area contained in this *hysteresis loop* is equal to the work that was necessary to reverse the direction of the magnetization of the crystal.

[1] See J. A. Stratton, "Electromagnetic Theory," chap. II, McGraw-Hill Book Company, Inc., New York, 1941.

The actual shape and area of the hysteresis loop depend on the details of the internal structure and composition of the ferromagnet crystal under observation. We shall not be concerned with these details here except to note that, as the material becomes more (magnetically) pure, the lattice plays less of a role with regard to the response of the magnetization to the applied field. Thus, the area contained in the hysteresis loop becomes smaller. In the ideal case, the hysteresis loop (Fig. 5.6*a*) collapses into the discontinuous curve shown in Fig. 5.6*b* (that is, $M_s \to -M_s$ at $H_a = 0$). This discontinuity in the magnetization curve disappears when the temperature is raised to a critical value T_C, when the crystal ceases to be ferromagnetic (becoming paramagnetic). The temperature T_C is called the Curie temperature.

A first attempt to explain the properties of the ferromagnet might be to assume that one has an array of 10^{24} atomic magnetic moments $\boldsymbol{\mu}$, each in the same sort of (averaged-out) magnetic environment (thus reducing the many-atom problem to the one-body problem). The magnetic interaction energy would then be

$$\sum_{i=1}^{N} - \boldsymbol{\mu} \cdot \mathbf{H}_{eff} \qquad (|\boldsymbol{\mu}| = \mu_0 J = g\beta J)$$

with $\mathbf{H}_{eff}$ being the net magnetic field, including all internal fields (forming the largest part of the field) and the internal magnetic field that is induced by the applied field. If the effective field is due merely to the magnetic dipole-dipole interactions between a given ion and its neighbors, then the expression for the magnetization of the crystal takes the same form as did that for the paramagnetic magnetization and follows from the partition function according to the relation[1]

$$<M> = kT \frac{\partial}{\partial H} (\ln Z) \tag{5.30}$$

In the limit where the atomic magnetic moments can be considered uncoupled, this expression is, according to (5.16), (5.17), and (5.30),

$$<M> = N\mu_0 J B_J \left(\frac{\mu_0 H}{2k}\right) \tag{5.31}$$

where

$$B_J(x) = \frac{1}{2J} \left[(2J + 1) \coth \frac{(2J + 1)x}{T} - \coth \frac{x}{T} \right] \tag{5.32}$$

is Brillouin's function. (At room temperature, $kT \gg \mu_0 H$ and, as we have seen earlier, $<M> \propto NJ(J + 1)\mu_0^2 H/3kT$.)

[1] This follows from the general relation in terms of the density matrix

$$\mathbf{M} = \mathrm{Tr}\,(\rho\hat{\boldsymbol{\mu}})$$

where $\hat{\boldsymbol{\mu}}$ is the quantum-mechanical operator for the constituent moment of the statistical ensemble (see Appendix B).

According to (5.31), if **H** represents the field due to the magnetic dipole moments of neighboring atoms, then

$$\frac{M_s}{N\mu_0} \sim \frac{10^{-3}}{T} \tag{5.31'}$$

The predictions of the classical theory then suffer from three discrepancies with respect to the observed properties:

1. The magnetization is of the order of 10^4 times larger than that predicted by (5.31′).
2. The saturation magnetization M_s does not depend on T^{-1}. Rather, it is very insensitive to the temperature of the crystal.
3. The classical theory does not predict the discontinuity in magnetization that occurs at the Curie temperature T_C.

The Weiss Theory of Ferromagnetism

The first attempt to solve this (apparent) paradox was made by Weiss.[1] According to Weiss, the effective magnetic field at an ion site is not merely the effective field H_e due to the other constituent magnetic dipoles of the lattice. Rather, there is an additional internal field, much larger than H_e, which is proportional to the crystal magnetization, so that the actual effective field is

$$H_e^* = H_e + \frac{kT_C}{J\mu_0} \frac{\langle M \rangle}{M_s} \tag{5.33}$$

The additional term (arising from some unforeseen fields in the crystal) could then account for the "observed" behavior of the internal field H_e^*, if $\langle M \rangle$ were sufficiently large. (The magnetization $\langle M \rangle$ is called the *Weiss field.*) The resulting expression for the statistical average of the magnetization then has the same form as (5.31) except that H is replaced by H_e^*, that is,

$$\langle M \rangle = N\mu_0 J B_J \left(\frac{\mu_0 H_e}{2k} + \frac{T_C}{2J} \frac{\langle M \rangle}{M_s} \right) \tag{5.34}$$

or, in the absence of an external field and magnetic dipole-dipole interactions,[2]

$$\langle M \rangle = N\mu_0 J B_J \left(\frac{T_C}{2J} \frac{\langle M \rangle}{M_s} \right) \tag{5.35}$$

In the case in which the spin of the individual atoms is $\frac{1}{2}$ the limiting

[1] P. Weiss, *J. Phys. Radium*, **6**: 667 (1907).

[2] See R. H. Fowler and E. A. Guggenheim, Statistical Thermodynamics, p. 676, Cambridge University Press, New York, 1956.

value $B_J(\infty) = 1$, thus $M_s = N\mu_0 J$. Eq. (5.35) then takes the form

$$\frac{<M>}{M_s} = \tanh\left(\frac{T_C}{T}\frac{<M>}{M_s}\right) \tag{5.36}$$

(The demonstration of this result will be left as an exercise for the reader.)

If $T_C/T < 1$, the solution of (5.36) is $<M> = 0$, as expected. However, when $T_C/T > 1$ there are two solutions of (5.36), of which one is zero. The other (nonzero) solution corresponds to the minimum free energy of the system and describes a state of magnetization. Thus, the Weiss theory leads, in agreement with experiment, to a magnetization below a critical temperature T_C and no magnetization above this temperature.

When the external magnetic field H_e is nonzero, then, for $\mu_0 H_e \ll kT$, the following result is obtained:

$$\frac{<M>}{M_s} \sim \frac{\mu_0 H_e}{kT} + \frac{T_C}{T}\frac{<M>}{M_s} \tag{5.37}$$

or

$$\frac{<M>}{H_e} = \chi \propto \frac{1}{T - T_C} \tag{5.38}$$

The behavior of the paramagnetic susceptibility according to (5.38) is called the Curie-Weiss law. This law is found, experimentally, to be valid only at temperatures which are not close to and are above the Curie temperature. [Also, the mgnitude of T_C in (5.38) is not in agreement with the observed magnitude of the temperature at which the crystal becomes ferromagnetic.]

The Weiss theory, while containing features which agree with experiment, is still an empirical theory since it does not explain the origin of the Weiss field. Classical considerations of the magnetization of a sample would indeed give a term in the effective magnetic field which is proportional to the magnetization of the crystal. This term, however, only introduces the correction factor $(4\pi/3)$ whereas the corresponding correction factor in the Weiss theory is of the order of 10^4. The origin of the Weiss field was not given a plausible explanation until Heisenberg applied the quantum theory to the description of the ferromagnet.

The Heisenberg Theory of Ferromagnetism

It was Heisenberg who first recognized that the quantum theory would provide a physical explanation for the large magnitude of the Weiss field.[1] Because of the requirement imposed by the Pauli exclusion principle that the wave function describing a system of electrons be

[1] W. Heisenberg, *Z. Physik*, **49**: 619 (1928). Also see Van Vleck, *op. cit.*, p. 322.

antisymmetric, an extra electrostatic-energy term appears in the hamiltonian for the system. This term, depending on the overlap of the wave functions of the adjacent particles, is called the electrostatic exchange interaction and was first discussed by Heisenberg.[1] It also depends on the relative orientation of the spins of the adjacent particles and therefore contributes to the ferromagnetic effect. In a crystal in which each ion has a nonzero spin, such an effect is large enough to account for the magnitude of the Weiss field. It should be emphasized that such an effect has no classical counterpart and the success of the Heisenberg model represents one further striking success of the quantum theory.

We shall now outline the mathematical development of the Heisenberg theory. First we consider the Schroedinger wave equation for a system of two noninteracting atoms. The stationary states of each atom [(1) and (2)] are determined by identical wave equations

$$\begin{aligned} \mathcal{H}_0^{(1)}\psi_n(\mathbf{r}_1) &= E_n\psi_n(\mathbf{r}_1) \\ \mathcal{H}_0^{(2)}\psi_m(\mathbf{r}_2) &= E_m\psi_m(\mathbf{r}_2) \end{aligned} \tag{5.39}$$

where the quantum states identified by n and m are two of a complete set of eigenfunctions of $\mathcal{H}_0$. It clearly follows from (5.39) that the total system is described by the wave equation

$$(\mathcal{H}_0^{(1)} + \mathcal{H}_0^{(2)})\psi_n(\mathbf{r}_1)\psi_m(\mathbf{r}_2) = (E_n + E_m)\psi_n(\mathbf{r}_1)\psi_m(\mathbf{r}_2) \tag{5.39$'$}$$

[since $\mathcal{H}_0^{(1)}$ operates only on $\psi(\mathbf{r}_1)$ and $\mathcal{H}_0^{(2)}$ operates only on $\psi(\mathbf{r}_2)$]. Since n and m are any two of a complete set of states, the wave equation (5.39′), with m and n interchanged, is also a solution, i.e.,

$$(\mathcal{H}_0^{(1)} + \mathcal{H}_0^{(2)})\psi_m(\mathbf{r}_1)\psi_n(\mathbf{r}_2) = (E_n + E_m)\psi_m(\mathbf{r}_1)\psi_n(\mathbf{r}_2) \tag{5.39$''$}$$

Since $\psi_n(\mathbf{r}_1)\psi_m(\mathbf{r}_2)$ and $\psi_m(\mathbf{r}_1)\psi_n(\mathbf{r}_2)$ are two distinct orthogonal solutions of the same differential equation, the energy eigenvalue $E_n + E_m$ has a double degeneracy with respect to the interchange of n and m between the wave functions for neighboring atoms. This degeneracy is removed by the Coulomb interaction acting between the two atoms, having the form

$$\mathcal{H}^{(1,2)} = \frac{e^2}{|\mathbf{r}_1 - \mathbf{r}_2|} \tag{5.40}$$

The effect of the perturbation (5.40) on the energy levels of the system may then be obtained by means of the standard technique of degenerate perturbation theory.[2] The removal of the 2-fold degeneracy is accom-

[1] W. Heisenberg, *Z. Physik*, **38**: 411 (1926).

[2] See, for example, L. I. Schiff, "Quantum Mechanics," p. 153, McGraw-Hill Book Company, Inc., New York, 1955.

plished by diagonalizing the secular determinant

$$\begin{vmatrix} \langle \mathcal{H}_0 + \mathcal{H}^{(1,2)} \rangle_{11} - \epsilon & \langle \mathcal{H}^{(1,2)} \rangle_{12} \\ \langle \mathcal{H}^{(1,2)} \rangle_{21} & \langle \mathcal{H}_0 + \mathcal{H}^{(1,2)} \rangle_{22} - \epsilon \end{vmatrix} = 0 \qquad (5.41)$$

where

$$\langle \mathcal{H} \rangle_{pq} \equiv \int \psi_p^* \mathcal{H} \psi_q \, dV$$
$$\psi_1 \equiv \psi_n(\mathbf{r}_1)\psi_m(\mathbf{r}_2)$$
$$\psi_2 \equiv \psi_m(\mathbf{r}_1)\psi_n(\mathbf{r}_2)$$

are the unperturbed eigenfunctions. Since

$$J_{mn} \equiv \langle \mathcal{H}^{(1,2)} \rangle_{12} = \langle \mathcal{H}^{(1,2)} \rangle_{21} = \int \psi_n^*(\mathbf{r}_1)\psi_m^*(\mathbf{r}_2) \frac{e^2}{|\mathbf{r}_1 - \mathbf{r}_2|} \psi_m(\mathbf{r}_1)\psi_n(\mathbf{r}_2) \, d\mathbf{r}_1 \, d\mathbf{r}_2 \qquad (5.42a)$$

$$K_{mn} \equiv \langle \mathcal{H}^{(1,2)} \rangle_{11} = \langle \mathcal{H}^{(1,2)} \rangle_{22} = \int \psi_n^*(\mathbf{r}_1)\psi_m(\mathbf{r}_2) \frac{e^2}{|\mathbf{r}_1 - \mathbf{r}_2|} \psi_n(\mathbf{r}_1)\psi_m(\mathbf{r}_2) \, d\mathbf{r}_1 \, d\mathbf{r}_2 \qquad (5.42b)$$

the secular equation (5.41) gives the two eigenvalues

$$\epsilon_{\pm} = E_{mn} + K_{mn} \pm J_{mn}$$

where

$$E_{mn} = E_m + E_n$$

is the unperturbed energy eigenvalue.

The corresponding eigensolutions of the total hamiltonian

$$\mathcal{H} = \mathcal{H}_0^{(1)} + \mathcal{H}_0^{(2)} + \mathcal{H}^{(1,2)}$$

which diagonalize the determinant are the symmetric and antisymmetric functions

$$\psi^{(+)} = \frac{1}{\sqrt{2}} (\psi_1 + \psi_2) \qquad (5.43a)$$

$$\psi^{(-)} = \frac{1}{\sqrt{2}} (\psi_1 - \psi_2) \qquad (5.43b)$$

The treatment presented thus far neglects the fact that each of the interacting atoms has spin coordinates as well as configurational coordinates. If it is assumed that there is no coupling between the particle spins and their motion (i.e., if spin-orbit interactions are neglected), the total wave function which describes the two-atom system must be a product of the space part [Eqs. (5.43)] and a spin part.

Let us assume, for simplicity, that each atom has a single electron in the $3d$ shell. The spin of each electron is $\frac{1}{2}$, and, according to the way in which angular momenta combine, the total spin system is characterized either by a triplet state ($S = S_1 + S_2 = 1$) or by a singlet state ($S = S_1 - S_2 = 0$).

The possible values for the z component of total spin of two atoms are 1, 0, −1. The spin functions are then described as follows:

$$\begin{array}{llll} & (1)\quad(2)\qquad\quad(1)\quad(2) & & \\ S_z = 1 & (\uparrow\quad\uparrow) & & \\ S_z = -1 & (\downarrow\quad\downarrow) & \chi(S=1) & (5.44a) \\ S_z = 0 & \dfrac{1}{\sqrt{2}}\left\{(\uparrow\quad\downarrow) + (\downarrow\quad\uparrow)\right. & & \\ & \dfrac{1}{\sqrt{2}}\left\{(\uparrow\quad\downarrow) - (\downarrow\quad\uparrow)\right\} & \chi(S=0) & (5.44b) \end{array}$$

where the arrows represent the z component of each particle spin. The first three terms in (5.44) are clearly symmetric with respect to an interchange of particles (1) and (2). Since the symmetrical or antisymmetrical character of the wave function is dependent on the total-spin quantum number S, and not on S_z, the first three terms in (5.44) must correspond to the triplet state $S = 1$, while the fourth term describes the singlet state $S = 0$.[1]

The total wave function for the two-atom system is then given by products of the space functions (5.43) with the spin functions (5.44) (when it is assumed that there is no coupling of the electron spin to the motion of either electron).

Since the Pauli exclusion principle requires that the total wave function be antisymmetric, the symmetric spin function (5.44a) may be coupled only to the antisymmetric space function (5.43b), whereas the antisymmetric spin function (5.44b) may be coupled only to the symmetric space function (5.43a). Thus

$$^{(3)}\Psi = \frac{1}{\sqrt{2}}(\psi_1 - \psi_2)\chi(S = 1) \qquad (5.45a)$$

$$^{(1)}\Psi = \frac{1}{\sqrt{2}}(\psi_1 + \psi_2)\chi(S = 0) \qquad (5.45b)$$

correspond, respectively, to

$$^{(3)}\epsilon = E + K - J \qquad (5.45a')$$

$$^{(1)}\epsilon = E + K + J \qquad (5.45b')$$

[in (5.45) and henceforth the subscripts mn are dropped but will be implied].

Since

$$\mathbf{S}_1 \cdot \mathbf{S}_2 = \tfrac{1}{2}[(S_1 + S_2)^2 - S_1^2 - S_2^2]$$

[1] This result follows rigorously from a consideration of the second-rank spinors which are constructed from the direct product of ordinary spinors. The symmetric second-rank spinor $S^{(+)}(\sigma_1\sigma_2)$ transforms under rotations like a vector (the triplet state) while the antisymmetric second-rank spinor $S^{(-)}(\sigma_1\sigma_2)$ transforms like a scalar (the singlet state).

and also, since the eigenvalues of the squares are

$$<(S_1 + S_2)^2> \;=\; S(S+1) = \begin{cases} 0 \text{ for the singlet state} \\ 2 \text{ for the triplet state} \end{cases}$$

$$<S_i^2> \;=\; S_i(S_i + 1) = \tfrac{3}{4}$$

we have

$$<\mathbf{S}_1 \cdot \mathbf{S}_2> \;=\; \begin{cases} -\tfrac{3}{4} \text{ singlet state} \\ +\tfrac{1}{4} \text{ triplet state} \end{cases} \tag{5.46}$$

and (5.45a') and (5.45b') may then be combined in the general form

$$\epsilon = (E + K - \tfrac{1}{2}J) - 2J\mathbf{S}_1 \cdot \mathbf{S}_2 = \epsilon_D + \epsilon_H \tag{5.47}$$

Thus we have managed to express the energy eigenvalues of this two-atom system in terms of the spin-coupling term ϵ_H depending on $\mathbf{S}_1 \cdot \mathbf{S}_2$. It is this term, according to the Heisenberg model, which gives rise to the Weiss field. It is, of course, very difficult in practice to evaluate the exchange integral J (or even to determine its sign) since such a calculation entails the requirement of solving the many-electron-atom problem. (If the model is correct, the sign of J must be positive for the transition metals.)

The problem is, of course, further complicated when we consider these atoms to be constituent parts of a crystal, since one must now take into account all the neighbors of a given atom instead of considering a single pair of atoms at a time. Thus, the Heisenberg exchange operator (for the entire crystal) takes the form ($\boldsymbol{\hat{\sigma}} \equiv 2\mathbf{S}$)

$$\hat{\epsilon}_H = - \sum_{i<k=1}^{N} J_{ik} \boldsymbol{\hat{\sigma}}_i \cdot \boldsymbol{\hat{\sigma}}_k \tag{5.48}$$

where the sum is taken over all $\dfrac{N(N-1)}{2}$ pairs of ions in the crystal.

The evaluation of (5.48) can be further simplified if we assume that the overlap of the $3d$ electron wave functions between ions beyond the nearest neighbors may be neglected. In this case, $J_{ik} = J$ is the same for all interactions, and the Heisenberg energy operator takes the form

$$\hat{\epsilon}_H = -\tfrac{1}{2}J \sum_{i,k} \boldsymbol{\hat{\sigma}}_i \cdot \boldsymbol{\hat{\sigma}}_k \tag{5.49}$$

In order to determine the magnetization of the crystal according to the statistical formula (5.2), it is necessary to evaluate the energy eigenvalues of $\hat{\epsilon}_H$ [Eq. (5.48)]. These eigenvalues depend in turn on different spin configurations of the lattice. Such an evaluation has never been carried out for a real crystal, but approximate methods of evaluating these energy levels have been developed. These will be discussed presently.

If the spin-orbit coupling may be neglected, the total spin of the lattice

$$\mathbf{S} = \tfrac{1}{2} \sum_{i=1}^{N} \boldsymbol{\sigma}_i \tag{5.50}$$

is a constant of the motion. Also, if the magnetic dipole-dipole inter-actions (which are indeed quite small in comparison with the Coulomb energy) are neglected, the energy of the crystal is independent of the orientation of the total spin $\mathbf{S}$. Thus

$$S_z = \tfrac{1}{2} \sum_{i=1}^{N} (\sigma_z)_i \tag{5.51}$$

is also a constant of the motion and can take on $2S + 1$ values.

The magnetization of the crystal depends on the quantum number S_z. For a given S_z, $N/2 + S_z$ atoms have $(S_z)_i = +\tfrac{1}{2}$ while $N/2 - S_z$ atoms have $(S_z)_i = -\tfrac{1}{2}$. Thus, the number of states of the crystal for a given value of S_z is just the number of ways in which N things may be taken $N/2 - S_z$ at a time. Calling this quantity $\Omega(S_z)$, we have

$$\Omega(S_z) = \frac{N!}{(N/2 + S_z)!(N/2 - S_z)!} \tag{5.52}$$

The quantum numbers S_z may be expressed in terms of a "box-diagonal" matrix in which the dimensionality of each box (shown in parentheses) represents the total number of states to be associated with that value of S_z. Thus

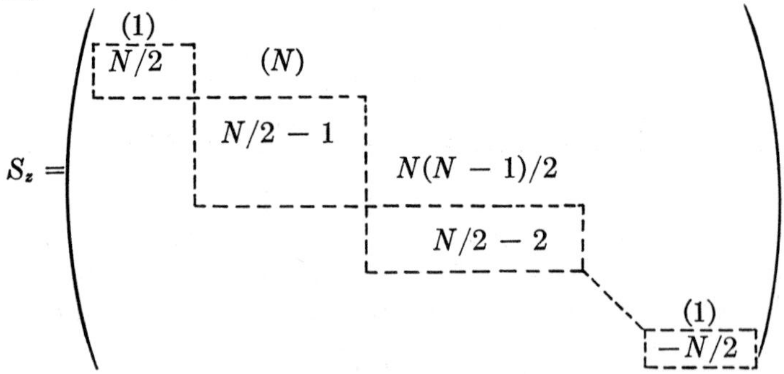

$$S_z = \begin{pmatrix} \overset{(1)}{N/2} & (N) & & & \\ & N/2-1 & & & \\ & & N(N-1)/2 & & \\ & & & N/2-2 & \\ & & & & \overset{(1)}{-N/2} \end{pmatrix} \tag{5.53}$$

In accordance with (5.50), the total spin S may be represented by a matrix similar to (5.53). However, each box of the matrix of S will contain all possible states for which $S \geq S_z$. Thus, if the number of states in a box for a particular $S_z + 1$ is subtracted from those in a box with the spin S_z, where $S_z = S$, we obtain the number of states associated with a given value S. Denoting the latter by $\omega(S)$, we have

$$\omega(S) = \Omega(S_z = S) - \Omega(S + 1)$$

or
$$\omega(S) = \frac{N!}{(N/2 + S)!(N/2 - S)!} \frac{2S + 1}{N/2 + S + 1} \tag{5.54}$$

We are now in a position to formulate the partition function for the ferromagnet and then to evaluate the magnetization of the crystal. The partition function may be expressed in terms of a sum of partition functions, each associated with a given spin configuration (i.e., a given S). Thus,

$$Z = \sum_{S=N/2,N/2-1,\ldots} Z_S \tag{5.55}$$

where

$$Z_S = \sum_{\nu} e^{-\epsilon_\nu/kT} = \omega(S)\langle e^{-E_S/kT}\rangle_S \tag{5.56}$$

where ν refers to all crystalline energy states, ϵ is an energy level of the crystal, and E_S are the energy levels associated with a given S. The right-hand side of Eq. (5.56) follows from the assumption that all spin configurations of the lattice which correspond to the same S are energetically equivalent. The total magnetic moment of the crystal then follows from the statistical formula (5.2), with the denominator given by (5.55).

The first difficulty encountered in determining Z is the problem of evaluating the energy levels of the crystal. For this purpose, Heisenberg made two approximations. The first was that

$$\langle e^{-E_S/kT}\rangle \simeq e^{-\langle E_S\rangle/kT} \tag{5.57a}$$

where $\langle E_S\rangle$ is the average energy for all states of a given S. In this approximation the population differences as a function of temperature have been disregarded.

The second of Heisenberg's approximations was to replace the discrete energy levels of a given S by a continuous Gaussian distribution. Thus, the following replacement is made:

$$\langle e^{-E/kT}\rangle = \int_0^\infty e^{-E/kT}\frac{1}{\sqrt{2\pi\Delta_S}}e^{-(E-\langle E_S\rangle)^2/2\Delta_S}\,dE = e^{-\langle E_S\rangle/kT+\Delta_S/2k^2T^2} \tag{5.57b}$$

where Δ_S is the mean-square deviation associated with the Gaussian distribution of energy levels within a given S manifold of states.

Now we consider the effect of applying an external magnetic field H_e. Under such a condition, the partition function (5.56) [in view of the approximation (5.57)] takes the form [see Eq. (5.17)]

$$\begin{aligned} Z_S &= \omega(S)e^{-\langle E_S\rangle/kT+\Delta_S/2k^2T^2}\sum_{S_z=-S}^{S} e^{2H_e\mu_0 S_z/kT} \\ &= \omega(S)e^{-\langle E_S\rangle/kT+\Delta_S/2k^2T^2}\frac{\sinh\,[(2S+1)\mu_0 H_e/kT]}{\sinh\,(\mu_0 H_e/kT)} \end{aligned} \tag{5.58}$$

$(\mu_0 \equiv g\beta/2)$

and, using (5.54), $\ln N! \sim N \ln N$,

$$\ln Z_S = -N\left(\frac{1}{2}+\frac{S}{N}\right)\ln\left(\frac{S}{N}+\frac{1}{2}\right) - N\left(\frac{1}{2}-\frac{S}{N}\right)\ln\left(\frac{1}{2}-\frac{S}{N}\right) + \ln(2S+1) - \ln\left(\frac{N}{2}+S+1\right) - \frac{<E_S>}{kT} + \frac{\Delta_S}{2k^2T^2} + \ln\sinh\left[\frac{(2S+1)\mu_0 H_e}{kT}\right] - \ln\sinh\left(\frac{\mu_0 H_e}{kT}\right) \quad (5.59)$$

In the case of the ferromagnet $S \sim N$ and for large N the following approximation can be made:

$$\ln Z_S = -N\left(\frac{S}{N}+\frac{1}{2}\right)\ln\left(\frac{S}{N}+\frac{1}{2}\right) - N\left(\frac{1}{2}-\frac{S}{N}\right)\ln\left(\frac{1}{2}-\frac{S}{N}\right) - \frac{<E_S>}{kT} + \frac{\Delta_S}{2k^2T^2} + \frac{(2S+1)\mu_0 H_e}{kT} \quad (5.60)$$

If we now assume that the equilibrium spin configuration corresponds to that value of S ($= S_0$) which minimizes the free energy of the system (see Appendix B) (and therefore maximizes $\ln Z_S$), we obtain

$$S_0 = \frac{N}{2}\tanh\left[\frac{1}{2}\left(-\frac{1}{kT}\frac{\partial<E_S>}{\partial S} + \frac{1}{2k^2T^2}\frac{\partial\Delta_S}{\partial S} + \frac{2H_e\mu_0}{kT}\right)\right] \quad (5.61)$$

Regarding S as a function of the applied field H_e, the magnetization is then obtained from the relation (5.30):

$$<M> = kT\frac{\partial}{\partial H}(\ln Z) = kT\left[\frac{\partial}{\partial H_e}(\ln Z) + \frac{\partial}{\partial S}(\ln Z)\frac{\partial S}{\partial H_e}\right] \quad (5.62)$$

In the equilibrium situation, $S = S_0$, and the second term on the right-hand side of (5.62) is zero, giving

$$<M> = \frac{NkT\mu_0(2S_0+1)}{kT} = N\mu_0(2S_0) \quad (5.63)$$

[In (5.63) we have taken $2S_0 \gg 1$. This is valid since S is assumed to be of the order N.] The result (5.63) indicates that for large S the most probable spin configurations are those in which most of the lattice spins line up in the same direction. Since $S \sim N \sim 10^{24}$, the Heisenberg result leads naturally to an enormous value of the Weiss field and agrees with the order of magnitude predicted by experiment.

Let us now determine $<M>$ as a function of temperature, according to the Heisenberg approximations made above. Combining (5.63) with (5.61), we have

$$\frac{<M>}{N\mu_0} = \tanh\left[\frac{1}{2}\left(-\frac{1}{kT}\frac{\partial<E_S>}{\partial S} + \frac{1}{2k^2T^2}\frac{\partial\Delta_S}{\partial S} + \frac{2H_e\mu_0}{kT}\right)\right] \quad (5.64)$$

Next, we must determine $<E_S>$. It is shown by Heisenberg (and in another way, by Van Vleck[1]) that if ν represents the number of nearest neighbors of a given atom in the lattice,

$$<E_S> = \nu \frac{J}{N} S^2 \tag{5.65}$$

$$\Delta_S = \nu J^2 \frac{(N^2 - 4S^2)(3N^2 - 4S^2)}{8N^3} \tag{5.66}$$

where J is the exchange integral [given by Eq. (5.42*a*)]. Combining (5.65) and (5.66) with (5.64), $<M>$ takes the form

$$\frac{<M>}{N\mu_0} = \tanh\left[\frac{\mu_0 H_e}{kT} + \frac{<M>}{2N\mu_0}\left(\rho - \frac{\rho^2}{\nu}\right) + \frac{<M>^3\rho^2}{4\nu(N\mu_0)^3}\right] \tag{5.67}$$

where

$$\rho \equiv \frac{\nu J}{kT} \tag{5.68}$$

Consider now (5.67) in the case when there is no applied field. The terms in (5.67) which are linear in ρ arise from the first Heisenberg

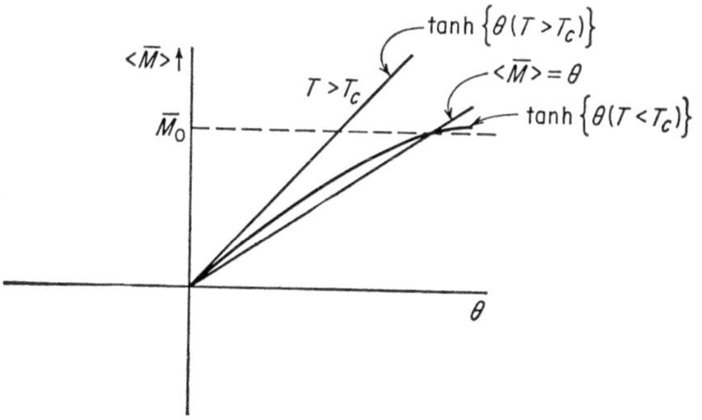

Fig. 5.7. Graphical solution of Heisenberg's equation (5.67), indicating spontaneous magnetization. The abscissa is

$$\theta(T > T_C) = <\bar{M}> \frac{\rho}{2} \qquad \theta(T < T_C) = \frac{<\bar{M}>}{2}\left(\rho - \frac{\rho^2}{\nu}\right) + \frac{<\bar{M}>^3}{4}\frac{\rho^2}{\nu}$$

with $<\bar{M}> = <M>/N\mu_0$.

approximation (5.57*a*) while the quadratic terms ρ^2 arise from the second Heisenberg approximation (5.57*b*). When the temperature is high, ρ is small and the terms in ρ^2 can be neglected. Under this condition, the only solution of (5.67) occurs at $<M> = 0$. As the temperature is lowered sufficiently, the ρ^2 terms cannot be neglected; there are then two solutions of (5.67), one at $<M> = 0$ and the other at a nonzero value M_s. This is illustrated in Fig. 5.7. By the argument similar to

[1] Van Vleck, *op. cit.*, p. 342.

that given in the discussion of the Weiss field, the latter corresponds to the stable solution and describes the spontaneous magnetization of the lattice which occurs below the critical (Curie) temperature T_C.

The Curie temperature occurs as the slopes of both tanh θ curves (Fig. 5.7) approach each other at $<M> = 0$. Thus, applying the condition

$$\frac{d<M>}{d\theta} = 0 \qquad \text{at } T = T_C \tag{5.69}$$

we obtain

$$T_C = \frac{J}{k}\frac{2}{1 - \sqrt{1 - 8/\nu}} \tag{5.70}$$

According to (5.70), T_C is a real number only if

$$\nu \geq 8$$

Thus, Heisenberg concluded that the number of nearest neighbors in a ferromagnetic material (i.e., the coordination number) must be at least 8. The transition-group metals (iron, nickel, cobalt), which are strongly ferromagnetic, do indeed meet this requirement. However, there are ferromagnetic alloys for which $\nu = 6$. This indicates a weakness in the approximations that were used in the Heisenberg derivation. A list of ferromagnetic materials and their associated values of M_s and T_C are given in Table 5.1.

TABLE 5.1 *Saturation Magnetization and Curie Temperature for Some Ferromagnetic Materials*

Substance	M_s *at room temp.*	M_s *at* 0°K	T_C,°K
Fe	1707	1752	1043
Co	1400	1446	1400
Ni	485	510	631
Gd	1090	1980	289
Dy	1830	—	105
Cu_2MnAl	430	580	603
$NiOFe_2O_3$	240	—	863
UH_3	—	230	180

The Curie-Weiss law (5.38) follows from (5.67) (with $H_e \neq 0$). Thus, the Heisenberg model does indeed provide a mechanism which explains the large Weiss field and gives agreement with the observed temperature dependence of the susceptibility at temperatures removed from the Curie temperature.

5.3 Antiferromagnetism

We have seen in the preceding section that the behavior of a ferromagnetic material may be explained quantum-mechanically in terms of the exchange interaction

$$\epsilon_H = -J \sum_{i<k=1}^{N} \boldsymbol{\sigma}_i \cdot \boldsymbol{\sigma}_k$$

It was, however, tacitly assumed in this derivation that the exchange integral J is positive. This assumption is required if the energy of the pair interaction with spins parallel is to be lower than the pair interaction describing the spins as antiparallel. There are, however, specific crystals which normally exhibit a paramagnetic behavior, and as the temperature is lowered to some critical value T_C, the magnetization *drops* very sharply to zero as the temperature is decreased from T_C. Such a behavior may be explained by a negative exchange integral. For in this case the spontaneous effect at the transition temperature would be (at equilibrium) to align the adjacent spins antiparallel to their neighbors, thus eliminating the net magnetization of the crystal. Typical examples of antiferromagnetic materials are transition-metal oxides (FeO, NiO, CoO, MnO), and a plot of the susceptibility of MnO as a function of temperature is shown in Fig. 5.8.

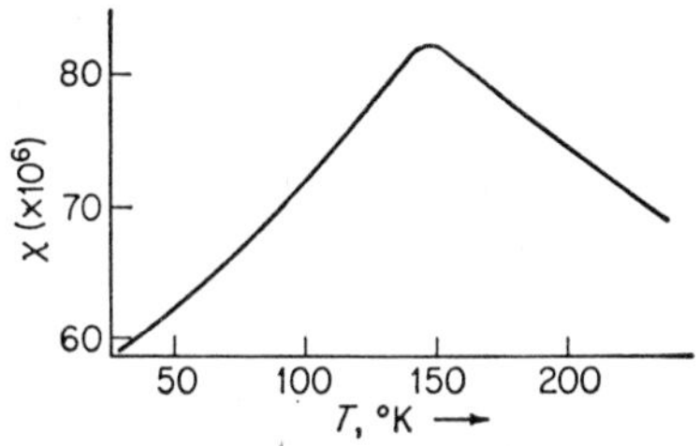

Fig. 5.8. Magnetic susceptibility of MnO (H_a = 5,000 gauss).

The temperature at which a crystal becomes antiferromagnetic is called the Néel temperature T_N. The Néel temperature is not the same as the Curie temperature. The latter is defined in terms of the magnetic susceptibility, according to the Curie-Weiss law for antiferromagnetic materials,

$$\chi = \frac{C}{T + T_C} \tag{5.71}$$

[The change in sign between (5.71) and (5.38) follows from the change in sign of J.] A tabulation of properties of typical antiferromagnetic materials is given in Table 5.2.

TABLE 5.2 *Néel and Curie Temperatures for Antiferromagnetic Crystals*

Crystal	T_N(°K)	T_C(°K)	T_N/T_C
MnO	610	122	5.0
FeO	570	198	2.9
NiO	—	523	
CoO	—	291	
CrSb	725	1000	1.4

5.4 Ferrimagnetism

There is a group of magnetic alloys which exhibit the property of a magnetization that varies with the relative percentage of composition of the different constituent atoms making up the alloy. A typical example of this type of alloy is the group of ferrites represented by the chemical formula

$$R\mathrm{OFe_2O_3}$$

with $$R = \mathrm{Mn, Co, Ni, Cu, Mg, Zn, Cd, or\ Fe^{++}}$$

These crystals all belong to the cubic-symmetry groups.

A plausible mechanism for the ferrimagnetic properties of crystals has been proposed by Néel.[1] According to the Néel theory, one can

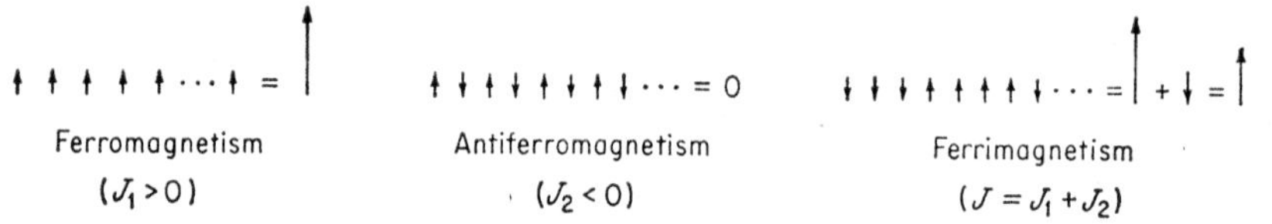

Fig. 5.9. Three types of magnetic mechanisms. (*a*) Ferromagnetism, (*b*) antiferromagnetism, and (*c*) ferrimagnetism.

imagine the ferrite as an interpenetration of different magnetic ion lattices. If one type of lattice is antiferromagnetic and another ferromagnetic, the net amount of magnetization would depend on the relative amounts of each type of atom (in agreement with the observed facts). Néel observed that the saturation magnetization ($M_s = 485$) for FeO-$\mathrm{Fe_2O_3}$ agrees with the situation in which the $\mathrm{Fe^{3+}}$ ions are antiparallel to each other while the $\mathrm{Fe^{++}}$ ions are parallel to each other. Thus, the $\mathrm{Fe^{3+}}$ lattice (arising from the $\mathrm{Fe_2O_3}$ radical in the ferrites) contributes to a decrease in the ferromagnetism of the entire ferrite, according to the Néel model.

Summarizing, the (ferro-, ferri-, and antiferromagnetic) types of magnetic crystal may be illustrated as in Fig. 5.9.

Our object in this chapter has been to discuss fundamental mechanisms that are responsible for some of the magnetic properties of solids. It should be stressed once again, however, that this discussion should not be taken as an exhaustive treatment of the subject. Rather, it should serve only as an introduction to the quantum theory of magnetism.

[1] L. Néel, *Ann. Phys.* (*Paris*), **3**: 137 (1948). Also see C. Kittel, "Introduction to Solid State Physics," p. 443, John Wiley & Sons, Inc., New York, 1953.

6 free-electron theory of metals

ONE MECHANISM responsible for binding a large group of atoms to form a stable crystalline structure has been shown to be intimately connected with the detailed electronic structure of the constituent atoms themselves. Thus far, we have discussed the more simple types of bonding mechanisms in which a given electron does not partake in the bonding of more than a few ions. The electron which partakes in the ionic and covalent bonds is primarily localized to a microscopic region which contains only a few atoms out of the entire macroscopic crystal. The metallic bond, on the other hand, may be characterized by an insufficient number of valence electrons to bind even a few ions in a microscopic region of the crystal. As a result, any given electron must pass freely from one ion to the other throughout the entire crystal in order to cause a net binding effect. In view of this picture of the metallic bond, it becomes convenient, in the first order of approximation, to consider a metal as a periodic array of positively charged ions immersed in a sea of freely moving electrons.

6.1 Classical free-electron model

The Wiedemann-Franz Law

Near the turn of this century, not long after the discovery of the electron, Drude[1] suggested that the electrical and thermal properties of metals should be interpreted in terms of a free-electron model, assuming that the free-electron gas is in thermal equilibrium with the positive-ion lattice and that the electrical and thermal properties of the metal are determined essentially by the properties of the free-electron gas. The electron gas was treated as a perfect gas and electron-electron interactions were neglected. On the basis of this model, Drude derived approximate expressions for the electrical conductivity σ and the thermal conductivity

[1] P. Drude, *Ann. Physik*, **1**: 566 (1900).

K and found that the ratio

$$\frac{K}{\sigma} = CT \tag{6.1}$$

(where C is constant, independent of the type of metal and the temperature) agreed with the experimentally verified Wiedemann-Franz law.[1] Some experimental values of K/σ are given in Table 6.1. The agreement with experiment gave some credence to the free-electron model of metals. The calculation which was carried out by Drude will be described below as an introduction to our treatment of the free-electron model of metals.

TABLE 6.1* *Experimental values of the Wiedemann-Franz Constant C (in units of* 10^{-8} *volt degrees)*

Metal	273°K	373°K
Cu	2.23	2.33
Mo	2.61	2.79
Pd	2.59	2.74
Ag	2.31	2.37
Sn	2.52	2.49
Pt	2.51	2.60
Bi	3.31	2.89

* *Handbuch Metallphysik,* **1:** 379 (1935).

Electrical Conductivity

Electrical conductivity, for an isotropic medium, is defined as the absolute value of the ratio of the magnitudes of the current density **j** to the applied electric field intensity $\boldsymbol{\varepsilon}$,

$$\sigma = \frac{|\mathbf{j}|}{|\boldsymbol{\varepsilon}|} \tag{6.2}$$

The current density is given by the product of the electron flux $n\mathbf{v}_D$ and the electrostatic charge e (which is carried by an electron), where n is the number of charge carriers per cubic centimeter and $\mathbf{v}_D$ is the average drift velocity per electron in the direction of the applied field. The electrical conductivity is then expressed in the form

$$\sigma = ne\frac{|\mathbf{v}_D|}{|\boldsymbol{\varepsilon}|} = ne\mu \tag{6.3}$$

The average drift velocity per applied field strength μ is appropriately referred to as the *mobility*, since it is intimately related to the resistance

[1] G. Wiedemann and R. Franz, *Ann. Physik* **89:** 497 (1853).

which the lattice offers to the flow of electrons on their course through the crystal. It will be shown in the following chapter that the motion of free electrons is unimpeded by a static periodic lattice. In the realistic case, however, the lattice is not static but rather is a dynamic system analogous to a large assemblage of hard spheres, connected by springs and oscillating about their equilibrium lattice positions. The amplitude of vibration of the lattice ions depends on the temperature of the lattice, with a minimum at the absolute zero temperature. (Contrary to the classical prediction, there is a small but finite zero-point oscillation at the absolute zero-degree temperature.) Consequently, this crude model would predict a finite temperature-dependent mobility.

Before the electric field is applied to the crystal, a given constituent electron in the electron gas moves in an arbitrary direction and the average current is therefore zero. As soon as an electric field is applied, an average current density j_z is established. This electron (on an average) moves along the z axis only until it is scattered by the lattice, at which time it once again moves in a random direction relative to the other constituent electrons. If one defines τ to be the time between two scattering events in the crystal, the component of the electron velocity in the direction of the applied field will, on an average, be zero just after the scattering event, and it will acquire a magnitude v_D in the time τ. The average drift velocity is then, according to the equation of motion of an electron in an electric field, given by the proportionality

$$\mathbf{v}_D \propto \frac{e\mathcal{E}}{m}\tau \tag{6.4}$$

The time τ may also be expressed in terms of a mean free path λ, according to the relation

$$\tau = \frac{\lambda}{v} \tag{6.5}$$

where v (as distinguished from v_D) is the average charge-carrier velocity.

The mobility, which is denoted by μ, may then be expressed in the form

$$\mu = \frac{|\mathbf{v}_D|}{|\boldsymbol{\mathcal{E}}|} = \frac{e\lambda}{mv}$$

and the conductivity is

$$\sigma = \frac{|\mathbf{j}|}{|\boldsymbol{\mathcal{E}}|} = \frac{ne^2\tau}{m} = \frac{ne^2\lambda}{mv} \tag{6.6}$$

It is assumed above that the mean free path λ is independent of the electron velocity. Using the familiar result from statistical mechanics[1]

[1] See, for example, R. C. Tolman, "The Principles of Statistical Mechanics," chap. IV, Oxford University Press, Fair Lawn, N.J., 1938.

that the average kinetic energy per particle in a perfect gas is related to the gas temperature in the following way,

$$\langle \tfrac{1}{2}mv^2 \rangle = \tfrac{3}{2}kT \tag{6.7}$$

Drude takes v, which appears in the expression for the conductivity, to be $(3kT/m)^{1/2}$ and obtains the proportionality

$$\sigma \propto \frac{ne^2\lambda}{\sqrt{mkT}} \tag{6.8}$$

This result would indicate that $\sigma \propto T^{-1/2}$, a variation with temperature which is not in agreement with experimental observations. The variation $\sigma \propto T^{-1}$ is closer to the experimental facts. Drude's supposition that λ is independent of velocity was based on the assumption that the electron's mean free path must be proportional to a mean lattice spacing r_0 in the crystal. The validity of this assumption would rule out the possibility of the variation $\lambda \propto T^{-1/2}$ since r_0 must be directly, rather than inversely, proportional to some power of the temperature. It was at this stage of the calculation that the classical free-electron model of metals first broke down.

Thermal Conductivity

The thermal conductivity of the electron gas is defined in a fashion analogous to the definition of electrical conductivity, as the ratio of the energy flux to the temperature gradient which gives rise to the flow of energy. Thus, the thermal conductivity is

$$K = \frac{H}{dT/dz} \tag{6.9}$$

where H is the thermal energy carried by the electrons, per unit area per second, and where the temperature gradient is applied in the z direction. We shall now calculate the flux H that crosses a plane which is perpendicular to the z direction. We assume that, on an average, the component of an electron velocity in the z direction is zero at the scattering center and that this electron acquires a velocity v_D after it has traveled the distance of one mean free path λ, at which time it once again is scattered by a lattice ion.

The amount of energy flux that crosses a plane between the solid angles Ω and $\Omega + d\Omega$ from the scattering center which is located in the volume increment dV is

$$dH = Uf(\Omega)\, d\Omega \tag{6.10}$$

where U is the energy carried per electron and where $f(\Omega)\, d\Omega$ is the number of electrons per square centimeter per second, which are found in the solid-angle increment $d\Omega$ (see Fig. 6.1).

According to our assumption, the velocities of electrons in dV are all distributed equally with regard to their directions. The velocity vectors may then be represented by points on a sphere whose center is at P. If the number of electrons per unit volume is n, the number of electrons which cross the plane S per square centimeter per second along the normal direction is $nv_D \cos\theta$. The number of electrons which are

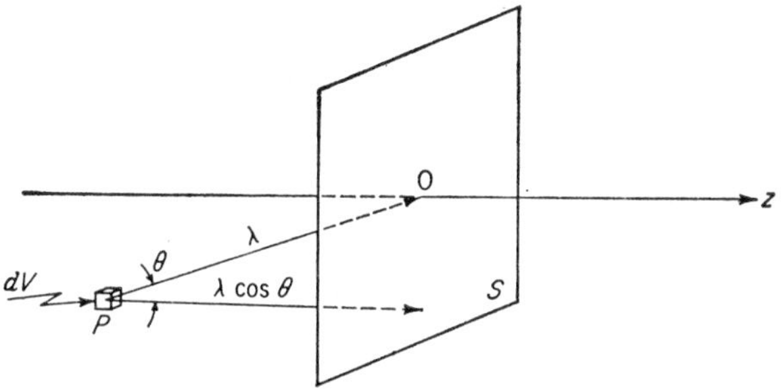

Fig. 6.1. Energy flux crossing a plane.

found in the solid-angle increment $d\Omega$ is (integrating out the azimuthal angle ϕ)

$$f(\Omega)\,d\Omega = nv_D \cos\theta \frac{d\Omega}{4\pi} = \frac{1}{2} nv_D \cos\theta \sin\theta \, d\theta \qquad (6.11)$$

The energy carried per electron across the plane S in the z direction may be expressed in terms of a Taylor expansion of $U(z)$ taken about the point $z = 0$:

$$U = U(0) + \lambda \cos\theta \left(\frac{\partial U}{\partial z}\right)_{z=0} + \cdots \qquad (6.12)$$

If it is assumed that the energy U varies by a very small amount over distances comparable with a mean free path, the series (6.12) will converge rapidly, and we may take the first two terms as a fair approximation to the correct value of the energy. Substituting Eqs. (6.11) and (6.12) into Eq. (6.10) and integrating dH over the entire solid angle, we obtain the total flux of energy which crosses the plane.

$$\begin{aligned} H = \int dH &= \int_0^\pi \left[U(0) + \lambda \cos\theta \left(\frac{\partial U}{\partial z}\right)_{z=0} \right] \left[\frac{1}{2} nv_D \cos\theta \sin\theta \right] d\theta \\ &= \frac{1}{2} nv_D\lambda \left(\frac{\partial U}{\partial z}\right)_{z=0} \int_0^\pi \cos^2\theta \sin\theta \, d\theta \\ &= \frac{1}{3} nv_D\lambda \left(\frac{\partial U}{\partial z}\right)_{z=0} \end{aligned} \qquad (6.13)$$

The variation of electron energy with z is due to the presence of a temperature gradient which causes a thermal diffusion of electrons in the z direction. Thus, we have

$$n\left(\frac{\partial U}{\partial z}\right)_{z=0} = n\frac{\partial U}{\partial T}\frac{dT}{dz} = C_v\frac{dT}{dz}$$

where C_v is the specific heat of the electron gas. The heat flux may then be expressed in the form

$$H = \frac{1}{3}v_D\lambda C_v\frac{dT}{dz}$$

and, in accordance with (6.9), the thermal conductivity has the form

$$K = \tfrac{1}{3}v_D\lambda C_v \qquad (6.14)$$

In the case of the perfect (classical) gas, the specific heat is simply $\frac{3}{2}nk$, where k is Boltzmann's constant, and

$$K = \tfrac{1}{2}nkv_D\lambda \qquad (6.15)$$

The assumption that the specific heat of a metal is determined solely by the specific heat of a classical electron gas is subject to experimental verification. The result that $C_v = \frac{3}{2}nk$ for the metal predicts a specific heat and thermal conductivity which are many orders of magnitude larger than the experimentally measured quantities at high temperatures and does not predict the experimentally observed drop in C_v with temperature, at low temperatures. Thus, the prediction of the Drude model for the behavior of thermal conductivity, as well as the electrical conductivity, with temperature, is in sharp contrast to the experimental observations.

The Wiedemann-Franz ratio, as predicted by Drude, is given by the ratio of K [Eq.(6.15)] to σ [Eq.(6.6)]. Assuming that $\langle v\rangle^2 \propto kT/m$, we have the proportionality

$$\frac{K}{\sigma} \propto \left(\frac{k}{e}\right)^2 T \qquad (6.16)$$

This result not only gives the correct dependence of K/σ on the temperature, but the constant $(k/e)^2$ is also in fairly good numerical agreement with the experimental data.

In spite of the success of Drude's classical electron-gas model of metals, the inability of this model to predict separately the correct magnitudes and functional dependence of the electrical and thermal conductivities with the temperature presented a dilemma which remained until the onset of the quantum theory.

6.2 Quantum-mechanical free-electron model

Qualitative Discussion

The predictions of the properties of a free-electron gas by the quantum theory are due to A. Sommerfeld.[1] His results agreed with the experimental observations and appeared to solve the dilemma presented by the classical theory. The two main consequences of the quantum theory which led to a theoretical agreement with the temperature dependence of the thermal and electrical conductivities are as follows:

1. Only the very small fraction of electrons that have velocities near a fixed maximum are allowed to absorb energy and contribute to the electrical and thermal conductivities.
2. The mean free path for electrons in the metal is *inversely* proportional to the mean-square amplitude of vibration of the lattice ions, which is, in turn, proportional to the first power of the temperature.

These predictions indicate that the velocity v which appears in the expression for the electrical conductivity [Eq. (6.6)] is essentially constant in temperature and that the mean free path $\lambda \propto T^{-1}$, so that $\sigma \propto T^{-1}$; this result is an agreement with experimental observations. The Wiedemann-Franz ratio is proportional to the mean kinetic energy of those available electrons which can absorb energy. The mean kinetic energy is still proportional to the temperature of the nonclassical electron gas so that there is no basic disagreement with the experimentally observed variation of the Wiedemann-Franz ratio with temperature, i.e.,

$$\frac{K}{\sigma} \sim \frac{k}{e^2} \langle mv^2 \rangle \sim 3 \left(\frac{k}{e}\right)^2 T \qquad (6.16')$$

The feature of the quantum theory which leads to prediction 1 is the Pauli exclusion principle. This principle states that no two electrons may be in the same state of motion and position simultaneously. The energy states of a free-electron gas depend on the kinetic energies and the spin states of all the constituent electrons. Since there are two possible spin states available to any given electron, only two electrons in the same region may have the same kinetic energy. Thus, in a fashion analogous to the buildup of atoms, we may build up a free-electron gas by dropping electrons into a macroscopic box, one by one. The walls of the box play the role of the binding potential for the free-electron gas, just as the Coulomb attraction of the nucleus plays the major role in binding the atomic electrons. The first two electrons will assume opposite spin states and the lowest kinetic energy available

[1] A. Sommerfeld, *Z. Physik*, **47**: 1 (1928); A. Sommerfeld and H. A. Bethe, "Handbuch der Physik," vol. 26, no. 2, Springer-Verlag OHG, Berlin, 1933.

(let us call this energy E_0). The next two electrons in the same region as the first two will never be able to have the kinetic energy E_0, because of the exclusion principle, but will have to assume a slightly higher kinetic energy value $E_0 + \delta$. Once this upper energy level at $E_0 + \delta$ is filled, the electrons in the lower energy state at E_0 will not be permitted to absorb an amount of energy δ since, according to the exclusion principle, they cannot occupy the energy level at $E_0 + \delta$. These electrons would have to absorb an amount of energy greater than δ in order to be excited out of their ground state. If we now continue the process of adding electrons to the box, always bringing them into the same region as the other electrons, until all the valence electrons available have been added, the last pair of electrons would have a maximum energy E_F, which would necessarily depend on the number of electrons in the box. [This energy (the Fermi energy) is the chemical potential $(U - TS + pV)$ of Gibbs, see Appendix B.] The electrons in the ground state E_0 would now need an excitation energy greater than the difference $E_F - E_0$ in order to get out of the ground state. As we consider electrons which have kinetic energies E_i greater than E_0, the difference $E_F - E_i$ becomes smaller and consequently it would take less energy to excite them from their normal energy states. In actual metals, the difference $E_F - E_0$ is of the order of electron volts while the energy available from ordinary laboratory sources (such as an applied electric field, electromagnetic radiation, or a temperature gradient) is of the order of hundredths of electron volts. Thus, under ordinary circumstances, only those electrons which have energies near the maximum energy level (or near the top of the so-called *Fermi sea*) are available to absorb energy from an outside source. Consequently, the electrons which we observe to carry energy in electrical or thermal conduction processes are only those electrons which have velocities near the maximum velocity v_F. We shall see later on that this velocity (the Fermi velocity) is a constant at $T = 0°K$ and that it has a very slight temperature variation at higher temperatures.

In the case of the monovalent metals, such as the alkali metals, there are only N valence electrons present, while there are $2N$ electronic energy levels available to them. If we consider that each of the valence electrons is in one of two possible spin orientations and that a given state is characterized by this kinetic energy and definite spin orientation, then the N electrons can be in any of $2N$ electronic states with ith electron occupying the state $\psi(\mathbf{k}^i,\sigma^i = \pm 1)$. Consequently the *energy band* will be only half full, and there will be many empty contiguous energy levels available to the electronic gas. Therefore, such a substance would normally be a good conductor of electrical and thermal energy. On the other hand, a divalent solid would normally be a very poor conductor of electrical and thermal energy, since all $2N$ of the energy levels would be full, leaving no available energy levels to the valence electrons. Such a material is a good electrical insulator. The properties of energy bands in crystals will be explored in much greater detail in the following two chapters.

The normal modes of vibration of a crystal lattice may be described, quantum-mechanically, in terms of a gas composed of particles which obey the same statistics as the photon gas of the electromagnetic field. The analogous field may be referred to as the acoustic field and the quantized lattice vibrations as phonons. The primary source of electrical resistance in a metal is the interaction between electrons and phonons.[1] Just as the mean kinetic energy per electron is proportional to the first power of the temperature (at high T), so the mean kinetic energy per phonon is also proportional to the first power of the temperature. This result leads to the inverse linear temperature dependence of the electron mean free path and is the justification for our statement of prediction 2.

Further predictions of the quantum theory which contradict the predictions of the classical theory deal with any phenomena involving the absorption of energy by the metal. For example, the heat capacity (or specific heat) of a free classical electron gas would be simply

$$C_v = \frac{dU}{dT} = \frac{3}{2} Nk$$

as mentioned in the previous section. The derivation of this result depends on the supposition that all electrons in the gas are equivalently available to absorb thermal energy. We have just seen, however, that the quantum theory will allow only a small fraction of the constituent electrons to absorb energy. Consequently, the quantum theory predicts, correctly, that the specific heat of an electron gas should be several orders of magnitude smaller than the prediction of the classical theory.

In a similar fashion, one can argue that the paramagnetic susceptibility of an electron gas would be much smaller than predicted by the classical theory. This is due to the fact that the spins of the electrons of a classical electron gas are oriented at random and are all available to accept magnetic energy, whereas the majority of the electrons in a quantum-mechanical electron gas have their spins paired off in oppositely oriented directions and are not available to accept magnetic energy. Thus the only paramagnetism which can arise must be due to the few electrons (which are near the maximum energy level E_F) that would be allowed to flip their spins by the absorption of magnetic energy. We shall calculate both the specific heat and the paramagnetic susceptibility of a quantum-mechanical electron gas later in this chapter.

[1] See, for example, J. M. Ziman, "Electrons and Phonons," Oxford University Press, Fair Lawn, N.J., 1960.

These predictions were among the first to substantiate the quantum theory as a precise description of phenomena that involve the behavior of nonrelativistic microscopic systems.

Quantitative Discussion

In the preceding discussion we have seen, in a qualitative fashion, how the quantum free-electron theory indicates the correct behavior of metals. Now we shall study the detailed properties of this model in a quantitative fashion. In the following chapter a more realistic model of the metal is adopted, in which the influence of the periodic lattice potential on the motion of the valence electrons is taken into account.

Free Electrons in a Box

As a zeroth-order approximation to the description of the electronic behavior of metals, let us assume that the metal may be described by a free-electron gas which is confined to an impenetrable cubic box which is L cm on the side. Further, let us assume that the influence of the electrons on each other may be neglected so that we need consider only the motion of *one electron at a time* in the box.

Under the assumptions imposed to describe this model, the properties of the free-electron gas may be obtained from a solution of the one-particle Schroedinger wave equation

$$\nabla^2\psi + \frac{2m}{\hbar^2}(E - V)\psi = 0 \tag{6.17}$$

with

$$V = 0 \qquad 0 < (x,y,z) < L \tag{6.18a}$$

$$V = \infty \qquad \text{elsewhere} \tag{6.18b}$$

where V is the potential energy which binds the electron in the box. The only additional information required in order to solve the wave equation is the set of boundary conditions on the wave function ψ. This is obtained from the physical interpretation of the wave function in terms of a probability density. In order to interpret the wave function as a probability, it is required that ψ be finite and continuous at all points in space.[1] Because of the infinite value of the potential V at the boundaries of the box, the product $V\psi$ which appears in the wave equation will be infinite unless $\psi = 0$ at the walls of the box. If $V\psi$ is infinite, then the kinetic energy E must also be infinite in order that ψ be a continuous function (i.e., in order that $\nabla^2\psi$ be finite). An infinite kinetic energy is inadmissible (according to the postulates of the special theory of relativity); thus the physical situation demands that the wave function ψ vanish at the walls of the box.

[1] In view of this interpretation, the gradient of ψ must also be finite and continuous in order that the probability density function $\psi^*\psi$ shall follow from an equation of continuity.

The solution of the wave equation (6.17) is obtained in a manner identical to the solution of the hydrogen-atom problem.[1] In the latter problem, because of the central symmetry of the potential $V(|\mathbf{r}|)$, we are able to solve the problem by expressing the solution as a product of three separate functions of the polar coordinates $R(r)\Theta(\theta)\Phi(\phi)$. Similarly, the problem of free electrons in a box involves a potential which is defined in terms of functions of the x, y, and z cartesian coordinates, separately. Thus, we solve Eq. (6.17) by expressing the wave function as a product of three separate functions of the cartesian coordinates $X(x)Y(y)Z(z)$; according to the argument of the preceding paragraph, each of these functions is subject to the boundary condition that it vanish at the walls of the box (x, y, z = 0, L).

The solution of (6.17) and (6.18) is then readily obtained, giving

$$\Psi_{n_x n_y n_z}(x,y,z) = \left(\frac{8}{\Omega}\right)^{1/2} \sin \kappa_x x \sin \kappa_y y \sin \kappa_z z \qquad (6.19)$$

$$\begin{pmatrix} \kappa_x \\ \kappa_y \\ \kappa_z \end{pmatrix} = \begin{pmatrix} n_x \\ n_y \\ n_z \end{pmatrix} \frac{\pi}{L} = \begin{pmatrix} \pm 1, \pm 2, \ldots \\ \pm 1, \pm 2, \ldots \\ \pm 1, \pm 2, \ldots \end{pmatrix} \frac{\pi}{L} \qquad (6.20)$$

are the square roots of the separation constants appearing in the solutions of the wave equations for the three respective functions $X(x)$, $Y(y)$, and $Z(z)$. These three numbers may be considered to be the three components of a wave vector $\boldsymbol{\kappa}$. The solution with n_x, n_y, or $n_z = 0$ is mathematically permissible; it is, however, contradictory to the probability interpretation of the wave function. Thus, the statement that any electron is confined to the box leads to the requirement

$$\int_{\text{Box}} |\Psi_{n_x n_y n_z}|^2 \, dV = 1 \qquad (6.21)$$

and, of course, the right-hand side of Eq. (6.19) is zero for n_x, n_y, or $n_z = 0$. The factor $\sqrt{8/\Omega}$ which appears in the wave function [Eq. (6.19)] is the normalization factor and Ω is the volume of the box. The energy eigenvalue which corresponds to the state $(n_x n_y n_z)$ has the form

$$E(\boldsymbol{\kappa}) = \frac{\hbar^2 \kappa^2}{2m} = \frac{\hbar^2}{2m}\left(\frac{\pi}{L}\right)^2 (n_x^2 + n_y^2 + n_z^2) \qquad (6.22)$$

and according to the above argument,

$$|n_x|, |n_y|, |n_z| \geq 1$$

[1] See, for example, L. I. Schiff, "Quantum Mechanics," p. 80, McGraw-Hill Book Company, Inc., New York, 1955.

Problem

Suppose that the surface of a (one-dimensional) metal is taken into account by specifying the conduction electron to be subjected to the potential

$$V = \begin{cases} 0 & 0 < x < L_1 \\ -|V_0| & L_1 < x < L_2 \\ \infty & \text{elsewhere} \end{cases}$$

(*a*) Determine the transcendental equation that relates the states in the surface region to V_0.

(*b*) Calculate the electronic charge density in the metal.

Energy-level separations as a function of the dimensions of the box The functional dependence of the energy value $E(n_1,n_2,n_3)$ on the size of the box [Eq. (6.22)] indicates that, if the box has laboratory dimensions, the separation between energy levels is sufficiently small so as to allow them to be considered in a quasi continuum, whereas a box of atomic dimensions leads to the result that the energy levels would be widely spaced and discrete. For example, let us compare the energy-level separations between two energy states of a system of electrons in (1) a cubic box which is 1 cm on the side and (2) a cubic box which is 5 Å on the side. In the first case, Eq. (6.22) gives for the difference between the $E(2,1,1)$ and the $E(1,1,1)$ energy levels

$$\begin{aligned} \Delta E = E(2,1,1) - E(1,1,1) &= (18 - 9)10^{-15} \\ &= 9 \times 10^{-15} \text{ ev} \end{aligned} \tag{6.23}$$

In the second case, the quantities in Eq. (6.23) must be multiplied by the factor $(5 \times 10^{-8})^{-2}$, giving for the corresponding energy-level separation

$$\Delta E = 7.2 - 3.6 = 3.6 \text{ ev} \tag{6.24}$$

Thus, as the size of the box is diminished from laboratory dimensions (~1 cm) to atomic dimensions (~Å), the energy-level spectrum passes from a quasi continuum to a set of states with the typical atomic energy-level separations of electron volts.

The filling up of the energy levels Let us now consider the energy distribution of the N available valence electrons after they have been dropped into a macroscopic box, one by one. According to the Pauli exclusion principle, no more than one electron is permitted to be in a given state of the system at a given time. The "state" of the system denotes the momentum of the particle, the orientation of the spin of the particle (up or down with respect to an arbitrary direction), and the location of the particle. Thus, the first electron which is dropped into the box will take on the minimum kinetic energy

$$E(1,1,1) = \frac{3\hbar^2\pi^2}{2mL^2} \tag{6.25}$$

The next electron which is dropped into the same region of the box will also be able to take on the minimum kinetic energy $E(1,1,1)$ but only on condition that it orients its intrinsic spin antiparallel to the spin orientation of the first electron. The third electron which is dropped into the box in the same region of space as the first two electrons (i.e., so that all three electrons remain indistinguishable) cannot take on this kinetic energy since it has already been taken up by two electrons; thus it will occupy the slightly higher energy level

$$E(2,1,1) = \frac{6\hbar^2\pi^2}{2mL^2} \tag{6.26}$$

The fourth electron which is dropped into the same region of the box as the first three will then take on the kinetic energy $E(2,1,1)$ but orient its spin antiparallel to the spin of the other electron in this kinetic-energy state. Thus, if this process is continued until all N of the valence electrons have been used up, the first $N/2$ energy levels will be filled. Since electrons are free to move about within the walls of the box, there will be many more than two electrons which have the same energy; these electrons will, however, be separated from each other by distances which are greater than their corresponding De Broglie wavelengths. Consequently, the maximum kinetic energy which is taken up by the last electron [in the $(N/2)$-th energy level] will be many orders of magnitude smaller than the energy $(\hbar^2\pi^2/2mL)(N/2)$ which would be the maximum energy in the event of all electrons being closer together than their respective De Broglie wavelengths. The maximum energy which is taken up by the last of these electrons is called the Fermi energy and will be determined below in accordance with the methods of quantum statistics.

It is of interest to note the further contradiction between the predictions of the quantum and classical theories with regard to the mean energy of the electron gas at $T = 0°K$. The quantum theory predicts that the mean energy of the electron gas is of the order of the Fermi energy (which is of the order of a few electron volts) while the classical theory predicts that all the constituent electrons of the gas are at rest at $T = 0°K$!

Energy-level degeneracy as a function of the symmetry of the box
We have seen in the preceding discussion that a large number of electrons (say 10^{24}) contained in a box of laboratory dimensions fall into energy levels which are so close together, in comparison with the total width of the energy band, that these energy levels may be considered to be in a quasi-continuous spectrum. Because of the very large density of levels, we could hardly suppose that the shape of the box could have any gross effect on the electronic properties of this system. On the other hand, there is one effect that the shape of the box has on the energy-

level scheme which, although unimportant at this stage, will be found to be quite important when we discuss the more detailed behavior of electrons in more realistic crystals. This effect is the dependence of the degeneracy of the energy levels on the shape of the box; it will be described here for two reasons: (1) to give a more complete analysis of the properties of energy levels in the box and (2) to serve as an introduction to the more detailed description of degenerate energy bands in three-dimensional crystals (given in Chap. 8).

Instead of confining the electrons to a cubic box, let us first assume that the box is orthorhombic ($L_x \neq L_y \neq L_z$). In this case, the wave vector is given by

$$\boldsymbol{\kappa} = \begin{pmatrix} \kappa_x \\ \kappa_y \\ \kappa_z \end{pmatrix} = \begin{pmatrix} \dfrac{n_x}{L_x} \\ \dfrac{n_y}{L_y} \\ \dfrac{n_z}{L_z} \end{pmatrix} \pi \qquad (6.20')$$

and the energy eigenvalues are

$$E(\boldsymbol{\kappa}) = \frac{\hbar^2\kappa^2}{2m} = \frac{\hbar^2\pi^2}{2m}\left[\left(\frac{n_x}{L_x}\right)^2 + \left(\frac{n_y}{L_y}\right)^2 + \left(\frac{n_z}{L_z}\right)^2\right] \qquad (n_x,n_y,n_z) > 0 \qquad (6.22')$$

Comparing the energy expressions for the cubic box [Eq. (6.22)] with that for the orthorhombic box [Eq. (6.22′)], we see that there are, in general, many more different eigenfunctions [different sets (n_x,n_y,n_z)] which correspond to the same energy eigenvalue in the cubic case than there are in the orthorhombic case. For example, in the orthorhombic crystal, $E(2,1,1) \neq E(1,2,1) \neq E(1,1,2)$. As the symmetry of the box is increased to the tetragonal shape by making two sides equal in length ($L_x = L_y \neq L_z$), some degeneracy appears, since in this case

$$E(2,1,1) = E(1,2,1) \neq E(1,1,2)$$

Finally, when the symmetry is further increased to the cubic case, in which all sides of the box are equal in length, there is complete degeneracy:

$$E(2,1,1) = E(1,2,1) = E(1,1,2)$$

These results are a consequence of a general feature of quantum-mechanical systems that *the degree of degeneracy depends directly on the degree of symmetry of the system.* In the case described above, three nondegenerate energy levels of the orthorhombic system collapse into one nondegenerate and one 2-fold degenerate level in the tetragonal box which in turn collapse into one 3-fold degenerate level in the cubic box (see Fig. 6.2). (The degeneracies indicated pertain to each spin direction separately; thus the total degeneracy is actually double the degeneracy indicated above.) These results are illustrated in Fig. 6.2.

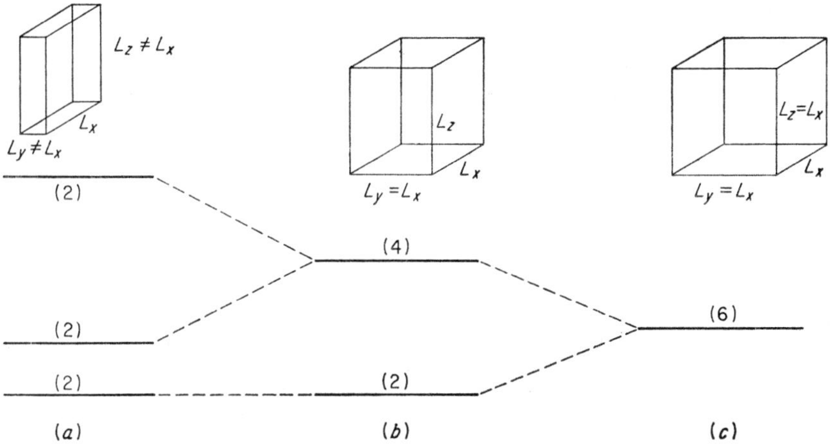

Fig. 6.2. Electronic energy levels for the state with $n = \sqrt{6}$ of an electron gas in a box with (*a*) orthorhombic symmetry ($L_x \neq L_y \neq L_z$), (*b*) tetragonal symmetry ($L_x = L_y \neq L_z$), and (*c*) cubic symmetry ($L_x = L_y = L_z$). The spacings between the energy levels were arbitrarily chosen.

6.3 Application of Fermi-Dirac statistics

The classical Boltzmann distribution function (derived in Appendix B) is based on four assumptions.

1. The total number of particles in the system is constant.
2. The particles have a constant total energy.
3. The particles are distinguishable (i.e., the precise coordinates and momentum of each particle are specified at any given time).
4. Any number of particles may be located in the same cell of phase space at any given time.

The first assumption will always hold for electrons, and the second assumption is merely a statement of the conservation of energy. A quantum-mechanical system made up of fermions, however, will not obey assumption 4. The fourth assumption is contrary to the statement of the Pauli exclusion principle. Let us now consider the third assumption.

According to elementary quantum mechanics, the motion of a particle must be described in terms of an accompanying probability wave with a characteristic De Broglie wavelength $\lambda = h/p$. A given particle cannot be identified unless one complete wavelength can be associated with that particle. Consider the case in which an electron gas is so dense that the average spacing between any two electrons is less than the De Broglie wavelength of one of the particles. In this case, we cannot distinguish which electron should be associated with the observed wave. So long as the electrons themselves are considered to be uncoupled, the wave function Ψ for the electron gas may be represented by the product of individual-particle wave functions

$$\Psi(\mathbf{r}_1,\mathbf{r}_2, \ldots ,\mathbf{r}_N) = \prod_{i=1}^{N} \psi(\mathbf{r}_i) \tag{6.27}$$

If we cannot associate with a particular spatial distribution of electrons a wave which corresponds to a particular energy eigenvalue, then the exchange of any two particle coordinates in the wave function Ψ will result in a wave function which corresponds to the same energy eigenvalue. Thus there are a great many degenerate wave functions Ψ which belong to the same energy eigenvalue.[1] For this reason, such a gas which is characterized by the wave function Ψ is referred to as a *degenerate gas*. If r_0 is the radius of a sphere in the electron gas which is of such a size that, on an average, only one electron is found within it at any given time, and if n is the number of electrons per cubic centimeter, then the average spacing between electrons in the gas is of the order

$$r_0 = \left(\frac{3}{4\pi n}\right)^{1/3} \tag{6.28}$$

The criterion for the gas to be considered degenerate is the inequality

$$r_0 \ll \lambda \tag{6.29}$$

In metals, a typical value for the charge-carrier concentration is $n \sim 10^{22}$ cm^{-3}, giving $r_0 \sim 10^{-8}$ cm, while the De Broglie wavelength for charge carriers is of the order 10^{-7} cm. Thus the criterion for describing an electron gas as degenerate is valid in the case of metals. As we consider materials with decreasing charge-carrier concentrations, the average spacing between electrons becomes greater than the De Broglie wavelength, and in the case of semiconductors, where $n \sim 10^{17}$ cm^{-3}, it becomes adequate to treat the electron gas as nondegenerate.

It is shown in Appendix B that the relaxation of assumptions 3 and 4 results in the Fermi-Dirac distribution function of the form

$$f^{F\text{-}D}(\epsilon) = [e^{(\epsilon-\epsilon_F)/kT} + 1]^{-1}g(\epsilon) \tag{6.30}$$

[1] This was discussed in the preceding chapter in connection with the Heisenberg theory of ferromagnetism.

where ϵ_F is a coefficient which is characteristic of the properties of the electron gas; it is the Fermi energy. [We shall henceforth drop the superscript $(F\text{-}D)$.]

According to its definition, this distribution function represents the number of electrons which are to be found in the energy range between ϵ and $\epsilon + d\epsilon$, and the mean value of any physical property of the system is obtained by weighting it with $f(\epsilon)$, integrating over all energy states in the continuum, and summing over all discrete energy states. Thus, for the electron gas,

$$\langle Q \rangle = \int_{\text{continuum}} Q(\epsilon)f(\epsilon)\,d\epsilon + \sum_n Q(\epsilon_n)f(\epsilon_n) \tag{6.31}$$

The function $g(\epsilon)$ is

$$g(\epsilon) = 2\rho(\epsilon) \tag{6.32}$$

where $\rho(\epsilon)$ is the density of states in the (continuum) electron gas, and the inherent-degeneracy factor 2 accounts for the two possible spin states of the electron.

The Density of States of an Electron Gas

In calculating the density of states of an electron gas, we must confine ourselves to the points $\boldsymbol{\kappa}$ which are contained within the surface

$$\kappa_x^2 + \kappa_y^2 + \kappa_z^2 - \frac{2m\epsilon}{\hbar^2} = 0 \tag{6.33}$$

In the preceding section we found that, when electrons were confined by the rigid walls of a box, the solution of the wave equation gave rise to standing waves [Eq. (6.19)] and that the allowed values of the wave vector $\boldsymbol{\kappa}$ were expressible in terms of a set of three nonzero integers (n_x,n_y,n_z) [Eq. (6.20)].

We now wish to determine the number of allowed energy levels in terms of the number of different sets of integers (n_x,n_y,n_z) which give rise to *independent* solutions of the wave equation. First, the reversal of the signs of any of the three integers does not transform the eigensolution [Eq. (6.19)] into another independent solution. Thus, we need consider only that portion of the volume of a sphere in $\mathbf{n}$ space with $(n_x,n_y,n_z) > 0$ and which is bounded by the surface

$$n_x^2 + n_y^2 + n_z^2 - \frac{2m}{\hbar^2}\frac{L^2}{\pi^2}\epsilon = 0 \tag{6.34}$$

[We have tacitly assumed that the energy levels could be approximated by a continuum. This assumption has been shown to be valid [Eqs. (6.23) and (6.24)] if the box is large enough (i.e., if the box is of the order of macroscopic dimensions).]

Thus, the number of states may be taken to be simply the volume of the first octant of the sphere in **n** space which is bounded by according to the surface (6.34). If we denote the total number of states at the energy ϵ by $\nu(\epsilon)$, then, using Eq. (6.34),

$$\nu(\epsilon) = \frac{1}{8}\frac{4\pi}{3}n^3 = \frac{\pi}{6}\left(\frac{2m}{\hbar^2}\frac{L^2}{\pi^2}\epsilon\right)^{3/2}$$

$$= \frac{1}{6\pi^2}\left(\frac{2m}{\hbar^2}\right)^{3/2} V\epsilon^{3/2} \tag{6.35}$$

and

$$\rho(\epsilon) \equiv \frac{d\nu(\epsilon)}{d\epsilon} = \frac{1}{4\pi^2}\left(\frac{2m}{\hbar^2}\right)^{3/2} V\epsilon^{1/2} \tag{6.36}$$

Thus, according to Eqs. (6.32) and (6.36), the total density of states per unit volume is

$$g(\epsilon) = \frac{1}{2\pi^2}\left(\frac{2m}{\hbar^2}\right)^{3/2} \epsilon^{1/2} \tag{6.37}$$

and the average value of any physical property $Q(\epsilon)$ of the electron gas (per unit volume) is

$$<Q> = \frac{1}{2\pi^2}\left(\frac{2m}{\hbar^2}\right)^{3/2} \int_0^\infty \frac{Q(\epsilon)\epsilon^{1/2}\,d\epsilon}{e^{(\epsilon-\epsilon_F)/kT}+1} \tag{6.38}$$

The more realistic models which describe the behavior of electrons in a crystal reveal an inconsistency between the equations of motion of an electron in a crystal lattice and the behavior as described by the present free-electron model. It will be shown in the next chapter that the inertial mass with which an electron resists a change of its state by an externally applied field is not strictly a constant, independent of its velocity. The energy of charge carriers that are near energy-band extrema may not be generally expressed by the simple parabolic relation between $\epsilon(\boldsymbol{\kappa})$ and $\boldsymbol{\kappa}$ as given in Eq. (6.22); rather, the energy $\epsilon(\boldsymbol{\kappa})$ is expressed more accurately in terms of a power series expansion in κ which depends on the particular point in $\boldsymbol{\kappa}$ space in which the electron is found; it also depends on the symmetry of the crystal lattice. The deviation of the energy-momentum relation from the free-electron case will in turn cause a corresponding change in the expression for the density of states (6.37). These points will be covered in more detail in the discussion of the properties of Brillouin zones in the following chapters.

Problem

Using the expression for electrical conductivity

$$\sigma = \frac{ne^2\tau}{m}$$

and assuming that the relaxation time has the momentum-dependent form

$$\tau = \tau_0 + \tau_2 p^2 + \tau_4 p^4$$

calculate the mean value of σ for a degenerate Fermi-Dirac gas at $T = 0°K$.

Free-electron Concentration

Our primary objective now is to determine the behavior of the Fermi energy ϵ_F and, consequently, the Fermi-Dirac distribution function as a function of the known properties of the electron gas, such as the charge-carrier concentration n and the temperature T.

The concentration of free electrons is, according to Eq. (6.30), given by the following equation:

$$n = \frac{1}{2\pi^2}\left(\frac{2m}{\hbar^2}\right)^{3/2}\int_0^\infty \frac{\epsilon^{1/2}\,d\epsilon}{e^{(\epsilon-\epsilon_F)/kT}+1} \tag{6.39}$$

Let us investigate the two limiting cases of a nondegenerate and a degenerate gas.

(*i*) ***Nondegenerate case*** If n is sufficiently small and T sufficiently high, the distribution function must approach the form of the classical Boltzmann function. In this case, we calculate ϵ_F from the equation

$$n = \frac{1}{2\pi^2}\left(\frac{2m}{\hbar^2}\right)^{3/2}\int_0^\infty \epsilon^{1/2}e^{-(\epsilon-\epsilon_F)/kT}\,d\epsilon = 2\left(\frac{mkT}{2\pi\hbar^2}\right)^{3/2} e^{\epsilon_F/kT} \tag{6.40}$$

giving

$$e^{-\epsilon_F/kt} = \frac{2}{n}\left(\frac{mkT}{2\pi\hbar^2}\right)^{3/2} \tag{6.41}$$

If T is large and n is small, the right-hand side of Eq. (6.41) is large compared with unity, and consequently the coefficient ϵ_F, which appears in the exponential of the left-hand side of this equation, must be a negative quantity. Choosing ϵ_F to be a negative quantity, the following relation is obtained from Eq. (6.41):

$$\epsilon_F = kT \ln \frac{2(2\pi mkT)^{3/2}}{nh^3} \tag{6.42}$$

These relations between charge-carrier concentration and the temperature in a nondegenerate electron gas will be discussed further in Chap. 9 where the properties of semiconductors will be explored.

(*ii*) ***Degenerate case*** If the charge-carrier concentration is sufficiently large ($\sim 10^{22}$ electrons/cm^3), the inequality (6.29) will be valid and, according to Eq. (6.39), the ratio ϵ_F/kT will be large compared with unity and ϵ_F must be a positive quantity. Let us first consider the properties of the Fermi-Dirac distribution function in the limit where $T = 0$°K. For a positive Fermi energy, the distribution function has the following values in the limit of zero-degree temperature:

$$\lim_{T\to 0}\frac{f(\epsilon)}{g(\epsilon)} = \lim_{T\to 0}\,[e^{(\epsilon-\epsilon_F)/kT}+1]^{-1} = \begin{cases} 1 & \epsilon < \epsilon_F \\ 0 & \epsilon > \epsilon_F \\ \frac{1}{2} & \epsilon = \epsilon_F \end{cases} \tag{6.43}$$

Thus, at $T = 0$°K the distribution function is the discontinuous step function defined by Eq. (6.43). The vanishing of $f(\epsilon)$ for energies greater than the Fermi energy means that no electrons within the degenerate gas are permitted to have energies greater than ϵ_F at $T = 0°K$. This situation is represented schematically by a Fermi sea with a depth ϵ_F (Fig. 6.3*b*). As the temperature is increased from 0°K, the discontinuity at $\epsilon = \epsilon_F$ vanishes, and the distribution function becomes rounded off near ϵ_F with a slope which is of the order $(kT)^{-1}$ (see Fig. 6.3*a*).

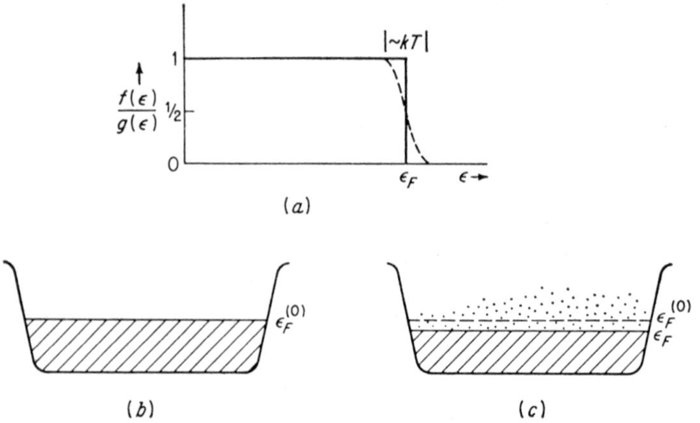

Fig. 6.3. (*a*) The Fermi-Dirac distribution function. (*b*) The Fermi sea at $T = 0°K$. (*c*) The Fermi sea at $T > 0°K$.

The charge-carrier concentration for a degenerate electron gas at 0°K ($n^{(0)}$), obtained from Eqs. (6.39) and (6.43), is given by the following equation:

$$n^{(0)} = \frac{1}{2\pi^2}\left(\frac{2m}{\hbar^2}\right)^{3/2} \int_0^{\epsilon_F^{(0)}} \epsilon^{1/2}\, d\epsilon = \frac{1}{3\pi^2}\left(\frac{2m}{\hbar^2}\right)^{3/2} (\epsilon_F^{(0)})^{3/2} \tag{6.44}$$

where the superscript (0) refers to the fact that the value of the Fermi energy is defined at $T = 0°K$. Thus, from (6.44),

$$\epsilon_F^{(0)} = \frac{\hbar^2}{2m}(3\pi^2 n^{(0)})^{2/3} = \frac{\hbar^2 \kappa_F^2}{2m} = \frac{1}{2} m v_F^2 = kT_F \tag{6.45}$$

where $|\boldsymbol{\kappa}_F| = (3\pi^2 n^{(0)})^{1/3}$ is the Fermi wave vector for the degenerate electron gas at $T = 0°K$. Equation (6.45) also defines the so-called Fermi temperature T_F and the Fermi velocity v_F.

Number of Electrons per Energy Interval at $T = 0°K$

The number of electrons per energy interval has the same functional form as the density of states at $T = 0°K$, since $f(\epsilon < \epsilon_F) = g$. Thus

$$\rho = \frac{dn}{d\epsilon} = \frac{1}{2\pi^2}\left(\frac{2m}{\hbar^2}\right)^{3/2} \epsilon^{1/2} \qquad \epsilon < \epsilon_F$$
$$= 0 \qquad \epsilon > \epsilon_F \tag{6.46}$$

This function rounds off at the discontinuity (in the same fashion as does the distribution function) as the temperature is increased from $T = 0°K$ (see Fig. 6.4). The area enclosed in this curve represents the total number of charge carriers in the gas.

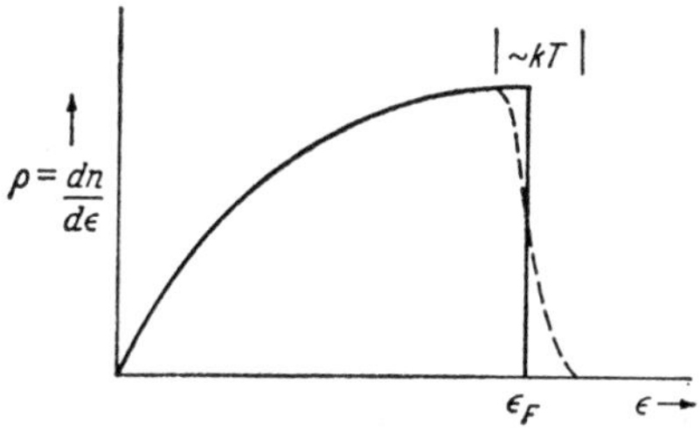

Fig. 6.4. The number of electrons in a metal per energy state and the density of states of the free-electron gas.

Mean Kinetic Energy of the Fermi Gas at $T = 0°K$

The mean kinetic energy of the Fermi gas is obtained by weighting the electron energy with the number of electrons per energy interval $f(\epsilon)$ and integrating over all energies. Thus,

$$<\epsilon^{(0)}> = \int_0^{\epsilon_F{}^{(0)}} \epsilon g(\epsilon)\, d\epsilon = \frac{1}{2\pi^2}\left(\frac{2m}{\hbar^2}\right)^{3/2} \int_0^{\epsilon_F{}^{(0)}} \epsilon^{3/2}\, d\epsilon$$

or

$$<\epsilon^{(0)}> = \frac{1}{5\pi^2}\left(\frac{2m}{\hbar^2}\right)^{3/2} (\epsilon_F{}^{(0)})^{5/2} = \frac{3}{5}\, n\epsilon_F^{(0)} \tag{6.47}$$

This result will be used later in connection with our calculation of the specific heat of a degenerate electron gas.

The Properties of a Degenerate Fermi Gas at $T > 0°K$

We have been careful to label the quantities calculated in the preceding discussion with a superscript (0) in order to emphasize that these quantities are defined at $T = 0°K$. As the temperature increases from 0°K, these quantities become temperature-dependent in a fashion indicated in Figs. 6.3 and 6.4. As has previously been pointed out, the departure of n and f from their values at 0°K is small for normal temperatures and is completely negligible at energies far removed from the Fermi energy ϵ_F. This result is due to the inability of thermal fluctuations to excite electrons from the deeper states to unoccupied states. Now we shall derive an expression for the average value of any function $Q(\epsilon)$ (referring to a property of the electron gas), defined in terms of the Fermi distribution function $f(\epsilon)$ according to the equation

$$<Q(\epsilon)> = \int_0^\infty \varphi(\epsilon)\bar{f}(\epsilon)\,d\epsilon \tag{6.48}$$

with

$$\varphi(\epsilon) = Q(\epsilon)g(\epsilon)$$

$$\bar{f}(\epsilon) = \frac{f(\epsilon)}{g(\epsilon)} = [e^{(\epsilon-\epsilon_F)/kT} + 1]^{-1}$$

and subject to the condition that $\epsilon_F \gg kT$.

The Fermi energy $\epsilon_F^{(0)}$ is of the order of magnitude of 1 ev for the typical electron concentrations in metals of 10^{22} cm^{-3}. The temperature which corresponds to 1 ev is of the order of 12,000°K!

On the other hand, room temperature is of the order of 0.025 ev, which is only 2.5 per cent of $\epsilon_F^{(0)}$. Thus, the energy range in which the electron concentration rounds off is very narrow indeed at normal temperatures and does not appreciably alter the distribution function until it reaches the depth of the Fermi sea (which occurs when the temperature is raised to the order of 10^4°K). The Fermi sea at room temperature may be represented schematically by a small concentration of the constituent electrons of the gas seen at any given time at some small height above the surface of the Fermi sea (see Fig. 6.3*c*). This is in analogy with the vapor observed above the surface of a liquid at a finite temperature T.

The electron concentration n is defined at an arbitrary temperature in terms of the Fermi energy by the integral relation given by Eq. (6.39). It has been pointed out in the preceding paragraph that, in metals, $kT \ll \epsilon_F$ at ordinary temperatures. In this case, then, $n(T)$ may be approximated at ordinary temperatures by expanding the distribution function as a power series in kT/ϵ_F.

Consider the integral

$$I = \int_0^\infty \bar{f}(\epsilon)\,\frac{dG(\epsilon)}{d\epsilon}\,d\epsilon \tag{6.49}$$

where $G(\epsilon) = \int_0^\epsilon \varphi(\epsilon')\,d\epsilon'$ is an arbitrary function which satisfies the boundary condition

$$G(0) = 0 \tag{6.50}$$

Integrating by parts, the integral (6.49) becomes

$$I = \bar{f}(\epsilon)G(\epsilon)\Big|_0^\infty - \int_0^\infty G(\epsilon)\,\frac{d\bar{f}}{d\epsilon}\,d\epsilon \tag{6.51}$$

If the arbitrary function $G(\epsilon)$ is restricted to the class of functions that may not approach infinity more rapidly than $\bar{f}(\epsilon)$ approaches zero as ϵ approaches infinity, the first term on the right-hand side of Eq. (6.51), evaluated at the upper limit, will vanish. The lower limit in the first term will also vanish in view of (6.50). Thus, the integral takes the form

$$I = -\int_0^\infty G(\epsilon)\,\frac{d\bar{f}}{d\epsilon}\,d\epsilon \tag{6.52}$$

Making the transformation

$$x = \frac{\epsilon - \epsilon_F}{kT} \tag{6.53}$$

taking the derivative

$$\frac{d\bar{f}}{d\epsilon} = -\frac{1}{kT}\frac{e^x}{(e^x+1)^2} \tag{6.54}$$

and expressing G as a Taylor expansion about $x = 0$, we have

$$G(x) = \sum_{s=0}^{\infty} \frac{x^s}{s!}\left(\frac{d^sG(x)}{dx^s}\right)_{x=0} \tag{6.55}$$

The integral I then takes the form of an infinite sum of integrals

$$I = \sum_{s=0}^{\infty} I_s \tag{6.56}$$

where

$$I_s = \frac{1}{s!}\left(\frac{d^sG(x)}{dx^s}\right)_{x=0}\int_{-a}^{\infty}\frac{x^se^x\,dx}{(e^x+1)^2} \tag{6.57}$$

and where

$$a = \frac{\epsilon_F}{kT} \tag{6.58}$$

It has been pointed out previously that, for typical electron concentrations in metals, the ratio $a = \epsilon_F/kT$ is of the order of magnitude of 10^2 at room temperature ($\sim$300°K). Because of the large value for a, the lower limit on the integral given in Eq. (6.57) may be replaced by $-\infty$ without appreciably altering the magnitude of the integral. The quantitative expression for the error which is introduced when this assumption is made is shown below.[1]

[1] It can be shown that the fractional error introduced in replacing $-a$ by $-\infty$ in I_s [Eq. (6.57)] (i.e., the integral evaluated between 0 and a divided by I_s) is

$$\Delta_{2s} < 2\,\frac{s+1}{(2s+1)!}\,a^{2s+1}e^{-a} \qquad a > s$$

and

$$\Delta_{2s} < (s+1)e^{-a} \qquad a < s$$

Thus, for $a \sim 100$, the inequalities indicate that $\Delta_{2s} \ll 1$ and may be neglected to a very high degree of precision for all terms up to $s \sim 125$. On the other hand, the rapid convergence of the Taylor expansion of $G(x)$ about $x = 0$ for most practical problems indicates that the series [Eq. (6.59)] may be terminated at $s = 4$ without losing too much accuracy. According to the first inequality indicated above, for $a = 100$, the error introduced at $s = 4$ (the largest error in the series) is

$$\Delta_8 \simeq 10^{-29}$$

The integral in Eq. (6.57) (with the lower limit $-a$ replaced by $-\infty$) may now be readily evaluated. The integrand is observed to be an odd function for odd integral values of s and an even function for even integral values of s. Thus the integral evaluated between $-\infty$ and ∞ will vanish for odd s and will have the following form for even s:

$$\int_{-\infty}^{\infty} \frac{e^x x^s\,dx}{(e^x+1)^2} = 2\int_0^{\infty} \frac{e^x x^s\,dx}{(e^x+1)^2}$$

$$= 2\sum_{n=1}^{\infty} (-1)^{n+1}\, n \int_0^{\infty} x^s e^{-nx}\,dx = 2(s!)\sum_{n=1}^{\infty} \frac{(-1)^{n+1}}{n^s} \tag{6.59}$$

The final summation which appears in Eq. (6.59) may be expressed in terms of the Riemann zeta function[1] $\zeta(s)$ as follows:

$$\sum_{n=1}^{\infty} \frac{(-1)^{n+1}}{n^s} = (1 - 2^{(1-\zeta)})\zeta(s) \tag{6.60}$$

Combining Eqs. (6.59), (6.60), and (6.57) and the assumption that the error in replacing $-a$ by $-\infty$ is small,[2] we have

$$I_s \simeq \begin{cases} 2\left(\dfrac{d^sG(x)}{dx^s}\right)_{x=0} (1 - 2^{(1-\zeta)})\zeta(s) & s \text{ even} \quad (6.61) \\ 0 & s \text{ odd} \quad (6.62) \end{cases}$$

The values of some of the Riemann ζ functions are given in Table 6.2.

TABLE 6.2* *Riemann Zeta Functions for Even s*

s	0	2	4	6	8
$\zeta(s)$	$-\frac{1}{2}$	$\pi^2/6$	$\pi^4/90$	$\pi^6/945$	$\pi^8/9450$

* E. T. Whittaker and G. N. Watson, "A Course of Modern Analysis," chap. 12, Cambridge University Press, New York, 1952; Janke and Emde, "Tables of Functions," p. 269, Dover Publications, Inc., New York.

Several of the macroscopic properties of a degenerate electron gas which has a characteristic parameter

$$a = \frac{\epsilon_F}{kT} \geq 3$$

may be determined quite accurately from our expression (6.61) by choosing the appropriate form for the function $G(x)$.

[1] E. T. Whittaker and G. N. Watson, "A Course of Modern Analysis," chap. 12, Cambridge University Press, New York, 1952.

[2] See footnote 1 on preceding page.

Electron concentration Choosing the function $G(x)$ to have the form

$$G(x) = \frac{1}{3\pi^2}\left(\frac{2m}{\hbar^2}\right)^{3/2} (kTx + \epsilon_F)^{3/2} \tag{6.63}$$

the electron concentration may be written in terms of the power series in kT/ϵ_F according to Eqs. (6.56), (6.57), (6.59), and Table 6.2, giving

$$n = \sum_{t=0}^{\infty} n_{2t} = n^{(0)}\left[1 + \frac{\pi^2}{8}\left(\frac{kT}{\epsilon_F}\right)^2 + \frac{7\pi^4}{640}\left(\frac{kT}{\epsilon_F}\right)^4 + \cdots\right] \tag{6.64}$$

with

$$n^{(0)} = G(x = 0) = \frac{1}{3\pi^2}\left(\frac{2m}{\hbar^2}\right)^{3/2} \epsilon_F^{3/2} \tag{6.65}$$

The general expression for ϵ_F is obtained from the polynomial equation (6.64). At low temperatures, $(kT/\epsilon_F) \ll 1$, and we may cut off this series after the second term without losing a great deal of accuracy. Combining the resulting truncated series with Eq. (6.65) and assuming that

$$\left(\frac{kT}{\epsilon_F}\right)^2 \sim \left(\frac{kT}{\epsilon_F^{(0)}}\right)^2 \ll 1 \tag{6.66}$$

the Fermi energy is evaluated to have the form

$$\epsilon_F \simeq \epsilon_F^{(0)}\left[1 - \frac{\pi^2}{12}\left(\frac{kT}{\epsilon_F^{(0)}}\right)^2\right] \tag{6.67}$$

with $\epsilon_F^{(0)}$ defined by Eq. (6.45).

The specific heat of an electron gas It was indicated earlier in the chapter that Drude's classical free-electron model of metals predicted that the specific heat of a metal

$$C_v = \tfrac{3}{2}nk$$

is far greater than the observed value. It was then pointed out that the quantum-mechanical model predicts, in agreement with experiment, a much smaller value for the specific heat and also a temperature dependence at low temperatures which behaves in the proper way. We are now in a position to evaluate the specific heat at low temperatures with the aid of the general integral (6.49) in terms of the representation of I given in Eqs. (6.56) and (6.57).

The internal energy of a free-electron gas is the mean kinetic energy of the gas

$$<\epsilon> = \int_0^{\infty} \epsilon \bar{f}(\epsilon) g(\epsilon)\, d\epsilon \tag{6.68}$$

The specific heat of the electron gas is the rate of change of the internal energy $<\epsilon>$ of the electrons with the temperature,

$$C_v = \frac{d<\epsilon>}{dT} \tag{6.69}$$

Thus we may evaluate C_v from the internal energy $<\epsilon(T)>$. The internal energy $<\epsilon^{(0)}>$ was calculated in a previous subsection and is given by Eq. (6.47). We are now able to evaluate $<\epsilon>$ at arbitrary temperatures which are small compared with ϵ_F/k by choosing the function $G(x)$ to have the form

$$G(x) = \frac{1}{5\pi^2}\left(\frac{2m}{\hbar^2}\right)^{3/2}(kTx + \epsilon_F)^{5/2} \tag{6.70}$$

Substituting this form of $G(x)$ into the general equation (6.56), assuming that the series may be cut off after the first two terms without losing a great deal of accuracy, and assuming the inequality (6.66), we obtain

$$<\epsilon> = \frac{1}{5\pi^2}\left(\frac{2m}{\hbar^2}\right)^{3/2}\epsilon_F^{5/2}\left[1 + \frac{5\pi^2}{8}\left(\frac{kT}{\epsilon_F^{(0)}}\right)^2\right] \tag{6.71}$$

If we now substitute the following expansion for $\epsilon_F^{5/2}$ [from Eq. (6.67)]

$$\epsilon_F^{5/2} = (\epsilon_F^{(0)})^{5/2}\left[1 - \frac{5}{24}\pi^2\left(\frac{kT}{\epsilon_F^{(0)}}\right)^2\right] \tag{6.72}$$

and Eq. (6.47) into Eq. (6.71), the following result is obtained:

$$<\epsilon> = <\epsilon^{(0)}>\left[1 + \frac{5}{12}\pi^2\left(\frac{kT}{\epsilon_F^{(0)}}\right)^2\right] \tag{6.73}$$

The specific heat is then, using Eq. (6.47),

$$C_v = \frac{d<\epsilon>}{dT} = \frac{5\pi^2}{6}\frac{k^2<\epsilon^{(0)}>}{(\epsilon_F^{(0)})^2}T = \frac{\pi^2}{2}nk\left(\frac{T}{T_F}\right) \tag{6.74}$$

It is observed that the specific heat is now given by the product of a term approximately equal to the classical value $\frac{3}{2}nk$ and the ratio T/T_F (which is very small for a degenerate electron gas) and is calculated to be of the order 10^{-4} for most metals.[1] The ratio T/T_F may be interpreted as proportional to that small fraction of electrons near the surface of the Fermi sea which are allowed to absorb thermal energy and thereby contribute to the specific heat of the metal. The observed values of C_v are often larger than this by approximately a factor of 10. This discrepancy may be attributed to the error in our assumptions of describing a metal in terms of a free-electron gas. When the interactions between the electrons and the lattice ions and between the electrons themselves are taken into account and also when one considers the capacity of the lattice vibrations to absorb thermal energy, this discrepancy in the

[1] For a tabulation of actual experimental values of T/T_F for metals, see C. Kittel, "Introduction to Solid State Physics," p. 259, John Wiley & Sons, Inc., New York, 1953.

prediction of the specific heat as derived from the free-electron model is diminished.[1]

The spin paramagnetism of an electron gas The paramagnetic susceptibility of a crystal which is made up of magnetic moments may be derived by means of classical statistics to have the form (see Chap. 5)

$$\chi = \frac{1}{3}\frac{n\mu_0^2}{kT} \tag{6.75}$$

where n is the number of magnetic moments per unit volume and μ_0 is the magnetic moment associated with one lattice site. Since we know that an isolated electron has an intrinsic spin associated with it, it follows from the classical free-electron model that the free-electron gas should have a paramagnetic susceptibility of the form given by Eq. (6.75), with μ_0 representing the free-electron magnetic moment and n representing the electron concentration.

The validity of the classical paramagnetic-susceptibility expression applied to a free-electron gas is equivalent to the statement that an application of a constant magnetic field $\mathbf{H}$ to a free-electron gas would have the effect of lining up the magnetic moments of the fraction $e^{\boldsymbol{\mu}_0\cdot\mathbf{H}/kT}Z^{-1}$ of the electrons with the field, and the fraction $e^{-\boldsymbol{\mu}_0\cdot\mathbf{H}/kT}Z^{-1}$ of the electrons against the field where the partition function is

$$Z = e^{\boldsymbol{\mu}_0\cdot\mathbf{H}/kT} + e^{-\boldsymbol{\mu}_0\cdot\mathbf{H}/kT}$$

This statement implies that any of the electrons, irrespective of its kinetic energy, may absorb the sufficient amount of magnetic energy to allow an alignment of its spin into a favored position. This result is contrary to the predictions of the quantum-mechanical free-electron model in which the Pauli exclusion principle would forbid the absorption of energy by an electron in the gas other than the few electrons that are near the surface of the Fermi sea. All other electrons have their spins paired off (i.e., for each electron in a given kinetic-energy state with a spin up, there is another electron, in the same kinetic-energy state, with its spin down); thus all other electrons in the Fermi sea contribute nothing to the magnetic moment of the gas. We should then expect the magnitude of the paramagnetic susceptibility, according to the quantum-mechanical model, to be approximately T/T_F times smaller than the classical expression near $T = 0°\text{K}$.[2] The susceptibility should have the temperature-independent form at 0°K.

$$\chi^{(0)} = \frac{n\mu_0^2}{kT_F} \tag{6.76}$$

[1] See, for example, Ziman, *op. cit.*

[2] This was first shown by W. Pauli, *Z. Physik*, **41:** 81 (1927).

This result is substantiated by experimental observations, where a temperature-independent paramagnetic susceptibility of the order 10^{-6} is measured. This is in contrast to the classical (theoretical) result which predicts a susceptibility of the order 10^{-4} at room temperature, and a variation with temperature as T^{-1}.

The calculation of χ at arbitrary temperatures (with $T \ll \epsilon_F/k$) is straightforward and parallels the calculations of the electron concentration and the specific heat carried out in the previous two sections. The net magnetization of a free-electron gas which is subject to a constant applied magnetic field $\mathbf{H}$ is

$$\mathbf{M} = \boldsymbol{\mu}_0(n_{\parallel} - n_{\nparallel}) \tag{6.77}$$

and the paramagnetic susceptibility is

$$\chi_i = \frac{\partial M_i}{\partial H_i} \tag{6.78}$$

where $n_{\parallel}$ is the total number of electrons with their spins parallel to the applied field, and $n_{\nparallel}$ is the total number of electrons with their spins antiparallel to the applied field. Choosing the corresponding G functions as

$$G_{\parallel}(x) = \frac{1}{6\pi^2}\left(\frac{2m}{\hbar^2}\right)^{3/2}(kTx + \mu_0 H + \epsilon_F)^{3/2} \tag{6.79a}$$

$$G_{\nparallel}(x) = \frac{1}{6\pi^2}\left(\frac{2m}{\hbar^2}\right)^{3/2}(kTx - \mu_0 H + \epsilon_F)^{3/2} \tag{6.79b}$$

the application of the general equation (6.56) results in the following expression for the paramagnetic susceptibility of a free-electron gas (for $\mu_0 H \ll kT, \epsilon_F$):

$$\chi = \chi^{(0)}\left[1 + \frac{\pi^2}{6}\left(\frac{kT}{\epsilon_F}\right)^2 + O(H)\right] \tag{6.80}$$

with

$$\chi^{(0)} = \frac{3n\mu_0^2}{2kT_F} \tag{6.81}$$

and where the remainder term $O(H)$ may be obtained by making use of the power series expansion given by Eq. (6.56) and Eqs. (6.77) to (6.79).

Problem

Estimate the magnitude of the remainder term $O(H)$.

In a more exact calculation of the susceptibility the following modifications of the free-electron model must be made:

1. The fact that the electron magnetic moment is different in a metal than outside the metal, because of a different apparent mass of the electron in the crystal, must be taken into account.

2. The fact that the electron-electron interactions and the presence of the magnetic field alter the free-electron wave function, which in turn affects the expectation value of the paramagnetic susceptibility, must be taken into account.

The De Haas-van Alphen effect In the preceding discussion we calculated the paramagnetic susceptibility of a free-electron gas, due to the intrinsic magnetic moment associated with each of the electrons. The question that we now wish to answer pertains to the orbital motion of electrons in a strong magnetic field and the corresponding diamagnetic susceptibility of the system. According to classical electrodynamics, the free-electron gas should exhibit no diamagnetism.[1] However, the quantization of the electron orbits in the magnetic field do indeed give rise to a nonzero diamagnetism.[2] This again represents a striking difference in the predictions of the quantum theory from the classical theory.

The diamagnetic susceptibility is related to the free energy F of the system as follows (Appendix B):

$$\chi \equiv \frac{\partial M}{\partial H} = - \frac{\partial^2 F}{\partial H^2}$$

where[3]

$$F = N\epsilon_F - 2kT \sum_i \ln \left(1 + e^{(\epsilon_F - \epsilon_i)/kT}\right) \tag{6.82}$$

The quantized energy levels ϵ_i depend on the applied magnetic field $\mathbf{H}$. If $\mathbf{H}$ is applied in the z direction, then ϵ_i is an eigenvalue of the wave equation

$$\frac{1}{2m} [p_x^2 + (p_y + m\omega x)^2 + p_z^2]\psi_i = \epsilon_i \psi_i \tag{6.83}$$

and has the values

$$\epsilon_i \equiv \epsilon_{n,k_z} = (n + \tfrac{1}{2})\hbar\omega + \frac{\hbar^2 k^2}{2m} \tag{6.84}$$

In (6.84) the integer n and k_z signify the quantum state,[4] and $\omega = eH/mc$ is the cyclotron frequency. Thus ϵ_i and, in turn, F depend on the applied magnetic field, according to (6.82) and (6.84).

Evaluating the free energy then yields the result that, at sufficiently

[1] The proof of this was first shown by N. Bohr, Dissertation, University of Copenhagen. See N. F. Mott and H. Jones, "The Theory of the Properties of Metals and Alloys," chap. 6, Dover Publications, Inc., New York, 1959.

[2] This was first shown by L. Landau, *Z. Physik*, **64:** 629 (1930).

[3] See A. H. Wilson, "The Theory of Metals," chap. 6, Cambridge University Press, New York, 1954. Also see Appendix B.

[4] See A. H. Kahn and H. P. R. Frederikse, in F. Seitz and D. Turnbull (eds.), "Solid State Physics," vol. 9, Academic Press Inc., New York, 1960.

large **H** and low T, the diamagnetic susceptibility should depend on $1/H$ in a periodic fashion, somewhat like the function $\sin(a + b/H)$. This was discovered experimentally by De Haas and Van Alphen[1] in 1930 and the effect named after these authors.

The main point to be emphasized here is that the De Haas-Van Alphen effect is very sensitive to the details of the electronic motion in the solid, and such high-magnetic-field experiments would therefore provide an efficient probe into the behavior of mobile electrons in (metallic) solids.

The determination of the theoretical expression for the observed effect depends on the detailed evaluation of the partition function and free energy. Such a calculation due to Landau is outlined in Wilson's book.[2] The procedure followed by Landau in evaluating the free energy is to express this function in terms of the classical partition function. The expression for F is thereby determined in terms of an expression in harmonic functions. To represent the motion of the electron in the crystal, the mass m is replaced by the effective mass m^*. The resulting expression for the diamagnetic susceptibility then becomes

$$\chi = \frac{1}{12\pi^2}\frac{e^2}{\hbar c}\left(\frac{2\epsilon_F}{m^*c^2}\right)^{1/2}\left[3\left(\frac{m^*}{m}\right)^2 - 1 - \frac{3kT\pi}{\hbar\omega}\left(\frac{2\epsilon_F}{\hbar\omega}\right)^{1/2}\sum_{r=1}^{\infty}\frac{(-1)^r\cos\dfrac{r\pi m^*}{m}\sin\left(\dfrac{2\pi r\epsilon_F}{\hbar\omega} - \frac{1}{2}\right)}{r^{1/2}\sinh\dfrac{2\pi^2 rkT}{\hbar\omega}}\right] \tag{6.85}$$

where $\omega = eH/m^*c$ is the cyclotron frequency.

The third term in (6.85) represents the oscillating part of χ and clearly vanishes as $\mathbf{H} \to 0$ (as required by experiment). Also, it is seen that (because of the sinh function in the denominator) of this expression the effect is optimized when (1) T becomes small and (2) m^*/m becomes small.

The next question that may arise pertains to the effect of the departure from the free-electron model on the De Haas-Van Alphen effect. That is, the electron-electron interactions would be thought at first hand to alter the expression for the free energy and thereby correspondingly alter the expression for the diamagnetic susceptibility. The very interesting result has been derived by Kohn[3] that the electron-electron interactions have no effect on the expression for the De Haas-Van Alphen effect (to

[1] W. J. de Haas and P. M. van Alphen, *Proc. Acad. Sci. Amsterdam*, **33:** 1106 (1930).

[2] Wilson, *loc. cit.*

[3] W. Kohn, *Phys. Rev.*, **123:** 1242 (1961). This proof is carried out for a two-dimensional gas.

any order perturbation), as was predicted above by the free-electron model.

6.4 The wave-packet description of electron motion in a metal[1]

The behavior of free electrons in a metal has been described thus far in terms of the solution of the Schroedinger wave equation (6.17), with the electron potential defined by Eqs. (6.18). The solution (6.19) is valid only if it is meaningful to assign to an electron a specific value of momentum

$$\mathbf{p} = \frac{\hbar\pi}{L}(\hat{\mathbf{i}}n_x + \hat{\mathbf{j}}n_y + \hat{\mathbf{k}}n_z) \tag{6.86}$$

for any particular mode, labeled by the three integers (n_x,n_y,n_z). The Heisenberg uncertainty principle predicts that it is impossible to specify the exact momentum and the exact location of a particle simultaneously. Further, the product of the uncertainties of both the momentum and the location is subject to the inequality

$$\Delta p_i \, \Delta x_i \geq h \qquad i = 1, 2, 3$$

so that the more accurately the momentum (or location) is known, the less accurately the location (or momentum) is known. The assignment of the exact momentum (6.86) to a constituent electron of the metal then implies that our knowledge of the location of the electron in the metal is completely unknown or that there is an equal probability for the electron to occur at any point within the boundaries of the macroscopic crystal.

It is often convenient to localize a particle in space somewhat more definitely than does the plane-wave description. According to the *uncertainty principle*, any localization of an electron would necessarily entail a sacrifice of our exact knowledge of the electron momentum. Thus we may localize the particle to a greater extent by constructing a wave packet which is made up of monochromatic waves, each with a slightly different momentum and energy but each with approximately the same amplitude. The wider the range of electron momenta which characterize the wave packet, the more exact is our description of the electron location.

In order to illustrate this point, let us start by adding only two plane waves, with slightly different momenta $\hbar\kappa_1$ and $\hbar\kappa_2$ and energies ϵ_1 and ϵ_2 but with the same amplitudes A. Let these waves be labeled φ_1 and φ_2 and let us consider, for simplicity, a one-dimensional crystal. The

[1] For an extensive discussion of the wave-packet description, see D. Bohm, "Quantum Theory," Prentice-Hall, Englewood Cliffs, N.J., 1951.

wave which is made up of the addition of these two waves has the form

$$\begin{aligned}\varphi = \varphi_1 + \varphi_2 &= A[e^{i(\kappa_1 z - \epsilon_1 t/\hbar)} + e^{i(\kappa_2 z - \epsilon_2 t/\hbar)}] \\ &= A\left\{\left[\cos\left(\kappa_1 z - \frac{\epsilon_1 t}{\hbar}\right) + \cos\left(\kappa_2 z - \frac{\epsilon_2 t}{\hbar}\right)\right]\right. \\ &\qquad \left. + i\left[\sin\left(\kappa_1 z - \frac{\epsilon_1 t}{\hbar}\right) + \sin\left(\kappa_2 z - \frac{\epsilon_2 t}{\hbar}\right)\right]\right\} \end{aligned} \tag{6.87}$$

Using the trigonometric identities

$$\begin{aligned}\sin\alpha + \sin\beta &= 2\sin\tfrac{1}{2}(\alpha+\beta)\cos\tfrac{1}{2}(\alpha-\beta) \\ \cos\alpha + \cos\beta &= 2\cos\tfrac{1}{2}(\alpha+\beta)\cos\tfrac{1}{2}(\alpha-\beta)\end{aligned}$$

and assuming that

$$\begin{aligned}\kappa_1 + \kappa_2 &= 2\kappa \qquad & \kappa_1 - \kappa_2 &= \delta\kappa \\ \epsilon_1 + \epsilon_2 &= 2\epsilon \qquad & \epsilon_2 - \epsilon_2 &= \delta\epsilon\end{aligned} \tag{6.88}$$

the wave function takes the form

$$\varphi = 2A\cos\tfrac{1}{2}\left(\delta\kappa z - \frac{t}{\hbar}\,\delta\epsilon\right)e^{i(\kappa z - \epsilon t/\hbar)} \tag{6.89}$$

Thus the resulting wave function describes a traveling wave $e^{i(\kappa z - \epsilon t/\hbar)}$ which is modulated by the varying amplitude $2A\cos\frac{1}{2}[\delta\kappa z - (t/\hbar)\,\delta\epsilon]$. The velocity associated with this packet of two waves is called the group velocity. Since the wave function φ has the same amplitude at points where the argument $[\delta\kappa z - (t/\hbar)\,\delta\epsilon]$ is constant, the velocity of the maximum amplitude of the wave is obtained by setting this argument equal to zero.

$$\delta\kappa z = \frac{t}{\hbar}\,\delta\epsilon \tag{6.90}$$

and the group velocity takes the form

$$v_z = \frac{z}{t} = \frac{1}{\hbar}\frac{\partial\epsilon}{\partial\kappa_z} \tag{6.91}$$

The group velocity of the wave packet has the following form in the three-dimensional case:

$$\mathbf{v} = \frac{1}{\hbar}\nabla_{\boldsymbol{\kappa}}\epsilon(\boldsymbol{\kappa}) \tag{6.92}$$

where $\nabla_{\boldsymbol{\kappa}}$ refers to the gradient operator in $\boldsymbol{\kappa}$ space. In the case of a free particle, the group velocity of the electron wave packet is identical with its classical velocity $(\mathbf{p}/m)$. This may be seen as follows:

$$|\mathbf{v}| = \frac{1}{\hbar}\frac{d}{d\kappa}\left(\frac{\hbar^2\kappa^2}{2m}\right) = \frac{\hbar\kappa}{m} = \frac{p}{m} \tag{6.93}$$

Problem

(*a*) Derive an expression for the specific heat of a degenerate electron gas as a function of temperature, assuming that the energy-momentum relationship is in one case

A: $$E = \frac{\hbar^2}{2m}\left[\alpha_\perp(\kappa_x^2 + \kappa_y^2) + \alpha_\|\kappa_z^2\right]$$

and in another case

B: $$E = \frac{\hbar^2}{2m}\left[\alpha_1(\kappa_x^2 + \kappa_y^2) + \alpha_2\kappa_z^2 + \alpha_3\kappa_1\kappa_2\right]$$

(*b*) Calculate the components of the group velocity of electrons in cases A and B.

On the other hand, we shall discover in the chapters which follow that an electron which moves about under the influence of the periodic

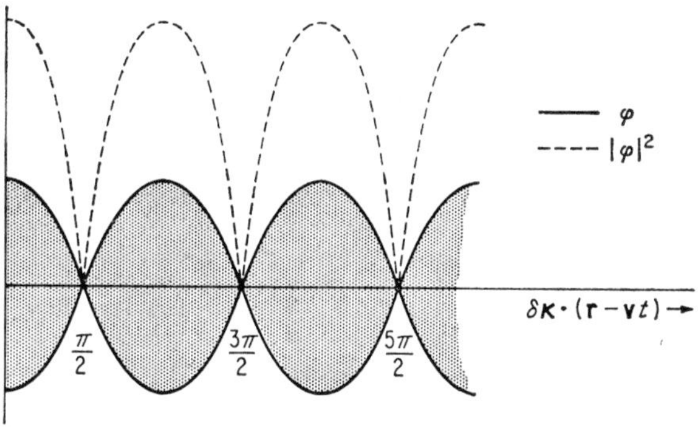

Fig. 6.5. A wave packet constructed from two monochromatic waves with slightly different frequencies.

potential of a crystal lattice cannot be considered as perfectly free. Rather, in this case the electron energy depends on its momentum in a very complicated way. This result will in turn prevent us from associating the wave-packet velocity **v** with the classical velocity of the electron. It is nevertheless possible in many cases to treat the electron as though it were classical by assigning an effective mass m^* (different from the free-electron mass m) to the particle in the crystal.

The three-dimensional expression for the wave packet which is made up of two waves is

$$\varphi = \pm\left[2A\cos\frac{\delta\boldsymbol{\kappa}}{2}\cdot(\mathbf{r} - \mathbf{v}t)\right]e^{i(\boldsymbol{\kappa}\cdot\mathbf{r} - \epsilon t/\hbar)} \tag{6.89'}$$

The absolute square $|\varphi|^2$ represents the probability per volume of finding a particle at a location **r**. It is apparent from Fig. 6.5 that we have not done a very good job in localizing the particle, since $|\varphi|^2$ has a maximum at distances of π apart throughout the entire crystal.

Nevertheless, there are also locations which are π apart at which $|\varphi|^2$ vanishes; these are locations where a particle cannot appear.

Thus we have managed to localize the particle to a somewhat greater extent than does the plane-wave description. The localization is only slight, since we have added only two waves to obtain the result. The construction of a wave packet from more than two waves of different momenta should result in an increased amount of localization of the electron. As a next step, let us imagine that we have a set of plane waves with a continuous variation of wave vector $\boldsymbol{\kappa}$ from $\boldsymbol{\kappa} - \delta\boldsymbol{\kappa}$ to

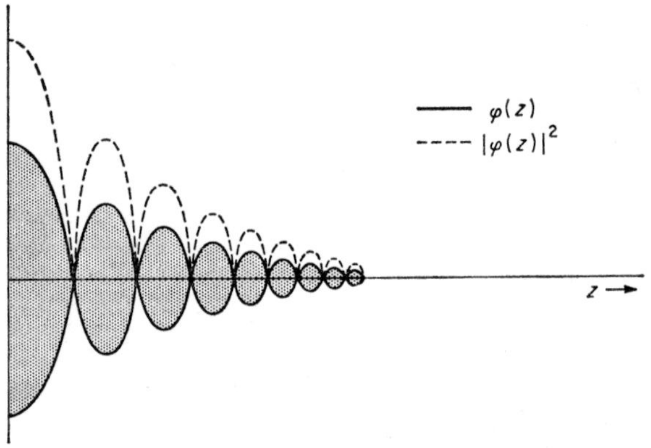

Fig. 6.6. A wave packet that is localized in space according to $1/z$.

$\boldsymbol{\kappa} + \delta\boldsymbol{\kappa}$, where $|\delta\boldsymbol{\kappa}| \ll |\boldsymbol{\kappa}|$, and let us construct the resultant wave by integrating over these waves:

$$\varphi(z) = \pm A \int_{\kappa-\delta\kappa}^{\kappa+\delta\kappa} e^{i(\kappa z - \epsilon t/\hbar)}\, d\kappa = \pm 2A \frac{\sin \delta\kappa z}{z} e^{i(\kappa z - \epsilon t/\hbar)} \tag{6.94}$$

It is clear that this representation of the electron wave function describes a localization of the electron much more precisely than the previous addition of only two waves. This is due to a modulating amplitude $2A[(\sin \delta\kappa z)/z]$ which falls off rapidly with the coordinate z (see Fig. 6.6).

In general, an electron is localized by integrating the product of the plane-wave solution $e^{i\boldsymbol{\kappa}\cdot\mathbf{r}}$ and an arbitrary modulation function $\mu(\boldsymbol{\kappa} - \boldsymbol{\kappa}_0)$ which has the property of being large near $\boldsymbol{\kappa} = \boldsymbol{\kappa}_0$ and dropping to a very small value in a short increment $\delta\kappa$. The function of spatial coordinates is then

$$\varphi(\mathbf{r}) = \int_{-\infty}^{\infty} \mu(\boldsymbol{\kappa} - \boldsymbol{\kappa}_0) e^{i(\boldsymbol{\kappa}-\boldsymbol{\kappa}_0)\cdot\mathbf{r}}\, d\boldsymbol{\kappa} \tag{6.95}$$

At $\mathbf{r} = 0$ the argument of the exponential is zero for all κ and the total contribution to $\varphi(\mathbf{r})$ comes from μ which is constructed to be large at the origin. As $\mathbf{r}$ increases from zero, the rapidly oscillating behavior of the exponential function leads to destructive interference and the vanishing of the wave function $\varphi(\mathbf{r})$. Thus, $|\varphi|$ is large only at $\mathbf{r} \sim 0$.

In the limit where we choose the modulating function to be the Dirac delta function (see Chap. 7), the wave function reduces to the solution for an unlocalized electron, i.e.,

$$\varphi(\mathbf{r}) = A \int \delta(\boldsymbol{\kappa} - \boldsymbol{\kappa}_0) e^{i\boldsymbol{\kappa}\cdot\mathbf{r}}\, d\boldsymbol{\kappa} = A e^{i\boldsymbol{\kappa}_0\cdot\mathbf{r}}$$

A popular choice for the modulating function μ is the Gaussian function

$$\mu(|\boldsymbol{\kappa} - \boldsymbol{\kappa}_0|) = e^{-(\kappa-\kappa_0)^2/2(\delta\kappa)^2}$$

giving for the electron wave function

$$\varphi = \int_{-\infty}^{\infty} e^{i\boldsymbol{\kappa}\cdot\mathbf{r}-(\kappa-\kappa_0)^2/2(\delta\kappa)^2}\, d\kappa = \sqrt{2\pi}\,\delta\kappa\, e^{i\boldsymbol{\kappa}_0\cdot\mathbf{r}-\frac{1}{2}r^2(\delta\kappa)^2}$$

We have discussed in this chapter the successes and failures of the classical free-electron model, and we have seen how the quantum theory explains the behavior with temperature of the so-called static properties of a free-electron gas, such as the charge-carrier concentration, the specific heat, and the paramagnetic spin susceptibility. We have also seen that the quantum theory leads to an approximately constant charge-carrier velocity and a proper temperature dependence of the electrical and thermal conductivities. Thus the predictions of Sommerfeld's quantum-mechanical free-electron model of metals does indeed indicate that it is a fairly good (first) approximation to the more realistic description of the behavior of electrons in solids.

In the chapter which follows we shall continue our discussion of the wave nature of the behavior of electrons in crystals. We shall, however, introduce there the effect of the periodic potential of the crystal lattice so as to obtain a more realistic description of behavior of electrons in actual crystals.

7 quasi-free-electron theory: electrons in a periodic lattice

MANY OF the features of the macroscopic properties of those crystals which contain freely moving electrons are determined by a free-electron theory (Chap. 6). At first sight, this result seems quite surprising since the free-electron theory has taken no account of the scattering effect of the lattice ions on the electrons. Rather, the only potential which is assumed in this theory is that which tends to confine the electrons to within the boundaries of the macroscopic crystal. We have seen that this model predicts that the electrons are allowed to occupy a quasi continuum of energy levels only up to a maximum energy E_F (the Fermi energy) which necessarily depends on the number of electrons present. Thus, one may think of the free-electron theory as predicting a one-energy-band model with electron energies allowed only within the energy band $0 \leq E \leq E_F$.

Our discussion of ionic crystals (Chap. 3) revealed the fact that the energies of mobile electrons in crystals fall into certain allowed energy bands separated by regions of energy which are forbidden. We shall discover in this chapter that this feature is distinctive of any crystal in which there are mobile electrons present. In the case of the ionic crystal, we initially considered the valence electrons to be bound to their parent ions and then analyzed the effect on these electrons of a surrounding ionic lattice. The approach which we shall adopt here is that of the free-electron theory, where the electrons that are mobile in the crystal may not be identified with any particular parent ion in the lattice but are free to move about without any preference for any particular region of the crystal. We shall, however, carry our analysis of the free-electron model one step further by taking into account the scattering effect which a *rigid* lattice has on the electron motion. Under this further restriction we shall see that the electrons may not be regarded as perfectly free; for this reason we refer to this analysis as the *quasi-free-electron theory.*

We shall determine in the remainder of this chapter that the effect of a static periodic potential is to introduce within the one-energy band of the free-electron model regions of energy which are forbidden to the mobile electrons in the crystal. Thus, just as the Pauli exclusion principle leads to the one-energy-band description, so the further restriction imposed by the periodic potential of the crystal leads to the many-energy-band description.

Many of the qualitative features of electron behavior in actual crystals will be derived in this chapter, in a rigorous fashion, by considering the one-dimensional crystal. We shall investigate specifically the wave nature of electrons in crystals and the associated properties of energy bands. In Chap. 8 we shall proceed to the three-dimensional crystal where we shall concentrate on the properties of the electronic-wave nature and energy bands as a function of the rotational symmetry of the crystal.

We shall start by developing a formalism for the treatment of the scattering of electrons by a single atom and then proceed to the problem of the one-dimensional crystal.

7.1 Free-electron scattering by a single atom

The De Broglie wave which describes the motion of an electron that is not acted upon by any external force may be represented by a plane wave Ψ which is a product of a space-dependent part and a time-dependent part

$$\Psi(\mathbf{r},t) = \psi(\mathbf{r})e^{-(i/\hbar)Et} \tag{7.1}$$

The space-dependent part of the wave function is a solution of the Schroedinger equation

$$\nabla^2\psi(\mathbf{r}) + \kappa_0^2\psi(\mathbf{r}) = 0 \tag{7.2}$$

where

$$\kappa_0^2 = \frac{2mE}{\hbar^2} \tag{7.3}$$

and (because of the absence of an external potential) E is the kinetic energy of the electron. The solution of the wave equation (7.2) may be given in terms of the sum of the sine and cosine solutions,

$$\psi(\mathbf{r}) = A \cos \boldsymbol{\kappa}_0 \cdot \mathbf{r} + B \sin \boldsymbol{\kappa}_0 \cdot \mathbf{r} \tag{7.4}$$

or, in terms of the sum of two progressive waves, one proceeding to the right and one to the left,

$$\psi(\mathbf{r}) = A_+e^{i\boldsymbol{\kappa}_0\cdot\mathbf{r}} + A_-e^{-i\boldsymbol{\kappa}_0\cdot\mathbf{r}} \tag{7.5}$$

In the preceding chapter we studied the behavior of electrons in a finite box. Because of the vanishing of the wave functions at the walls of the box, it was appropriate to choose the sine and cosine solutions in order to give the required standing-wave solutions. In this chapter we shall be dealing with an infinite crystal, which is made up of equivalent cells. Because of this equivalence, the restrictions on the electron wave function are those of periodicity within the cells of the crystal (along with the requirement that the wave function shall not diverge at any point in space). In view of these new boundary conditions, it becomes more appropriate, for the present purposes, to adopt the progressive-wave solution (7.5). Further, we shall consider only the properties of the one-dimensional crystal in this chapter, so that the wave function within the confines of a cell will be taken to have the form

$$\psi_{\pm}(z) = A_+ e^{i\kappa_0 z} + A_- e^{-i\kappa_0 z} \qquad (7.5')$$

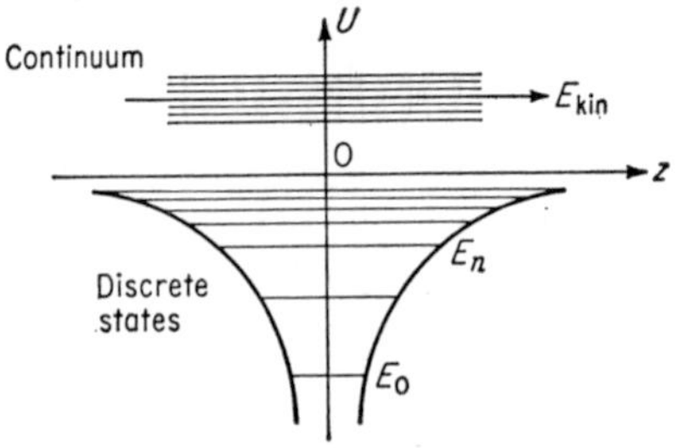

Fig. 7.1. The scattering potential of an atom. The horizontal lines represent energy levels of the system.

Let us suppose that an atom is located at the origin of our coordinate system, and let us first determine the behavior of the electron De Broglie wave in the immediate vicinity of this atom. The atom will offer a potential barrier to the free motion of the electron and will thus have the effect of impeding its motion by trapping it (electron capture) or by scattering it elastically or inelastically. The actual detailed effect of the atomic potential on the electron motion depends on the shape of the atomic potential well and on the bound states associated with this well.

The potential energy of the atom, being of electrostatic origin, has a typical Coulomb shape, as shown in Fig. 7.1. Because the bound states of a complex atom are very numerous and the shape of the potential would introduce unnecessary mathematical complications into our problem, let us approximate the actual potential by a much simpler potential which would, however, lead to the same qualitative behavior of its scattering effect on impinging De Broglie waves.

Dirac-delta-function Potential[1]

We replace the actual potential barrier which the atom presents to the moving electron by a potential which is infinite in depth but infinitesimal in width, so that the product of the well depth and the well width is a finite number. Such a function is known as the Dirac delta function

[1] Much of the discussion that follows in this chapter, relating to the delta-function model, was drawn from work done originally by D. S. Saxon and R. A. Hutner, *Philips Res. Rept.*, **4**: 81 (1949).

and is represented by the symbol $\delta(z - z_0)$.[1] The delta function is zero everywhere except at $z = z_0$, where it is infinite, and the function is a meaningful concept only when used in an integration process. The dimensions of the delta function $\delta(z - z_0)$ are in reciprocal centimeters. The following are further properties of the Dirac delta function:

$$\delta(|z| - z_0) = 0 \qquad |z| \neq z_0 \tag{7.6}$$

$$\int_{-\infty}^{\infty} \delta(z - z_0)\, dz = 1 \tag{7.7}$$

$$\int_{-\infty}^{\infty} f(z)\delta(z - z_0)\, dz = f(z_0) \tag{7.8}$$

We shall now solve the Schroedinger wave equation for an electron which is in the vicinity of an atom, whose potential energy may be represented by a Dirac-delta-function form

$$V = -\eta\delta(z) \tag{7.9}$$

where the coefficient η measures the strength of the potential [and has the dimensions (energy) $\times$ (length)]. The Schroedinger wave equation then takes the following form for electrons inside the potential well (setting $z_0 = 0$):

$$\frac{d^2\psi_i(z)}{dz^2} + \kappa_0^2\psi_i(z) = \frac{2m}{\hbar^2}\eta\delta(z)\psi_i(z) \tag{7.10}$$

It takes the form of Eq. (7.2) outside of the well:

$$\frac{d^2\psi_o(z)}{dz^2} + \kappa_0^2\psi_o(z) = 0 \tag{7.2'}$$

The wave vector κ_0 is defined in terms of the electron energy by Eq. (7.3).

The true electron wave for this problem is now obtained by solving Eqs. (7.10) and (7.2′) for ψ_i and for ψ_o, respectively, and then by matching their magnitudes and slopes at the potential barrier. The latter operation is a boundary condition imposed by the probability interpretation of the wave function and by the equation of continuity, which requires the wave function and its gradient to be finite continuous functions throughout all of space. This problem differs from the usual one in that the boundary condition is imposed only at one point ($z = 0$) instead of the usual two points (the two sides of a one-dimensional box).

We proceed to solve the wave equation (7.10) by integrating it from $-\epsilon$ to $+\epsilon$, where ϵ is a very small number which is allowed to go to zero after the integration. Carrying out this integration, we have

$$\int_{-\epsilon}^{\epsilon} \frac{d^2\psi_i}{dz^2}\, dz + \kappa_0^2 \int_{-\epsilon}^{\epsilon} \psi_i\, dz = \frac{2m}{\hbar^2}\eta \int_{-\epsilon}^{\epsilon} \delta(z)\psi_i(z)\, dz \tag{7.11}$$

[1] See L. I. Schiff, "Quantum Mechanics," p. 50, McGraw-Hill Book Company, Inc., New York, 1955.

As the number ϵ approaches zero, the limit of the second integral on the left-hand side of (7.11) is

$$\lim_{\epsilon \to 0} \int_{-\epsilon}^{\epsilon} \psi_i \, dz = 0 \tag{7.12}$$

Combining (7.12) with (7.8), the integrated wave equation (7.11) takes the following form as $\epsilon \to 0$:

$$\left. \frac{d\psi_i}{dz} \right|_{0+} - \left. \frac{d\psi_i}{dz} \right|_{0-} = \frac{2m}{\hbar^2} \psi_i(0) \tag{7.13}$$

The exterior solution ψ_o of the wave equation (7.2′) has the form of a progressive wave moving to the right,

$$\psi^{(+)} = A_+ e^{i\kappa_0 z} \tag{7.14a}$$

or a progressive wave moving to the left,

$$\psi^{(-)} = A_- e^{-i\kappa_0 z} \tag{7.14b}$$

In the absence of the δ-function well, ψ_o is a free-electron wave function and the amplitudes A_+ and A_- may be taken to be the same and will be set equal to unity.

Let us then denote the exterior wave function by

$$\psi_o^{(\pm)} = e^{\pm i\kappa_0 z} \tag{7.14c}$$

remembering that $\psi^{(\pm)}$ represents two independent solutions. The slope of ψ_o is then

$$\frac{d\psi_o^{(\pm)}}{dz} = \pm i\kappa_0 e^{\pm i\kappa_0 z} \tag{7.15}$$

We shall now determine the energy eigenvalues for electrons trapped inside a δ-function well by making use of the boundary conditions

$$\psi_o(z = 0) = \psi_i(z = 0) = 1 \tag{7.16}$$

and Eq. (7.13), with

$$\left. \frac{d\psi_i}{dz} \right|_0 = \left. \frac{d\psi_o}{dz} \right|_0 = \pm i\kappa_0 \tag{7.17}$$

Inserting Eqs. (7.16) and (7.17) into Eq. (7.13), we have

$$\pm i\kappa_0 \mp i\kappa_0 = \frac{2m}{\hbar^2} \eta \tag{7.18}$$

Of the four possible ways of combining the + and − signs on the left-hand side of Eq. (7.18) two nonzero results come from the choice of like signs in front of each term, giving

$$\pm i\kappa_0 = \frac{m}{\hbar^2} \eta \tag{7.19}$$

Thus the interior wave function takes the form

$$\psi_i^{(\pm)} = e^{\pm(m\eta/\hbar^2)z} \tag{7.20}$$

In order to satisfy the condition that the wave function shall not diverge, the two independent solutions given by Eq. (7.20) must be valid only in the following regions:

$$\psi^{(+)} = e^{(m\eta/\hbar^2)z} \qquad z < 0 \qquad (7.20')$$

$$\psi^{(-)} = e^{-(m\eta/\hbar^2)z} \qquad z > 0 \qquad (7.20'')$$

The total wave function is then represented in Fig. 7.2 where it is compared with the free-particle wave function.

From Eq. (7.19) we have the following energy relationship:

$$\kappa_0^2 = \frac{2mE_0}{\hbar^2} = \frac{-m\eta^2}{\hbar^4}$$

or $$E_0 = -\left(\frac{2m}{\hbar^2}\right)\frac{\eta^2}{4} \tag{7.21}$$

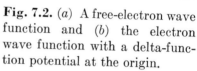

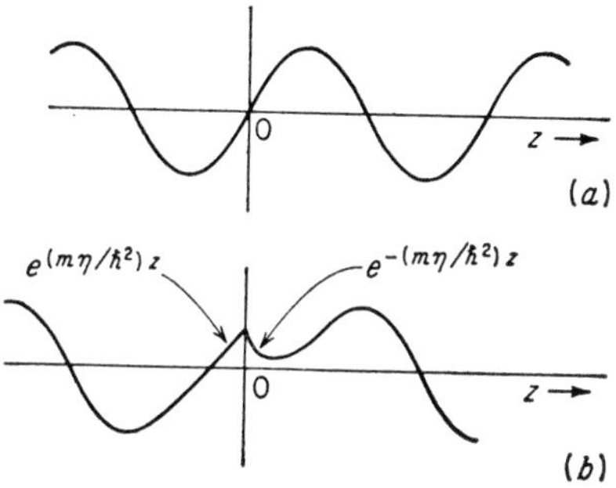

Fig. 7.2. (*a*) A free-electron wave function and (*b*) the electron wave function with a delta-function potential at the origin.

The energy E_0 is the only bound state which is associated with the Dirac-delta-function potential.

We shall make use of these results later in this chapter, when we discuss the scattering of electrons by a periodic array of Dirac-delta-function potentials.

The Arbitrary-scattering-potential Solution in Terms of the S Matrix

Let us now consider the general formulation of the problem of the scattering of electron De Broglie waves by an arbitrary scattering potential. Wheeler[1] has introduced an approach to this problem which allows a formulation in terms of the asymptotic behavior of the wave function and a scattering operator S which relates the wave function in the remote past ($t = -\infty$) to the wave function in the distant future ($t = \infty$) (the scattering event is assumed to take place at $t = 0$). Thus,

$$\psi(t = \infty) = S\psi(t = -\infty) \tag{7.22}$$

In its matrix form, the scattering operator is referred to as the S matrix, and it is completely determined by the details of the scattering potential U. As far as the scattering potential is concerned, the wave at $t = -\infty$ is regarded as an incoming wave, and the wave at $t = +\infty$ is regarded as an outgoing wave.

[1] J. A. Wheeler, *Phys. Rev.*, **52**: 1107 (1937). Wheeler's application is to nuclear scattering; his formalism is, however, the same.

Some useful properties of the S matrix may be derived on the basis of general considerations, independent of the shape of the scattering potential. These properties, which are derived in Appendix C, are based on the following fundamental assumptions:

1. The Schroedinger wave equation presents an accurate description of particle wave behavior (in the nonrelativistic energy region).
2. The interaction energy operator is invariant under time reversal.
3. The total number of particles in a closed system is conserved (continuity condition).

The properties of the S matrix which follow from these assumptions are as follows:

1. The S matrix is unitary, i.e.,

$$S^{\dagger}S = 1 \qquad S^{\dagger}_{ij} \equiv S^{*}_{ji} \tag{7.23}$$

2. The S matrix is symmetric, i.e.,

$$S = \tilde{S} \qquad \tilde{S}_{ij} \equiv S_{ji} \tag{7.24}$$

The combination of (7.23) and (7.24) leads to the property

$$SS^{*} = 1 \equiv \begin{pmatrix} 1 & & & & \\ & 1 & & & \\ & & \cdot & & \\ & & & \cdot & \\ & & & & \cdot \\ & & & & & 1 \end{pmatrix} \tag{7.25}$$

Let us now look for the solutions of the one-dimensional Schroedinger wave equation

$$\frac{d^2\psi}{dz^2} + \left(\kappa_0^2 - \frac{2mU}{\hbar^2}\right)\psi = 0 \tag{7.26}$$

in terms of the S matrix, where U is an arbitrary scattering potential, localized around $z = 0$. Let the amplitudes of the incoming waves from the left and from the right be denoted by A_+ and A_-, respectively, and the outgoing waves proceeding to the left and to the right by B_- and B_+, respectively (Fig. 7.3). The outgoing wave $B_-e^{-i\kappa_0 z}$ may be considered to be made up of a reflected part of the incoming wave $A_+e^{i\kappa_0 z}$ and the part of the incoming wave $A_-e^{-i\kappa_0 z}$ which is transmitted through the potential barrier.

Similarly, the outgoing wave $B_+e^{i\kappa_0 z}$ may be considered to be made up of a reflected part of the incoming wave $A_-e^{-i\kappa_0 z}$ and a transmitted part of the incoming wave $A_+e^{i\kappa_0 z}$.

Because of the linearity of the wave equation, we are permitted to express the outgoing-wave amplitudes B_+ and B_- as linear combinations of the incoming-wave amplitudes A_+ and A_-. The constants of proportionality between the incoming- and outgoing-wave amplitudes must necessarily depend on the transmission and reflection characteristics of the potential barrier. Let us call the reflection coefficient ρ, and the transmission coefficient τ ($= \sqrt{1 - \rho^2}$). Also, let us assume that the potential is symmetric about $z = 0$. The scattering potential will have the effect of shifting the phase of the impinging wave by an amount α.

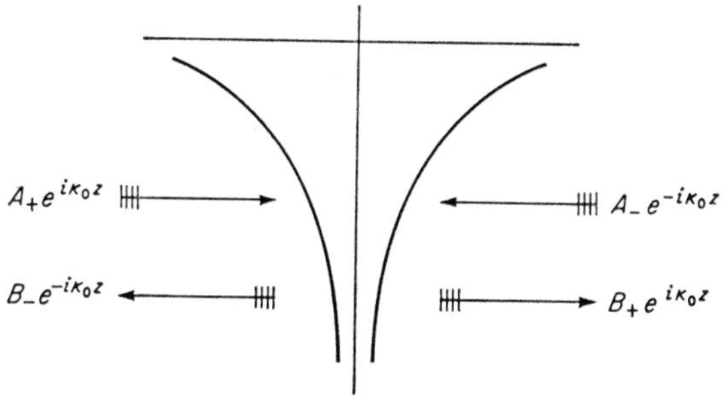

Fig. 7.3. The scattering of waves by a one-dimensional arbitrary potential.

We may then relate the outgoing to the incoming wave by the following set of equations:

$$B_- = (\rho A_+ - i\tau A_-)e^{i\alpha} \tag{7.27}$$
$$B_+ = (-i\tau A_+ + \rho A_-)e^{i\alpha} \tag{7.28}$$

The factor of i is introduced to ensure that

$$|B_+|^2 + |B_-|^2 = |A_+|^2 + |A_-|^2 \tag{7.29}$$

(i.e., the number density of incoming particles must equal the number density of outgoing particles if no new particles are to be created!).

According to our definition of the S operator [Eq. (7.22)], the following identification may be made between the matrix elements of the S operator and the reflection and transmission coefficients in Eqs. (7.27) and (7.28):

$$\begin{pmatrix} B_- \\ B_+ \end{pmatrix} = \begin{pmatrix} \rho e^{i\alpha} & -i\tau e^{i\alpha} \\ -i\tau e^{i\alpha} & \rho e^{i\alpha} \end{pmatrix} \begin{pmatrix} A_+ \\ A_- \end{pmatrix} = \begin{pmatrix} S_{11} & S_{12} \\ S_{21} & S_{22} \end{pmatrix} \begin{pmatrix} A_+ \\ A_- \end{pmatrix} \tag{7.30}$$

It is clear that (since ρ and τ are real numbers) the requirements on the properties of the S matrix, given by Eqs. (7.23) to (7.25), are fulfilled, i.e.,

$$S_{11}S_{11}^* + S_{12}S_{21}^* = S_{22}S_{22}^* + S_{12}S_{21}^* = 1 \tag{7.31}$$
$$|S_{11}| = |S_{22}| \tag{7.32}$$
$$S_{12} = S_{21}$$
$$S_{11}S_{12}^* + S_{12}S_{22}^* = 0$$

In order to evaluate the elements of the scattering matrix S, we apply the boundary condition that the wave function ψ be continuous and finite throughout all of space. The wave function which describes the electron motion on the left-hand side of the scattering center,

$$\psi_l = A_+ e^{i\kappa_0 z} + B_- e^{-i\kappa_0 z} \tag{7.33}$$

and the wave function which describes the electron motion on the right-hand side of the scattering center

$$\psi_r = B_+ e^{i\kappa_0 z} + A_- e^{-i\kappa_0 z} \tag{7.34}$$

must be matched to the wave function which describes the electron motion inside the region of the scattering potential. An exact knowledge of the details of the scattering potential would enable an evaluation of the latter wave function which in turn would lead to the amplitudes A and B and thence, from Eq. (7.30), to the elements of the S matrix itself.

We shall illustrate this method of calculation by once again considering the scattering potential to have the Dirac-delta-function behavior given by Eq. (7.9). At $z = 0$, the requirement of continuity at the origin gives

$$\psi_l(0) = \psi_r(0)$$

or, from Eqs. (7.33) and (7.34),

$$A_+ + B_- = B_+ + A_- \tag{7.35}$$

Also, the boundary condition on the slope of the wave function at $z = 0$, as given by Eq. (7.13), yields

$$i\kappa_0(B_+ - A_-) - i\kappa_0(A_+ - B_-) = \frac{2m}{\hbar^2}\,\eta\,(B_+ + A_-) \tag{7.36}$$

Combining Eqs. (7.35) and (7.36), we may solve for each of the two amplitudes B_+ and B_- in terms of a linear combination of the amplitudes A_+ and A_-. Thus, we obtain

$$\begin{pmatrix} B_- \\ B_+ \end{pmatrix} = \begin{pmatrix} \dfrac{\gamma}{i-\gamma} & \dfrac{i}{i-\gamma} \\ \dfrac{i}{i-\gamma} & \dfrac{\gamma}{i-\gamma} \end{pmatrix} \begin{pmatrix} A_+ \\ A_- \end{pmatrix} = \begin{pmatrix} S_{11} & S_{12} \\ S_{21} & S_{22} \end{pmatrix} \begin{pmatrix} A_+ \\ A_- \end{pmatrix} \tag{7.37}$$

where

$$\gamma = \frac{m\eta}{\hbar^2\kappa_0} = \frac{\eta\kappa_0}{2E} \tag{7.38}$$

The elements of the S matrix, given by Eq. (7.37), may be written in terms of the reflection coefficient ρ and the phase angle α by comparing

Eq. (7.37) with Eq. (7.30). We obtain for the reflection and transmission coefficients

$$\rho = \frac{\gamma}{(1+\gamma^2)^{1/2}} \qquad \tau = (1-\rho^2)^{1/2} = \frac{1}{(1+\gamma^2)^{1/2}} \tag{7.39}$$

and for the phase angle

$$\alpha = \cot^{-1}\gamma \tag{7.40}$$

Thus, we would expect strong reflection (weak transmission) of the electron De Broglie wave through the potential barrier in the strong potential barrier limit, where

$$\gamma = \frac{\eta}{\hbar^2\kappa_0/m} = \frac{\eta\kappa_0}{2E} \gg 1 \tag{7.41}$$

whereas a weak reflection (strong transmission) would occur in the weak potential barrier limit, where

$$\frac{\eta\kappa_0}{2E} \ll 1 \tag{7.42}$$

with
$$E = \frac{\hbar^2\kappa_0}{2m}$$

The scattering of electron De Broglie waves by a Dirac-delta-function potential has thus been determined in terms of the scattering operator S. This operator will be discussed further in the next section in connection with the determination of effects of impurities in a perfect lattice as a function of singularities in the S matrix.

In order to determine energy spectra, it is useful to define another matrix R, which relates the electron waves on the right-hand side to those on the left-hand side of the scattering potential. Thus, R is defined by the following equation:

$$\begin{pmatrix} B_+ \\ A_- \end{pmatrix} = R\begin{pmatrix} A_+ \\ B_- \end{pmatrix} \tag{7.43}$$

When Eqs. (7.43) and (7.30) are combined (it will be left as an exercise for the reader to show this), the S and R matrices relate to each other in the following manner:

$$(R) \equiv \begin{pmatrix} R_{11} & R_{12} \\ R_{21} & R_{22} \end{pmatrix} = \begin{pmatrix} \dfrac{S_{12}^2 - S_{11}S_{22}}{S_{12}} & \dfrac{S_{22}}{S_{12}} \\ -\dfrac{S_{11}}{S_{12}} & \dfrac{1}{S_{12}} \end{pmatrix} \tag{7.44}$$

The R matrix has the property that its determinant is equal to unity (i.e., it is unimodular). Using Eq. (7.30), we see that the R matrix is related to the reflection and transmission coefficients in the following way:

$$(R) \equiv \begin{pmatrix} R_{11} & R_{12} \\ R_{21} & R_{22} \end{pmatrix} = \begin{pmatrix} \dfrac{e^{i\alpha}}{i\tau} & \dfrac{\rho}{-i\tau} \\ \dfrac{\rho}{i\tau} & \dfrac{e^{-i\alpha}}{-i\tau} \end{pmatrix} \tag{7.45}$$

7.2 Free-electron scattering in a one-dimensional crystal[1]

Let us now suppose that, instead of a single scattering center, an electron is moving through a one-dimensional lattice which is made up of a periodic array of equivalent scattering potentials, separated from each other by the lattice parameter z_0. Such a situation would be encountered by an electron moving through a one-dimensional static monatomic lattice. We have already determined the qualitative way in which a single atom scatters an electron De Broglie wave. The question which arises at this point is the following: As the electron wave proceeds through the crystal lattice, will the scattering at each lattice point produce a successive set of noncoherent scattered waves or will the scattered waves add in a coherent way so as to produce a net progressive wave in the crystal? Offhand, one would be tempted to say that the scattering effect of the lattice on the De Broglie waves would be noncoherent, and this is indeed the case under the condition that the lattice ions are not fixed in a periodic array but, rather, have freedom to move about in a random fashion. However, we know from various experimental data (e.g., X-ray diffraction analysis of solids) that the constituent atoms in a crystal arrange themselves in a regular periodic array and that their freedom to move from their fixed equilibrium positions is not great. We shall see in the paragraphs which follow that, under the ideal conditions of a static lattice, the motion of electrons through a crystal may indeed be described by a net progressive wave in the lattice. The momentum associated with this wave is not, however, the free-electron momentum $\hbar\kappa_0$; rather it is a momentum $\hbar\kappa$ which depends on the details of the lattice potential. We shall also see that the plane-wave characteristic of the wave function is modified by a modulating function which is periodic throughout the crystal lattice. It should be emphasized at this point that the perfect translational symmetry of the crystal lattice is the saving factor which enables us to reduce

[1] This model was first investigated by R. de L. Kronig and W. G. Penney, *Proc. Roy. Soc.* (*London*), *Ser. A*, **130:** 499 (1931). The Dirac-delta-function potential was applied to the Kronig-Penney model by Saxon and Hutner, *loc. cit.* Also, see H. Jones, "The Theory of Brillouin Zones and Electronic States in Crystals," North Holland Publishing Company, Amsterdam, 1960.

the impossible task of treating the interaction of all 10^{23} particles of the macroscopic system to the relatively simple problem of treating the interaction of only a very few particles.

The prediction that a wave will be scattered by the perfect periodic potential of a lattice in such a way as to produce a coherent progressive wave with an associated crystal momentum $\hbar\kappa$ follows from the Bloch-Floquet theorem. According to this theorem, two linearly independent wave functions which describe the electron motion in a periodic potential have the form

$$\psi_{\boldsymbol{\kappa}}^{(\pm)}(\mathbf{r}) = e^{\pm i\boldsymbol{\kappa}\cdot\mathbf{r}}u_{\boldsymbol{\kappa}}(\mathbf{r}) \tag{7.46}$$

where the factor $u_{\boldsymbol{\kappa}}(\mathbf{r})$ which multiplies the progressive wave function $e^{i\boldsymbol{\kappa}\cdot\mathbf{r}}$ is the modulating function which is identical in each cell of the crystal. The function (7.46) is referred to as the Bloch wave function. In the next subsection we shall prove the Bloch-Floquet theorem for the case of the one-dimensional crystal.

Bloch-Floquet Theorem

We shall now show that the progressive wave given by the Bloch form (7.46) does indeed describe the motion of electrons through a perfect periodic lattice. Let us consider once again a one-dimensional crystal lattice in which the constituent ions are separated by a distance z_0. We shall analyze the wave behavior of an electron in the vicinity of two neighboring ions in the lattice. Because the ion potential has translational symmetry throughout the crystal, i.e.

$$V(z) = V(z + nz_0) \qquad n = \text{any integer} \tag{7.47}$$

the solution of the Schroedinger equation (7.26) is identical for any cell in the crystal. In each cell (i.e., in between the lattice points) the wave function is taken to be a linear combination of incoming and outgoing waves. The wave amplitudes in each cell are then adjusted in order to satisfy the continuity condition on the wave function across the scattering potential. The wave behavior of the electron in the vicinity of two neighboring constituent ions of the lattice is thus shown in Fig. 7.4.

The electron De Broglie wave in cell (1) is described in terms of the amplitudes A_+ and B_- for waves traveling to the right and to the left, respectively. The wave function just on the right-hand side of atom (1) is

$$\psi_r^{(1)} = A_+^{(1)}e^{i\kappa_0 z} + B_-^{(1)}e^{-i\kappa_0 z} \tag{7.48}$$

where $A_+^{(1)}$ and $B_-^{(1)}$ are the amplitudes of the electron wave in cell (1). The wave function just on the left-hand side of ion (2) is obtained by making the transformation $z \rightarrow z + z_0$:

$$\psi_l^{(2)} = A_+^{(1)}e^{i\kappa_0(z+z_0)} + B_-^{(1)}e^{-i\kappa_0(z+z_0)} \tag{7.49}$$

We shall denote the wave function for an electron in cell (2) by the amplitudes $A_-^{(2)}$ and $B_+^{(2)}$. The wave function on the right-hand side of ion (2) is then given by the expression

$$\psi_r^{(2)} = B_+^{(2)} e^{i\kappa_0 z} + A_-^{(2)} e^{-i\kappa_0 z} \tag{7.50}$$

Our object now is to determine the amplitudes of the wave function in cell (2) in terms of the amplitudes of the wave function in cell (1). This may be done in terms of the R matrix according to the definition (7.43), giving

$$B_+^{(2)} = R_{11} A_+^{(1)} e^{i\kappa_0 z_0} + R_{12} B_-^{(1)} e^{-i\kappa_0 z_0} \tag{7.51a}$$
$$A_-^{(2)} = R_{21} A_+^{(1)} e^{i\kappa_0 z_0} + R_{22} B_-^{(1)} e^{-i\kappa_0 z_0} \tag{7.51b}$$

Once we know the amplitudes $A_+^{(1)}$ and $B_-^{(1)}$, which belong to the wave in cell (1), we can determine the amplitudes $A_-^{(2)}$ and $B_+^{(2)}$, which belong

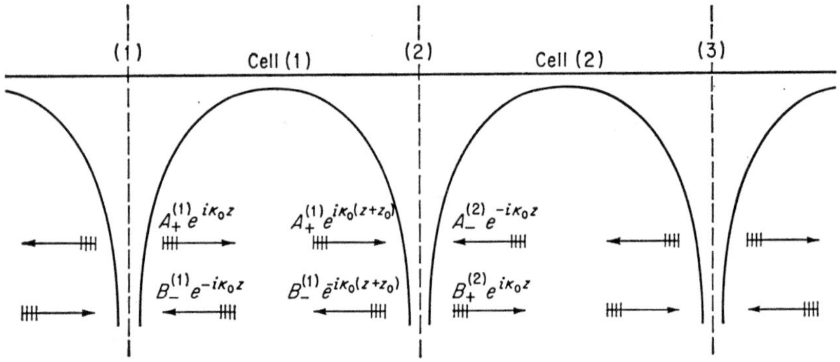

Fig. 7.4. Wave behavior in a one-dimensional periodic lattice.

to the wave in cell (2), from Eqs. (7.51). We may then continue this process to cell (3), cell (4), etc., until we have a descripion of the electron wave function in the entire crystal. We cannot, of course, obtain any quantitative results until we have evaluated the elements of the R matrix. This evaluation depends on the detailed behavior of the potential energy that an electron feels in the presence of one of the constituent ions of the lattice.

Because of the periodicity of the lattice potential from cell to cell in the crystal and the linearity of the Schroedinger wave equation (7.26), the wave function in one cell must be linearly proportional to the wave function in any other cell of the crystal. Let us define β to be the constant of proportionality between the electron wave function in one cell and the electron wave function in its neighboring cell, i.e.,

$$\psi(z + z_0) = \beta\psi(z) \tag{7.52}$$

where the constant β is a complex number. Combining Eq. (7.52) with

Eqs. (7.48) and (7.50), we obtain the following further relationship between the wave amplitudes in adjacent cells:

$$\psi_r^{(2)} = B_+^{(2)} e^{i\kappa_0 z} + A_-^{(2)} e^{-i\kappa_0 z} = \beta \psi_r^{(1)} = \beta(A_+^{(1)} e^{i\kappa_0 z} + B_-^{(1)} e^{-i\kappa_0 z})$$

or

$$B_+^{(2)} = \beta A_+^{(1)} \tag{7.53a}$$

$$A_-^{(2)} = \beta B_-^{(1)} \tag{7.53b}$$

If we now combine Eqs. (7.53) with Eqs. (7.51) and note that the determinant of R is unity, we obtain the following quadratic equation in β:

$$\beta^2 - \beta(R_{11} e^{i\kappa_0 z_0} + R_{22} e^{-i\kappa_0 z_0}) + 1 = 0 \tag{7.54}$$

The two roots of Eq. (7.54), β_+ and β_-, are

$$\beta_\pm = \frac{\varepsilon}{2} \pm \sqrt{\left(\frac{\varepsilon}{2}\right)^2 - 1} \tag{7.55}$$

where

$$\varepsilon = R_{11} e^{i\kappa_0 z_0} + R_{22} e^{-i\kappa_0 z_0} \tag{7.56}$$

It is readily verified that the solutions β_+ and β_- are the reciprocals of each other:

$$\beta_+ = \frac{1}{\beta_-} \tag{7.57}$$

Since there are two values of β, Eq. (7.52) is equivalent to the two equations

$$\psi_+(z + z_0) = \beta_+ \psi_+(z) \tag{7.52$'a$}$$

$$\psi_-(z + z_0) = \beta_- \psi_-(z) \tag{7.52$'b$}$$

These relations may now be extended to cover the entire crystal. In general, for a point in the nth cell $(z + nz_0)$, the wave function is

$$\psi_+(z + nz_0) = \beta_+ \psi_+(z + (n-1)z_0) = \cdots = \beta_+^n \psi_+(z) \tag{7.58a}$$

Similarly,

$$\psi_-(z + nz_0) = \beta_-^n \psi_-(z) \tag{7.58b}$$

It is clear from Eqs. (7.58) that, if $|\beta_+| > 1$, then $\psi_+(z + nz_0)$ will diverge to infinity as n becomes very large, and if $|\beta_+| < 1$, the reciprocal relation between β_+ and β_- indicates that $\psi_-(z + nz_0)$ would diverge to infinity as n becomes very large. Since the wave function must remain finite at all points in space because of its probabilistic interpretation, the form of Eqs. (7.58) indicates that the absolute values of β_+ and β_- must both be unity:

$$|\beta_+| = |\beta_-| = 1 \tag{7.59}$$

The most general expression for β is then given by the exponential function

$$\beta_\pm = e^{\pm i\kappa z_0} \tag{7.60}$$

where κ is a real number, different from the free-electron wave number κ_0. Thus, the solutions (7.52′) reduce to the form

$$\psi_+(z + z_0) = e^{i\kappa z_0}\psi_+(z) \tag{7.52′c}$$
$$\psi_-(z + z_0) = e^{-i\kappa z_0}\psi_-(z) \tag{7.52′d}$$

and Eq. (7.58*a*) can be written in the form

$$\psi_+(z) = e^{i\kappa n z_0}\psi_+(z - nz_0) \tag{7.58c}$$

If we now substitute $z' = z - nz_0$ in Eq. (7.58*c*), we have

$$\psi_+(z) = e^{i\kappa z}[e^{-i\kappa z'}\psi_+(z')] = e^{i\kappa z}u_\kappa(z) \tag{7.61}$$

where the function $u_\kappa(z)$ is identical from one cell to the next throughout the entire crystal because of the periodicity of z' in the crystal. Thus, in accordance with the statement of the Bloch-Floquet theorem, the solution of the wave equation (7.26), with U being a periodic potential, is made up of two linearly independent solutions ψ_+ and ψ_-,

$$\psi_\pm = e^{\pm i\kappa z}u_\kappa(z)$$

which is in the form of a progressive wave modulated by a function which has the periodicity of the lattice. The plus and the minus signs refer to waves which move to the right and to the left, respectively. In the case of the three-dimensional crystal (Chap. 8), the Bloch wave function has the form

$$\psi_\pm(\mathbf{r}) = e^{\pm i\boldsymbol{\kappa}\cdot\mathbf{r}}u_{\boldsymbol{\kappa}}(\mathbf{r}) \tag{7.62}$$

Electronic Energy Bands in a One-dimensional Crystal

The free-electron theory (Chap. 6) predicts that electrons in crystals may have the energy

$$E(\kappa_0) = \frac{\hbar^2\kappa_0^2}{2m} \tag{7.63}$$

(so long as this energy state is not occupied by another electron with the same spin) up to a maximum energy E_F (the Fermi energy), with an associated momentum $\hbar\kappa_0$. The only restrictions imposed on the electrons in this model, besides the Pauli exclusion principle, are due to the potential defined by the walls of the macroscopic crystal which act to confine the electrons within the crystal.

The quasi-free-electron theory which we are now discussing differs from the free-electron theory because of the imposition of the additional potential due to the periodic array of lattice ions. We have determined that the wave functions which describe the electrons are no longer of the plane-wave form but rather have the modulated plane-wave form of the Bloch wave function (7.62). The next question which we wish to answer deals with the way in which the electron energy levels of the quasi-free-electron model differ from those of the free-electron model. We have already determined that the momentum $\hbar\kappa$ of electrons in a periodic potential can differ from the free-electron momentum $\hbar\kappa_0$. Let us now calculate the electron energy $E(\kappa)$ as a function of this new momentum.

The energy eigenvalues for electrons in a periodic potential may be determined in terms of the elements of the R matrix. Dividing Eq. (7.54) through by β, we have

$$\beta + \frac{1}{\beta} - (R_{11}e^{i\kappa_0 z_0} + R_{22}e^{-i\kappa_0 z_0}) = 0 \tag{7.54'}$$

If we now substitute either one of the two values of β (β_+ or β_-) into Eq. (7.54′), we have

$$\cos \kappa z_0 = \tfrac{1}{2}(R_{11}e^{i\kappa_0 z_0} + R_{22}e^{-i\kappa_0 z_0}) \tag{7.64}$$

The right-hand side of Eq. (7.64) may be expressed in terms of the reflection and transmission coefficients ρ and τ, respectively. Combining Eqs. (7.45) and (7.64), we have

$$\cos \kappa z_0 = \cos \kappa_0 z_0 + \frac{\sin \alpha - \tau}{\tau} \cos \kappa_0 z_0 + \frac{\cos \alpha}{\tau} \sin \kappa_0 z_0 \tag{7.65}$$

The derivation of the form of the factor β given by Eq. (7.60) is based on the requirement that the wave number κ be a real number, since an imaginary component in κ would cause the solution (7.59) to break down and lead to a divergent wave function. Since κ is real, the magnitude of the left-hand side of Eq. (7.64) ($|\cos \kappa z_0|$) cannot be greater than unity. On the other hand, there are indeed values of electron energy which correspond to values of the free-electron wave number κ_0 which would force the right-hand side of Eq. (7.64) to be greater than unity. These values of electron energy are therefore forbidden so as to ensure compatibility with Eq. (7.65).

The net result of this analysis is that the energy spectrum of mobile electrons which move under the influence of a periodic potential is characterized by allowed and forbidden regions. The electron wave number which corresponds to the energy discontinuity is determined from the condition that

$$|\cos \kappa_d z_0| = 1 \tag{7.66}$$

or that

$$\kappa_d = \pm \frac{m\pi}{z_0} \qquad m = 0, 1, 2, \ldots \tag{7.67}$$

Exact Calculation for the Dirac-delta-function-model Crystal

As an example, let us carry out the energy-band calculation for the case of the periodic potential of the Dirac-delta-function form. The phase angle α is related to the reflection and transmission coefficients for the case of the delta-function potential in the following way [see Eqs. (7.39) to (7.41)]:

$$\sin\alpha = \tau \qquad \cos\alpha = \rho \qquad \frac{\rho}{\tau} = \gamma = \frac{\eta\kappa_0}{2E} \tag{7.68}$$

If we now substitute Eq. (7.68) into Eq. (7.65) we obtain the following transcendental equation:

$$\cos\kappa z_0 = \cos\kappa_0 z_0 + \gamma\sin\kappa_0 z_0 \tag{7.69a}$$

which is, in terms of the electron energy, given in the following form:[1]

$$\cos\kappa z_0 = \cos\left[\left(\frac{2mE}{\hbar^2}\right)^{1/2} z_0\right] + \left(\frac{m\eta^2}{2\hbar^2 E}\right)^{1/2}\sin\left[\left(\frac{2mE}{\hbar^2}\right)^{1/2} z_0\right] \tag{7.69b}$$

This equation relates the electron momentum $\hbar\kappa$ to its energy E. The strength of the Dirac delta function η is related to the potential V by the equation

$$|V| = \eta \sum_{n=-N/2}^{N/2} \delta(z - nz_0) \tag{7.70}$$

It is readily verified that the strength function η is merely the product

$$\eta = \langle V\rangle z_0 \tag{7.71}$$

where $\langle V\rangle$ is the value of the crystal potential averaged over the entire crystal.

It is clear that, as the strength function $\eta \to 0$, $\kappa \to \kappa_0$, and we have once again the free-electron energy-momentum relation (7.63). It is also easily verified from Eq. (7.69*b*) that the electron velocity, defined by Eq. (6.93), vanishes at the edges of the energy band. The results obtained in this and in the succeeding discussion are illustrated in Fig. 7.6.

Combining Eqs. (7.45), (7.51), (7.53), (7.54), and (7.68), we find that the wave function (7.48) is given by the expression

$$\psi_r^{(\pm)}(z) = A_+^{(1)}\left[e^{\pm i\kappa_0 z} + \frac{e^{i\kappa z} - (1 + i\gamma)e^{i\kappa_0 z_0}}{i\gamma e^{-i\kappa_0 z_0}}\, e^{\mp i\kappa_0 z}\right] \tag{7.48'}$$

The wave function (7.48′) may now be expressed in the Bloch form

$$\psi(z) = \gamma\psi(0)e^{i\kappa(z-z')}\,\frac{e^{i\kappa z_0}\sin\kappa_0 z' - \sin\kappa_0(z' - z_0)}{\cos\kappa z_0 - \cos\kappa_0 z_0} \tag{7.72}$$

[1] Note that, according to Eq. (7.21), the coefficient of the second term on the right-hand side of Eq. (7.69*b*) is $(E_0/E)^{1/2}$, where E_0 is the energy of the bound state in the delta-function potential.

The complete derivation of the wave function (7.72) *will be left as an exercise for the reader.*

Another general method of deriving this Bloch wave function for the periodic δ-function model utilizes the method of Green's functions. Such a calculation has also been carried out by Saxon and Hutner.[1]

Electron Motion near Energy-band Edges

It is observed that the discontinuities in electron energy are determined by the same equation that determines the condition for the interference of reflected X rays from adjacent lattice points (or lattice planes in the three-dimensional case) of a crystal (see Chap. 1). The condition (7.67) is referred to as the Bragg condition. The behavior of electrons and the behavior of X rays in a periodic lattice are analogous. The electron-energy discontinuity corresponds to those wave numbers κ that give rise to interference of the De Broglie waves which are incident and reflected from a lattice point and would correspond to a vanishing electron group velocity at the edge of the energy band. We have determined in the preceding chapter that in the free-electron case the classical velocity of the electron and the group velocity of its corresponding wave packet are identical and related to the electron energy by the following equation:

$$v = \frac{1}{\hbar}\frac{dE}{d\kappa} \tag{7.73}$$

The vanishing of the electron velocity at the band edge indicates that the electron velocity (and therefore $dE/d\kappa$) starts to decrease for wave numbers which are near $\pm m\pi/z_0$, and it continues to decrease until κ reaches the value $\pm m\pi/z_0$ at which time v vanishes. Thus, if an electric field is applied to the crystal, the electron absorbs energy and increases its velocity only if its kinetic energy does not correspond to wave vectors near the edge of the energy band. If the absorption of energy gives the electron a net energy which is near a band edge, it will decrease its velocity instead of increasing it. Should the electron absorb exactly enough energy to reach the band edge, its velocity would vanish. A very physical description of this effect may be given by considering the motion of a wave packet near a band edge (Fig. 7.5).

As we have seen in the preceding chapter, a localization of an electron in space requires a sacrifice of the exact knowledge of its momentum $\hbar\kappa$. We thus describe an electron in a crystal in terms of a wave packet which is made up of a number of monochromatic waves, each with a slightly different wave number κ and with the packet centering about some average wave number $\bar{\kappa}$. Such a packet is shown in Fig. 7.5*a* where it is assumed that there is an external electric field applied to the crystal.

[1] Saxon and Hutner, *loc. cit.*

Suppose now that an electric field with sufficient magnitude to cause the wave packet just to surpass the band edge is applied. Those parts of the wave packet which have a maximum value of wave vector will be diffracted (i.e., their momenta will change direction from $\hbar\pi/z_0$ to $-\hbar\pi/z_0$) and will represent a negative contribution to the total wave packet. Such a wave packet, shown in Fig. 7.5*b*, with the positive contributions on the right and the negative contributions to the left, represents a slowing down of the electron. A zero velocity for the electron would correspond to equal amounts of positive and negative contributions to the wave packet (Fig. 7.5*c*).

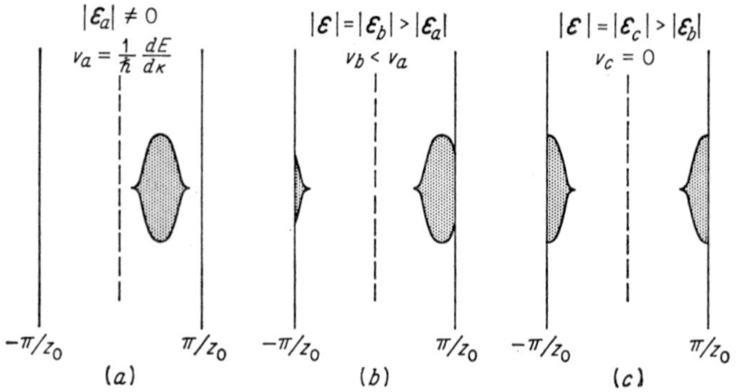

Fig. 7.5. The motion of an electron wave packet near a band edge.

The presence of the electric field changes the electron distribution function because of an alteration of the energy appearing in the Boltzmann factor. The result is that there are more states which correspond to positive momentum than there are states which correspond to negative momentum. For this reason, a further increase in the value of the electric field cannot cause the electron wave packet which was originally moving in the positive direction now to move in the negative direction. Thus, Fig. 7.5*c* represents the limiting effect of the application of an electric field to the electron wave packet (unless, of course, enough energy is supplied to excite the electron to a higher band).

The foregoing description of the behavior of electrons in crystals indicates that these electrons do not appear to obey the classical Newtonian equations of motion in the region of momentum space which is near the energy-band extrema. We shall return to this question later in this section when we discuss the concept of effective mass.

Bandwidth and Electron Freedom

The width of the energy bands depends on the relative freedom which the electrons have in the crystal. The energy bands to which the low-energy electrons (i.e., low kinetic energy in deep potential wells) belong should therefore be narrow. In the limit where an electron has practically no freedom to move about in the crystal (such as a 1*s* electron of Na in Na metal) the electron energy band collapses into a discrete energy level of the crystal. On the other hand, the kinetic energy of electrons increases if the electrons are not so tightly bound to the ions in the lattice and thus move about with much more relative freedom. The greater the electron kinetic energy (and therefore the greater the magnitude of the wave number κ), the wider is the energy band. This result was also obtained in our analysis of the energy-level structure of ionic crystals (Chap. 3) and is, in general, a feature of the behavior of

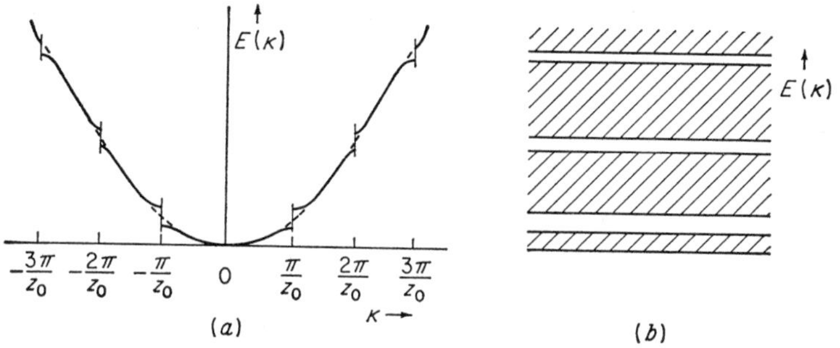

Fig. 7.6. (*a*) Electronic energy as a function of the wave vector in a one-dimensional crystal. (*b*) Energy bands.

mobile electrons in any structure which is characterized by a periodic potential.

The actual widths of the energy bands are calculated from the transcendental equation (7.64) [or (7.65)] which relates the electron energy (through its relation to κ_0) to the actual momentum $\hbar\kappa$ of the electron in the crystal.

Number of Energy Levels in an Energy Band

Let us now assume that we have a finite one-dimensional crystal, containing N atoms each separated from each other by a distance z_0. The length of such a crystal is then Nz_0. The boundary conditions imposed by the requirement that the electrons be confined to within this crystal leads to a restriction on κ which is identical to that of the case of electrons in a one-dimensional box of length Nz_0. This problem was treated in the preceding chapter in connection with the free-electron theory. We found there that the boundary conditions at the edges of the box lead to the requirement that $\sin \kappa(Nz_0) = 0$, which is satisfied when $\kappa = \pm m\pi/Nz_0$ (where m is any integer). The number of energy levels in an energy band is equal to the number of nodes in the electron wave function, which in turn is equal to the maximum value of the integer $m = \bar{m}$.[1] Thus, if $\bar{m}$ represents the number of energy levels in an energy band, the maximum value of the absolute value of the wave vector $\boldsymbol{\kappa}$ is $\bar{m}\pi/Nz_0$. However, according to our previous analysis, the absolute value of the magnitude $|\kappa|$ is confined to a range of π/z_0 for any energy band, and therefore the maximum value of $|\kappa|$ is also π/z_0. Thus, we have the equality

$$|\kappa_{\max}| = \frac{\pi}{z_0} = \frac{\bar{m}\pi}{Nz_0}$$

or

$$\bar{m} = N$$

i.e., the number of energy levels in a given energy band is equal to the number of atoms in the crystal.

According to the Pauli exclusion principle, these N energy levels can be filled with $2N$ electrons (each level may be occupied by two electrons, each electron with an opposite spin orientation). Thus we see once again that in the case of a monovalent metal, where there is only one electron per ion, the electrons occupy the lower half of the lowest energy band. The electrons at the top of this distribution have contiguous energy levels available to them so that electric fields readily excite them and give rise to electrical conduction. Consequently, a monovalent metal is a good electrical conductor. On the other hand, a divalent material is characterized by a filling of the lowest energy band, leaving no nearby energy levels available to the electrons. Such a material should be a good electrical insulator (unless, of course, the energy bands overlap). We may continue this process to a trivalent metal which is characterized by a full lower band and an upper band which is half full. Such a material should, once again, be a good electrical conductor.

Hole and Electron Current

Let us, for the moment, consider an insulating material with its lowest band filled with electrons but with the next energy band close enough so that the amount of energy available in the laboratory is sufficient to excite electrons into it. Suppose that, of the $2N$ electrons in the lowest energy band, n have been excited into the next higher energy band. Let us label the states which are filled by the $2N - n$ electrons as μ and the unfilled states by ν (see Fig. 7.7). If an external electric field is applied in the z direction, a current j_z will be induced. In the case where the energy band is full, there can be no current, since electrons within the full band cannot absorb energy. Let us express this

[1] This follows from the *oscillation theorem*. For a proof see P. M. Morse and H. Feshbach, "Methods of Theoretical Physics," Pt. I, chap. 6, McGraw-Hill Book Company, Inc., New York, 1953.

vanishing current in terms of current due to electrons in the μ states and electrons in the ν states.

$$j_z = -e \sum_{\mu} v_z^{(\mu)} - e \sum_{\nu} v_z^{(\nu)} = 0$$

or

$$-e \sum_{\mu} v_z^{(\mu)} = +e \sum_{\nu} v_z^{(\nu)}$$

Suppose now that the states ν are emptied by supplying the sufficient amount of energy to excite them into the next higher energy band. The

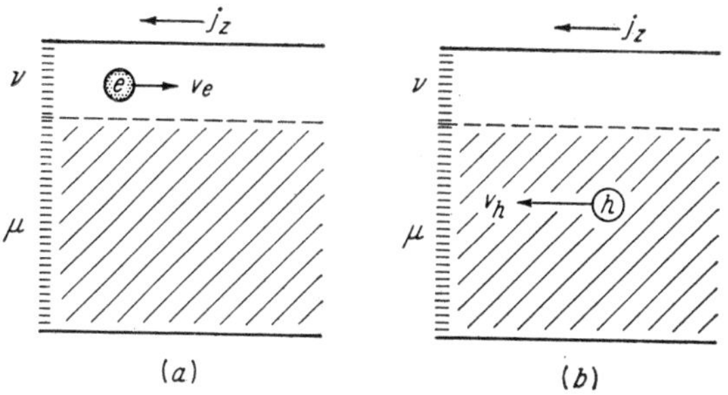

Fig. 7.7 Positive-hole current. Equivalent representations of an electrical current in a partially filled energy band is shown in (a) where the electron ⓔ is moving to the right in the ν-energy region and (b) the electron vacancy ⓗ is moving to the left in the μ-energy region.

application of a small electric field will now be able to excite μ electrons into the unfilled ν-energy levels and give rise to an electrical current

$$j_z = -e \sum_{\mu} v_z^{(\mu)} = +e \sum v_z^{(\nu)}$$

This excitation of electrons out of the μ states and into the ν states leaves vacancies which will be filled by other μ electrons. Thus, as the negative electrons move in one direction, giving rise to a current, *positive holes* will move in the opposite direction. This result is seen by combining the two equations above. The electrical current which is carried by the negative electrons from the μ states may thus be equally well described by electrical current which is carried by electron vacancies (positive holes) from the ν states, under the assumption that no other charges are present in the energy band (see Fig. 7.7). This concept is referred to as *positive-hole current* and is an essential property of p-type semiconductors (see Chap. 9).

Effective Mass

It was pointed out earlier in this section that in the regions of momentum space near the energy-band discontinuities the electrons do not appear to obey Newton's classical equations of motion. We shall now elaborate on this by considering the effect of an external force on an electron (which is described in terms of its wave-packet representation). We have discovered previously that the group velocity of the wave packet which describes the mobile electron is the same as the classical velocity of this electron (in the free-electron case). This result was obtained by combining the expression for the group velocity (6.93) with the energy-momentum relationship of a free electron (7.63). However, the free-electron energy-momentum relationship is no longer valid if we are considering the motion of an electron in a periodic potential. The true energy-momentum relationship (for the one-dimensional crystal) is rather given by the transcendental equation (7.65) [which in the case of the Dirac-delta-function potential reduces to the form of Eqs. (7.69)]. The electrons that have energies near the center of the energy band come very close to obeying the form of the classical equations of motion, since in this region the energy-momentum relationship is parabolic, as it is in the free-electron case. However, we do not usually observe the electrons when they are in the center of nearly filled energy bands, since they are unable to absorb small amounts of energy and thereby interact with externally applied fields. We can observe these electrons in nearly filled bands only if they are given sufficient energy to excite them out of the region of filled energy levels. Thus we often observe effects of the interaction between externally applied fields and the mobile electrons which are near the edges of the energy bands (electrons near the top of the lower energy band or near the bottom of the next higher band). Since the energy-momentum relationship is not necessarily parabolic near band edges, there is no longer any reason to expect that the group velocity of the wave packets which describe the electron motion can be identified with the classical velocity of the electron (which is defined as the ratio of the electron momentum to its mass). In the special cases where the energy-momentum relationship is parabolic at the band edge, it is possible to associate an effective mass with the electron (not necessarily equal to the free-electron mass).

Let us then consider the effect of an external force on the motion of electrons which are near the edge of an energy band. We shall assume that the external force F acts on a wave packet during an increment of time δt. The increment of energy which is given to the wave packet in this time is [using Eq. (6.93)]

$$\delta E = Fv\,\delta t = \frac{F}{\hbar}\frac{dE}{d\kappa}\,\delta t \tag{7.74}$$

The application of the external force to the wave packet produces a corresponding change in the wave number κ by an amount of $\delta\kappa$. Thus the increment of energy given to the wave packet may also be expressed in the form

$$\delta E = \frac{dE}{d\kappa}\,\delta\kappa \tag{7.75}$$

Equating the right-hand sides of Eqs. (7.74) and (7.75), we have the following equation of motion for the wave packet:

$$F = \hbar\frac{d\kappa}{dt} \tag{7.76}$$

The equation of motion (7.76) for the wave packet replaces the Newtonian equation of motion $F = ma$. The applied force causes the group velocity of the wave packet to change in time at the rate

$$\frac{dv}{dt} = \frac{1}{\hbar}\frac{d}{dt}\frac{dE}{d\kappa} = \frac{1}{\hbar}\frac{d^2E}{d\kappa^2}\frac{d\kappa}{dt} = \frac{1}{\hbar^2}\frac{d^2E}{d\kappa^2}F \tag{7.77}$$

This equation was obtained with the aid of Eqs. (6.93) and (7.76). According to Newton's first law, the acceleration produced in a particle which was initially moving at a constant velocity v (or was at rest) and is acted upon by a force F is directly proportional to the magnitude of the force, with a constant of proportionality being defined as the inverse of the inertial mass of the particle. Thus, *if it is possible to express the equation of motion* (7.77) *in the Newtonian form,* we can define an effective mass according to the equation[1]

$$\frac{1}{m^*} = \frac{1}{\hbar^2}\frac{d^2E}{d\kappa^2} \tag{7.78}$$

If the right-hand side of Eq. (7.78) is a constant, independent of the electron momentum, the equation of motion is exactly of the Newtonian form, although the effective mass m^* is not necessarily the same as the inertial mass of the particle in free space. In this case, as a result of its interaction with the crystal lattice, the electron would behave as though it had a constant inertial mass m^*, different from the free-electron inertial mass m_0. For the case of the free particle, the use of the free-particle energy-momentum relation (7.63) in Eq. (7.78) leads to the obvious equality of the effective mass and the free-particle inertial mass.

The effective mass of electrons near the edges of an energy band as defined by Eq. (7.78) is not, in general, a constant; rather it is a complicated function of the electron momentum $\hbar\kappa$. This is in accordance with a nonparabolic energy-momentum relationship. The actual form of the effective mass for electrons in a one-dimensional crystal may

[1] A criticism of the effective-mass theory is given by E. N. Adams and P. N. Argyres, *Phys. Rev.*, **102:** 605 (1956). They find that (7.78) is valid only to the first order in the applied fields. A generally rigorous treatment is given by J. M. Luttinger and W. Kohn, *Phys. Rev.*, **97:** 869 (1955).

be obtained by combining its definition (7.78) with the energy-momentum relation (7.69). In the chapter which follows, we shall obtain the equation of motion for an electron in a three-dimensional crystal. We shall discover there that, in its most general form, the proportionality between the force applied to a wave packet and the acceleration which is thereby produced is given by the so-called *effective-mass tensor*

$$\frac{1}{m_{ij}} = \frac{1}{\hbar^2} \frac{\partial^2 E(\boldsymbol{\kappa})}{\partial \kappa_i \partial \kappa_j} \qquad i, j = 1, 2, 3 \tag{7.79}$$

A nonvanishing of the off-diagonal elements of this tensor indicates that, in a crystal, the acceleration of a wave packet produced by an applied force is not necessarily parallel to that force. We shall also see in Chap. 8 how symmetry in the elements of the effective-mass tensor is intimately related to the spatial symmetry of the crystal lattice. Thus, in the most general case, the effective mass of an electron in a three-dimensional crystal is not only dependent on the magnitude of the electron momentum, but it is also dependent on its direction.

The behavior of electrons which have energies near the edge of an energy band and which are under the influence of an external force is one of the simplest and oldest examples of momentum-dependent forces existing inside a medium which contains a high density of particles. [Brueckner and his collaborators have shown that the introduction of momentum-dependent forces between nucleons, inside complex nuclei (the sources of these forces being, of course, entirely different from those in the crystal case) and the resulting introduction of an effective mass of the nucleons were able to account for several nuclear phenomena, among them being the saturation of nuclear forces.[1]]

7.3 The imperfect crystal: effects of substitutional impurities

In the preceding sections of this chapter we have analyzed the behavior of electrons which are under the influence of the potential of a perfect one-dimensional crystal. Let us now suppose that we have a one-dimensional crystal in which there is a substitutional foreign impurity. That is to say, one of the lattice sites will be assumed to be occupied by a different type of atom (with a correspondingly different potential) than the rest of the lattice sites. Under such conditions, we would like to determine the energy-level spectrum of the mobile electrons in the crystal.

Before carrying out a mathematical analysis of this problem, we can say, from a qualitative point of view, what will happen to the energy-level spectrum. We have found that the potential of a perfect periodic lattice would give rise to an electron wave function which has the form

[1] K. A. Brueckner, *Phys. Rev.*, **97**: 1353 (1955).

of a progressive wave and to an associated energy-band spectrum. The introduction of a foreign impurity in the lattice and its associated nonconforming potential would destroy the perfect periodicity of the lattice and would thereby destroy the progressive-wave solution for the electron wave function. One would therefore expect that a foreign impurity should have the effect of causing a peaking of the electron wave function in its vicinity and also introduce corresponding discrete energy levels in the forbidden-energy gap of the perfect-crystal solution. From the point of view of the electron motion, we would interpret this result as meaning that, as the freely moving electron comes into the vicinity of a foreign atom, it may be trapped in a bound state of that atom and remain in this state until it is ejected by the interaction with another freely moving electron. Also, the impurity atom may hinder the motion of the conduction electron by repelling it, thereby destroying the homogeneous description of the electron as a progressive wave in the crystal. In either case, one would expect the misbehaving electron to have associated with it discrete energy levels within the forbidden region. These are referred to as *impurity states.* The electron density (the square of the electron wave function) should therefore be greater in the vicinity of the foreign impurities than it would be in the vicinity of the normal ion in the lattice.

We may analyze this problem from a mathematical point of view by considering the conditions under which the electron wave becomes resonant within the potential well of the foreign impurity. In terms of the scattering of waves, the resonant condition may be characterized by an outgoing attenuated wave with a finite amplitude and no corresponding incoming wave (i.e., the wave vector $\boldsymbol{\kappa}$ which is associated with the outgoing wave must be a pure imaginary number; otherwise we would be describing the impurity as a source of electrons). The outgoing wave must be attenuated to a negligible amplitude within some characteristic distance $1/\kappa$ from the center of the foreign-impurity atom. According to the energy-momentum relationship (7.65), an imaginary wave vector $\boldsymbol{\kappa}$ would correspond to an energy level (an impurity state) within the forbidden gap. We shall see in Chap. 9 how the existence of impurity states in the forbidden-energy gap is very crucial to the operation of one type of semiconductor.

According to the definition of the S matrix, we see that the resonance condition is met only when the S matrix is singular.[1] Thus we can calculate the position of the impurity state in the forbidden-energy gap

[1] This general idea has been investigated recently in elementary particle theory in relation to the identification of the poles of the S matrix with the creation of particles in elementary particle-decay schemes. For a general discussion and bibliography on recent work in this area, see G. F. Chew, "S-Matrix Theory of Strong Interactions," W. A. Benjamin, Inc., New York, 1961.

by requiring that each element of the S matrix be infinite. For the purpose of illustration, we shall once again consider the case in which the potential energy of each lattice ion may be assumed to have the Dirac-delta-function form. Let us denote the unscattered waves to the left and to the right of the impurity center by $\varphi_-(z)$ and $\varphi_+(z)$, respectively. Then the total wave function on the left-hand side and on the right-hand side of the scattering potential has forms which are generalizations of Eqs. (7.33) and (7.34):

$$\psi_l = A_+\varphi_+(z) + B_-\varphi_-(z) \tag{7.33'}$$
$$\psi_r = B_+\varphi_+(z) + A_-\varphi_-(z) \tag{7.34'}$$

According to the definition of the S matrix,

$$B_- = S_{11}A_+ + S_{12}A_- \tag{7.27a}$$
$$B_+ = S_{21}A_+ + S_{22}A_- \tag{7.27b}$$

Let us assume that the impurity atom is located at the position $z = z_i$ and that its potential has the Dirac-delta-function form. Applying the boundary conditions (7.13) and (7.16) at $z = z_i$, we have

$$A_+\varphi_+(z_i) + B_-\varphi_-(z_i) = B_+\varphi_+(z_i) + A_-\varphi_-(z_i) \tag{7.80}$$
$$A_+\varphi_+'(z_i) + B_-\varphi_-'(z_i) - B_+\varphi_+'(z_i) - A_-\varphi_-'(z_i) = \frac{2m}{\hbar^2}\eta_i[A_+\varphi_+(z_i) + B_-\varphi_-(z_i)] \tag{7.81}$$

where $\eta_i \neq \eta$ is the strength of the Dirac-delta-function potential at the impurity site. We have used the symbol $\varphi'(z_i)$ to denote the derivative of φ with respect to z, evaluated at the impurity site $z = z_i$. If we now combine Eqs. (7.80), (7.81), and (7.27), we obtain the elements of the S matrix as follows:

$$S_{11} = \frac{-[(2m/\hbar^2)\eta_i]\varphi_+(z_i)\varphi_+(z_i)}{W + [(2m/\hbar^2)\eta_i]\varphi_+(z_i)\varphi_-(z_i)} \tag{7.82}$$
$$S_{22} = S_{11}\frac{\varphi_-(z_i)\varphi_-(z_i)}{\varphi_+(z_i)\varphi_+(z_i)} \tag{7.83}$$
$$S_{12} = S_{21} = 1 + S_{11} = \frac{W}{W + [(2m/\hbar^2)\eta_i]\varphi_+(z_i)\varphi_-(z_i)} \tag{7.84}$$

where
$$W = \varphi_+(z_i)\varphi_-'(z_i) - \varphi_-(z_i)\varphi_+'(z_i) \tag{7.85}$$

is the Wronskian.

According to the discussion above, a bound state is determined by the condition that the S matrix be singular. This is the case when the denominators of the elements of the S matrix vanish or when

$$W = -\frac{2m}{\hbar^2}\eta_i\varphi_+(z_i)\varphi_-(z_i) \tag{7.86}$$

Let us choose the impurity atom to be located at the origin ($z_i = 0$) and take the functions φ_+ to be the Bloch wave functions (7.72),

$$\varphi_+ = C[e^{i\kappa z_0} \sin \kappa_0 z - \sin \kappa_0(z - z_0)] \tag{7.87}$$
$$\varphi_- = C[e^{-i\kappa z_0} \sin \kappa_0 z - \sin \kappa_0(z - z_0)] \tag{7.88}$$

where C is a constant, independent of the coordinate z (and will cancel out in the calculation). If we now substitute Eqs. (7.87) and (7.88) into Eq. (7.86), we have

$$-2i\kappa_0 \sin \kappa z_0 + \left(\frac{2m}{\hbar^2}\,\eta_i\right) \sin \kappa_0 z_0 = 0 \tag{7.89}$$

We now take κ to have the complex form

$$\kappa = \frac{m\pi}{z_0} + i\xi \tag{7.90}$$

where ξ is a positive real number. The energy-band equation (7.69a) then takes the form

$$(-1)^m \cosh \xi z_0 = \cos \kappa_0 z_0 + \gamma \sin \kappa_0 z_0 \tag{7.91}$$

and Eq. (7.89) takes the form

$$(-1)^m \sinh \xi z_0 = -\gamma_i \sin \kappa_0 z_0 \tag{7.92}$$

where

$$\gamma = \frac{\eta \kappa_0}{2E}$$

and

$$\gamma_i = \frac{\eta_i \kappa_0}{2E}$$

Squaring Eqs. (7.91) and (7.92) and making use of the identity

$$\cosh^2 x - \sinh^2 x = 1$$

we obtain the following relationship which determines the energy of the impurity states as a function of the strength of the impurity potential:

$$\cot \kappa_0 z_0 = \frac{1}{2\gamma}\,[1 + (\gamma_i^2 - \gamma^2)] \tag{7.93}$$

This equation may now be expressed in the following energy-dependent form:

$$\cot \left(\frac{E}{E_0}\right)^{1/2} = \frac{E_0 E}{<V>}\left(1 + \frac{\eta_i^2 - \eta^2}{4z_0^2 E_0 E}\right) \qquad \eta_i \neq \eta \tag{7.94}$$

where

$$E_0 \equiv \frac{\hbar^2}{2mz_0^2} \cong \frac{3.8}{z_0^2(\text{Å})} \quad \text{ev}$$

and where $<V>$ is the average value of the crystal potential.[1] *The values of energy E which satisfy Eq.* (7.94) *are the locations of the discrete impurity energy levels in the forbidden-energy gap.*

It is interesting to note that E_0 is of the same order of magnitude as the Fermi energy E_F [Eq. (6.45)]. Since E cannot be greater than E_F in metals, the maximum value of the ratio E/E_0 cannot be far different from unity. Also, for $\eta_i > \eta$, the right-hand side of Eq. (7.94) is always positive. Since $\cot x < 0$ for $(\pi/2) < x < \pi$, the solutions of Eq. (7.94) may be obtained by considering E only within the restricted range

$$0 < E < \left(\frac{\pi}{2}\right)^2 E_0 \tag{7.95}$$

We have chosen to consider the effect of an imperfection in a perfect crystal due to the substitutional foreign impurity only for the purposes of simplicity in illustrating some of the effects of imperfections in crystals. Some of the other types of imperfections in crystals which give rise to discrete states in the forbidden-energy gap are due to (1) the existence of the natural surface of the crystal, (2) interstitial foreign impurities in the crystal, (3) ion vacancies, (4) internal cracks, (5) ionic displacements, and (6) dislocations. We shall elaborate more on imperfections in crystals in Chap. 9 in our discussion of semiconductors.

7.4 Conclusions

In this chapter we have investigated the qualitative behavior of quasi-free electrons, which move about in a crystal, under the influence of the periodic potential of the lattice ions. We have discussed the case of the one-dimensional crystal simply because we can solve this problem exactly (once the potential has been specified) and with a minimum amount of mathematical detail. Many of the qualitative features of the behavior of electrons in one-dimensional crystals are not changed when we extend our model to the real three-dimensional crystal. There are, however, many features of electron behavior in three-dimensional crystals which cannot possibly be explored in an analysis of the one-dimensional crystal. These are related to the effects on the electron behavior due to the rotational symmetry properties that are associated with a three-dimensional lattice. We shall stress the effects of rotational symmetry in the following chapter where we shall treat the problem of the behavior of electrons in a three-dimensional periodic lattice.

[1] To be more exact, $<V>^{-1}$ should be replaced by (z_0/η). These two quantities may be shown to be equal only in the case of a perfect crystal [Eq. (7.71)]. However, if the number of impurity atoms is very small in comparison with the total number of atoms in the crystal, the difference between $<V>^{-1}$ and z_0/η would be correspondingly small.

8 quasi-free-electron theory: electrons in a three-dimensional periodic lattice

LET US continue our discussion of the behavior of electrons in a periodic lattice by extending the properties of the one-dimensional model (discussed in the preceding chapter) to the (more realistic) three-dimensional model. The multidimensional nature of the crystal does not destroy the essential features of the electron behavior which were derived previously. Thus, the Bloch wave function for the crystal in the three-dimensional periodic lattice now has the form

$$\psi_{\mathbf{k}}(\mathbf{r}) = u_{\mathbf{k}}(\mathbf{r})e^{i\mathbf{k}\cdot\mathbf{r}} \tag{8.1}$$

The modulating function $u_{\mathbf{k}}(\mathbf{r})$ satisfies the periodic condition for the real crystal

$$u_{\mathbf{k}}(\mathbf{r}) = u_{\mathbf{k}}(\mathbf{r} + \mathbf{n}r_0) \tag{8.2}$$

where $\mathbf{n}r_0$ is a vector which translates the location of any given lattice ion to any other (see Chap. 2).

The discontinuities in the energy as a function of the wave vector k_z occurred in the one-dimensional crystal at the multitude of *points* in k space

$$k_z = \frac{m\pi}{z_0} \qquad m = 0, \pm 1, \pm 2, \ldots$$

Similarly, the discontinuities in a two-dimensional crystal would occur along *lines* in **k** space, whereas the discontinuities in a three-dimensional crystal would lie along *planes* in **k** space. Roughly speaking, one would expect that these planes would be obtained by a superposition of three "broken-parabola" curves (Fig. 7.6) for each of the three components of the wave vector **k**. [This is not exactly the case in those crystals which are characterized by more than one atom per cell (see Chap. 2), because of the destructive interference of the scattered electron waves from each of the atoms in the unit cell. This will be discussed more fully below.]

In any case, the allowed energy values for electrons in a three-dimensional periodic lattice may be described in terms of sets of intersecting planes of discontinuity.

The condition on the electron wave vector **k** that implies an energy discontinuity follows from a generalization of the result for the one-dimensional crystal (7.67). The generalization is

$$\mathbf{k} \cdot \hat{\mathbf{n}} = \frac{m\pi}{r_0} \qquad m = 0, \pm 1, \pm 2, \ldots \tag{8.3}$$

where $\hat{\mathbf{n}}$ is a unit vector normal to a lattice plane. This condition (the Bragg condition) will be discussed more fully below.

This relation is identical with the Bragg condition for the constructive interference of reflected X rays from a set of lattice planes, separated by r_0 (see Chap. 1). Thus,

$$\mathbf{k} \cdot \hat{\mathbf{n}} = |\mathbf{k}| \cos\theta = \frac{2\pi}{\lambda} \cos\theta = \frac{m\pi}{r_0} \tag{8.3'}$$

or

$$m\lambda = 2r_0 \cos\theta$$

Considering all possible orders of reflection (i.e., different values of m) and all possible reflecting planes (r_0), Eq. (8.3) describes a set of intersecting planes in **k** space. The volume (in **k** space) which is enclosed by a given set of intersecting planes is called a *Brillouin zone.*[1]

Clearly, because of the sensitivity of physical properties on **k**, it is more convenient in a study of the behavior of electrons in a (three-dimensional) crystal to describe physical variables in **k** space than in ordinary (configuration) space. The symmetry properties of the Brillouin zones play a significant role in the electronic behavior of the solid. They are determined by the symmetry properties of the ordinary lattice. (The symmetry types which describe crystal lattices have been discussed in Chap. 2.)

8.1 The reciprocal lattice

In order to determine the nature of the Brillouin zones it is most convenient first to describe the unit cells of the ordinary lattice in terms of unit cells of a lattice in **k** space. This is possible because of the reciprocal relation between the wave vector **k** and the lattice dimensions

[1] As a general reference, see H. Jones, "The Theory of Brillouin Zones and Electronic States in Crystals," North Holland Publishing Company, Amsterdam, 1960.

[as determined by the wave vector for X rays (see Chap. 1) or by the electron wave vector] according to the Bragg condition (8.3′) or (8.3).

We have seen in Chap. 2 that the unit cell for a crystal may be defined in terms of the three noncoplanar basis vectors $(\mathbf{b}_1,\mathbf{b}_2,\mathbf{b}_3)$ from which any lattice point may be located with respect to a fixed lattice point $\mathbf{r}(0,0,0)$, according to the transformation

$$\mathbf{r}(n_1,n_2,n_3) = \mathbf{r}(0,0,0) + n_1\mathbf{b}_1 + n_2\mathbf{b}_2 + n_3\mathbf{b}_3 \tag{8.4}$$

It is recalled that (8.4) defines a *simple Bravais lattice*, while those lattices with more than one atom per cell can be described by the set of vectors

$$\mathbf{r}^{(\nu)}(n_1,n_2,n_3) = \mathbf{r}_0^{(\nu)} + n_1\mathbf{b}_1 + n_2\mathbf{b}_2 + n_3\mathbf{b}_3$$

where $\mathbf{r}_0^{(\nu)}$ represents the different atoms in the unit cell. For example, in the body-centered-cubic cell, $\mathbf{r}_0^{(\nu)}$ takes two values (i.e., two displaced vectors)

$$\begin{aligned} \mathbf{r}_0^{(1)} &= \mathbf{r}(0,0,0) \\ \mathbf{r}_0^{(2)} &= \mathbf{r}(\tfrac{1}{2},\tfrac{1}{2},\tfrac{1}{2}) \end{aligned} \tag{8.5}$$

Let us now define the set of reciprocal vectors $(\mathbf{c}_1,\mathbf{c}_2,\mathbf{c}_3)$ as follows:

$$\mathbf{c}_1 = 2\pi\frac{\mathbf{b}_2 \times \mathbf{b}_3}{(b_1b_2b_3)} \qquad \mathbf{c}_2 = 2\pi\frac{\mathbf{b}_3 \times \mathbf{b}_1}{(b_1b_2b_3)} \qquad \mathbf{c}_3 = 2\pi\frac{\mathbf{b}_1 \times \mathbf{b}_2}{(b_1b_2b_3)} \tag{8.6}$$

(the factor 2π is introduced for convenience), where

$$(b_1b_2b_3) = \mathbf{b}_1 \cdot \mathbf{b}_2 \times \mathbf{b}_3 \tag{8.7}$$

is the volume of the unit cell. The set of reciprocal basis vectors $(\mathbf{c}_1,\mathbf{c}_2,\mathbf{c}_3)$ has the property that each vector $\mathbf{c}_i$ is the perpendicular to the plane defined by the two vectors $\mathbf{b}_j$ and $\mathbf{b}_k (i \neq j \neq k = 1, 2, 3)$,[1]

$$\mathbf{b}_i \cdot \mathbf{c}_j = 2\pi\delta_{ij} \tag{8.6′}$$

Thus, an identification may be made with the direction of $\mathbf{c}_i$ and the direction of the wave vector **k** which describes a constructive interference according to the Bragg condition (8.3).

The parallelepiped spanned by the reciprocal basis vectors $(\mathbf{c}_1,\mathbf{c}_2,\mathbf{c}_3)$ is called the unit cell of the *reciprocal lattice.* It is readily verified that the volume of this cell is proportional to the reciprocal of the volume of the ordinary unit cell, i.e.,

$$\mathbf{c}_1 \cdot \mathbf{c}_2 \times \mathbf{c}_3 = \frac{(2\pi)^3}{\mathbf{b}_1 \cdot \mathbf{b}_2 \times \mathbf{b}_3} \tag{8.8}$$

[1] According to the standard notation, if (by definition) $\mathbf{b}_i$ are contravariant vectors then $\mathbf{c}_i$ are the associated covariant vectors.

Analogous to the construction of the lattice from the unit cell, according to (8.4), the reciprocal lattice is constructed from the unit cell according to a set of transformations in **k** space such that

$$\mathbf{k} + \mathbf{K}(m_1,m_2,m_3) = \mathbf{k} + m_1\mathbf{c}_1 + m_2\mathbf{c}_2 + m_3\mathbf{c}_3 \tag{8.9}$$

translates any point **k** to an equivalent point in the reciprocal lattice.

Clearly, the symmetry properties of the reciprocal lattice, defined by (8.9), are directly related to the symmetry properties of the ordinary lattice. In particular, let us now calculate the reciprocal lattices which are associated with the simple-cubic (sc), face-centered-cubic (fcc), body-centered-cubic (bcc), and hexagonal-close-packed (hcp) lattices (see Figs. 2.3 and 2.11). The latter three of these symmetry types are very commonly associated with conducting crystals.

The Simple-cubic (sc) Lattice

The simple-cubic lattice (Fig. 2.11*a*) is defined by the unit cell constructed with the three mutually orthogonal basis vectors shown in Fig. 8.1*a*. The unit cell itself is defined as that volume bounded by the set of intersecting planes that are normal to the basis vectors, contain their end points, and enclose the proper number of atoms to generate the entire lattice by translation transformations. Thus it is clear that the unit cell for the simple-cubic lattice is a cube of side r_0.

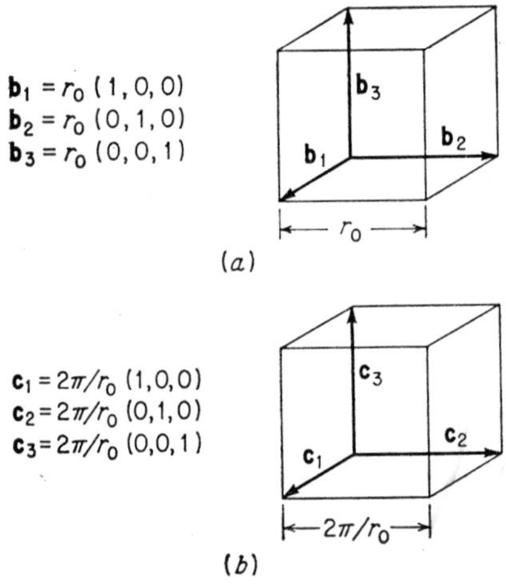

Fig. 8.1. (*a*) The unit cell of the simple-cubic lattice. (*b*) The unit cell of the reciprocal simple-cubic lattice—a simple-cubic lattice.

According to (8.6), the unit cell of the reciprocal lattice is defined by the basis vectors shown in Fig. 8.1*b*, and it is also a simple cube, with the lattice constant $2\pi/r_0$.

Diatomic lattices (such as CsCl) are frequently described in terms of an interpenetration of simple-cubic lattices, with the different atoms at the relative points (0,0,0), $(r_0/2)(1,1,1)$. Simple-cubic monatomic crystals have not been observed in nature.

The Face-centered-cubic (fcc) Lattice

The unit cell of the fcc lattice contains four atoms (see Fig. 2.11*c*) and is described by the basis vectors shown in Fig. 8.2*a*. The unit cell is then given by the volume enclosed by the intersection of the 12 planes

$$\pm x \pm y = r_0 \qquad \pm x \pm z = r_0 \qquad \pm y \pm z = r_0$$

Such a figure is called a rhombododecahedron and is shown in Fig. 8.2*b*.

The unit cell associated with the reciprocal lattice is then, according to (8.6), defined by the three basis vectors shown in Fig. 8.3*a*. These

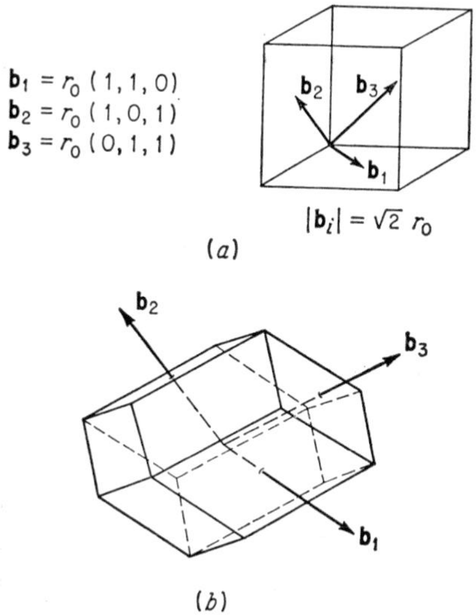

Fig. 8.2. (*a*) The basis vectors for the face-centered-cubic lattice. (*b*) The rhombododecahedron—the unit cell for the face-centered-cubic structure and the reciprocal lattice for the body-centered-cubic structure.

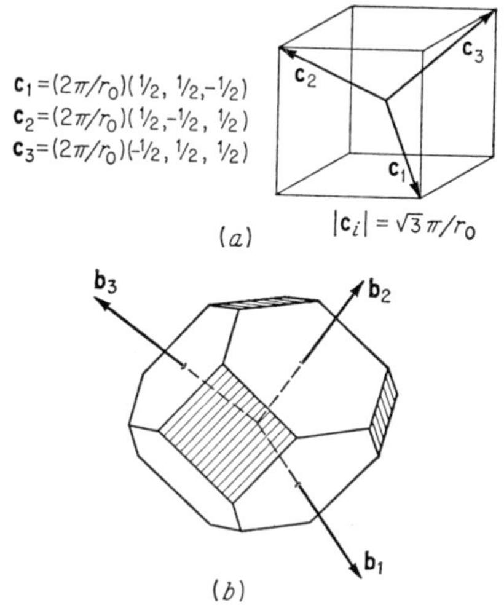

Fig. 8.3. (*a*) The basis vectors for the reciprocal face-centered-cubic structure. (*b*) The truncated octahedron—the unit cell for the body-centered-cubic structure and the reciprocal lattice for the face-centered-cubic structure.

basis vectors, however, define the unit cell of a body-centered-cubic lattice. The unit cell of the reciprocal lattice is then given by the volume enclosed by the following 14 intersecting planes:

$$k_x, k_y, k_z = \frac{\pm\pi}{r_0} \qquad \pm k_x \pm k_y \pm k_z = \frac{3\pi}{2r_0}$$

This is a truncated octahedron and is shown in Fig. 8.3*b*.[1]

[1] The reason that the octahedron is truncated by the sides of the cube (the shaded portion in Fig. 8.3*b*) is the necessity that the bcc cell can contain only two nonequivalent sites [i.e., any dimension internal to the cell must be less than or equal to the length of the body diagonal of the cube which is $2\pi/r_0$ on the side (Fig. 8.3*a*)].

Examples of fcc lattices are as follows:

1. The monatomic crystals Ca, Cu, Pb.

2. The NaCl structure may be considered as an interpenetration of two fcc lattices for each kind of ion [with the relative positions Na^+: $r_0 = (0,0,0)$; Cl^-: $r_0 = (1,0,0)$].

3. The zinc blende structure of ZnS is characterized by the interpenetration of Zn and S fcc lattices with the relative positions Zn^{++}: $r_0 = (0,0,0)$ and $S^=$; $(r_0/2)(1,1,1)$.

4. The calcium-fluoride-type crystal (CaF_2) is characterized by three interpenetrating fcc lattices, with the relative positions Ca^{2+}: $(0,0,0)$ and the two fluorine ions at $(r_0/2)(1,1,1)$ and $(r_0/2)(1,1,-1)$, respectively.

The Body-centered-cubic (bcc) Lattice

The unit cell of the bcc lattice is defined by the basis vectors shown in Fig. 8.4. The unit cell for this lattice is the truncated octahedron, defined by the 14 planes

$$x, y, z = \pm r_0 \qquad \pm x \pm y \pm z = \frac{3r_0}{2}$$

and is sketched in Fig. 8.3b.

$$\mathbf{b}_1 = r_0(1, 1, -1)$$
$$\mathbf{b}_2 = r_0(1, -1, 1)$$
$$\mathbf{b}_3 = r_0(-1, 1, 1)$$

$$|\mathbf{b}_i| = \sqrt{3}\, r_0$$

$$\mathbf{c}_1 = 2\pi/r_0\,(\tfrac{1}{2}\ \tfrac{1}{2}\ 0)$$
$$\mathbf{c}_2 = 2\pi/r_0\,(\tfrac{1}{2}\ 0\ \tfrac{1}{2})$$
$$\mathbf{c}_3 = 2\pi/r_0\,(0\ \tfrac{1}{2}\ \tfrac{1}{2})$$

$$|\mathbf{c}_i| = \sqrt{2}\,\pi/r_0$$

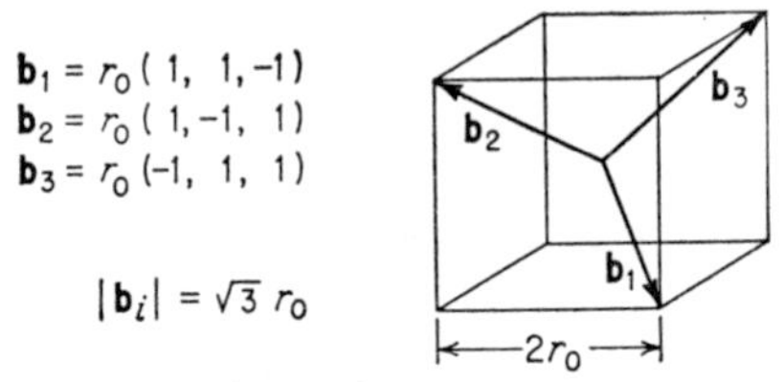

Fig. 8.4. The basis vectors for the body-centered-cubic structure.

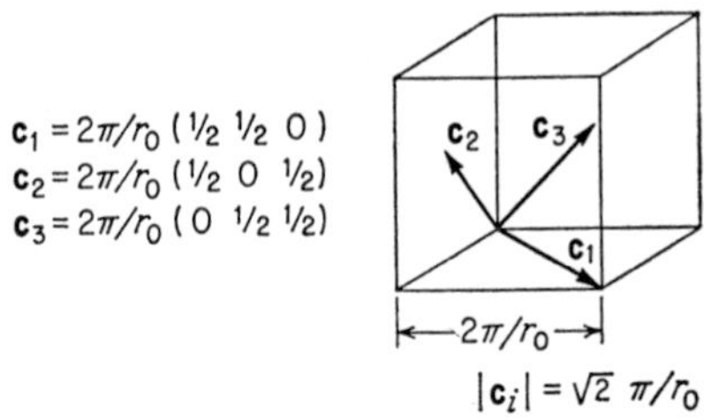

Fig. 8.5. The basis vectors for the reciprocal body-centered-cubic structure.

In accordance with (8.6), the unit cell of the reciprocal lattice is defined by the basis vectors shown in Fig. 8.5. Thus, the lattice that is reciprocal to the bcc structure is the fcc structure. The unit cell of the lattice is described by the 12-sided rhombododecahedron,

$$\pm k_x \pm k_y = \frac{\pi}{r_0} \qquad \pm k_x \pm k_z = \frac{\pi}{r_0} \qquad \pm k_y \pm k_z = \frac{\pi}{r_0}$$

and is sketched in Fig. 8.2b. The most common bcc lattices are the (monatomic) metals Na, Cs, Ba.

The Hexagonal-close-packed (hcp) Lattice

The hcp lattice (Fig. 2.3c) is defined by the basis vectors shown in Fig. 8.6. This lattice is characterized by two atoms per unit cell, and the unit cell is a hexagonal prism, bounded by the eight planes

$$x = \frac{\pm a_1}{2} \qquad y = \frac{\pm a_2}{2} \qquad y + \sqrt{3}\, z = \frac{\pm a_2}{2} \qquad \sqrt{3}\, y + z = \frac{\pm a_2}{2}$$

The reciprocal lattice is then, according to (8.6), defined by the basis vectors shown in Fig. 8.7. The unit cell of the reciprocal lattice

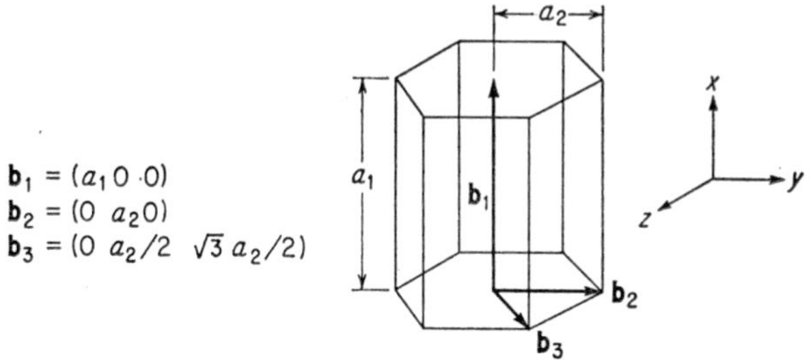

Fig. 8.6. The basis vectors for the hexagonal-close-packed structure.

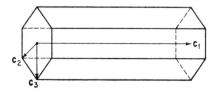

Fig. 8.7. The basis vectors for the reciprocal hexagonal-close-packed structure.

is therefore also a hexagonal prism, bounded by the eight planes

$$k_x = \frac{\pm\pi}{a_1} \qquad k_z = \frac{\pm 2\pi}{\sqrt{3}\, a_2} \qquad k_y + \sqrt{3}\, k_z = \frac{\pm 4\pi}{\sqrt{3}\, a_2}$$

$$\sqrt{3}\, k_y + k_z = \frac{\pm 4\pi}{\sqrt{3}\, a_2}$$

Typical solids which have the hcp structure are the divalent metals Zn, Cd, Be, Mg.

8.2 Planes of discontinuity in a three-dimensional lattice

Thus far, we have prescribed a set of rules which tell us how we may formally construct a **k**-space lattice (the reciprocal lattice) from the symmetry properties of the space (Bravais) lattice. It was indicated that such a construction would be a natural one to consider because of our interest in the motion of electrons in the lattice as a function of their wave vectors **k**. We shall now apply these considerations to a determination of the planes of discontinuity which occur in the three-dimensional lattice. This will then lead to the determination of the Brillouin zones.

Consider once again the Bloch form for the electron wave function [Eq. (8.1)]. Since we are concerned here only with the stationary-state problem, this function is the solution of the time-independent Schroedinger wave equation

$$\mathcal{H}\psi_{\mathbf{k}}(\mathbf{r}) \equiv \left[-\frac{\hbar^2}{2m}\nabla_r^2 + V(\mathbf{r})\right]\psi_{\mathbf{k}}(\mathbf{r}) = \epsilon(\mathbf{k})\psi_{\mathbf{k}}(\mathbf{r}) \tag{8.10}$$

where $V(\mathbf{r})$ is the electrostatic potential of the lattice, satisfying the periodicity condition [according to (8.4)]

$$V(\mathbf{r}) = V(\mathbf{r} + n_1\mathbf{b}_1 + n_2\mathbf{b}_2 + n_3\mathbf{b}_3) \tag{8.11}$$

We now wish to determine the planes in **k** space which correspond to discontinuities in the electron-energy eigenvalues $\epsilon(\mathbf{k})$ of the hamiltonian given in Eq. (8.10) [and in accordance with the periodicity of the potential (8.11)].

Because of its periodicity, the lattice potential is most conveniently treated in terms of the Fourier expansion

$$V(\mathbf{r}) = \sum_{m_1m_2m_3} V_{\mathbf{K}}e^{-i\mathbf{K}(\mathbf{m})\cdot\mathbf{r}} \tag{8.12}$$

where the integers $(m_1m_2m_3)$ predict all the points of the reciprocal lattice (characterized by the basis vectors $\mathbf{c}_1$, $\mathbf{c}_2$, $\mathbf{c}_3$) according to Eq. (8.9) and $V_{\mathbf{K}}$ is the Fourier coefficient associated with the particular reciprocal lattice point **K**. (The sign of the exponential factor is chosen for mathematical convenience.) The verification that (8.12) is compatible with the periodicity condition (8.11) is as follows:

$$V(\mathbf{r} + n_1\mathbf{b}_1 + n_2\mathbf{b}_2 + n_3\mathbf{b}_3) = \sum_{m_1m_2m_3} V_{\mathbf{K}}e^{-i\mathbf{K}\cdot\mathbf{r}}e^{-i\mathbf{K}\cdot(n_1\mathbf{b}_1+n_2\mathbf{b}_2+n_3\mathbf{b}_3)} \tag{8.13}$$

But, in accordance with (8.6′) and (8.9),

$$\mathbf{K}\cdot(n_1\mathbf{b}_1 + n_2\mathbf{b}_2 + n_3\mathbf{b}_3) = 2\pi(m_1n_1 + m_2n_2 + m_3n_3)$$
$$= 2\pi \times (\text{integer}) \tag{8.14}$$

Thus, $$e^{-i\mathbf{K}\cdot(n_1\mathbf{b}_1+n_2\mathbf{b}_2+n_3\mathbf{b}_3)} = e^{-2\pi i(\text{integer})} = 1$$

and the right-hand side of (8.13) thereby reduces to $V(\mathbf{r})$ [defined by (8.12)]. We now see how the periodic potential $V(\mathbf{r})$ may be expressed in terms of the *geometry* of the reciprocal lattice.

It is clear that any function which has the periodicity of the lattice may be expanded in a Fourier series. In particular, the modulating factor of the Bloch wave function $u_{\mathbf{k}}(\mathbf{r})$ has the periodicity of the lattice and may be expressed as a Fourier expansion:

$$u_{\mathbf{k}}(\mathbf{r}) = \sum_{m_1m_2m_3} a_{\mathbf{K}}e^{-i\mathbf{K}\cdot\mathbf{r}} \qquad \mathbf{K} = m_1\mathbf{c}_1 + m_2\mathbf{c}_2 + m_3\mathbf{c}_3 \tag{8.15a}$$

Thus, the Bloch wave function takes the form

$$\psi(\mathbf{k},\mathbf{r}) = \sum_{m_1m_2m_3} a_{\mathbf{K}}e^{-i(\mathbf{K}-\mathbf{k})\cdot\mathbf{r}} \tag{8.15b}$$

Let us now investigate some of the physical consequences of these periodic properties of $V(\mathbf{r})$ and $\psi_{\mathbf{k}}(\mathbf{r})$.

In the preceding chapter, we answered the question of the behavior of a quasi-free electron moving about under the influence of a perfectly periodic one-dimensional potential. This was accomplished by considering the scattering of the (otherwise free) electrons by the lattice ions. Extending this line of approach to the three-dimensional lattice, we generalized the point of discontinuity in energy to a plane of discontinuity. The particular planes may then be determined by a consideration of the scattering effect of a three-dimensional potential $V(\mathbf{r})$ on the (otherwise free) electrons.

In accordance with this approach, we consider the probability that the lattice potential will cause a transition from the initial free-electron state $\psi(\mathbf{k}_i) \equiv e^{i\mathbf{k}_i\cdot\mathbf{r}}$ to the final state $\psi(\mathbf{k}_f) \equiv e^{i\mathbf{k}_f\cdot\mathbf{r}}$.[1] Quantum-mechanical considerations[2] predict that such a transition probability depends on the square of the matrix element

$$\int e^{-i\mathbf{k}_f\cdot\mathbf{r}}V(\mathbf{r})e^{i\mathbf{k}_i\cdot\mathbf{r}}\,d\mathbf{r} \tag{8.16}$$

Substituting the Fourier expansion (8.12) into (8.16), we have

$$\int \psi_f^* V(\mathbf{r})\psi_i\,d\mathbf{r} = \sum_{m_1m_2m_3} V_{\mathbf{K}} \int e^{-i\mathbf{k}_f\cdot\mathbf{r}-i\mathbf{K}\cdot\mathbf{r}+i\mathbf{k}_i\cdot\mathbf{r}}\,d\mathbf{r} \tag{8.17}$$

The right-hand side of (8.17) vanishes unless

$$\Delta\mathbf{k} \equiv \mathbf{k}_i - \mathbf{k}_f = \mathbf{K} \tag{8.18}$$

Thus (8.18) represents a *selection rule* which is imposed because of the translational symmetry of the lattice. This rule says that an electron cannot be excited (*elastically*) by the lattice potential unless the momentum of the excited state differs from that of the initial state by precisely a

[1] Choosing the (more exact) Bloch wave function would not alter the result derived below.

[2] See, for example, L. I. Schiff, "Quantum Mechanics," chap. VIII, McGraw-Hill Book Company, Inc., New York, 1955.

vector of the reciprocal lattice (multiplied by $\hbar$). This is a statement of the coherence of the scattered electron waves from the lattice ions.

In view of the periodicity of the Bloch wave functions, it is clear [according to (8.15)] that the same selection rule would have been obtained had we chosen the Bloch wave functions to represent the free-electron states.

The planes of discontinuity occur [according to the Bragg condition (8.3)] whenever the lattice potential causes a total reflection of the electron wave, thus maintaining a constant energy in the incident and reflected waves. A constant energy in the initial and final waves in turn corresponds to the condition

$$k_i^2 = k_f^2 = |\mathbf{k}_i - \mathbf{K}|^2 \qquad (8.19)$$

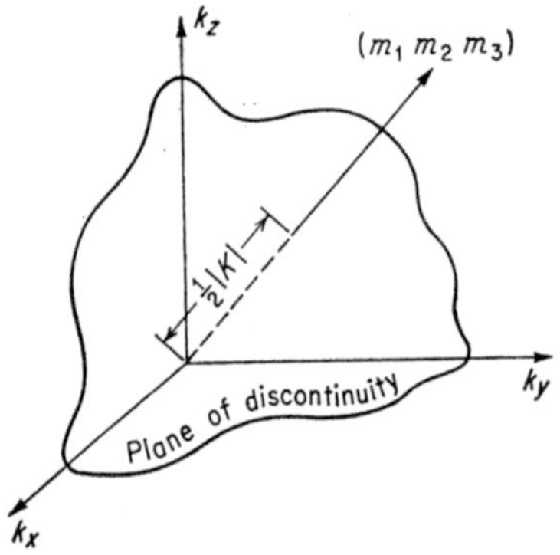

Fig. 8.8. Planes of energy discontinuity in a three-dimensional lattice.

where the right-hand side of (8.19) follows from the selection rule (8.18). This result is equivalent to the following condition:

$$\mathbf{k}_i \cdot \mathbf{K} = \tfrac{1}{2}K^2 \qquad (8.20)$$

But this is the equation for a set of planes [one for each set of integers (m_1,m_2,m_3)] in the space of the reciprocal lattice (**k** space). A particular plane, corresponding to (m_1,m_2,m_3), is perpendicular to the vector which joins the point $\mathbf{m} = (m_1,m_2,m_3)$ (in **k** space) to the origin and is a distance $\frac{1}{2}|\mathbf{K}|$ from the origin (see Fig. 8.8).

8.3 Brillouin zones

A given order of reflection [i.e., a set (m_1,m_2,m_3)] will correspond to a particular set of planes of energy discontinuity in the reciprocal lattice which are defined according to Eq. (8.20). This set of planes are the boundaries of a volume in **k** space in which the interior points are the states of the electrons (i.e., the allowed values of **k**) for the order of reflection **m**. The points on the boundaries (i.e., the reflection points) correspond to those values of electron momenta which vanish. The volume of **k** space (for each reflection order **m**) is called a Brillouin zone. In general, there is an energy gap between the upper edge of one Brillouin zone and the lower edge of the next zone. In a perfectly periodic crystal, there are no energy levels in this gap; thus there exists, as in the one-dimension problem (Chap. 7), a threshold value for the excitation of mobile electrons which are near a zone edge. [There are, however, many instances in which there is an overlap between zones (see Fig. 8.11*b*).] If all points **k** in this zone are occupied, the crystal is not a conductor.

The Reduced Zone

The addition of the wave vector **K** (i.e., any point in the reciprocal lattice) to the electron wave vector **k** introduces the factor $e^{i\mathbf{K}\cdot\mathbf{r}}$ into the Bloch wave function (8.1). This factor has the periodicity of the lattice and therefore it can be included in the modulating function $u_{\mathbf{k}}(\mathbf{r})$. Thus the translational symmetry of the lattice can be described by taking the wave functions to be multivalued functions of **k** within the unit cell of the reciprocal lattice. Consequently, since all properties of the system are determined by these wave functions, it is only the unit cell of the reciprocal lattice which need be considered. This cell (the first Brillouin zone) is called the *reduced zone.* Thus it has been illustrated once again how the inherent symmetry of the system permits a reduction from the problem which entails many ($\sim 10^{24}$) atoms to the single- (or few-) atom system.

The Structure Factor

The existence of more than one atom per unit cell of the Bravais lattice introduces the possibility that particular Fourier coefficients $V_{\mathbf{K}_0}$ of the lattice potential might vanish. This is due to a phase cancellation of the reciprocal lattice vectors associated with the different atoms in the unit cell. Under such conditions, the plane of discontinuity, defined by the equation,

$$\mathbf{k}_i \cdot \mathbf{K}_0 = \tfrac{1}{2}K_0^2 \tag{8.20$'$}$$

would be absent from the bounding surfaces of the reduced zone.

If the unit cell of the Bravais lattice contains s atoms, defined by the displacement vectors [see Eq. (8.5)]

$$\mathbf{R}_t = (u_t\mathbf{b}_1, v_t\mathbf{b}_2, w_t\mathbf{b}_3) \qquad \begin{array}{l} t = 1, 2, \ldots, s \\ u_0 = v_0 = w_0 = 1 \end{array} \tag{8.21}$$

then the Fourier coefficient $V_{\mathbf{K}}$ may be expanded in the form

$$V_{\mathbf{K}} = \sum_{t=1}^{s} U_{\mathbf{K}t} e^{2\pi i(m_1u_t + m_2v_t + m_3w_t)} \equiv \sum_{t=1}^{s} U_{\mathbf{K}t} e^{2\pi i\mathbf{K}\cdot\mathbf{R}_t} \tag{8.21$'$}$$

In the particular case in which the different atoms in the unit cell are all of the same type, the coefficients $U_{\mathbf{K}t}$ are the same for each of these atoms. In this case, the coefficients $U_{\mathbf{K}t} = U_{\mathbf{K}}$ may be taken out of the summation in (8.21′) and we have

$$V_{\mathbf{K}} = U_{\mathbf{K}} S_{\mathbf{m}}$$

where
$$S_{\mathbf{m}} = \sum_{t=1}^{s} e^{2\pi i(m_1 u_t + m_2 v_t + m_3 w_t)} \tag{8.22}$$

is called the *structure factor*. (This function is used extensively in X-ray analysis in determining the set of planes of a crystal which are associated with the intensity pattern of the reflected X rays.)

Thus those cases in which the structure factor vanishes correspond to a vanishing Fourier coefficient $V_{\mathbf{K}_0}$ and define a plane of the reciprocal lattice which satisfies (8.20) but is not a plane of discontinuity which bounds the reduced zone.

Construction of the reduced zone The reduced zone is constructed by the following procedure:

1. Determine all possible planes of discontinuity, according to (8.20).
2. Pick out all such planes whose structure factors are nonzero, and whose intersections enclose the smallest volume in **k** space.

As an example, let us now apply this prescription to the construction of the reduced zone for the three cubic Bravais lattices.

THE CUBIC LATTICES. According to our previous consideration of the cubic structure, the primitive basis vectors of the reciprocal lattice have the magnitudes

$$|\mathbf{c}_1| = |\mathbf{c}_2| = |\mathbf{c}_3| = \frac{2\pi}{r_0} \tag{8.23}$$

Thus
$$\begin{aligned} \mathbf{K} &= m_1\mathbf{c}_1 + m_2\mathbf{c}_2 + m_3\mathbf{c}_3 \\ &= \frac{2\pi}{r_0}(m_1\hat{\mathbf{i}} + m_2\hat{\mathbf{j}} + m_3\hat{\mathbf{k}}) \end{aligned} \tag{8.24}$$

and Eq. (8.20) reduces to

$$m_1k_x + m_2k_y + m_3k_z = \frac{\pi}{r_0}(m_1^2 + m_2^2 + m_3^2) \tag{8.25}$$

The symbol $\{|m_1|\,|m_2|\,|m_3|\}$ will be used to denote all possible planes which are a distance $\sqrt{m_1^2 + m_2^2 + m_3^2}$ from the origin. We shall consider the

$$\begin{aligned} &6 \text{ planes } \{100\} \equiv (\pm1,0,0),\ (0,\pm1,0),\ (0,0,\pm1) \\ &12 \text{ planes } \{110\} \equiv (\pm1,\pm1,0),\ (0,\pm1,\pm1),\ (\pm1,0,\pm1) \\ &8 \text{ planes } \{111\} \equiv (\pm1,\pm1,\pm1) \\ &6 \text{ planes } \{200\} \equiv (\pm2,0,0),\ (0,\pm2,0),\ (0,0,\pm2) \end{aligned} \tag{8.26}$$

(i) *The Simple-cubic Lattice.* Since there is only one atom per cell in the sc lattice, the structure factor is unity for all planes. The six planes

{100} correspond, according to (8.25), to the planes

$$\pm k_x = \frac{\pi}{r_0} \qquad \pm k_y = \frac{\pi}{r_0} \qquad \pm k_z = \frac{\pi}{r_0} \tag{8.27}$$

which bound a cube $(2\pi/r_0)$ on the side and with a volume $(2\pi/r_0)^3$. Thus the reduced zone for the simple-cubic lattice is also a simple cube. This means that only those electrons with the wave vectors whose three components are $\pm\pi/r_0$ are diffracted. The others will all propagate through the lattice as though they are free.

(ii) *The Face-centered-cubic Lattice.* Here we have a case in which there are four atoms in the unit cell, with displacement vectors defined by

$$(u_t,v_t,w_t) = (0,0,0),\ (0,\tfrac{1}{2},\tfrac{1}{2}),\ (\tfrac{1}{2},0,\tfrac{1}{2}),\ (\tfrac{1}{2},\tfrac{1}{2},0)$$

[according to the definition (8.21)]. Thus, according to (8.22), the structure factor is

$$\begin{aligned} S_{\mathbf{m}} &= \sum_{t=1}^{4} e^{2\pi i(m_1u_t+m_2v_t+m_3w_t)} \\ &= 1 + e^{\pi i(m_2+m_3)} + e^{\pi i(m_1+m_3)} + e^{\pi i(m_2+m_2)} \end{aligned} \tag{8.28}$$

or

$$\begin{aligned} S_{100} &= 1 + e^0 + e^{\pi i} + e^{\pi i} = 0 \\ S_{110} &= 1 + e^{\pi i} + e^{\pi i} + e^{2\pi i} = 0 \\ S_{111} &= 1 + e^{2\pi i} + e^{2\pi i} + e^{2\pi i} = 4 \\ S_{200} &= 1 + e^0 + e^{2\pi i} + e^{2\pi i} = 4 \end{aligned} \tag{8.28$'$}$$

The {100} and {110} planes are therefore excluded as planes of energy discontinuity. The remaining eight {111} and six {200} planes describe the 14-sided truncated octahedron (shown in Fig. 8.3*b*), which is the reduced zone in question.

(iii) *The Body-centered-cubic Lattice.* The bcc lattice has two atoms in the unit cell, defined by the displacement vectors

$$(u_t,v_t,w_t) = (0,0,0),\ (\tfrac{1}{2},\tfrac{1}{2},\tfrac{1}{2})$$

The structure factor then takes the form

$$S_{\mathbf{m}} = 1 + e^{\pi i(m_1+m_2+m_3)} = \begin{cases} 0 & m_1+m_2+m_3 \text{ odd} \\ 2 & m_1+m_2+m_3 \text{ even} \end{cases} \tag{8.29}$$

or

$$\begin{aligned} S_{100} &= S_{111} = 0 \\ S_{110} &= S_{200} = 2 \end{aligned} \tag{8.29$'$}$$

Since the 12 {110} planes enclose a minimal volume, the {200} planes need not be taken into account. Consequently, the reduced zone for the bcc lattice is the 12-sided figure (the rhombododecahedron) shown in Fig. 8.2*b*.

It should be noted that, in proceeding from the sc lattice to the bcc lattice and then to the fcc lattice, the volume of the reduced zone increases, because of the elimination of certain planes as planes of discontinuity. The increase in the volume of the reduced zone means that the number of states is increased. This is, of course, anticipated since the procedure entails an increase in the number of atoms per cell from one to two to four.

The incremental number of states per volume for a free-electron gas is

$$d\nu = 2\frac{d\mathbf{p}}{h^3} = \frac{2}{(2\pi)^3}\,d\mathbf{k} \tag{8.30}$$

Thus the number of states in the reduced zone of the simple cube, for example, is obtained by integrating (8.30) over the cubic volume which is $2\pi/r_0$ on the side. Combining this result with the definition of r_0: $r_0^{-3} = N$ (N is the number of cells per volume), we have

$$\nu = \frac{2}{(2\pi)^3}\left(\frac{2\pi}{r_0}\right)^3 = 2N \tag{8.31}$$

This result is a general one and says that the number of states (per volume) in the reduced zone (the first Brillouin zone) is just twice the number of unit cells per volume. Thus, as we have seen earlier in the text, a monovalent monatomic solid would be characterized by a half-full energy band (the first Brillouin zone) whereas a divalent monatomic solid (such as sulfur) would be characterized by a full band.

Symmetry Points in the Reduced Zone

The eigensolutions of the wave equation (8.10) depend on the symmetry properties associated with any given point **k** in the Brillouin zone because of the symmetry properties of $V(\mathbf{r})$ that are induced in the reciprocal lattice. Also, the corresponding energy values, as a function of **k**, must be determined by these symmetry points in a manner analogous to that with which the ordinary potential of the ionic lattice was treated (Chap. 4). In order to determine the underlying space group, it is necessary to know (1) the point group **G** which is associated with the reciprocal lattice and (2) the subgroup **G**(**k**) of **G** whose elements leave **k** invariant. The latter is referred to as the "group of **k**." For discussions of "the group of **k**" associated with any particular vector of the reduced zone and the associated electron wave functions, the reader is referred to Bouckaert, Smoluchowski, and Wigner;[1] Bell;[2] and Sachs.[3] Examples of the point groups associated with the reciprocal lattice points of cubic lattices are given in Table 8.1.

The symmetry points and the associated electron wave functions

[1] L. P. Bouckaert, R. Smoluchowski, and E. P. Wigner, *Phys. Rev.*, **50**: 59 (1936).
[2] D. G. Bell, *Rev. Mod. Phys.*, **26**: 311 (1954).
[3] M. Sachs, *Phys. Rev.*, **107**: 437 (1957).

$\psi(\mathbf{k},\mathbf{r})$ for the different points in the reciprocal lattice determine many of the physical properties of a crystal. Consider, for example, a semiconducting crystal (see Chap. 9) which is described by a band structure in which the top of the lowest (valence) band is at the particular reciprocal lattice point $\mathbf{k}_0$. The bottom of the next (conduction) band is also at $\mathbf{k}_0$ but is a minimum of $\Delta\epsilon$ ev above the valence band at $\mathbf{k} = \mathbf{k}_0$. Thus, an electron at the top of the valence band can be excited into the conduction band if it absorbs a minimum of $\Delta\epsilon$ ev (so as to conserve energy) and *also* absorbs a sufficient amount of angular momentum so as to comply with the conservation of angular momentum. The latter is determined

TABLE 8.1 *Point Groups Associated with Reciprocal Lattice Points* $(0 < \alpha < 1)$

Simple-cubic		*bcc*		*fcc*	
k	*Group*	**k**	*Group*	**k**	*Group*
(0,0,0) $\pi/r_0(1,1,1)$	$\mathbf{O}_h$	(0,0,0)	$\mathbf{O}_h$	(0,0,0,)	$\mathbf{O}_h$
$\pi/r_0(\alpha,1,1)$	$\mathbf{C}_{4v}$	$\pi/r_0(1,0,0)$	$\mathbf{O}_h$	$\pi/2r_0(1,2,0)$	$\mathbf{D}_{2d}$
$\pi/r_0(0,1,1)$	$\mathbf{D}_{4h}$	$\pi/2r_0(1,1,1)$	$\mathbf{T}_d$	$\pi/2r_0(\alpha,0,0)$	$\mathbf{C}_{4v}$
$\pi/r_0(1,0,0)$	$\mathbf{D}_{4h}$	$\pi/r_0(\alpha,0,0)$	$\mathbf{C}_{4v}$	$\pi/r_0(1,0,0)$	$\mathbf{D}_{4h}$
				$\pi/2r_0(1,2-\alpha,\alpha)$	$\mathbf{C}_2$

by the angular momentum associated with the wave function of the initial and final states and with the absorbed energy. The angular momenta of the initial and final states (i.e., the electron in the valence and conduction bands) are described by the crystal quantum numbers, associated with the irreducible representations of "the group of $\mathbf{k}_0$." These may generally be expressed in terms of a linear combination of atomic-orbital states. If the energy absorbed comes from an electromagnetic radiation field, its angular momentum is associated with the various multipole components of this field (and their respective polarizations). Thus, one should expect to be able to investigate the anisotropic behavior of energy bands by studying the absorption of polarized radiation by mobile electrons in crystals.[1] The process described here is called a *direct absorption process*, since, in going from the initial to the final state, **k** does not change in magnitude (nor does the group of **k** change). It is also possible for the electrons to be excited to a state in the conduction band where **k** does change, if the excitation occurs by means of a series

[1] Sachs, *loc. cit.*

of collisions (say, with phonons) in which the electron can gain or lose energy (to these phonons) *on the way*. These are called *indirect absorption processes* (see Chap. 9).

8.4 Energy bands

In the preceding chapter we have seen how the restricting influence of a perfectly periodic lattice potential on an otherwise free-electron gas led to the existence of regions in **k** space where there were no energy levels available to the electrons (i.e., the forbidden-energy gaps). In this chapter we have thus far generalized the one-dimensional problem to the three-dimensional problem by prescribing the construction of the planes of discontinuity which bound the reduced zone. As we have seen above, the symmetry properties of the energy-band extrema can be very influential in determining many of the finer details of the electronic properties of a solid. Let us now consider the behavior of the electrons near energy-band extrema. For this purpose, we first reconsider the role played by the inertial mass of the conduction electrons when they are subjected to an external force field in a three-dimensional crystal.

Effective-mass Theory

The effective mass was defined in the preceding chapter as the proportionality between the force exerted on the conduction electron (that is, $<\dot{\mathbf{p}}>$ for a wave packet) and its resulting acceleration. The result obtained was given by Eq. (7.78). Let us now rederive this result for the three-dimensional crystal, making use of the Bloch form for the electron wave function.

Using the Bloch wave function (8.15*b*), the expectation value for the electron momentum takes the form

$$\begin{aligned} <\mathbf{p}> &= \int \psi_{\mathbf{k}}^*(\mathbf{r})[-i\hbar\,\nabla\psi_{\mathbf{k}}(\mathbf{r})]\,d\mathbf{r} \\ &= \sum_{\mathbf{K},\mathbf{K}'} a_{\mathbf{K}'}^* a_{\mathbf{K}} \hbar(\mathbf{k}-\mathbf{K}) \int e^{-i(\mathbf{K}-\mathbf{K}')\cdot\mathbf{r}}\,d\mathbf{r} \\ &= \sum_{\mathbf{K}} \hbar|a_{\mathbf{K}}|^2(\mathbf{k}-\mathbf{K}) \end{aligned} \tag{8.32a}$$

Using the normalization condition

$$\int \psi_{\mathbf{k}}^*(\mathbf{r})\psi_{\mathbf{k}}(\mathbf{r})\,d\mathbf{r} = \sum_{\mathbf{K}} |a_{\mathbf{K}}|^2 = 1$$

Eq. (8.32*a*) takes the form

$$<\mathbf{p}> = \hbar\left(\mathbf{k} - \sum_{\mathbf{K}} \mathbf{K}|a_{\mathbf{K}}|^2\right) \tag{8.32b}$$

Suppose now that a constant external electric field $\boldsymbol{\varepsilon}_0$ is applied to this electron for a time increment Δt. The corresponding impulse that acts on the electron is

$$\int_0^{\Delta t} \mathbf{F}\, dt = e\mathcal{E}_0 \, \Delta t = \Delta \mathbf{P}_t = \Delta \mathbf{P}_c + \Delta \mathbf{p} \tag{8.33}$$

where $\Delta \mathbf{P}_t$ is the total increment of momentum, $\Delta \mathbf{P}_c$ is the incremental momentum imparted to the crystal, and $\Delta \mathbf{p}$ is the momentum imparted to the electron.

Correspondingly, the electron wave vector changes from $\mathbf{k}$ at $t = 0$ to $\mathbf{k} + \Delta \mathbf{k}$ at $t = \Delta t$. Thus, for a free electron it will be shown that

$$\Delta \langle \mathbf{P}_c \rangle + \Delta \langle \mathbf{p} \rangle = \hbar \, \Delta \mathbf{k} \tag{8.34}$$

If, now, the electron should have the proper momentum so as to undergo a Bragg reflection, i.e.,

$$\hbar \mathbf{k} \rightarrow \hbar(\mathbf{k} - \mathbf{K}) \tag{8.35}$$

then, to conserve momentum, the crystal must undergo a momentum change $\hbar \mathbf{K}$. Thus, from (8.35) and (8.32*a*)

$$\Delta \langle \mathbf{P}_c \rangle = \hbar \sum_{\mathbf{K}} \mathbf{K} \nabla_{\mathbf{k}} |a_{\mathbf{K}}|^2 \cdot \Delta \mathbf{k} \tag{8.36}$$

and from (8.32*b*)

$$\Delta \langle \mathbf{p} \rangle = \hbar \Big(\Delta \mathbf{k} - \sum_{\mathbf{K}} \mathbf{K} \nabla_{\mathbf{k}} |a_{\mathbf{K}}|^2 \cdot \Delta \mathbf{k} \Big) \tag{8.37}$$

Equation (8.34) follows from (8.33), (8.36), and (8.37).

The corresponding energy change is

$$\Delta \epsilon_t = \frac{(\Delta \langle \mathbf{P}_c \rangle)^2}{2M_L} + \frac{(\Delta \langle \mathbf{p} \rangle)^2}{2m} \tag{8.38}$$

where M_L is the mean mass of the lattice ions and m is the inertial mass of the electron. Since $M_L \gg m$, it is clear that the greatest portion of the kinetic-energy change following the Bragg reflection goes to the electron. For this reason, we shall neglect the change in the ionic kinetic energy. It then follows that the velocity change of the electron is

$$\Delta \langle \mathbf{v} \rangle \simeq \frac{\Delta \langle \mathbf{p} \rangle}{m} \tag{8.39}$$

On the other hand, the momentum change of the electron wave packet in the same field is $\hbar \, \Delta \mathbf{k}$. Hence, for a free-electron wave packet with a momentum change $\hbar \, \Delta \mathbf{k}$ to have the velocity change (8.39), it would have to be described by a new mass m^*, according to the relation

$$\frac{\hbar \, \Delta \mathbf{k}}{m^*} = \frac{\Delta \langle \mathbf{p} \rangle}{m} \tag{8.40}$$

Thus, the Bloch electron is considered as a free electron with an *effective* mass m^*. From (8.40) and (8.37) we have for the general case

$$\left(\frac{m}{m^*}\right)_{ij} = \delta_{ij} - \sum_{\mathbf{K}} K_i \frac{\partial}{\partial k_j} |a_{\mathbf{K}}|^2 \qquad i, j = 1, 2, 3 \tag{8.41}$$

where m^*_{ij} is called the *effective-mass tensor*. According to (8.32*b*)

$$\hbar\left(k_i - \sum_{\mathbf{K}} K_i|a_{\mathbf{K}}|^2\right) = <p_i> = m\frac{\partial\epsilon}{\partial <p_i>} = \frac{m}{\hbar}\frac{\partial\epsilon}{\partial k_i}$$

or

$$\frac{m}{\hbar^2}\frac{\partial\epsilon}{\partial k_i} = k_i - \sum_{\mathbf{K}} K_i|a_{\mathbf{K}}|^2$$

Differentiating again with respect to k_j, we have

$$\frac{m}{\hbar^2}\frac{\partial^2\epsilon}{\partial k_i \partial k_j} = \delta_{ij} - \sum_{\mathbf{K}} K_i \frac{\partial}{\partial k_j} |a_{\mathbf{K}}|^2 = \left(\frac{m}{m^*}\right)_{ij} \tag{8.42}$$

where the last step in (8.42) follows from (8.41).

Thus, the effective-mass tensor

$$m^*_{ij} = \left[\frac{1}{\hbar^2}\frac{\partial^2\epsilon(\mathbf{k})}{\partial k_i \partial k_j}\right]^{-1} \tag{8.43}$$

provides a measure of the curvature of the electron energy surfaces $\epsilon(\mathbf{k})$. Much of the early work in solid state physics assumed that these energy surfaces were isotropic, so that

$$m^*_{ij} = \frac{1}{\hbar^2}\left[\frac{\partial^2\epsilon(k^2)}{\partial k^2}\right]^{-1} = m^*\delta_{ij} = m \tag{8.44}$$

i.e., the effective mass was taken to be constant, independent of the direction of electron motion. However, the discovery of the cyclotron-resonance technique along with the development of the proper electronic and cryogenic equipment (since World War II) permitted the investigation of the anisotropic character of the energy surfaces in semiconductors and metals, through the measurement of m^*_{ij}. This will be discussed more fully in Chap. 9.

Nondegenerate Energy Bands

The functional form of the electron energy $\epsilon(\mathbf{k})$ in the neighborhood of nondegenerate extremum states (i.e., near a band edge) can be obtained by considering the group of transformations which, when applied to the point $\mathbf{k}$ of the reduced zone, leaves $\epsilon(\mathbf{k})$ unchanged. In view of the discussion of effective mass given above, the most general expression for $\epsilon(\mathbf{k})$ can be written in the form[1]

$$\epsilon(\mathbf{k}) = \frac{\hbar^2}{2m} \sum_{i=1}^{3} T_{ii} k_i^2 + \sum_{\lambda=0}^{\infty} \sum_{\mu=-\lambda}^{\lambda} R_{\lambda\mu} k^\lambda Y_\lambda^\mu(\Omega_\mathbf{k}) \tag{8.45}$$

where T_{ii} is a diagonal component of the tensor

$$T_{ij} = \frac{m}{m_{ij}^*} \tag{8.46}$$

The argument of the spherical harmonic is the solid angle subtended by the vector $\mathbf{k}$ in the reciprocal lattice, and $R_{\lambda\mu}$ is a (complex) $\mathbf{k}$-independent coefficient.

Three restraints must be imposed on the right-hand side of Eq. (8.45). These are:

1. $\epsilon(\mathbf{k})$ *must be real.* This imposes the following condition on the coefficients $R_{\lambda\mu}$:

$$R_{\lambda\mu} = (-1)^\mu R_{\lambda-\mu}^* \tag{8.47}$$

Using (8.47) in (8.45), we have

$$\epsilon(\mathbf{k}) = \frac{\hbar^2}{2m} \sum_{i=1}^{3} T_{ii} k_i^2 + \sum_{\lambda=0}^{\infty} \sum_{\mu=0}^{\lambda} (\epsilon_{\lambda\mu} + \bar{\epsilon}_{\lambda\mu}) \tag{8.48}$$

where

$$\epsilon_{\lambda\mu} = (2 - \delta_{\mu 0}) R_{\lambda\mu}^{(r)} k^\lambda P_\lambda^\mu(\cos\theta) \cos\mu\phi \tag{8.49a}$$

$$\bar{\epsilon}_{\lambda\mu} = 2R_{\lambda\mu}^{(i)} k^\lambda P_\lambda^\mu(\cos\theta) \sin\mu\phi \tag{8.49b}$$

The superscripts (r) and (i) refer to the real and imaginary components of $R_{\lambda\mu}$ and $P_\lambda^\mu(\cos\theta)$ is an associated Legendre function [for the exact definition see Eq. (4.8)].

2. $\epsilon(\mathbf{k})$ *is invariant with respect to the elements of the "group of* $\mathbf{k}$." This restriction allows only particular values for the integers λ,μ in (8.48) and restricts the relation between the diagonal components of T_{ij}. The former is completely analogous to the situation occurring in the direct lattice, and the method of determining the invariant moments $\epsilon_{\lambda\mu}$ and $\bar{\epsilon}_{\lambda\mu}$ of the energy is precisely the same as that which was used in Chap. 4 for determining the potential moments $\varphi_{\lambda\mu}$ and $\bar{\varphi}_{\lambda\mu}$.

3. $\epsilon(\mathbf{k})$ *is invariant under time reversal.* This restriction follows from the assumption that the crystalline electrostatic potential completely describes the electromagnetic interaction between the mobile electrons and the lattice and that electromagnetic interactions, in general, are

[1] *Ibid.* The first term in (8.45) represents that part of $\epsilon(\mathbf{k})$ which maintains the Newtonian (velocity-independent) mass of the electron wave packet in the crystal. The second term is expressed as a spherical harmonic expansion because of its isomorphism with the irreducible representations of the rotation group.

described by a hamiltonian which is invariant under time reversal. The possible implications of a breakdown of this assumption have been discussed more fully in the literature.[1] Any possible violation of the law of time-reversal invariance would, however, introduce extra terms in the hamiltonian which may be safely neglected here, because of their relatively small effects in conducting solids. Such a restriction requires that

$$\epsilon(\mathbf{k}) = \epsilon(-\mathbf{k}) \tag{8.50}$$

and thereby restricts $\epsilon_{\lambda\mu}$ and $\bar{\epsilon}_{\lambda\mu}$ in (8.48) to even values of λ.

Summarizing, the electron energy $\epsilon(\mathbf{k})$ may be obtained from (8.48) by first determining which moments $\epsilon_{\lambda\mu}$ and $\bar{\epsilon}_{\lambda\mu}$ are compatible with the particular "group of **k**" and then eliminating all moments with odd λ. The former procedure follows in precisely the same way as carried out previously for the direct lattice (Chap. 4), and the proper moments may be determined from Table 4.2, substituting $\epsilon_{\lambda\mu}$, $\bar{\epsilon}_{\lambda\mu}$, and **k** for $\varphi_{\lambda\mu}$, $\bar{\varphi}_{\lambda\mu}$, and **r**.

Thus, for example, at a symmetry point of the reciprocal lattice characterized by the group $\mathbf{O}_h$, the electron energy is

$$\epsilon_{\mathbf{O}_h}(\mathbf{k}) = \frac{\hbar^2 k^2}{2m} T + R_4(k_x^4 + k_y^4 + k_z^4 - \tfrac{3}{5}k^4) + \cdots \tag{8.51}$$

where $m/T \equiv m^*$ is the (isotropic) effective mass of the electron.

For the symmetry point described by the tetragonal $\mathbf{D}_{2d}$ point group

$$\epsilon_{\mathbf{D}_{2d}}(\mathbf{k}) = \frac{\hbar^2}{2m}(T_{\parallel}k_z^2 + T_{\perp}k_{\perp}^2) + R_{20}^{(r)}k^2P_2^0 + R_{40}^{(r)}k^4P_4^0 + 2R_{44}^{(r)}k^4P_4^4\cos 4\phi + \cdots \tag{8.52}$$

where $m/T_{\parallel} = m_{\parallel}$ is the effective electron mass along the C axis of the crystal and $m/T_{\perp}$ is the effective electron mass perpendicular to the C axis.

If the symmetry point is described by the orthorhombic group $\mathbf{C}_{2v}$, the electron energy has the form

$$\begin{aligned}\epsilon_{\mathbf{C}_{2v}}(\mathbf{k}) = \frac{\hbar^2}{2m}(T_{11}k_x^2 + T_{22}k_y^2 + T_{33}k_z^2) + R_{20}^{(r)}k^2P_2^0 \\ + 2R_{22}^{(r)}k^2P_2^2\cos 2\phi + R_{40}^{(r)}k^4P_4^0 \\ + 2R_{42}^{(r)}k^4P_4^2\cos 2\phi + 2R_{44}^{(r)}k^4P_4^4\cos 4\phi + \cdots\end{aligned} \tag{8.53}$$

where $m/T_{ii} = m_i^*$ are the values for the electron effective mass in each of the three mutually orthogonal directions.

The discussion of the selection rules for the absorption of polarized

[1] M. Sachs, *Ann. Phys.* (*N.Y.*), **6:** 244 (1959); M. Sachs and S. L. Schwebel, *Ann. Phys.* (*N.Y.*), **8:** 475 (1959).

radiation by crystalline (bound) atomic electrons, given in Chap. 4, applies equally to the case of the (direct) absorption by mobile electrons in conductors, using here, of course, the symmetry properties of the point in the reciprocal lattice described by the "groups of **k**."

Degenerate Energy Bands

The preceding discussion of the electron energy did not take into account those cases in which the states of the electron gas near the surfaces of the Brillouin zone are inherently degenerate. [We did, however, take account of the 2-fold degeneracy in time direction by requiring that $\epsilon(\mathbf{k})$ be dependent only on even powers of **k**.] Such a degeneracy may result from states which are, in general, linear combinations of *p*-like, *d*-like, etc., atomic orbitals. [This character of energy bands has been discussed in connection with ionic crystals (Chap 3).] In general, the dimensionalities of the irreducible representations of the "group of **k**" indicate the actual degeneracies of the states, and the correspondence of these representations with appropriate linear combinations of spherical harmonics indicate the symmetry of the wave functions which are associated with the states. This is, of course, completely analogous to the direct lattice problem, which was treated in Chap. 4.

It is a straightforward matter to determine which atomic-orbital-like wave functions are associated with the irreducible representations of the "group of **k**." Such a calculation is again analogous to the direct lattice problem and was discussed in detail in Chap. 4. Making use of the results obtained there, we give in Table 8.2 (as an example) the atomic orbitals which are associated with the representations of the tetragonal $\mathbf{C}_{4v}$ group. [This group may be associated, for example, with the points $\mathbf{k} = \pi/r_0(\alpha,1,1)$ of the simple-cubic lattice, $\mathbf{k} = \pi/r_0$ $(\alpha,0,0)$ of the body-centered-cubic lattice, and $\mathbf{k} = \pi/2r_0\ (\alpha,0,0)$ of the face-centered-cubic lattice, where $0 < \alpha < 1$ (see Table 8.1).] The notation used in Table 8.2 for the irreducible representations of the $\mathbf{C}_{4v}$ group was introduced in Table 4.3 (no. 20).

An energy band may be characterized by linear combinations of atomic-orbital states, such as those shown above. (It is observed that the energy bands characterized by ${}^1\Gamma_1$, ${}^1\Gamma_3$, and ${}^1\Gamma_4$ are nondegenerate. On the other hand, the ${}^2\Gamma_5$ energy band is 2-fold degenerate.) Clearly, a perfectly quasi-free-electron gas would be described by these group representations made up of the infinite number of orbital states, *S*, *P*, *D*, *F*, *G* . . . , which comprise the plane wave. On the other hand, in the other extreme when the valence electrons become more tightly bound to their parent ions, the number of orbital states describing the band diminishes until the case of the ground state of a perfect ionic crystal is reached. In this situation the valence electrons are described by only one orbital state. The realistic problem lies between these two limits.

It should be emphasized at this point that the discussion of electron wave functions for various points in the reduced zone has thus far depended only on the spatial symmetry at those points. We have not yet taken into account the electron spin. If we assume that the electron spin does not couple to its orbital motion (through the spin-orbit interaction), then account may be taken of this property of the electron merely by assigning a doubly degenerate spin function to each of the

TABLE 8.2 *Association of the Atomic-orbital States (up to $l = 3$) with the Single-valued Representations of the Tetragonal* $\mathbf{C}_{4v}$ *Group*

Atomic-orbital $\psi(l,m_l)$		$\mathbf{C}_{4v}$ *group representation*
Orbital state	*Component*	
^1S	$\psi(0,0)$	$^1\Gamma_1$
^1P	$\psi(1,0)$	
^1D	$\psi(2,0)$	
^1F	$\psi(3,0)$	
^1D	$\psi(2,+2) + \psi(2,-2)$	$^1\Gamma_3$
^1F	$\psi(3,+2) + \psi(3,-2)$	
^1D	$\psi(2,+2) - \psi(2,-2)$	$^1\Gamma_4$
^1F	$\psi(3,+2) - \psi(3,-2)$	
^2P	$\psi(1,\pm 1)$	$^2\Gamma_5$
^2D	$\psi(2,\pm 1)$	
^2F*	$a_1(\psi(3,+3) \pm \psi(3,-3))$ $\pm a_2(\psi(3,+1) \pm \psi(3,-1))$	$^2\Gamma_5$
^2F	$a_2(\psi(3,+3) \pm \psi(3,-3))$ $\mp a_1(\psi(3,+1) \pm \psi(3,-1))$	$^2\Gamma_5$

* $|a_1|^2 + |a_2|^2 = 1$.

atomic orbitals discussed thus far and doubling each of the spatial degeneracies in order to obtain the total degeneracy of the energy band. Similarly, the expressions obtained above for the electron energy $\epsilon(\mathbf{k})$ in nondegenerate energy bands would hold for electrons of each spin direction. Again, the degeneracy in $\pm S_z$ is a consequence of the assumption of time-reversal invariance in electromagnetic interactions. (This follows from the fact that the electron-spin variable transforms like an angular-momentum vector.) Thus, the (spatially) nondegenerate energy bands discussed earlier are actually characterized by a (temporal) 4-fold degeneracy according to the following combinations of electron linear and spin angular momenta:

$$(+\hbar\mathbf{k},+S_z\hbar),\ (+\hbar\mathbf{k},-S_z\hbar),\ (-\hbar\mathbf{k},+S_z\hbar),\ (-\hbar\mathbf{k},-S_z\hbar)$$

The spin-orbit interaction has been found to have a significant effect on the band structure of crystals in which two allowed bands are very close in energy (e.g., in semiconductors) and where the energy shifts produced by this interaction in each of the bands is not the same.[1] Following the argument presented in Chap. 4, the introduction of the spin-orbit interaction into the quasi-free-electron hamiltonian necessitates the use of the double-valued group representations to describe the energy bands. Once again, let us consider the double-valued group $^2\mathbf{C}_{4v}$ (Table 8.3). We give in Table 8.3 a correspondence between atomic states (up to $J = \frac{7}{2}$) and the representations of the $^2\mathbf{C}_{4v}$ point group. Note that both of the irreducible representations $^2\Gamma_6$ and $^2\Gamma_7$ describe doubly degenerate energy bands.

TABLE 8.3 *Association of Atomic-orbital States* $\psi(J,M_J)$ *(up to* $J = \frac{7}{2}$*) with the Double-valued Representations of the Tetragonal* $\mathbf{C}_{4v}$ *Group*

J	*Atomic state*	$^2\mathbf{C}_{4v}$ *group representation*
$\frac{1}{2}$	$\psi(\frac{1}{2}, \pm\frac{1}{2})$	
$\frac{3}{2}$	$\psi(\frac{3}{2}, \pm\frac{1}{2})$	
$\frac{5}{2}$	$\psi(\frac{5}{2}, \pm\frac{1}{2})$	$^2\Gamma_6$
$*\frac{7}{2}$	$\begin{cases} a_1\psi(\frac{7}{2}, \pm\frac{7}{2}) + a_2\psi(\frac{7}{2}, \mp\frac{1}{2}) \\ a_2\psi(\frac{7}{2}, \pm\frac{7}{2}) - a_1\psi(\frac{7}{2}, \mp\frac{1}{2}) \end{cases}$	
$\frac{3}{2}$	$(\frac{3}{2}, \pm\frac{3}{2})$	
$*\frac{5}{2}$	$\begin{cases} b_1\psi(\frac{5}{2}, \pm\frac{5}{2}) - b_2\psi(\frac{5}{2}, \mp\frac{3}{2}) \\ b_2\psi(\frac{5}{2}, \pm\frac{5}{2}) + b_1\psi(\frac{5}{2}, \mp\frac{3}{2}) \end{cases}$	$^2\Gamma_7$
$*\frac{7}{2}$	$\begin{cases} c_1\psi(\frac{7}{2}, \pm\frac{5}{2}) - c_2\psi(\frac{7}{2}, \mp\frac{3}{2}) \\ c_2\psi(\frac{7}{2}, \pm\frac{5}{2}) + c_1\psi(\frac{7}{2}, \mp\frac{3}{2}) \end{cases}$	

* $|a_1|^2 + |a_2|^2 = |b_1|^2 + |b_2|^2 = |c_1|^2 + |c_2|^2 = 1.$

The considerations presented thus far are quite general and independent of the strength of binding of the valence electrons to their parent ions. The case in which the electrons "lose all knowledge of their original source" (i.e., when they are indeed quasi-free electrons) is known as the weak limit of binding. We have seen how the wave functions associated with these bands depend on spatial symmetry. One further symmetry requirement placed on these functions is that derived earlier from the translational invariance of the lattice potential. This is, of course, the requirement that the wave functions have the Bloch form, i.e.,

$$\psi_{\mathbf{k}}(\mathbf{r}) = u_{\mathbf{k}}(\mathbf{r})e^{i\mathbf{k}\cdot\mathbf{r}} \tag{8.1}$$

a result independent of the strength of binding. A calculation of the energy bands in the weak-binding approximation was carried out in the

[1] R. J. Elliott, *Phys. Rev.*, **96:** 206 (1954); **96:** 280 (1954).

preceding chapter for the one-dimensional model of the crystal. The extension to three dimensions (with an arbitrary potential) then yields the same qualitative features for the three-dimensional energy-band structure. This (weak-binding) limit entailed the assumption that the kinetic energy of the electrons is much larger than their Coulomb interaction with the lattice ions, thus causing little effect on the (almost free) electron motion. (It should be emphasized, however, that these energy bands must still maintain the properties imposed by spatial symmetry and time-reflection symmetry, as outlined above in the discussion of the nondegenerate energy bands.)

Let us now go to the other limit of binding in which the valence electrons are bound tightly enough to the vicinity of their parent ions so that all knowledge of their origin is not lost. This is called the *tight-binding approximation.*

The Tight-binding Approximation[1]

Since the tight-binding approximation implies the electron's knowledge of a center of force, one need take account only of energy bands associated with a single orbital state or possibly some combination of a small number of orbital states. In view of the translational periodicity of the lattice potential (with respect to any given ion), the electron wave function must still, however, maintain the Bloch form (8.1).

The tight-binding approximation is valid whenever the motion of the valence electron is influenced to a much greater extent by the Coulomb potential of its parent ion than by all other neighboring ions. This is the case if the lattice ions may be considered to be sufficiently separated or whenever the considered valence electrons are sufficiently imbedded in the parent ion. In any case, we shall see again (as we did in our discussion of ionic crystals in Chap. 3) that there are allowed and forbidden energy regions for the valence electrons. Let us now consider the s band, p band, and d band in the tight-binding approximation.

(*i*) ***The s band*** We now consider the solution of the Schroedinger wave equation

$$\nabla^2\psi_0 + \frac{2m}{\hbar^2}(\epsilon_0 - V_0)\psi_0 = 0 \tag{8.54}$$

which corresponds to the (spherically symmetric, nondegenerate) s wave. $V_0(\mathbf{r})$ is the lattice potential and so the solution ψ_0 is still that for an electron in the entire crystal. If $\mathbf{r}_i$ denotes the position of the nucleus of the ith atom, then, in view of the assumption that neighboring atoms have a very small effect on the electrons of the ith atom, the valence-electron wave function near the ith atom is *approximately* independent

[1] See, for further reading, N. F. Mott and H. Jones, "The Theory of the Properties of Metals and Alloys," chap. II, Oxford University Press, Fair Lawn, N.J., 1936.

of the other atoms and is therefore a function of $|\mathbf{r} - \mathbf{r}_i|$. The corrected crystalline wave function may then be expressed in the form of a superposition of atomic wave functions:

$$\psi_0(\mathbf{r}) = \sum_{i=1}^{N} c_i \phi_0(\mathbf{r} - \mathbf{r}_i) \tag{8.55}$$

where N is the number of lattice ions and where $\phi_0(\mathbf{r} - \mathbf{r}_i)$ is an atomic s-state wave function (and is the same for each atom of the crystal). In view of the requirement that the crystalline electron have the form of a Bloch wave function, the coefficient c_i must describe a progressive wave within the crystal lattice. For this reason we take c_i to be $e^{i\mathbf{k}\cdot\mathbf{r}_i}$,[1] and (8.55) takes the form

$$\psi_0(\mathbf{r}) = \sum_{i=1}^{N} e^{i\mathbf{k}\cdot\mathbf{r}_i} \phi_0(\mathbf{r} - \mathbf{r}_i) \tag{8.56}$$

The energy eigenvalue associated with this wave function is then

$$\epsilon_0 = \frac{\int \psi_0^* \hat{\mathcal{H}} \psi_0 \, d\mathbf{r}}{\int \psi_0^* \psi_0 \, d\mathbf{r}} \tag{8.57}$$

where, from (8.54) and (8.56),

$$\hat{\mathcal{H}}\psi_0 = \left(\frac{-\hbar^2}{2m} \nabla^2 + V \right) \psi_0 = \sum_{i=1}^{N} e^{i\mathbf{k}\cdot\mathbf{r}_i} \hat{\mathcal{H}} \phi_0(\mathbf{r} - \mathbf{r}_i) \tag{8.58}$$

Observing that the parent ions have the greatest influence on the valence electrons, it becomes convenient to separate $\hat{\mathcal{H}}$ into a *large* part, $\Sigma\hat{\mathcal{H}}_i$, and the *small* part $\hat{\mathcal{H}} - \Sigma\hat{\mathcal{H}}_i$. $\hat{\mathcal{H}}_i$ is the free-atom hamiltonian

$$\hat{\mathcal{H}}_i = -\frac{\hbar^2}{2m} \nabla_i^2 + V_0(\mathbf{r} - \mathbf{r}_i) \tag{8.59}$$

and

$$\hat{\mathcal{H}} - \hat{\mathcal{H}}_i = V(\mathbf{r}) - V_0(\mathbf{r} - \mathbf{r}_i) \tag{8.60}$$

Since

$$\hat{\mathcal{H}}_i \phi_0(\mathbf{r} - \mathbf{r}_i) = \epsilon_0^{(0)} \phi_0(\mathbf{r} - \mathbf{r}_i) \tag{8.61}$$

where $\epsilon^{(0)}$ is the unperturbed energy level, it follows from (8.58) that

$$\hat{\mathcal{H}}\psi_0 = \epsilon_0^{(0)} \psi_0 + \sum_i e^{i\mathbf{k}\cdot\mathbf{r}_i} (\hat{\mathcal{H}} - \hat{\mathcal{H}}_i) \phi_0(\mathbf{r} - \mathbf{r}_i) \tag{8.62}$$

[1] That this choice of c_i satisfies the Bloch requirement is seen as follows: From (8.56)

$$\begin{aligned} \psi(\mathbf{r} + \mathbf{b}) &= \sum_i e^{i\mathbf{k}\cdot\mathbf{r}_i} \phi(\mathbf{r} + \mathbf{b} - \mathbf{r}_i) = e^{i\mathbf{k}\cdot\mathbf{b}} \sum_i e^{i\mathbf{k}\cdot(\mathbf{r}_i - \mathbf{b})} \phi(\mathbf{r} - (\mathbf{r}_i - \mathbf{b})) \\ &= e^{i\mathbf{k}\cdot\mathbf{b}} \sum_i e^{i\mathbf{k}\cdot\mathbf{r}_i} \phi(\mathbf{r} - \mathbf{r}_i) = e^{i\mathbf{k}\cdot\mathbf{b}} \psi(\mathbf{r}) \end{aligned}$$

where $\mathbf{b}$ is a vector connecting two lattice points.

Thus, according to (8.57), the desired energy eigenvalue becomes

$$\epsilon_0 = \epsilon_0^{(0)} + \frac{\sum_{i=1}^{N} e^{i\mathbf{k}\cdot\mathbf{r}_i} \int \psi_0^*(\hat{\mathcal{H}} - \hat{\mathcal{H}}_i)\phi_0(\mathbf{r} - \mathbf{r}_i)\, d\mathbf{r}}{\int \psi_0^*\psi_0\, d\mathbf{r}} \tag{8.63}$$

where, in view of the assumed small effect of $\hat{\mathcal{H}} - \hat{\mathcal{H}}_i$, the second term on the right-hand side of (8.63) is small in comparison with $\epsilon_0^{(0)}$. If we completely neglect (in the first order) the overlap between the crystalline ion charge clouds, then $\int \psi_0^*\psi_0\, d\mathbf{r} = N$ and

$$\epsilon_0 = \epsilon_0^{(0)} + \frac{1}{N}\sum_{i=1}^{N} e^{i\mathbf{k}\cdot\mathbf{r}_i} \int \psi_0^*(\hat{\mathcal{H}} - \hat{\mathcal{H}}_i)\phi_0(\mathbf{r} - \mathbf{r}_i)\, d\mathbf{r} \tag{8.64}$$

Substituting for ψ_0^* from (8.56), we then have (in the first order)

$$\epsilon_0 = \epsilon_0^{(0)} + \frac{1}{N}\sum_{i,j} e^{i\mathbf{k}\cdot(\mathbf{r}_i - \mathbf{r}_j)} \int \phi_0^*(\mathbf{r} - \mathbf{r}_j)(\hat{\mathcal{H}} - \hat{\mathcal{H}}_i)\phi_0(\mathbf{r} - \mathbf{r}_i)\, d\mathbf{r} \tag{8.65}$$

Since the terms in the summation over i are identical (because of the periodicity of the lattice potential), we need consider only one term, and multiply by N. Thus, calling $\boldsymbol{\varrho}_j = \mathbf{r}_j - \mathbf{r}_i$ and substituting $V - V_0(\mathbf{r} - \mathbf{r}_i)$ for $\hat{\mathcal{H}} - \hat{\mathcal{H}}_i$ [according to (8.60)], we have, in the first order,

$$\epsilon_0 = \epsilon_0^{(0)} + \sum_j e^{-i\mathbf{k}\cdot\boldsymbol{\varrho}_j} \int \phi_0^*(\mathbf{r} - \boldsymbol{\varrho}_j)[V(\mathbf{r}) - V_0(\mathbf{r})]\phi_0(\mathbf{r})\, d\mathbf{r} \tag{8.66}$$

where $\mathbf{r}_i$ was taken to be the origin and $\boldsymbol{\varrho}_j$ connects the origin to the lattice point j.

Taking into account the effect of nearest neighbors on the electronic energy levels and calling

$$\begin{aligned} \int \phi_0^*(\mathbf{r})[V(\mathbf{r}) - V_0(\mathbf{r})]\phi_0(\mathbf{r})\, d\mathbf{r} &= -\alpha \\ \int \phi_0^*(\mathbf{r} + \boldsymbol{\varrho})[V(\mathbf{r}) - V_0(\mathbf{r})]\phi_0(\mathbf{r})\, d\mathbf{r} &= -\gamma \end{aligned} \tag{8.67}$$

(8.66) takes the form

$$\epsilon_0 = \epsilon_0^{(0)} - \alpha - \gamma \sum_j e^{-i\mathbf{k}\cdot\boldsymbol{\varrho}_j} \tag{8.68}$$

It is observed that, since the free-ion potential V_0 is more binding (i.e., more negative) than is the lattice potential $V(\mathbf{r})$, $V - V_0$ is always *negative* (and α and γ are always positive). Thus, $\epsilon_0 < \epsilon_0^{(0)}$. Let us now utilize these results in order to calculate the energy bands for the three cubic types of Bravais lattice.

(*a*) *The Simple-cubic Lattice.* Here, any given ion has six neighbors at

$$\boldsymbol{\varrho}_j = (\pm r_0,0,0),\ (0,\pm r_0,0),\ (0,0,\pm r_0) \tag{8.69a}$$

Substituting (8.69*a*) into (8.68), we have

$$\epsilon_0 = (\epsilon_0^{(0)} - \alpha) - 2\gamma(\cos k_x r_0 + \cos k_y r_0 + \cos k_z r_0) \qquad (8.69b)$$

(*b*) *The Body-centered-cubic Lattice.* The eight nearest neighbors are at

$$\boldsymbol{\varrho}_j = (\pm\tfrac{1}{2}r_0, \pm\tfrac{1}{2}r_0, \pm\tfrac{1}{2}r_0) \qquad (8.70a)$$

so that

$$\epsilon_0 = (\epsilon_0^{(0)} - \alpha) - 8\gamma \cos\frac{k_x r_0}{2} \cos\frac{k_y r_0}{2} \cos\frac{k_z r_0}{2} \qquad (8.70b)$$

(*c*) *The Face-centered-cubic Lattice.* Twelve nearest neighbors are at

$$\boldsymbol{\varrho}_j = (0,\pm r_0,\pm r_0),\ (\pm r_0,0,\pm r_0),\ (\pm r_0,\pm r_0,0) \qquad (8.71a)$$

and

$$\epsilon_0 = (\epsilon_0^{(0)} - \alpha) - 4\gamma\left(\cos\frac{k_y r_0}{2}\cos\frac{k_z r_0}{2} + \cos\frac{k_z r_0}{2}\cos\frac{k_x r_0}{2} + \cos\frac{k_x r_0}{2}\cos\frac{k_y r_0}{2}\right) \qquad (8.71b)$$

We see that the s band is described by a constant energy term $\epsilon_0^{(0)} - \alpha$ together with a term which depends on the electron wave vector **k**.

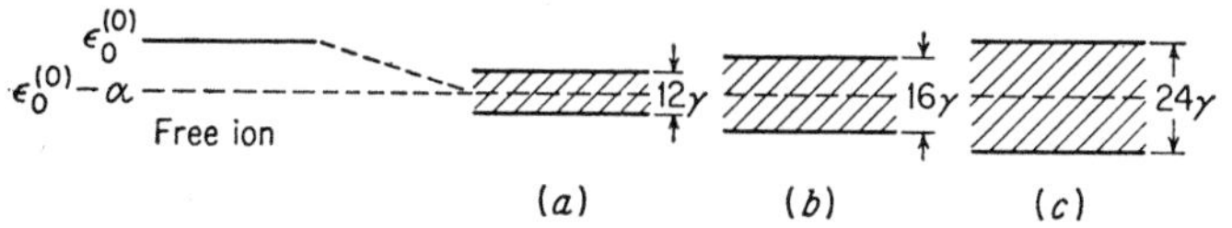

Fig. 8.9. s Bands for (*a*) simple-cubic, (*b*) body-centered-cubic, and (*c*) face-centered-cubic lattices in the tight-binding approximation.

Thus we have an energy band of width 12γ ev, centered about the energy $\epsilon_0^{(0)} - \alpha$ ev for the sc lattice. From our definition of γ [Eq. (8.67)], it is clear that the greater the overlap of the electron wave functions of neighboring ions, the greater is γ and thus the wider is the energy band. The tight-binding approximation, however, is based on the assumption that the charge clouds of neighboring ions overlap very little. Thus the considerations presented here apply only when γ is small, so that (in our approximation) the energy band is narrow. (In the other two cases, the energy bands have widths 16γ and 24γ, respectively; see Fig. 8.9.) Thus we see that in the tight-binding approximation each discrete free-atom energy level has an associated energy band. It is, of course, clear that the extension to more than the nearest neighbors would further widen the energy bands but to an increasingly small degree (according to our approximation).

The tight-binding approximation implies that the potential energy of the valence electrons in the field of their parent and neighboring ions is large compared with their kinetic energy. This result then implies that the separation between ions is small compared with the electron De Broglie wavelength, or

$$|\mathbf{k}|r_0 \ll 1$$

Using this approximation,

$$\cos kr_0 \simeq 1 - \tfrac{1}{2}(kr_0)^2$$

and the sc, bcc, and fcc energy levels take the form

$$\begin{aligned}\epsilon_0(\text{sc}) &= (\epsilon_0^{(0)} - \alpha) - 6\gamma + \gamma k^2 r_0^2 + \cdots \\ \epsilon_0(\text{bcc}) &= (\epsilon_0^{(0)} - \alpha) - 8\gamma + \gamma k^2 r_0^2 + \cdots \\ \epsilon_0(\text{fcc}) &= (\epsilon_0^{(0)} - \alpha) - 12\gamma + \gamma k^2 r_0^2 + \cdots\end{aligned} \tag{8.72}$$

In view of our general expression for the effective mass [Eq. (8.43)], we see that in each of these cases

$$m^* = \frac{\hbar^2}{\partial^2\epsilon/\partial k^2} = \frac{\hbar^2}{2\gamma r_0^2} \tag{8.73}$$

This indicates that, for a narrow band (i.e., small γ), the electron behaves as though it were extremely heavy, implying that these electrons are rather immobile with respect to motion throughout the crystal when under the influence of externally applied forces. This result is compatible with the tight-binding approximation.

It follows from the expressions for the energy surfaces given by Eqs. (8.69*b*), (8.70*b*), and (8.71*b*) and from Eq. (8.30) that the number of energy levels in the zone is equal to the number of atoms in the crystal (in agreement with this general result arrived at earlier). *A verification of this result for the energy surfaces* (8.69*b*), (8.70*b*), and (8.71*b*) *will be left as an exercise for the reader.*

(ii) The p band The calculation of the p band is complicated because of the inherent degeneracy that is present. The three degenerate p states are characterized by the functions

$$\left.\begin{matrix} xf(r) \\ yf(r) \\ zf(r) \end{matrix}\right\} \equiv \left\{\begin{matrix} \phi_1(\mathbf{r}) \\ \phi_2(\mathbf{r}) \\ \phi_3(\mathbf{r}) \end{matrix}\right. \tag{8.74}$$

In order to avoid excessive mathematical details, we shall consider only the simple-cubic lattice. In this case, from Sec. 8.1,

$$\mathbf{r}_j = r_0\mathbf{m} \tag{8.75}$$

where, as usual, $\mathbf{m} = (m_1m_2m_3)$ is a set of integers and r_0 is the lattice constant.

The extension of the form of the wave function given by (8.56) to the

p-like orbitals is accomplished by treating each of the three degenerate wave functions (8.74) separately. Thus, using (8.75), we have

$$\psi_n = \sum_{m_1 m_2 m_3} e^{ir_0(\mathbf{m}\cdot\mathbf{k})}\phi_n(r - \mathbf{m}r_0) \qquad n = 1, 2, 3 \tag{8.76}$$

We have seen in Chap. 4 that a crystal potential characterized by the transformations of a cubic group leaves the atomic p state triply degenerate (see Table 4.5). Thus the three eigenfunctions (ϕ_1,ϕ_2,ϕ_3) all correspond to the same energy level, and we need consider only one of them (say ϕ_1) in calculating the electron energy. If we call this energy ϵ_1, then, in a fashion completely analogous to the derivation of (8.66), we arrive at the following expression for the p-band energy:

$$\epsilon_1 = \epsilon_1^{(0)} - \alpha_1 + 2\gamma_1 \cos k_x r_0 + 2\gamma_1'(\cos k_y r_0 + \cos k_z r_0) \tag{8.77}$$

where

$$\begin{aligned}
\alpha_1 &= -\int \phi_1^*(\mathbf{r})(V - V_1)\phi_1(\mathbf{r})\, d\mathbf{r} \\
\gamma_1 &= \int \phi_1^*(x \pm r_0, y, z)(V - V_1)\phi_1(x,y,z)\, d\mathbf{r} \\
\gamma_1' &= \int \phi_1^*(x, y \pm r_0, z)(V - V_1)\phi_1(x,y,z)\, d\mathbf{r} \\
&= \int \phi_1^*(x, y, z \pm r_0)(V - V_1)\phi_1(x,y,z)\, d\mathbf{r}
\end{aligned} \tag{8.78}$$

The inequality between γ_1 and γ_1', implying interactions which are different for different neighboring ions, follows from the lack of spherical symmetry of the ϕ_1 component of the p-state wave function.

Once again, since the free-atom binding energy is greater than the potential energy of the lattice, it follows from (8.78) that α_1 is positive. The wave function $\phi_1 = xf(r)$ is an odd function along the x direction. Thus, midway between the neighboring atoms along the x axis, where the overlap integral γ_1 is a maximum, $\phi_1(x)$ and $\phi_1(x + r_0)$ have opposite signs. Since $V - V_1$ is negative, γ_1 must be positive. On the other hand, ϕ_1 is not an odd function with respect to the y direction, so that $\phi_1(y)$ and $\phi_1(y + r_0)$ are not of opposite sign midway between the atoms along the y axis. Thus, γ_1' is negative. Also, since $\phi_1(y)$ and $\phi_1(y + r_0)$ vanish along a plane containing both atoms, and γ_1 does not vanish anywhere, we have

$$|\gamma_1'| < \gamma_1$$

In view of these considerations, a qualitative plot of $\epsilon(\mathbf{k})$ along different $\mathbf{k}$ planes is given in Fig. 8.10.

If we now invoke the inequality

$$kr_0 \ll 1$$

inherent in the tight-binding approximation, (8.77) takes the form

$$\epsilon_1 = (\epsilon_1^{(0)} - \alpha_1 + 2\gamma_1 + 4\gamma_1') - \gamma_1 r_0^2 k_x^2 - \gamma_1' r_0^2 (k_y^2 + k_z^2) \tag{8.79}$$

When similar considerations are applied to the other two eigenstates ϕ_2 and ϕ_3, identical results are obtained, with the permutations of the three coordinate labels. As mentioned earlier, however, the cubic symmetry of the lattice potential requires that all three expressions be the same. This is equivalent to saying that a study of the motion of the electrons does not distinguish any one direction in space. This is *not the case* when the energy band is characterized by the *d* state, because, in this case, the cubic crystalline field does indeed split the 5-fold degenerate energy level into two separate levels (see Chap. 4).

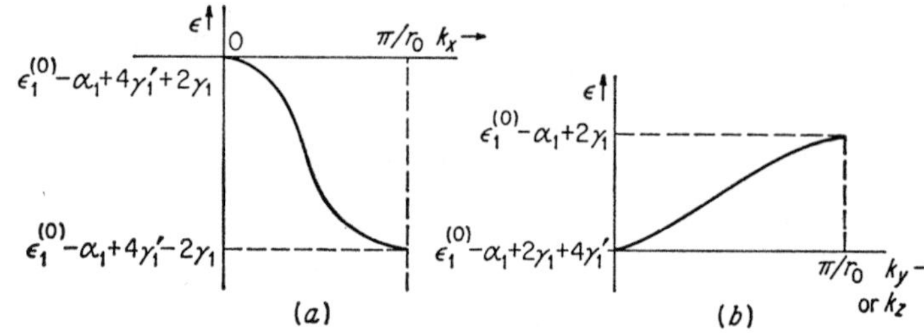

Fig. 8.10. $\epsilon(\mathbf{k})$ as a function of **k** for a *p*-band structure with the tight-binding approximation. (*a*) ϵ vs k_x and (*b*) ϵ vs k_y or k_z.

(iii) The s-p degenerate band Suppose now that the *s*-band width γ and the *p*-band widths γ_1, γ_1' are of such magnitude that each of these bands overlap. The resulting energy band is then degenerate in *s* and *p*-like orbitals. [We have already seen that such an overlap does indeed occur in the band structure of NaCl (Chap. 3).] In order to obtain the energy levels of this system it becomes necessary to use degenerate perturbation theory.[1]

Once again, denoting the *s*-like wave function by ϕ_0 and the *p*-like functions by ϕ_1, ϕ_2, ϕ_3, we construct the wave functions (for the simple-cubic lattice):

$$\psi_n = \sum_{\mathbf{m}} e^{ir_0(\mathbf{m}\cdot\mathbf{k})}\phi_n(\mathbf{r} - \mathbf{m}r_0) \qquad n = 0, 1, 2, 3$$

We now superpose the four functions ψ_n in order to build the wave function for the crystalline electron. Thus, we have

$$\Psi_p = \sum_n a_{pn}(\mathbf{k})\psi_n(\mathbf{k},\mathbf{r}) \tag{8.80}$$

and in the usual way arrive at the secular equation

$$|\mathcal{H}_{pn} - \epsilon\delta_{pn}| = 0 \tag{8.81}$$

[1] Schiff, *op. cit.*, chap. VII.

The diagonal elements $\mathcal{H}_{nn}$ are given by the energy eigenvalues (8.69*b*) and (8.77) for the nonoverlapping *s* and *p* states.

Since the nondiagonal elements arise, according to our assumption of only nearest-neighbor interactions, from the mixing of states with $\Delta l = 1$ (and not from the degenerate *p* states themselves), we have, in view of (8.56) and (8.76),

$$\mathcal{H}_{mn} = 0 \qquad m,n \neq 0$$

$$\mathcal{H}_{0n} = \frac{1}{N} \sum_{mm'} e^{-ir_0(\mathbf{m}-\mathbf{m}')\cdot\mathbf{k}} \int \phi_0^*(\mathbf{r} - r_0\mathbf{m})(\hat{\mathcal{H}} - \hat{\mathcal{H}}^{(0)})\phi_n(\mathbf{r} - r_0\mathbf{m}')\, d\mathbf{r} \tag{8.82}$$

Using (8.60), calling

$$\beta = \int \phi_0^*(x \pm r_0, y, z)(V - V^{(0)})\phi_n(x,y,z)\, d\mathbf{r}$$

and taking into account only nearest neighbors, (8.82) takes the form

$$\mathcal{H}_{0n} = 2i\beta \sin k_n r_0 \tag{8.83}$$

(The terms $\mathcal{H}^{(0)}$ and $V^{(0)}$ are the free-ion hamiltonian and potential, respectively.) The secular equation (8.81) then takes the form

$$\begin{vmatrix} \epsilon_0 - \epsilon & 2i\beta \sin k_x r_0 & 2i\beta \sin k_y r_0 & 2i\beta \sin k_z r_0 \\ -2i\beta \sin k_x r_0 & \epsilon_1 - \epsilon & 0 & 0 \\ -2i\beta \sin k_y r_0 & 0 & \epsilon_1 - \epsilon & 0 \\ -2i\beta \sin k_z r_0 & 0 & 0 & \epsilon_1 - \epsilon \end{vmatrix} = 0 \tag{8.84}$$

where ϵ_0 and ϵ_1 are given by Eqs. (8.69*b*) and (8.77), respectively. The solutions of (8.84) (i.e., the four roots of this secular equation) then give the energies of the *s* band and the three *p* bands as a function of **k**.

The fourth-order algebraic equation reduces to a quadratic equation when we consider the energy surfaces along one of the directions in **k** space. Thus, setting $k_y = k_z = 0$, (8.84) gives the two roots

$$\epsilon_\pm = \tfrac{1}{2}\{(\epsilon_0 + \epsilon_1) \pm [(\epsilon_0 - \epsilon_1) + 16\beta^2 \sin^2 k_x r_0]^{1/2}\} \tag{8.85}$$

These two bands are plotted in Fig. 8.11 together with the unmixed *s* and *p* bands. The two cases shown indicate the situations which arise when the unperturbed bands do not cross (*a*) and when they do cross (*b*) at some critical value of k_x.

Clearly, a superposition of all curves such as those shown in Fig. 8.11 will map the entire energy surface in **k** space for the tight-binding approximation considered.

(*iv*) ***The d band*** The procedure followed here is identical with that of the *p*-band calculation. Because of the 5-fold degeneracy of the atomic *d* state, the Bloch function in the tight-binding approximation takes the usual form (for the simple-cubic lattice) given by Eq. (8.76), except that $n = 1, 2, 3, 4, 5$, with

$$\phi_1 = (3z^2 - r^2)f(r) \qquad \phi_2 = (x^2 - y^2)f(r) \qquad \phi_3 = xyf(r)$$
$$\phi_4 = yzf(r) \qquad \phi_5 = zxf(r)$$

As we have seen earlier (Chap. 4), the cubic field splits the 5-fold degenerate d state into one triply degenerate energy level and one doubly degenerate energy level. These energy bands are then derived from the solution of a fifth-order secular equation.[1]

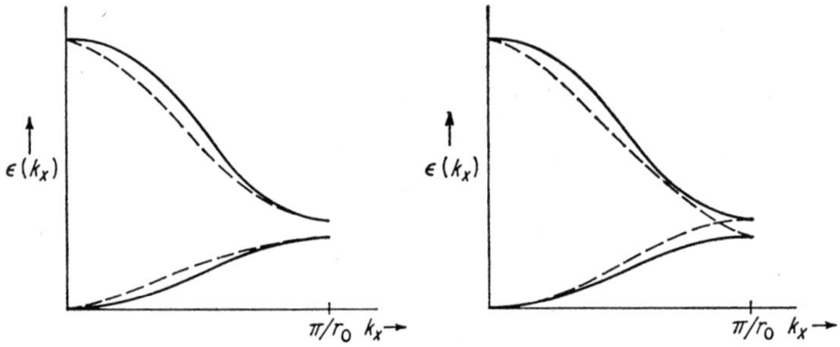

Fig. 8.11. $\epsilon(\mathbf{k})$ as a function of k_x in the tight-binding approximation. The full lines represent the *s-p* degenerate band [Eq. (8.85)], and the dotted lines are the unmixed s and p bands [Eqs. (8.69*b*) and (8.77)]. (*a*) and (*b*) are diagrams of energy bands that do not and do cross at some critical value for the wave vector k_x.

The Density of States

The density of states is the number of electron states per unit energy interval. The macroscopic properties of conducting solids (such as the electronic specific heat, paramagnetic susceptibility, etc.) depend sensitively on this function. We have seen this relation applied specifically to the free-electron model of metals (Chap. 6) in a calculation of various of its macroscopic properties. The reader is referred to the latter discussion as an introduction to the present one.

We now wish to modify the previous calculation for the free-electron gas, so as to take account of the nonspherical symmetry which is associated with the energy states in the **k** space of the reduced zone.

According to (8.30), the density of states is

$$g = \frac{d\nu}{d\epsilon} = \frac{2}{(2\pi)^3}\, d\mathbf{k}$$

[1] For a more detailed treatment of this case, see G. C. Fletcher and E. P. Wolfarth, *Phil. Mag.*, **42:** 106 (1951); Fletcher, *Proc. Phys. Soc.* (*London*), **A65:** 192 (1952).

Consider now that $d\mathbf{k}$ is bounded by the differential areas dS in the planes of discontinuity of the reduced zone, so that the volume increment of $\mathbf{k}$ space is expressible in the form

$$d\mathbf{k} = dS\,dk = dS\,\frac{dk}{d\epsilon}\,d\epsilon \tag{8.86}$$

Since $(dk/d\epsilon)^{-1} = |\nabla_{\mathbf{k}}\epsilon(\mathbf{k})|$, we have

$$g_S = \frac{d\nu}{d\epsilon} = \frac{2}{(2\pi)^3}\frac{dS}{|\nabla_{\mathbf{k}}\epsilon(\mathbf{k})|}$$

for an incremental energy surface dS. Thus the density of states for the energy band may be obtained by integrating over the entire surface of the reduced zone, so that

$$g = \oint_S g_S = \frac{2}{(2\pi)^3}\oint_S \frac{dS}{|\nabla_{\mathbf{k}}\epsilon(\mathbf{k})|} \tag{8.87}$$

where the integration is carried out over a constant energy ϵ. Equation (8.87) represents a general expression for the density of electron states in a three-dimensional crystal.

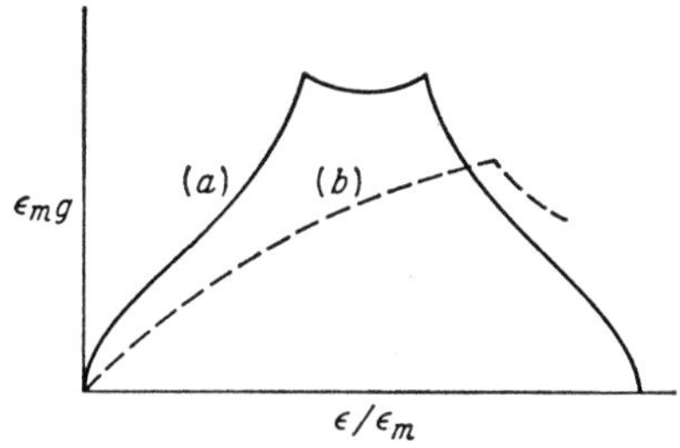

Fig. 8.12. The density of states $g(\epsilon)$ for the reduced zone of a simple-cubic lattice (a) for the s band in the tight-binding approximation and (b) for the free-electron gas. ϵ_m is the top of the s band $(\epsilon_0^{(0)} - \alpha + 6\gamma)$ [Eq. (8.69b)].

Let us consider, for example, the constant energy surface ϵ_0 of the s band (in the tight-binding approximation) for the simple-cubic lattice [Eq. (8.69b)]. In this case, a numerical integration of (8.87) gives the curve (a) shown in Fig. 8.12. A comparison with the free-electron density of states [Eq. (6.36)], which is cut off at the zone boundaries $(k_x,k_y,k_z) = (\pm\pi/r_0, \pm\pi/r_0, \pm\pi/r_0)$ is shown in this figure. The density of states in the actual crystal therefore must lie between the curves (*a*) and (*b*) for a description intermediate to the tight-binding and free-electron approximations.

In the general expressions for the energy surfaces as a function of **k**, the integration (8.87) would yield expressions which are functions of the undetermined constants (i.e., the effective-mass tensor m^*_{ij} and the coefficients $R^{(r)}_{\lambda\mu}$ and $R^{(i)}_{\lambda\mu}$) which describe the energy band. Consider, for example, the case in which ϵ is described by the surface of an ellipsoid [for example, the first term in (8.53)].

$$\epsilon(\mathbf{k}) = \frac{\hbar^2}{2m}(T_{11}k_x^2 + T_{22}k_y^2 + T_{33}k_z^2) \tag{8.88}$$

where

$$T_{ii} = \frac{m}{m^*_{ii}}$$

If we define new variables

$$q_x = \sqrt{T_{11}}\,k_x \qquad q_y = \sqrt{T_{22}}\,k_y \qquad q_z = \sqrt{T_{33}}\,k_z \tag{8.89}$$

then

$$\epsilon(\mathbf{q}) = \frac{\hbar^2}{2m}q^2 \tag{8.90}$$

Thus, since

$$d\mathbf{k} = \frac{d\mathbf{q}}{\sqrt{T_{11}T_{22}T_{33}}}$$

$$g(\epsilon)\,d\epsilon = \frac{2}{(2\pi)^3}\,d\mathbf{k} = \frac{2}{(2\pi)^3}\frac{d\mathbf{q}}{\sqrt{T_{11}T_{22}T_{33}}} = \frac{1}{2\pi^2}\left(\frac{2m}{\hbar^2}\right)^{3/2}\frac{\epsilon^{1/2}\,d\epsilon}{\sqrt{T_{11}T_{22}T_{33}}} \tag{8.91}$$

[The last part of (8.91) follows from (8.90).] Thus the density of states may be expressed, in this case, in terms of the product of electron effective masses in each of the three orthogonal directions.

$$g(\epsilon) = \frac{\sqrt{2m_{11}m_{22}m_{33}}}{\pi^2\hbar^3}\,\epsilon^{1/2} \tag{8.92}$$

Finally, let us consider the two-band structure, with each band described by the "free-energy"-like surface. As we have seen earlier, [Eq. (6.36)], the density of states for the free-electron gas (with "isotropic" effective mass m^*) is

$$g_1(\epsilon) = \frac{(2m^*)^{3/2}}{2\pi^2\hbar^3}\,\epsilon^{1/2} \tag{8.93}$$

Suppose now that the next band is ϵ_g ev below the bottom of the first band, so that the electron energy in the second band is

$$\epsilon_2(\mathbf{k}) = \epsilon_g - \frac{\hbar^2k^2}{2m^*}$$

(see Fig. 8.13). In the latter case, the density of states is

$$g_2(\epsilon) = \frac{1}{2\pi^2}\left(\frac{2m^*}{\hbar^2}\right)^{3/2}(\epsilon_g - \epsilon)^{1/2} \tag{8.94}$$

Consider now the density of states as a function of energy. Away from the band edge, $g_1(\epsilon)$ depends on $\epsilon^{1/2}$ [Eq. (8.93)] and $g_2(\epsilon)$ on $(\epsilon_g - \epsilon)^{1/2}$, as shown in Eq. (8.94). However, near the zone edges, the energy contours deviate from sphericity and $g(\epsilon)$ increases more rapidly than $\epsilon^{1/2}$.

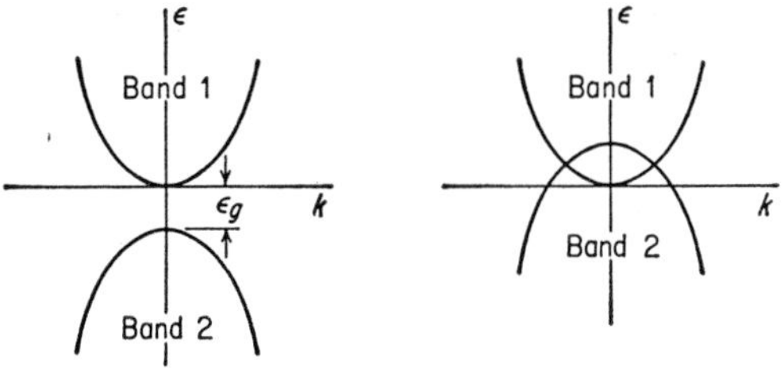

Fig. 8.13. Two-band diagram where (*a*) the energy bands do not overlap and (*b*) the energy bands do overlap.

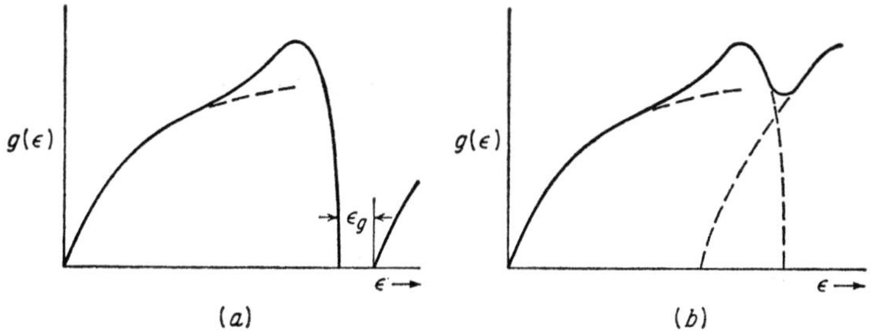

Fig. 8.14. The density of states for the two-band structure (*a*) with no band overlap and (*b*) with band overlap.

This is due to the fact that $g(\epsilon)$ must vanish at the zone boundary, in which case $dg/d\epsilon$ becomes infinite. Thus, $g(\epsilon)$ has the behavior indicated in Fig. 8.14*a*.

Suppose, now, that the two bands overlap. The corresponding energy curve would then be given by Fig. 8.13*b* and the density of states by Fig. 8.14*b*.

In the case of a metal with two overlapping bands, each associated with different effective masses, one has to consider the electrons in each of the overlapping bands simultaneously. In this case

$$g(\epsilon) = \frac{1}{2\pi^2\hbar^3}\left[2m_2(\epsilon_g - \epsilon)^{1/2} + 2m_1\epsilon^{1/2}\right]$$

where m_1 and m_2 are the effective masses for the electrons in each of the overlapping bands (see Fig. 8.15).

Summarizing this chapter, we have presented a discussion extending the one-dimensional periodic-lattice problem of the preceding chapter to the three-dimensional case. Much of the discussion of the physical ideas presented there has not been repeated in this chapter; rather, we have concentrated on an exploitation of the implications of the symmetry properties of the crystal lattice with respect to the energy-band structure. Thus the questions of the symmetry properties of quasi-free-electron wave functions, of the points in the Brillouin zones, of

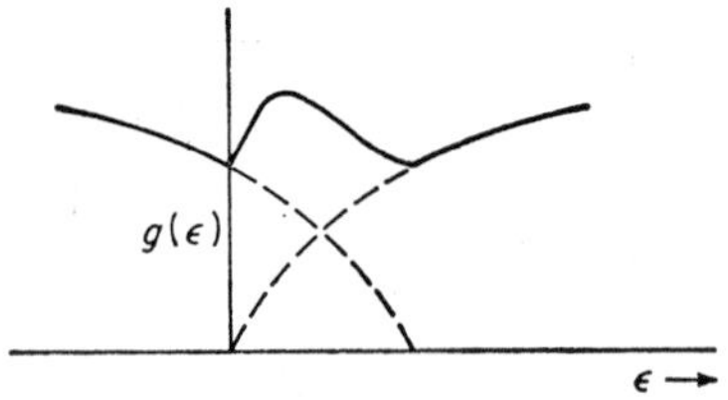

Fig. 8.15. The density of states for a metal with overlapping bands and correspondingly different effective masses.

degeneracy in energy bands, of selection rules for the absorption of radiation by conduction electrons in crystals, and of the tight-binding approximation all require the three-dimensional problem for discussion.

The absolute values for the electron energies corresponding to the *s* band, *p* band, etc., calculated here, according to the tight-binding approximation, may not be regarded as accurate but rather as a starting point for a more exact treatment. A discussion of methods which are evoked in calculating, in a more accurate way, the cohesive energy of a crystal will be presented in Chap. 10.

In the following chapter we shall consider the application of the band theory presented thus far to the treatment of many of the properties of semiconductors and metals.

9 quasi-free-electron theory: applications

IN THE three preceding chapters we have developed a logically consistent model of a solid, viewed as a cohesive system of a great many ions and electrons. The free-electron model, along with the requirements imposed by the Pauli exclusion principle (Chap. 6), gave us the one-energy-band description, with the maximum energy (i.e., the Fermi energy) determined by the electron concentration itself. This model totally disregarded the scattering effect of the constituent lattice ions on electron behavior and imposed only the restraint that the electrons be confined to the boundaries of the macroscopic crystal (i.e., the potential was taken to be infinite at the surfaces of the crystal but zero elsewhere). In Chap. 7 account was taken of the scattering effect of the (static) lattice potential, and, as a result, the electron-energy eigenvalues were found to be restricted to specific values, according to their momenta, thus giving rise to the energy-band picture in which there are alternately allowed and forbidden energy bands. Finally, in Chap. 8, symmetry aspects of the three-dimensional crystal were exploited in deciding their influence on the energy-band structure and other physical properties of the crystal.

In this chapter we consider a few of the important applications of this model of a crystal. The approach taken here is that we have already determined the band structure of solids in a rigorous fashion, according to the discussion of the preceding sections, and we now wish to predict some of the physical properties of such crystals. Three applications which we consider here are (1) the properties of semiconductors and their interaction with electromagnetic radiation, (2) thermionic emission, and (3) the properties of two different (electrical) types of solid which are in contact. The latter will lead, for example, to a discussion of the *p-n* junction and the transistor. These three topics have been selected to point out how three apparently unrelated phenomena in conducting solids are unified in terms of the band theory of solids.

9.1 Semiconductor theory

According to our discussion in Chap. 1, one way of classifying a solid is according to its electrical properties. A *conductor* and an *insulator* are first distinguished by their extreme values of electrical conductivity. In particular, a conductor has a conductivity of 10^4 to 10^6 ohm^{-1} cm^{-1} whereas insulators are characterized by conductivities less than 10^{-6} ohm^{-1} cm^{-1}. Second, the conductivity of a conductor decreases as its temperature increases while that of an insulator varies slightly (but does increase) with increasing temperature.

In addition to *conductors* and *insulators*, there is a class of solids with intermediate values of electrical conductivity (10^{-6} to 10^3 ohm^{-1} cm^{-1}) and whose conductivity increases (more strongly than insulators) with increasing temperature. Such solids (which resemble insulators only at temperatures near absolute zero) are called *semiconductors.* One further marked difference between a conductor and a semiconductor relates to the dependence on the degree of purity of the crystal of its electrical conductivity. The conductivity of a good conductor increases with purification (e.g., the elimination of foreign impurities from the crystal), whereas the conductivity of semiconductors generally decreases with purification. It is our object in this section to present a qualitative discussion explaining these properties of semiconductors and to discuss some of the experimental approaches which are taken in attempts to ascertain the behavior of electrons in semiconductors. We begin our discussion with a more detailed classification of semiconductors.

Classification of Semiconductors

There are two basic types of semiconductors. These are the *intrinsic type* and the *impurity type.* An intrinsic semiconductor is usually a pure monatomic or diatomic solid whereas the impurity type has electrical properties that depend on the type and amount of foreign-impurity atoms and/or an excess or deficiency of the normally constituent atoms (i.e., stoichiometric deviations). These are outlined in Table 9.1.

TABLE 9.1 *Classification of Semiconductors*

Type	*Typical examples*
Intrinsic	Si, Ge, Se, InSb
Impurity	
a. Foreign impurity	Si or Ge doped with Al or P
b. Stoichiometric deviations	
(i) Excess metallic	PbS, TiO_2
(ii) Excess nonmetallic	PbS, NiO, Cu_2O

The Intrinsic Semiconductor

Consider the perfect insulator. This property of a crystal has been explained, according to our quantum-mechanical description, by an energy band in which each of the $2N$ energy levels is occupied. The next band of allowed energy levels is unoccupied but is separated from the top of the occupied band by ϵ_g ev. At $T = 0°\text{K}$ such a material is a perfect insulator since all the energy levels are occupied so that the conduction electrons cannot absorb energy from an applied field[1] (so long as it does not exceed the potential difference ϵ_g/e) (see Fig. 9.1).

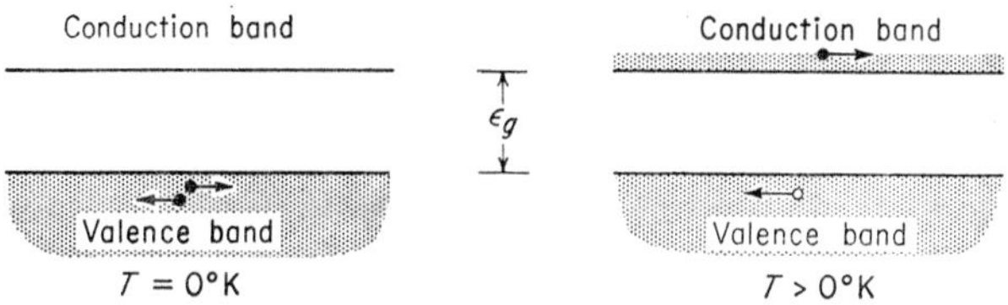

Fig. 9.1. Band structure of intrinsic semiconductors.

Suppose now that ϵ_g is sufficiently small that, as the temperature is raised from 0°K, a nonnegligible electron population in the upper band can be established (according to the Boltzmann law). Under such conditions, electrons in the upper band would now have as many available unoccupied energy levels as would the electron vacancies ("holes") left in the lower band by the departed (excited) electrons. Under such conditions electrical conductivity could occur for positive charge carriers (of the lower band) and for negative charge carriers (of the upper band). Such a crystal is called an *intrinsic semiconductor*. The lower and upper bands are called the *valence* and *conduction* bands, respectively. For the well-known intrinsic semiconductors, silicon and germanium, the minimum ϵ_g are 1.21 ev and 0.785 ev, respectively. The term *minimum* is emphasized since, in view of the theoretical development of the preceding chapter, the bands are described by energy *surfaces* (in **k** space). It is the region of **k** space around the minimum separation between energy bands that is very important in determining physical properties of a material. Only such regions of **k** space will be referred to in this chapter and in the energy-band diagrams (such as Fig. 9.1). Thus it is of interest to know the electron momenta $\hbar\mathbf{k}$ which correspond to the minimum band gap. [In fact, the minimum band gap in Si and Ge occurs at $\mathbf{k} = (0,0,0)$ and the energy surfaces here are spheroidal (i.e., the effective

[1] To estimate the order of magnitude of the applied electric field necessary to excite an electron from the conduction to the valence band, we take $\mathcal{E} \sim e/r^2$, where $r \sim 10a_0$ and a_0 is the radius of a crystalline ion. This gives $\mathcal{E} \sim 10^6$ volts/cm. Thus, $\mathcal{E}$ is of the same order of magnitude as those field values where dielectric breakdown occurs.

mass in the longitudinal direction differs from that in the transverse direction)] (see Fig. 9.9). Typical minimum band gaps are given in Table 9.2.

TABLE 9.2 *Typical Minimum Values of Energy-band Gaps in Semiconductors*

Material	ϵ_g, ev
Ge	0.78
Se	2.0
Si	1.21
Te	0.33
Cu_2O	1.0
InAs	0.5
InSb	2.3
UO_2	0.2
ZnS	3.6

Conductivity in intrinsic semiconductors Since both electrons and holes contribute to the electrical conductivity of an intrinsic semiconductor, the total conductivity [according to the general definition (6.3)] is

$$\sigma = n_e e \mu_e + n_h e \mu_h \tag{9.1}$$

where μ_e and μ_h are the electron and hole mobilities, respectively, while n_e and n_h are their concentrations.

The relation of the directions of electron and hole currents to the direction of the applied field is shown in Fig. 9.2.

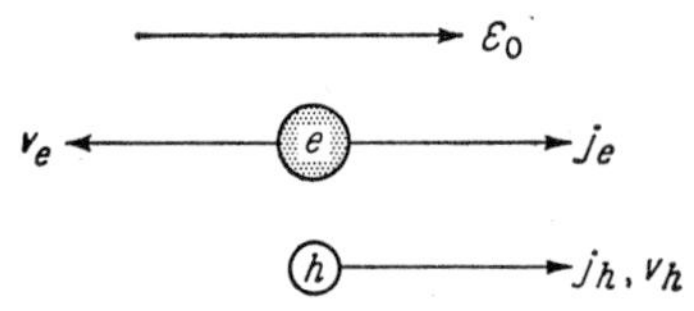

Fig. 9.2. Relative directions of the electron ⓔ and the hole ⓗ currents j_e and j_h and velocities v_e and v_h with respect to the direction of the applied electric field $\mathcal{E}_0$.

Let us now determine the electron and hole concentrations in the limit where n_e is so small and kT so large that the electron gas can be considered nondegenerate. The calculation has already been carried out for n_e [Eq. (6.40)]. Taking the zero of energy to be at the top of the valence band (Fig. 9.1) and using Eq. (8.94) for the density of states, the electron concentration is

$$\begin{aligned} n_e &= \int_{\epsilon_g}^{\infty} f_e(\epsilon)\, d\epsilon \\ &= \frac{1}{2\pi^2}\left(\frac{2m_e}{\hbar^2}\right)^{3/2} e^{\epsilon_F/kT} \int_{\epsilon_g}^{\infty} (\epsilon - \epsilon_g)^{1/2} e^{-\epsilon/kT}\, d\epsilon \\ &= 2\left(\frac{2\pi m_e kT}{h^2}\right)^{3/2} e^{(\epsilon_F - \epsilon_g)/kT} \end{aligned} \tag{9.2}$$

We now determine the Fermi energy ϵ_F by calculating the hole concentration n_h and requiring it to equal n_e.

For a nondegenerate gas, the Fermi-Dirac distribution function for the hole concentration is

$$\bar{f}_h = 1 - \bar{f}_e \simeq e^{(\epsilon - \epsilon_F)/kT} \qquad \bar{f} = f/g \tag{9.3}$$

and the corresponding density of states per unit volume is

$$g_h = \frac{1}{2\pi^2}\left(\frac{2m_h}{\hbar^2}\right)^{3/2}(-\epsilon)^{1/2} \tag{9.4}$$

Thus

$$n_h = \int_{-\infty}^{0} \bar{f}_h(\epsilon) g_h(\epsilon)\, d\epsilon = 2\left(\frac{2\pi m_h kT}{h^2}\right)^{3/2} e^{-\epsilon_F/kT} \tag{9.5}$$

Substituting the right-hand sides of (9.2) and (9.5) into

$$n_e = n_h \tag{9.6}$$

we obtain

$$e^{2\epsilon_F/kT} = \left(\frac{m_h}{m_e}\right)^{3/2} e^{\epsilon_g/kT}$$

or

$$\epsilon_F = \frac{1}{2}\epsilon_g + \frac{3}{4}kT \ln \frac{m_h}{m_e} \tag{9.7}$$

It is interesting to note that, if the effective masses m_e and m_h (at the minimum band separation) are equal, the Fermi energy is exactly in the center of the forbidden-energy gap. If $m_h \neq m_e$, ϵ_F lies above (or below) $\epsilon_g/2$ if m_h is greater (or less) than m_e. It is also noted that the separation of ϵ_F from $\epsilon_g/2$ is small (so long as $|m_h/m_e|$ is not large) since, at room temperature,

$$\frac{kT}{\epsilon_g} \sim \frac{0.025 \text{ ev}}{1 \text{ ev}} = \frac{1}{40}$$

If we now substitute (9.7) into (9.2) we have [in view of (9.6)]

$$n_e = n_h = 2\left(\frac{2\pi kT}{h^2}\right)^{3/2} (m_h m_e)^{3/4} e^{-\epsilon_g/2kT} \tag{9.8}$$

and the electrical conductivity is

$$\sigma = 2e\left(\frac{2\pi kT}{h^2}\right)^{3/2} (m_e m_h)^{3/4} e^{-\epsilon_g/2kT}(\mu_e + \mu_h) \tag{9.9}$$

The measurements on Ge and Si indicate the following empirical behavior of the product[1] $n_e n_h$:

Ge: $\quad n_e n_h = 3.10 \times 10^{32} T^3 e^{-0.785/kT}$

Si: $\quad n_e n_h = 1.5 \times 10^{33} T^3 e^{-1.21/kT}$

thus agreeing with the temperature dependence and giving a band gap of 0.785 ev for Ge and 1.21 ev for Si.

The problem of determining the electron and hole mobilities still

[1] F. J. Morin and J. P. Maita, *Phys. Rev.*, **94**: 1525 (1954).

remains. This entails the evaluation of the total cross section for electron and hole scattering (and thus a determination of the electron mean free path) in the crystal (see Sec. 6.1). This is indeed the most difficult (and as yet unsolved) part of the evaluation of σ.[1] Let it suffice at this point to remark that the electron and hole mobilities of intrinsic semiconductors depend very weakly on the temperature. This is evidenced by the experimental confirmation of the linear relationship between the logarithm of the resistivity $\ln \rho$ ($\equiv \ln \sigma^{-1}$) and $1/T$ in silicon and germanium. Such a relationship is seen to hold [according to (9.9)] if the temperature dependence of $T^{3/2}(\mu_e + \mu_h)$ may be neglected in comparison with the exponential term $e^{-\epsilon_g/2kT}$. Under such an approximation we have

$$\sigma^{-1} \equiv \rho = (\text{const})e^{\epsilon_g/2kT}$$

or

$$\ln \rho = \ln (\text{const}) + \frac{\epsilon_g}{2kT}$$

giving

$$\frac{d(\ln \rho)}{d(1/kT)} = \frac{\epsilon_g}{2} \tag{9.10}$$

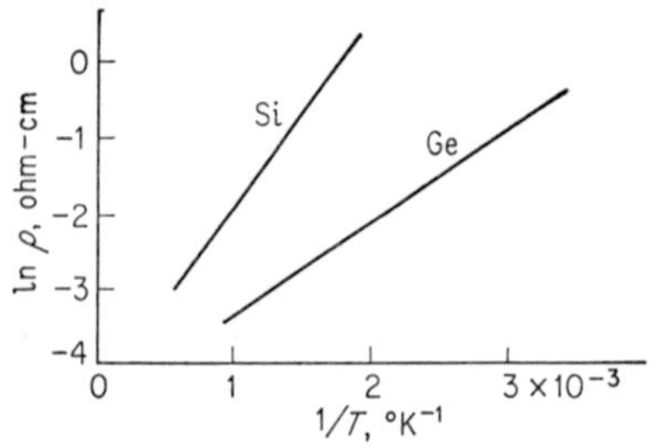

Fig. 9.3. Plot of the natural logarithm of the resistivity as a function of the reciprocal of the absolute temperature.

Typical graphs of $\ln \rho$ vs $1/T$ for intrinsic semiconductors are shown in Fig. 9.3. This linear relationship indicates that possibly the temperature dependence of $\mu_e + \mu_h$ is close to $T^{-3/2}$, thus canceling the $T^{3/2}$ term in the numerator of the expression for σ [Eq. (9.9)].

Seitz[2] finds the following result for the mobility of charge carriers in nonpolar crystals:

$$\mu_i = \frac{2^{1/2}6^{1/3}}{4\pi^{5/6}} \frac{n_i^{1/3} e\hbar^2 k^2 \Theta^2 M}{m_i^{5/2} c^2 (kT)^{3/2}} \qquad i \equiv e \text{ or } h \tag{9.11}$$

where Θ is the Debye temperature,

$$c = \frac{\hbar^2}{2m} \int |\nabla u|^2 \, dV$$

and u is the modulating factor of the Bloch wave function.

This expression was obtained by assuming that electron mobility arises only from interaction of the electron gas with the longitudinal

[1] For an extensive theoretical treatment of electron mobilities in solids, see the article by F. J. Blatt in F. Seitz and D. Turnbull (eds.), "Solid State Physics," vol. 4, Academic Press Inc., New York, 1957.

[2] F. Seitz, *Phys. Rev.*, **73**: 549 (1948).

phonons[1] (one at a time). Also, other restrictions were placed on the temperature range in arriving at (9.11). Although (9.11) agrees fairly well with the properties of diamond, it does not explain the properties of silicon or germanium and is not generally valid for semiconductors.

The deviations of μ from a $T^{-3/2}$ law can be seen from the following experimental results of Morin and Maita:[2] For Ge the drift mobilities for electrons and holes are

$$\mu_e = 4.90 \times 10^7 T^{-1.66} \qquad 100°\text{K} < T \leq 280°\text{K}$$
$$\mu_h = 1.05 \times 10^9 T^{-2.33} \qquad 100°\text{K} < T \leq 290°\text{K}$$

and for Si

$$\mu_e = 4.0 \times 10^9 T^{-2.6} \qquad 300°\text{K} < T < 400°\text{K}$$
$$\mu_h = 2.5 \times 10^8 T^{-2.3} \qquad 150°\text{K} < T < 400°\text{K}$$

The deviations from the $T^{-3/2}$ law are due to scattering mechanisms other than the one considered above. Thus, along with electron-longitudinal-phonon interactions, electrons can also interact, to some degree, with transverse acoustic phonons and optical phonons.[3] For a discussion of electron mobilities as a function of scattering mechanisms the reader is referred to the article by F. J. Blatt.[4]

From a practical standpoint, nature has provided us with relatively few solids which are intrinsic semiconductors. These are materials composed of elements in or around column IV of the periodic table. All that we can do to alter their electrical properties, as far as intrinsic semiconduction is concerned, is to vary the temperature. But such variation over the entire possible temperature range alters their electrical properties very little.

On the other hand, the operation of the other type of semiconductor, the impurity semiconductor, depends on the degree and type of impurity of the crystal. Since the purity of a crystal can be controlled (to some degree) in the laboratory, such semiconductors are of very practical value when a crystal with specific properties is required. Let us now examine some of the features of such semiconductors.

The Impurity Semiconductor

Consider now a material, characterized as an insulator at all temperatures (i.e., the forbidden-energy gap is too great for thermal excitations from the valence to the conduction band, even at the minimum energy-

[1] "Phonon" is the expression for a quantized lattice vibration. For an extensive treatment of electron-phonon interactions, see J. M. Ziman, "Electrons and Phonons," chap. 5, Oxford University Press, Fair Lawn, N.J., 1960.

[2] F. J. Morin and J. P. Maita, *Phys. Rev.*, **96:** 28 (1954).

[3] Acoustic phonons refer to in-phase motion of neighboring ions in a lattice vibration; optical phonons refer to out-of-phase motion of neighboring ions in a lattice vibration. See Ziman, *op. cit.*, chap. 1.

[4] Blatt, *op. cit.*, p. 199.

band separation). We have seen in Chap. 7 that the destruction of the perfect periodicity of the lattice potential by the introduction of impurity ions into the crystal has the effect of introducing extra energy levels into the normally forbidden-energy gap. Suppose now that the impurities are of such a type and occur in sufficient number that these extra energy levels appear close to the surfaces of the valence and/or conduction bands. If, now, the impurity-atom energy levels near the crystal conduction band are occupied (e.g., the 3*s* electron of Na) but are close enough to be thermally excited, the bound electron of these ions will move up into the conduction band (leaving behind an "immobile hole"). Also, of course, as electrons in the conduction band approach such an impurity ion, they can

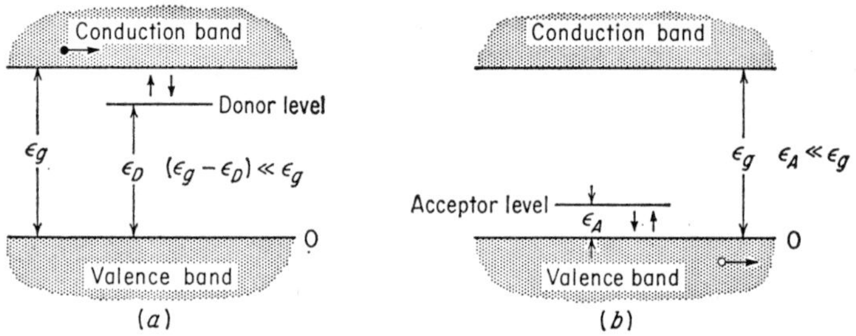

Fig. 9.4. Impurity semiconduction for (*a*) *n*-type and (*b*) *p*-type conductivity.

fall back into its outer shell. At any finite temperature there will be a continual flux of electrons between the conduction band and the impurity-ion "traps." A steady-state population in the conduction band will thereby be established, thus allowing the crystal to become conducting. Impurity states such as these are called *donor states*, and the resulting conduction process is called *n-type conduction* (see Fig. 9.4*a*).

A completely analogous situation occurs if the impurity atom is one which lacks an electron in its outer shell [such as $Cl(3p^5)$] and when this energy level is very close to the edge of the valence band. Under such conditions electrons may be thermally excited out of the valence band and "trapped" by these impurity ions. The resulting electron vacancy in the valence band (i.e., the "hole") is then free to contribute to the conductivity of electrical or thermal energy while the trapped electron remains immobile. Again, at finite temperatures a steady-state hole population is established in the valence band. Such impurity states are called *acceptor states*, and the resulting conduction process is called *p-type conduction* (see Fig. 9.4*b*).

Clearly, one could have a mixture of both *p*-type and *n*-type conduction for a crystal containing (naturally or purposely) both donor and acceptor ions. Generally, then, the impurity semiconductor differs from the intrinsic type because of the equal number of electrons and holes in the latter and an unequal number in the former. Since no crystal is perfect [any macroscopic crystal is imperfect if only because of the presence of its surface (see Chap. 1)], the limit of intrinsic semiconduction is never reached exactly but must refer only to the case in which the number of donor and/or acceptor states is of negligible importance in determining the crystal's electrical properties.

***n*-type conduction** The electrical conductivity for a purely *n*-type semiconductor is

$$\sigma = n_e e \mu_e \tag{9.1'}$$

taking the hole concentration to be exactly zero. Let us now consider the electron concentration n_e in such a crystal. We further particularize our crystal by specifying that each of the donor atoms contain one (weakly bound) electron to give to the conduction band. If N_D is the total number of donor ions per volume and $n_D(T)$ is the total number of those atoms which still hold onto their electrons (at a temperature T), then the number of conduction electrons per volume at this temperature is just

$$n_e(T) = N_D - n_D(T) \tag{9.12}$$

Thus, the remaining problem is to determine $n_D(T)$ in terms of N_D.

In Appendix B, we derive the Fermi-Dirac distribution function without regard to electron spin. It is tacitly assumed that all electrons have the same spin; the final expression for the distribution function is then doubled in order to take account of the double-spin degeneracy. The situation which confronts us now differs slightly from this one in that each of the donor atoms contains only *one* electron and this electron can be in either of the two spin states ($\sigma_z = +1$ or $\sigma_z = -1$). If N_D^+ of the N_D atoms contain electrons in the former spin state and N_D^- atoms have electrons in the latter spin state, the number of ways of distributing the N_D^+ ions among N_D atoms is

$$P^+ = \frac{N_D!}{N_D^+!(N_D - N_D^+)!} \tag{9.13}$$

while the number of ways of distributing the N_D^- ions among the remaining $N_D - N_D^+$ ions is

$$P^- = \frac{(N_D - N_D^+)!}{N_D^-!(N_D - N_D^+ - N_D^-)!} \tag{9.14}$$

Thus, the total number of ways of arranging the N_D^+ and N_D^- ions among the total number of donor atoms is, according to the law of combining independent probabilities, the product of (9.13) and (9.14), i.e.,

$$P = P^+P^- = \frac{N_D!}{N_D^+!N_D^-!(N_D - N_D^+ - N_D^-)!} \tag{9.15}$$

Following the same procedure as in Appendix B, we require that, at thermodynamic equilibrium, the total number of donor atoms $(N_D^+ + N_D^-)$ be constant, so that

$$\delta(N_D^+ + N_D^-) = 0 \tag{9.16}$$

and the total corresponding energy must be constant so that

$$\delta E_D = \delta[(N_D^+ + N_D^-)\epsilon_D] = 0 \tag{9.17}$$

where ϵ_D is the energy of the donor state, measured from the top of the valence band (see Fig. 9.4*a*). Finally, with the assumption of minimum entropy at equilibrium the standard variational procedure with N_D^+ and N_D^- varied independently [subject to (9.16) and (9.17)] gives $N_D^+ = N_D^-$,

$$\ln \frac{N_D - N_D^+ - N_D^-}{N_D^+} - \alpha - \beta\epsilon_D = 0$$

Thus
$$n_D \equiv N_D^+ + N_D^- = \frac{N_D}{\frac{1}{2}e^{\alpha+\beta\epsilon_D} + 1} \tag{9.18}$$

where α and β are the Lagrange multipliers to be determined. Again, we must have $\alpha = -\epsilon_F/kT$ and $\beta = 1/kT$ to ensure compatibility with the thermodynamic relations, giving

$$n_D(T) = \frac{N_D}{\frac{1}{2}e^{(\epsilon_D-\epsilon_F)/kT} + 1} \tag{9.19}$$

This is different from the normal expression because of the factor $\frac{1}{2}$ which appears in the denominator.

Finally, combining (9.19) and (9.12), we obtain the following result for the conduction electron concentration:

$$n_e = \frac{N_D}{2} \frac{e^{(\epsilon_D-\epsilon_F)/kT}}{\frac{1}{2}e^{(\epsilon_D-\epsilon_F)/kT} + 1} \tag{9.20}$$

We have already calculated n_e in terms of the zero of the conduction band occurring at ϵ_g [Eq. (9.2)]. Calling

$$n_e^{(0)} = 2\left(\frac{2\pi m_e kT}{h^2}\right)^{3/2} \tag{9.21}$$

and substituting Eqs. (9.21) and (9.2) into (9.20) we have

$$n_e^{(0)}e^{(\epsilon_F-\epsilon_g)/kT} = \frac{N_D}{1 + 2e^{(\epsilon_F-\epsilon_g)/kT}} \tag{9.22}$$

Calling $x = e^{\epsilon_F/kT}$, (9.22) takes the form of a quadratic equation

$$(2n_e^{(0)}e^{-(\epsilon_D+\epsilon_g)/kT})x^2 + (n_e^{(0)}e^{-\epsilon_g/kT})x - N_D = 0 \tag{9.23}$$

giving the root

$$x \equiv e^{\epsilon_F/kT} = \frac{e^{\epsilon_D/kT}}{4}\left[-1 + \left(1 + 8\frac{N_D}{n_e^{(0)}}e^{\epsilon_i/kT}\right)^{1/2}\right] \tag{9.24}$$

where

$$\epsilon_i = \epsilon_g - \epsilon_D \tag{9.24'}$$

is the ionization energy of the donor atom. [The plus sign in front of the second term on the right-hand side of (9.24) has been selected from the choice of plus and minus signs, obtained from the solutions of the quadratic equation (9.23), so as to make this side of the equation positive, in accordance with the sign on the left-hand side of the equation.]

Let us now consider two limiting cases. First we shall assume that N_D is small and T is large, so that

$$8\frac{N_D}{n_e^{(0)}}e^{\epsilon_i/kT} \ll 1 \tag{9.25}$$

In this case, (9.24) reduces to the approximate form

$$e^{\epsilon_F/kT} \simeq \frac{N_D}{n_e^{(0)}}e^{\epsilon_g/kT} \tag{9.26}$$

where we have used (9.24′) for ϵ_i. Thus, the Fermi energy is approximately

$$\epsilon_F \simeq \epsilon_g + kT\ln\frac{N_D}{n_e^{(0)}} \tag{9.27}$$

From (9.26) and (9.2), we then have

$$n_e^{(0)}e^{(\epsilon_F-\epsilon_g)/kT} = n_e \simeq N_D \tag{9.28}$$

Thus, under the condition (9.25), we see that the Fermi energy is only slightly above the bottom of the conduction band and that the concentration of conduction electrons is approximately the same as the concentration of donor atoms.

Consider now the opposite approximation in which N_D is large and the temperature T is low, so that

$$8\frac{N_D}{n_e^{(0)}}e^{\epsilon_i/kT} \gg 1 \tag{9.29}$$

In this case, (9.24) reduces to

$$e^{\epsilon_F/kT} \simeq \left(\frac{N_D}{2n_e^{(0)}}\right)^{1/2} e^{\epsilon_i/2kT}e^{\epsilon_D/kT}$$

so that, from (9.2) and (9.24),

$$n_e = \left(\frac{n_e^{(0)}N_D}{2}\right)^{1/2} e^{-\epsilon_i/2kT} \tag{9.30}$$

and

$$\begin{aligned}\epsilon_F &= \left(\epsilon_D + \frac{\epsilon_i}{2}\right) + \frac{kT}{2}\ln\frac{N_D}{2n_e^{(0)}} \\ &= \left(\epsilon_g - \frac{\epsilon_i}{2}\right) + \frac{kT}{2}\ln\frac{N_D}{2n_e^{(0)}}\end{aligned} \tag{9.31}$$

Thus, we see that, as the number of donor atoms increases and as the temperature decreases, n_e varies from an N_D dependence to an $\sqrt{N_D}$ dependence, and the Fermi energy is lowered somewhat toward the bound-state energy level of the donor atoms.

The results obtained for a p-type semiconductor are identical to those of the n-type material with N_A, m_h, ϵ_A (i.e., the acceptor ion concentration, the hole effective mass, and the energy required to excite electrons from the top of the valence band into the acceptor levels) replacing N_D, m_e, ϵ_i.

It should be emphasized again that these results apply when the donor (or acceptor) atoms have one electron (or vacancy) to contribute to n-type (or p-type) conduction. The existence of such impurity atoms is energetically more favorable than that of atoms with a pair of electrons (with opposite spins) in their outer valence shells, since the latter would generally correspond to an atom with outer electron binding tight enough that no such impurity levels would appear in the forbidden-energy gap.

Finally, we ask for the total concentration of charge carriers and Fermi energy, given a semiconductor with N_D donor atoms and N_A acceptor atoms [this is a mixed n-type–p-type (or np) semiconductor]. Using the assumption of charge neutrality, we determine the result from the addition to each side of Eq. (9.22) of the opposite sides of the corresponding equation for the acceptor atoms. Using (9.5) and following a similar procedure as above to derive n_A (the number of neutral acceptor atoms), we have

$$n_e^{(0)}e^{(\epsilon_F-\epsilon_g)/kT} + \frac{N_A}{1 + 2e^{(\epsilon_A-\epsilon_F)/kT}} = n_h^{(0)}e^{-\epsilon_F/kT} + \frac{N_D}{1 + 2e^{(\epsilon_F-\epsilon_D)/kT}} \tag{9.32}$$

The other factor (besides the charge-carrier concentration) that is required to predict the electrical conductivity is the charge-carrier mobility.

Once again, the mobility of electrons (or holes) in n- (or p-) type semiconductors is not a well-determined function. One example of a theoretical calculation of mobility in an impurity semiconductor is that of Conwell and Weisskopf.[1] They assume that the motion of electrons (or holes) is impeded only by their Coulomb scattering from the impurity ions. They find the following expression for the mobility in an n-type semiconductor:

$$\mu = \frac{2^{7/2}\epsilon^2(kT)^{3/2}\ln(1 + x^2)}{n_D\pi^{3/2}e^2m_e^{1/2}} \tag{9.33}$$

where

$$x = \frac{6\epsilon dkT}{e^2}$$

and $2d$ is the average distance between the pairs of ionized donor atoms.

[1] E. Conwell and V. Weisskopf, *Phys. Rev.*, **77**: 388 (1950).

The Hall Effect

One experimental method used in determining the charge-carrier mobility in a semiconductor is the combination of independent measurements of electrical conductivity and the Hall effect. The latter yields an independent value for the charge-carrier concentration, thus giving

$$\mu_H = \frac{\sigma_{exp}}{n_{exp}e} \tag{9.34}$$

Consider an electrical conductor subjected to a potential difference along the x direction. Suppose now that superposed on this voltage is a constant magnetic field in the z direction. The effect of the latter would be to cause the current, normally in the x direction, to curve about the z axis so that (for electron conduction) the negative charges would tend to pile up on one side of the wire, thus building up a counteracting electric field intensity $\mathcal{E}_y$ (see Fig. 9.5). The electric field intensity $\mathcal{E}_y$ would then build up until it is of a sufficient magnitude to cancel the force exerted on the electrons due to the magnetic field. In the steady state, a *Hall voltage* is thereby established in the y direction, causing the net force on the electron in that direction to vanish, i.e.,

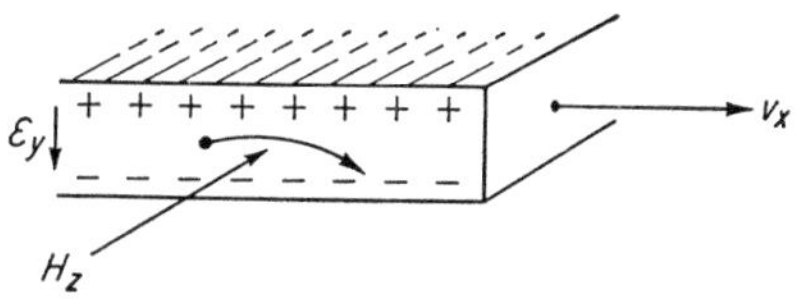

Fig. 9.5. The Hall effect.

$$F_y = e\left[\mathcal{E}_y + \frac{1}{c}(\mathbf{v} \times \mathbf{H})_y\right] = 0 \tag{9.35}$$

or

$$e\mathcal{E}_y = \frac{ev_x}{c} H_z \equiv \frac{j_x H_z}{nc}$$

Thus, the ratio

$$R_H = \frac{\mathcal{E}_y}{j_x H_z} = \pm\frac{1}{n|e|c} \tag{9.36}$$

must be constant. R_H is called the *Hall coefficient*, the + and − signs refer to positive and negative charge carriers, respectively, and n is their concentration.

Since the electrical conductivity depends on the square of the charge [Eq. (6.6)], its measurement does not reveal the type of conduction (p or n type). On the other hand, the measurement of the Hall coefficient does reveal the sign of the charge carriers, thus giving the conductivity type besides their concentration.

The above remarks apply to the impurity semiconductor in which there is only one type of charge carrier (i.e., pure electron or pure hole conduction). In the general case of n-type ($n_e > n_h$) or p-type ($n_h > n_e$) conduction, a more exact treatment of the transport of charge carriers, which scatter primarily from lattice vibrations, leads to a slight modification of (9.36), giving

$$R_H = \pm \frac{3\pi}{8} \frac{1}{n|e|c} \tag{9.37}$$

The assumption made here is that the charge carriers have a maxwellian distribution.[1] One other variable which is often used to describe the Hall effect is the ratio of the currents j_y to j_x. This is called the *Hall angle* and is, according to (9.36),

$$\theta = \frac{j_y}{j_x} = \frac{\sigma \mathcal{E}_y}{j_x} = \sigma R_H H_z = \frac{\mu_H H_z}{c} \tag{9.38}$$

where $\mu_H = \sigma R_H / c$ is called the Hall mobility.

Summarizing, a systematic determination of the Hall effect and electrical conductivity as a function of temperature gives, according to (9.1) or (9.1′), the behavior of the charge-carrier mobility μ as a function of temperature. Such experiments reveal significant deviations from the temperature dependences of the idealized Seitz model [Eq. (9.11)] for intrinsic semiconductors or the Conwell-Weisskopf model [Eq. (9.33)] for impurity semiconductors. It remains, then, to explain the data in terms of a more precise description of the interaction between the charge carriers and their total environment in the crystal. In practice, the experimentalist is interested in designing an experiment which will measure the electron (or hole) mobility as due to different types of scattering mechanisms in the crystal so as to enable him to study details of the transport of energy by the charge carriers. Thus, for example, the Hall mobility is distinguished from the "drift" mobility μ_D, where the latter is that due to electron-phonon scattering.[2] In principle, the total mobility must be calculated from the separate mobilities associated with all mechanisms which impede the motion of the charge carriers in the crystal.

A comparison of the electrical conductivities for intrinsic and impurity Ge and Si crystals is shown in Table 9.3.

A typical set of curves for the Hall mobility of n- and p-type Si as a function of sample purity is shown in Fig. 9.6.

[1] See A. H. Wilson, "Theory of Metals," chap. 8, Cambridge University Press, New York, 1954.

[2] In principle, the mobility must be calculated from the conductivity that one would derive using the nonequilibrium distribution function, i.e., the solution of the Boltzmann transport equation. A magnetic field present or not would give rise to correspondingly different expressions for the conductivity. Thus, in general, the drift and Hall mobilities differ. For a discussion of this point, see the article by Blatt, *op. cit.*, p. 243. It is shown by Blatt that one may express the ratio of the two mobilities as $\mu_H/\mu_D = \langle\tau^2\rangle/\langle\tau\rangle^2$, where τ is the relaxation time between collisions and the average is taken over a maxwellian distribution. Clearly, in the special case where τ is independent of velocity, the two mobilities are the same. This special case, however, cannot generally be assumed.

TABLE 9.3 *Typical Values of Electrical Conductivity for Intrinsic and Impurity Semiconductors. (Values are Given at Temperatures between 290 and 300°K.)*

Material	*Concentration, cm^{-3}*	*N_D or N_A, cm^{-3}*	*Donor or acceptor*	*Type*	*mho/cm*
Ge	4.41×10^{22}	Intrinsic			0.022*
		8×10^{13}	As(ϵ_i = 0.0127 ev)	n	0.05*
		1.5×10^{15}	As(ϵ_i = 0.0127 ev)	n	0.9*
		9×10^{13}	Ga(ϵ_A = 0.0108 ev)	p	0.03†
		8×10^{14}	Ga(ϵ_A = 0.0108 ev)	p	0.3†
Si	5.00×10^{22}	Intrinsic			1.57×10^{-5}
		5×10^{14}	As(ϵ_i = 0.049 ev)	n	0.1
		5×10^{15}	As(ϵ_i = 0.049 ev)	n	0.77
		5×10^{16}	As(ϵ_i = 0.049 ev)	n	3.3
		5×10^{14}	B(ϵ_A = 0.045 ev)	p	0.4
		5×10^{15}	B(ϵ_A = 0.045 ev)	p	3.3
		2×10^{16}	B(ϵ_A = 0.045 ev)	p	10.0

* P. P. Debye and E. M. Conwell, *Phys. Rev.*, **87:** 1131 (1952); **93:** 693 (1954).
† G. L. Pearson and J. Bardeen, *Phys. Rev.*, **75:** 865 (1949).
$\epsilon_i = \epsilon_g - \epsilon_D = (0.785 - \epsilon_D)$ ev; $\epsilon_D = 0.772$ ev. (Ge) (See Fig. 9.4.)
$\epsilon_i = \epsilon_g - \epsilon_D = (1.21 - \epsilon_D)$ ev; $\epsilon_D = 1.16$ ev. (Si)

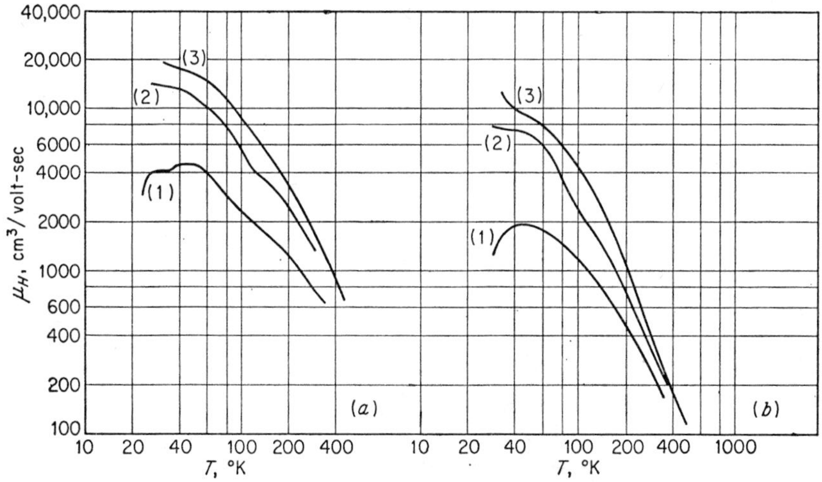

Fig. 9.6. Hall mobilities of (*a*) *n*-type, As-doped Si and (*b*) *p*-type, B-doped Si as a function of temperature and purity. The curves for the higher mobilities in both (*a*) and (*b*) correspond to increasingly pure samples. [*After F. J. Morin and J. Maita, Phys. Rev.*, **96:** 28 (1954).]

It is seen in Fig. 9.6 that, as the purity of the sample increases and as the temperature decreases, the charge carriers become more mobile. This is expected qualitatively since purification decreases the Coulomb scattering from impurity ions and the temperature decrease lowers the effective cross section for scattering from lattice vibrations. The actual (quantitative) sharpness of the drop in μ_H with decreasing temperature is not expected in terms of the ordinary scattering mechanisms.

Thus far we have examined the qualitative features of the mechanisms that predict the electrical properties of a semiconductor subjected to static fields. We have seen how certain measurements can lead to some of the quantitative properties of the band structure, especially near energy-band extrema. Let us now proceed to investigate the way in which such a quasi-free-electron gas will interact with a time-dependent electromagnetic radiation field. We shall see that such an analysis indicates further experiments which lead to finer details of the energy-band structure of semiconductors.

9.2 Interaction of a semiconductor with time-dependent fields

Consider first a quasi-free-electron gas which is not subject to any external forces. Let v_0 be the electron drift velocity just after a collision which normally impedes its motion (e.g., a collision with lattice vibrations or other electrons).[1] As this electron proceeds on its way in the lattice, further collisions attenuate its velocity. Let us make the assumption that the attenuation occurs in an exponential fashion so that, at any later time t,

$$v(t) = v_0 e^{-t/\tau} \tag{9.39}$$

This assumption is based on the supposition that the change in the electron's velocity within a time dt is directly proportional to this time interval and to its velocity at that time. Thus, the constant of proportionality $-1/\tau$ is assumed to be a true constant, independent of velocity, i.e.,

$$dv = -\frac{1}{\tau} v\, dt \tag{9.39'}$$

The only justification for this assumption is the degree of agreement between the experimental data and the implied properties obtained from the ensuing theory.[2]

[1] In Chap. 6, v was denoted by v_D. We shall drop the subscript here.

[2] One can justify (9.39) by calculating the average drift velocity with the distribution function obtained from the Boltzmann transport equation

$$\mathbf{v} \cdot \nabla_r f + \frac{e}{m} \left(\mathcal{E} + \frac{\mathbf{v}}{c} \times \mathbf{H}\right) \cdot \nabla_v f = \left(\frac{\partial f}{\partial t}\right)_{\text{coll}} = \frac{f - f_0}{\tau}$$

[f_0 is the equilibrium (Fermi-Dirac) distribution function] and by assuming that the

Equations of Motion

According to (9.39) or (9.39′), in the absence of external forces,

$$m\left(\dot{\mathbf{v}} + \frac{\mathbf{v}}{\tau}\right) = 0 \tag{9.40}$$

where m is the effective mass of the charge carriers. If we now assume that an external force $\mathbf{F}$ is present, (9.40) is generalized to the form

$$m\left(\dot{\mathbf{v}} + \frac{\mathbf{v}}{\tau}\right) = \mathbf{F} \tag{9.40′}$$

where the time variation $\dot{\mathbf{v}}$ is taken to follow the time variation of $\mathbf{F}$. Thus, $m\dot{\mathbf{v}}$ takes the form of a velocity-dependent force (this is analogous to the motion of particles through a viscous medium).

Consider now that $\mathbf{F}$ is the force imposed by a static external electric field $\boldsymbol{\varepsilon}_0$. In this case we have $\dot{\mathbf{v}} = 0$ and

$$\frac{m\mathbf{v}}{\tau} = e\boldsymbol{\varepsilon}_0$$

or

$$\mathbf{v} = \frac{e\tau}{m}\boldsymbol{\varepsilon}_0 \tag{9.41}$$

in agreement with (6.4).

Next, suppose that $\mathbf{F}$ is the force imposed by an oscillating electric field intensity. In this case, (9.40′) takes the form

$$m\left(\dot{\mathbf{v}} + \frac{\mathbf{v}}{\tau}\right) = e\boldsymbol{\varepsilon}_0 e^{i\omega t} \tag{9.42}$$

Complex Conductivity

Assuming now that the electron motion follows the oscillatory field (that is, $\mathbf{v} \propto e^{i\omega t}$), (9.42) takes the form

$$\left(i\omega + \frac{1}{\tau}\right)\mathbf{v} = \frac{e}{m}\boldsymbol{\varepsilon}_0 \tag{9.43}$$

The mobility is then (assuming an isotropic medium)

$$\mu = \frac{|\mathbf{v}|}{|\boldsymbol{\varepsilon}_0|} = \frac{e\tau}{m}\frac{1}{1 + i\omega\tau} \tag{9.44}$$

---

relaxation time τ is independent of energy. (See Wilson, *op. cit.*, chap. 1.) In the above approximation for $(\partial f/\partial t)_{\text{coll}}$ (the time rate of change of the electron distribution due to collisions) it is assumed that $(f - f_0)_t = (f - f_0)_{t=0}e^{-t/\tau}$ is a valid time behavior for this quantity. The validity of this assumption is justified by the agreement that it predicts with experiments.

and the conductivity is given by the complex form

$$\sigma = ne\mu = \frac{ne^2\tau}{m}\frac{1}{1 + i\omega\tau} = \sigma^{(r)} + i\sigma^{(i)} \tag{9.45}$$

where
$$\sigma^{(r)} = \frac{\sigma_0}{1 + (\omega\tau)^2} \tag{9.46a}$$

and
$$\sigma^{(i)} = -\frac{(\omega\tau)\sigma_0}{1 + (\omega\tau)^2} \tag{9.46b}$$

are the real and imaginary parts of the conductivity and

$$\sigma_0 = \frac{ne^2\tau}{m} \tag{9.47}$$

is the conductivity [derived previously in Eq. (6.6)] in the absence of a time-dependent external force.

Since σ is defined, according to Ohm's law, as the proportionality between the applied electric field intensity and the resulting current density, the complex conductivity implies a complex current vector. This, however, means nothing more than a current made up of two parts which are out of phase with each other.

According to the Maxwell field equations, the total current density which acts as a source of a magnetic field intensity is

$$\mathbf{j}_t = \mathbf{j} + \frac{1}{4\pi}\frac{\partial \mathbf{D}}{\partial t} \tag{9.48}$$

where the last term on the right is the displacement current. Since the electric induction vector is

$$\mathbf{D} = \mathcal{E} + 4\pi\mathcal{P} \equiv \epsilon_0\mathcal{E} \tag{9.49}$$

where $\mathcal{P}$ is the induced polarization vector of the crystal and ϵ_0 is the static dielectric constant, and since

$$\frac{\partial \mathcal{E}}{\partial t} = i\omega\mathcal{E} \tag{9.50}$$

we have

$$\begin{aligned} \mathbf{j}_t &= \sigma\mathcal{E} + \frac{\partial \mathcal{P}}{\partial t} + \frac{i\omega}{4\pi}\mathcal{E} \\ &= \left(\sigma^{(r)}\mathcal{E} + \frac{\partial \mathcal{P}}{\partial t}\right) + i\left(\sigma^{(i)} + \frac{\omega}{4\pi}\right)\mathcal{E} \\ &\equiv \mathbf{j}^{(r)} + i\mathbf{j}^{(i)} \end{aligned} \tag{9.51}$$

where $\mathbf{j}^{(r)}$ and $\mathbf{j}^{(i)}$ are the two current vectors, which are out of phase, and $\sigma^{(r)}$ and $\sigma^{(i)}$ are given by (9.46a) and (9.46b).

Complex Dielectric Constant

From (9.49) and (9.51), we can also express the total current vector in terms of the dielectric constant as follows:

$$\mathbf{j}_t = \frac{i\omega\epsilon}{4\pi}\,\boldsymbol{\mathcal{E}}$$

where

$$\begin{aligned}\epsilon = \epsilon_0 - \frac{4\pi i}{\omega}\sigma &= \epsilon_0 - \frac{4\pi i}{\omega}\frac{\sigma_0}{1 + i\omega\tau} \\ &= \epsilon^{(r)} + i\epsilon^{(i)} \end{aligned} \tag{9.52}$$

This is the expression for the complex dielectric constant of the conducting material. The explicit forms for the real and imaginary parts of ϵ are then

$$\epsilon^{(r)} = \epsilon_0 - \frac{4\pi\tau\sigma_0}{1 + (\omega\tau)^2} \tag{9.53a}$$

$$\epsilon^{(i)} = -\frac{4\pi}{\omega}\frac{\sigma_0}{1 + (\omega\tau)^2} \tag{9.53b}$$

To complete this aspect of the discussion, it is noted from physical optics that the propagation of the applied oscillating electric field through the crystal is described by the wave function

$$e^{i(\omega t - \rho\mathbf{k}\cdot\mathbf{r})} \tag{9.54}$$

where $\rho = \sqrt{\epsilon^{(r)}}$ is the index of refraction of the medium. We note from (9.53*a*) that for the critical value of frequency

$$\omega = \omega_0 \equiv \sqrt{\frac{4\pi\tau\sigma_0 - \epsilon_0}{\epsilon_0\tau^2}} \tag{9.55}$$

$\epsilon^{(r)}$ (and therefore the index of refraction) vanishes. This means that, when $\omega = \omega_0$, the applied electric radiation field does not propagate through the crystal; i.e., there is total reflection. On the other hand, when $\omega < \omega_0$, then $\epsilon^{(r)} < 0$ and ρ is purely imaginary, and when $\omega > \omega_0$, $\epsilon^{(r)} > 0$ and ρ is purely real. The former case corresponds to an opaque crystal (i.e., attenuation) and the latter to a transparent crystal. These results are indicated in Fig. 9.7.

In experimental investigations, it is frequently convenient to study the absorption of electromagnetic radiation at frequencies which satisfy the inequality

$$\omega\tau \gg 1 \tag{9.56}$$

This criterion means that, on an average, the electrons oscillate through a large number of cycles before they are stopped in collisions. By studying the dielectric constants of crystals as a function of temperature,

Benedict and Shockley[1] were able to establish, according to (9.52), that in germanium the temperature dependence of τ is $T^{-3/2}$. Thus, in general, one would expect that the lower the temperature, the smaller would be the required value of ω so as to satisfy (9.56). Experimentally, (9.56) is satisfied by infrared frequencies (in the 10-μ range) at room temperature and for the microwave range ($\lambda \sim 1$ to 10 cm) for $T < 10°$K.

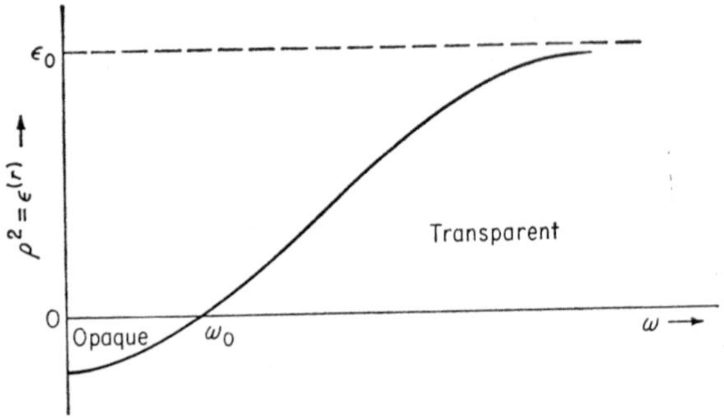

Fig. 9.7. Squared index of refraction of an electron gas as a function of the frequency of the impinging radiation.

Assuming (9.56) to be the case, (9.53a) gives

$$0 \simeq \epsilon_0 - \frac{4\pi\tau\sigma_0}{(\omega_0\tau)^2}$$

or

$$\omega_0^2 \simeq \frac{4\pi\sigma_0}{\tau\epsilon_0} = \frac{4\pi ne^2}{m\epsilon_0} \tag{9.57}$$

For typical charge-carrier concentrations in a semiconductor, $n \sim 10^{14}$ cm^{-3} (see Table 9.3), taking ϵ_0 to be of the order of 10 [ϵ_0(Ge) = 16, ϵ_0(Si) = 13], and taking the effective mass to be the free-electron mass, (9.57) gives

$$\nu_0 \equiv \frac{\omega_0}{2\pi} \simeq \frac{10^{11}}{2\pi} \cong 10^4 \text{ Mc/sec}$$

which is in the microwave frequency range. Thus, microwave-absorption experiments in semiconductors provide an accurate account of the behavior of charge carriers in these types of solids.

Cyclotron Resonance in Semiconductors[2]

Suppose now that the semiconductor is subjected to a constant magnetic field intensity in the z direction in addition to the linearly

[1] T. S. Benedict and W. Shockley, *Phys. Rev.*, **89**: 1152 (1953).

[2] For further reading on this topic, see B. Lax and J. G. Mavroides, in F. Seitz and D. Turnbull (eds.), "Solid State Physics," vol. 11, Academic Press Inc., New York, 1960.

polarized oscillating electric field in the x direction. In this case, our equation of motion (9.40′) takes the form

$$m\left(\dot{\mathbf{v}} + \frac{\mathbf{v}}{\tau}\right) = m\left(i\omega + \frac{1}{\tau}\right)\mathbf{v} = e\left(\boldsymbol{\mathcal{E}} + \frac{\mathbf{v}\times\mathbf{H}}{c}\right) \tag{9.58}$$

The second step in (9.58) follows again from the assumption that the electron motion follows the oscillatory behavior of the electric field intensity. Since $\boldsymbol{\mathcal{E}}$ is in the x direction and $\mathbf{H}_0$ in the z direction, (9.58) reduces to the following equations:

$$\begin{aligned} m\left(i\omega + \frac{1}{\tau}\right)v_x &= e\left(\mathcal{E}_x + \frac{v_y H_0}{c}\right) \\ m\left(i\omega + \frac{1}{\tau}\right)v_y &= -\frac{e}{c}v_x H_0 \end{aligned} \tag{9.59}$$

and v_z is unaffected by the applied $\boldsymbol{\mathcal{E}}$ and $\mathbf{H}$ fields. Equations (9.59) are then solved simultaneously for v_x and v_y, giving

$$\begin{aligned} v_x &= \left(\frac{e\tau}{m}\mathcal{E}_x\right)\frac{1 + i\omega\tau}{1 + 2i\omega\tau + \tau^2(\omega_c^2 - \omega^2)} \\ v_y &= \frac{-\omega_c\tau}{1 + i\omega\tau}v_x \end{aligned} \tag{9.59a}$$

where

$$\omega_c = \frac{eH_0}{mc} \tag{9.59b}$$

is called the *cyclotron frequency*. If we now combine (9.59*a*) with the equality

$$j_x = nev_x = \sigma\mathcal{E}_x$$

the following result is obtained for the complex conductivity of electrical current in the x direction:

$$\sigma = \sigma_0 \frac{1 + i\omega\tau}{1 + 2i\omega\tau + (\omega_c^2 - \omega^2)}$$

The observation relates to the real part of σ/σ_0

$$\mathcal{R}\left(\frac{\sigma}{\sigma_0}\right) = \frac{1 + 2(\omega\tau)^2 + (\omega_c^2 - \omega^2)\tau^2}{[1 + (\omega_c^2 - \omega^2)\tau^2]^2 + 4\omega^2\tau^2}$$

The cyclotron-resonance experiment is designed to detect a change in the power absorbed from an oscillating electric field (with constant frequency) as the dc magnetic field strength is varied. Since the power absorbed from the radiation field is proportional to $\mathcal{R}(\sigma/\sigma_0)$ [i.e., power absorbed $= \mathcal{R}(\sigma\mathcal{E}_x^2)$], such an experiment reveals quite accurately the cyclotron frequency $\omega_c = eH_0/mc$.

We shall now consider limiting values of $\mathcal{R}(\sigma/\sigma_0)$.

1. If $\omega = \omega_c$, we have

$$\frac{\sigma}{\sigma_0} = \frac{1 + i\omega_c\tau}{1 + 2i\omega_c\tau}$$

Further, if $\omega_c\tau \gg 1$, then

$$\frac{\sigma}{\sigma_0} = \frac{1}{2}$$

2. If now the magnetic field is turned off, so that $\omega_c = 0$, σ/σ_0 becomes

$$\frac{\sigma}{\sigma_0} = \frac{1 + i\omega\tau}{(1 + i\omega\tau)^2} = \frac{1 - i\omega\tau}{1 + \omega^2\tau^2}$$

and if $\omega\tau \gg 1$

$$\mathcal{R}\left(\frac{\sigma}{\sigma_0}\right) \simeq \frac{1}{\omega^2\tau^2}$$

Let us consider the shape of $\mathcal{R}(\sigma/\sigma_0)$ as a function of ω_c/ω. First, differentiating $\mathcal{R}(\sigma/\sigma_0)$ with respect to ω_c/ω, we find the maximum to occur at

$$\omega_c^{(m)} = \frac{1}{\tau}\left([1 + (\omega\tau)^2]\left\{2\left[\frac{1 + 2(\omega\tau)^2}{2(1 + (\omega\tau)^2)}\right]^{1/2} - 1\right\}\right)^{1/2} \tag{9.60}$$

This is the frequency at which the so-called *cyclotron resonance* occurs.

As ω_c increases from the maximum sufficiently so that $\omega_c^2 \gg \omega^2$, $\mathcal{R}(\sigma/\sigma_0)$ becomes proportional to $1/\omega_c^2\tau^2$ and therefore proportional to H_0^{-2}. This implies that at high magnetic fields the particle is slowed down by an increasing magnitude of the applied magnetic field. This is known as a *magnetoresistive effect.*

As ω_c decreases from the maximum, $\mathcal{R}(\sigma/\sigma_0)$ approaches the limiting value

$$\mathcal{R}\left(\frac{\sigma}{\sigma_0}\right)(\omega_c = 0) = \frac{1}{1 + \omega^2\tau^2} \tag{9.61}$$

when the applied magnetic field, and therefore ω_c, goes to zero.

In experiments of practical importance, the inequality (9.56) is usually valid. Under this condition, (9.60) and (9.61) take the forms

$$\omega_c^{(m)} \simeq \omega \tag{9.60$'$}$$

giving

$$\mathcal{R}\left(\frac{\sigma}{\sigma_0}\right) = \frac{1}{2} \tag{9.60$''$}$$

and

$$\mathcal{R}\left(\frac{\sigma}{\sigma_0}\right)(\omega_c = 0) = \frac{1}{\omega^2\tau^2} \tag{9.61$'$}$$

The relation (9.60″) implies that the power which is absorbed at resonance ($\omega \simeq \omega_c$) is one-half of the power that would be absorbed when both the frequency of the applied electric field and the applied magnetic field intensity are zero. In view of these calculations, the approximate shape of the power-absorption curve [which is the shape of $\Re(\sigma/\sigma_0)$] is shown in Fig. 9.8.

Thus an accurate measurement of the magnetic field at which the maximum power is absorbed by a semiconductor from the applied oscillating electric field intensity provides, in accordance with (9.60) [or (9.60′)], an accurate measure of ω_c. Such an experiment is carried out at microwave frequencies by properly orienting the semiconducting

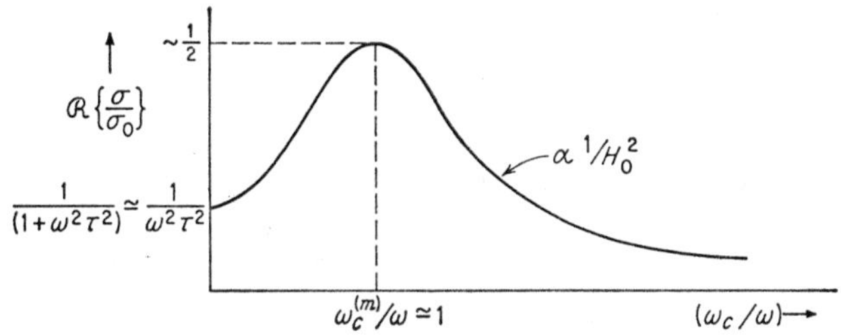

Fig. 9.8. Microwave power absorption in a cyclotron-resonance experiment.

crystal in a wave guide or cavity so as to optimize the absorption from an electric mode of the system.

The essential point in such an experiment is that a measure of ω_c for a particular orientation of H_0 provides a measure of the effective mass of electrons accelerated in that direction (i.e., the direction of the applied $\mathbf{H}_0$ field). Their unaccelerated motion is circular about the direction of $\mathbf{H}_0$. Thus, by varying the orientation of $\mathbf{H}_0$ relative to the crystal axes, it is possible to measure the components of the effective-mass tensor and thereby to draw conclusions about the symmetry properties of the energy-band structure near their extrema.

One piece of information about ω_c is missing from this analysis and that is its sign. The reason is that the linearly polarized $\boldsymbol{\mathcal{E}}$ field implies that $\Re(\sigma/\sigma_0)$ is proportional to ω_c^2. On the other hand, if the applied electric field intensity were circularly polarized, the resulting expression would be sensitive to the sign of ω_c. This is seen as follows:

The equations of motion (9.58) for $\boldsymbol{\mathcal{E}}$ in the xy plane are

$$
\begin{aligned}
m\left(i\omega + \frac{1}{\tau}\right)v_x &= e\left(\mathcal{E}_x + \frac{v_y H_0}{c}\right) \\
m\left(i\omega + \frac{1}{\tau}\right)v_y &= e\left(\mathcal{E}_y - \frac{v_x H_0}{c}\right)
\end{aligned}
\tag{9.62}
$$

and have the solution

$$v_x + iv_y = \frac{(e\tau/m)(\mathcal{E}_x + i\mathcal{E}_y)}{i(\omega + \omega_c)\tau + 1} \tag{9.63}$$

giving

$$\frac{\sigma}{\sigma_0} = \frac{1 - i(\omega + \omega_c)\tau}{1 + (\omega + \omega_c)^2\tau^2} \tag{9.64}$$

Thus,

$$\mathcal{R}\left(\frac{\sigma}{\sigma_0}\right) = \frac{1}{1 + (\omega + \omega_c)^2\tau^2} \tag{9.65}$$

for circularly polarized radiation and is indeed sensitive to the sign of ω_c. Again, such experiments may be carried out in the microwave frequency range by orienting the crystal in a properly excited mode of a cylindrical cavity.

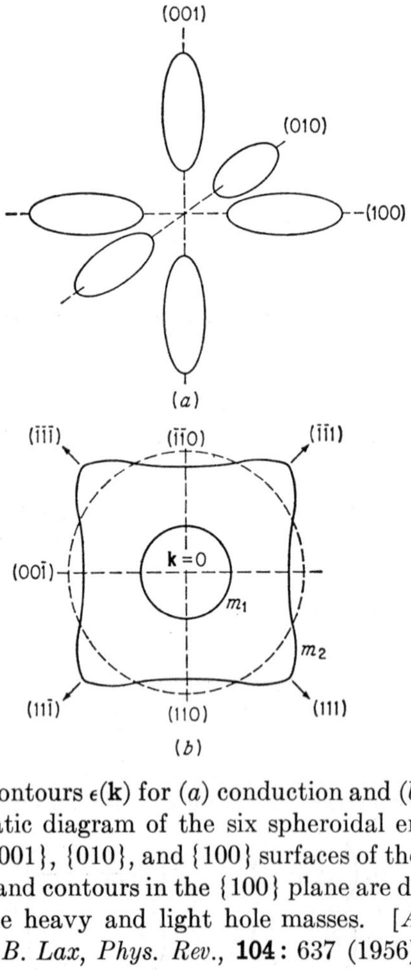

Fig. 9.9. Energy contours $\epsilon(\mathbf{k})$ for (*a*) conduction and (*b*) valence bands of Si. (*a*) A schematic diagram of the six spheroidal energy surfaces perpendicular to the {001}, {010}, and {100} surfaces of the conduction band. (*b*) The valence-band contours in the {100} plane are dotted about $\mathbf{k} = 0$. m_2 and m_1 are the heavy and light hole masses. [*After R. N. Dexter, H. J. Zeiger, and B. Lax, Phys. Rev.*, **104**: 637 (1956).]

In practice, the microwave frequency range is a very useful one with which to work, but it requires a very low lattice temperature, so as to make τ sufficiently large. Thus, much of the radio-frequency cyclotron-resonance work is carried out at liquid helium temperature ($\sim$4°K). As the temperature is increased, the maxima of power-absorption curves (such as are shown in Fig. 9.8), die out and eventually disappear because of the breakdown of the inequality (9.56).

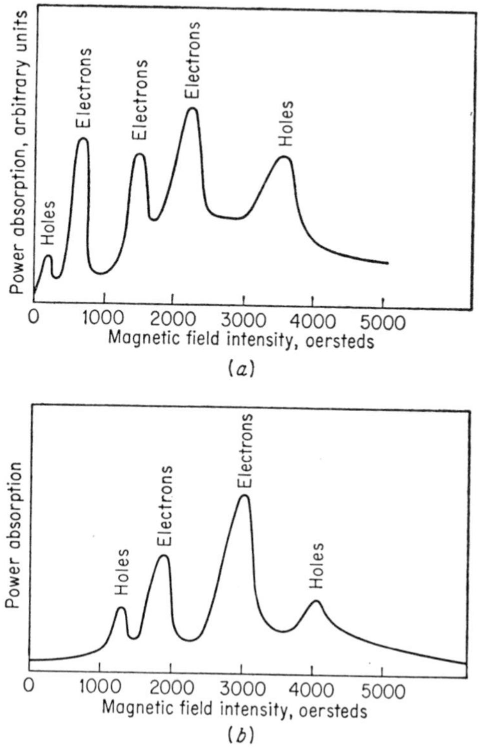

Fig. 9.10. Typical cyclotron-resonance curves for $\omega/2\pi = 2.4 \times 10^4$ Mc/sec at $T = 4$°K. (*a*) Ge with H_0 in the {100} plane at 60° from the (100) axis. (*b*) Si with H_0 in the {110} plane at 30° from the (100) axis. [*After G. Dresselhaus, A. F. Kip, and C. Kittel, Phys. Rev.*, **98**: 368 (1954).]

As a typical example of the results of such experiments, Fig. 9.9 illustrates the valence- and conduction-band structure of silicon along particular directions. The spheroidal surfaces are inferred from the measurements of $m_\parallel$ and $m_\perp$ which are significantly different. Typical experimental power-absorption curves for Ge and Si are shown in Fig. 9.10, and a plot of effective mass as a function of crystal orientation (for Ge and Si) is shown in Fig. 9.11.

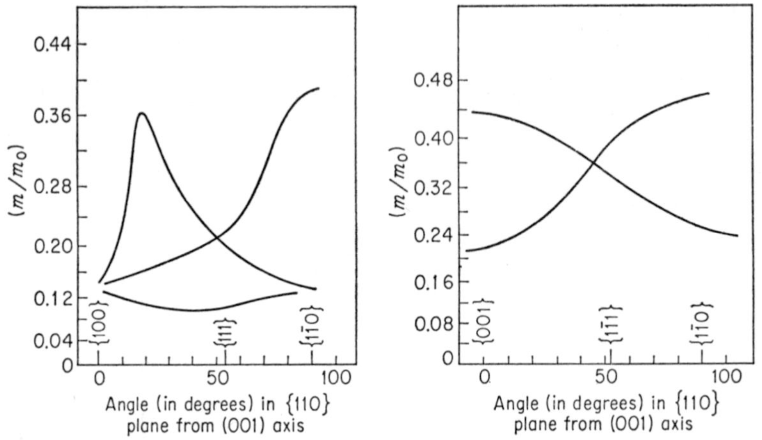

Fig. 9.11. Effective mass of electrons at $T = 4°K$ with H_0 in the $\{110\}$ plane for (*a*) Ge ($m_{\|}/m = 1.58$, $m_{\perp}/m = 0.082$) and (*b*) Si ($m_{\|}/m = 0.98$, $m_{\perp}/m = 0.19$). [*After G. Dresselhaus, A. F. Kip, and C. Kittel, Phys. Rev.,* **98**: 368 (1954).]

Cyclotron Resonance in Metals

Suppose we now consider the application of an oscillating electric field and a constant magnetic field to a metal. The equations derived in the preceding section for the cyclotron-resonance absorption in semiconductors would no longer be valid because of the fact that the electromagnetic field cannot penetrate a conducting solid, except for a skin depth, generally smaller than the mean free path of the electrons.[1] The actual skin depth δ is inversely proportional to the square root of the electrical conductivity and the frequency of impinging radiation. In copper, $\sigma \sim 10^{17}$ cgs and at microwave frequencies (that is, $\nu \sim 10^{10}$ cps) the skin depth is of the order of 10^{-5} cm. In this same metal, the mean free path λ for the electron is of the order 10^{-2} cm (thus, $\lambda \gg \delta$). Also of interest is the radius of the electron orbit about $\mathbf{H}$. This is of the order of $r \equiv v_F/\omega_c = \hbar k_F/m\omega_c \simeq 10^{-3}$ cm [see Eq. (6.45)]. This is also greater than δ. Thus, for a typical metal, $\delta < r < \lambda$, when the electromagnetic radiation is in the microwave region. Since the radius of curvature of the helical path of the electron is less than the mean free path of the electron, the particle will always return into the skin-depth region (see Fig. 9.12). Suppose now that, in addition to the dc magnetic field, an oscillating electric field is applied, parallel (or perpendicular) to H_{dc}. If the electric field vector is in phase with the cycle of the electron motion in the metal, the electron will be accelerated by this field each

[1] See, for example, J. A. Stratton, "Electromagnetic Theory," chap. 9, McGraw-Hill Book Company, Inc., New York, 1941.

time that it appears within the skin depth δ at the surface of the metal. Thus, a resonance occurs, causing the electron to gain energy. The rf field thereby suffers a power loss. This is analogous to the operation of the electron linear accelerator.[1] The experimental technique described above was first proposed by Azbel and Kaner[2] (the effect is named after them). It is also called the *anomalous skin resonance effect.*

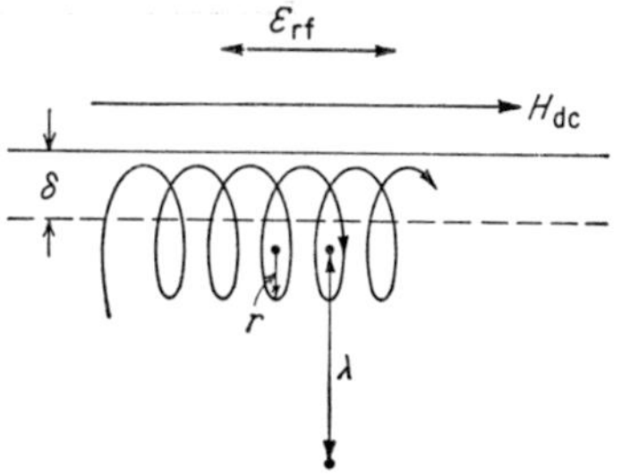

Fig. 9.12. Cyclotron resonance in metals. The skin depth for the radiation field is δ, r is the radius of the cyclotron orbit, and λ is the mean free path of the electrons in the metal.

Calculations of the surface impedance, which in turn gives the power absorption (i.e., the experimental measurement) have been carried out first by Azbel and Kaner and then by Mattis and Dresselhaus.[3] Let it suffice here to indicate that the surface impedance is found to take the form

$$R = \frac{16\pi\omega}{3^{3/2}c^2} \frac{\cos\left[\frac{1}{3}(\alpha+\pi)\right]}{(3\pi^2\sigma\omega/c^2v_F\tau)^2} \times \left[\frac{\sinh^2(\pi/\omega_c\tau)\cosh^2(\pi/\omega_c\tau)+\sin^2(\pi\omega/\omega_c)\cos^2(\pi\omega/\omega_c)}{[\cos^2(\pi\omega/\omega_c)\cosh^2(\pi/\omega_c\tau)+\sin^2(\pi\omega/\omega_c)\sinh^2\pi/\omega_c\tau]^2}\right]^{1/6}$$

where ω is the applied angular frequency, ω_c is the cyclotron frequency (eH/m^*c), and

$$\alpha = \tan^{-1}\frac{\sin(2\pi\omega/\omega_c)}{\sinh(2\pi/\omega_c\tau)}$$

R is plotted for $\omega\tau \simeq 10$, 1 in Fig. 9.13. A typical *experimental* plot of power absorption is shown in Fig. 9.14. Comparing Figs. 9.13 and 9.14, we see that the shape of the power-absorption curve duplicates that which is predicted by theory. It is clear that, just as in the case of cyclotron resonance in semiconductors, the actual shape of the absorption curve is sensitive to the magnitude of the components of the effective-mass tensor of the mobile charge carriers. Thus cyclotron-resonance experiments in metals provide a useful method of investigating properties of the energy-band extrema.

[1] The rf electric field could also be in phase with any number n of cycles of the electron motion. This would give rise in the power-absorption diagram to one large peak and additional peaks of diminishing amplitudes, corresponding to the higher harmonics of the fundamental frequency.

[2] M. I. Azbel and E. A. Kaner, *Soviet Phys. JETP*, **3**: 722 (1956); **5**: 730 (1957).

[3] D. C. Mattis and G. Dresselhaus, *Phys. Rev.*, **111**: 403 (1958).

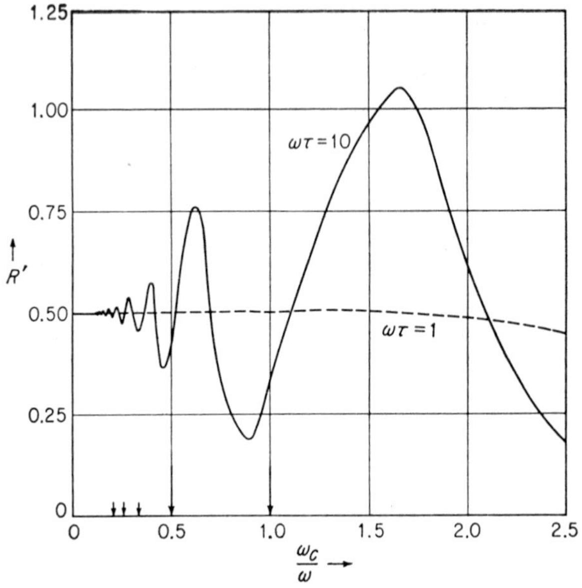

Fig. 9.13. Theoretical plot of the power absorption from cyclotron resonance in metals as a function of ω_c/ω. The curves shown are for $\omega\tau = 10$ and $\omega\tau = 1$. [*After D. C. Mattis and G. Dresselhaus, Phys. Rev.*, **111**: 403 (1958).]

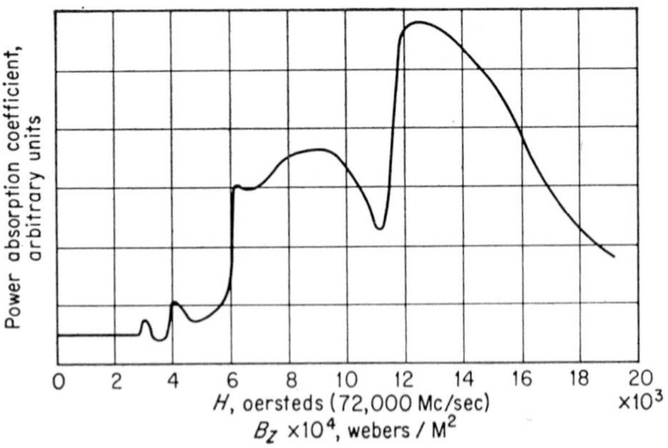

Fig. 9.14. Cyclotron resonance at 72,000 gauss and 1.3°K in zinc. The magnetic field strength is along a 2-fold axis of the crystal. [*After J. K. Galt, F. R. Merritt, W. A. Yager, and H. W. Dail, Jr., Phys. Rev. Letters*, **2**: 292 (1959).]

Optical Transitions in Semiconductors

One obvious way of measuring the energy gap between the valence and conduction bands of a semiconductor is to observe the threshold of optical radiation absorption. Thus, so long as $h\nu_{op} < \epsilon_g$ and ν_{op} is not in resonance with lattice vibrations, the radiation is reflected from the material. As soon as $\nu_{op} = \epsilon_g/h$, the electrons at the top of the valence band can absorb the radiation by their excitation to the conduction band. Thus, if no other processes are involved, the measured absorption coefficient increases very rapidly from zero, at $\nu = \epsilon_g/h$. This process has been discussed previously (Chap. 8), where it was pointed out that even further information about the symmetry properties of the energy bands may be extracted by studying the absorption of radiation which is polarized relative to the crystal axes.

The type of transition discussed above is the *direct transition* in which the following selection rule ho ds:

$$\mathbf{k}_i = \mathbf{k}_f + \mathbf{q} \tag{9.66}$$

where

$$\mathbf{q} = \frac{2\pi}{c}\nu_{op}\hat{\mathbf{q}}$$

and $\hat{\mathbf{q}}$ is the direction of propagation of the radiation field and $\mathbf{k}_i$ and $\mathbf{k}_f$ are the initial and final electron wave vectors.

The measured absorption coefficient depends on the transition probability for excitation between the (conduction-band and valence-band) states $\mathbf{k}_c$ and $\mathbf{k}_v$. This is shown, according to time-dependent perturbation theory, to have the form

$$W_{cv} = \frac{2\pi}{\hbar}|\mathcal{H}'_{cv}|^2 g(\epsilon) \tag{9.67}$$

where

$$\mathcal{H}'_{cv} \equiv \int \psi^*_{\mathbf{k}_c}\mathcal{H}'\psi_{\mathbf{k}_v}\,d\mathbf{r}$$

and $g(\epsilon)$, the density of final states, depends on the (conduction) energy-band structure, according to Eq. (8.87). If the transitions are direct, then the mechanism for electron excitation occurs by the direct coupling of the electron momentum to the radiation field, i.e.,

$$\hat{\mathcal{H}}' = \frac{-e\hbar}{imc}\mathbf{A}\cdot\nabla \tag{9.68}$$

where

$$\mathbf{A} = |\mathbf{A}_0|\hat{\mathbf{e}}_{\text{pol}}e^{i(\mathbf{q}\cdot\mathbf{r}-\omega_{op}t)}$$

is the electromagnetic vector potential of the radiation field.

On the other hand, it is possible that final states

$$\mathbf{k}_c \neq \mathbf{k}_v + \mathbf{q}$$

could be reached if one also takes account of the coupling between the electron motion and the lattice vibrations (i.e., electron-phonon coupling). This type of interaction is responsible for the so-called *indirect transition.*

If $\mathbf{q}_P$ is the wave vector of the phonon involved in such a transition, the new selection rule for indirect transitions is

$$\mathbf{k}_c = \mathbf{k}_v + \mathbf{q} \pm \mathbf{q}_P \tag{9.69}$$

where the $\pm$ refers to the absorption or emission (i.e., the destruction or creation) of a phonon. It is now clear that, although the measured

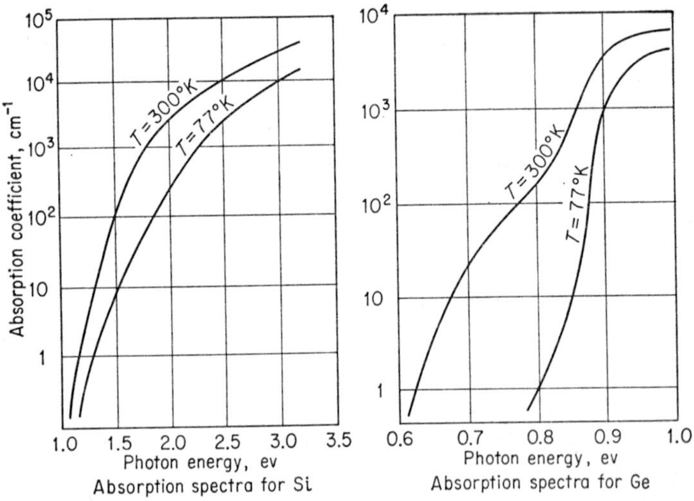

Fig. 9.15. Optical absorption coefficient as a function of frequency and temperature. [*After W. C. Dash and R. Newman, Phys. Rev.,* **99**: 1151 (1955).]

absorption coefficient would still be zero at frequencies below $\nu_{op} = \epsilon_g/h$, indirect transitions should cause a sharp change in the shape of the absorption curve at various optical frequencies. Such experimental results are illustrated in Fig. 9.15, where we also indicate the temperature dependence of the absorption coefficient. The transition probability (9.67) then depends on the matrix element

$$\mathcal{H}'_{cv} = \sum_I \frac{\mathcal{H}'_{vI}\mathcal{H}''_{Ic}}{\epsilon_I - \epsilon_v} \tag{9.70}$$

where the sum is taken over all intermediate states I which were arrived at by processes involving phonon creation or annihilation.

In (9.70), one of the matrix elements $\mathcal{H}'_{vI}$ depends on the mechanism of electron-photon coupling [Eq. (9.68)] while the matrix element $\mathcal{H}''_{Ic}$

depends on the electron-phonon coupling. The expression for this coupling has been derived from a number of different models. One of these models[1] assumes that the potential in a deformed crystal at a point $\mathbf{r}$ is $\varphi(\mathbf{r} - \mathbf{u})$ if $\varphi(\mathbf{r})$ is the potential in the undeformed crystal. The variable $\mathbf{u}$ is related to the displacement of the lattice ions in the crystal. Under the assumption of isotropy of forces in the crystal and after lattice vibrations are quantized, $\mathbf{u}$ has the form

$$\mathbf{u} = \frac{1}{\sqrt{N}} \sum_{\mathbf{q}} \sum_{j=1}^{3} \hat{\mathbf{e}}_{q_j}(a_{q_j}e^{i\mathbf{q}\cdot\mathbf{r}} + a^*_{q_j}e^{-i\mathbf{q}\cdot\mathbf{r}})$$

where N is the number of constituent ions, $\mathbf{q}$ is the wave vector for a *phonon* of momentum to $\hbar\mathbf{q}$, and $\hat{\mathbf{e}}_{q_j}$ is the polarization vector.[2] The normal coordinates a_{q_j} and $a^*_{q_j}$ correspond, respectively, to the *creation* and *annihilation* of phonons with momenta in the x_j direction. This is because the matrix elements of these operators connect the state of n phonons with the respective states of $n - 1$ and $n + 1$ phonons.

With this model, the electron-phonon interaction is obtained by expanding $\varphi(\mathbf{r} - \mathbf{u})$ in a Taylor series about $\varphi(\mathbf{r})$ and subtracting $\varphi(\mathbf{r})$. Thus,

$$\mathcal{H}''_{Ic} = <\varphi(\mathbf{r} - \mathbf{u})> - <\varphi(\mathbf{r})>_{Ic} = <-\mathbf{u} \cdot \nabla\varphi(\mathbf{r})>_{Ic} + \cdots$$

where the matrix element above is related to the matrix elements of the annihilation *operator*

$$<n_q - 1|a_q|n_q> = \sqrt{\frac{\hbar n_q}{2M\omega_q}}\, e^{-i\omega_q t}$$

and those of the creation operator

$$<n_q + 1|a^*_q|n_q> = \sqrt{\frac{\hbar(n_q + 1)}{2M\omega_q}}\, e^{i\omega_q t}$$

which are in turn related to the respective transition probabilities for decreasing and increasing $n_\mathbf{q}$ phonons (with momentum $\hbar\mathbf{q}$) by one.

Typical indirect transitions are illustrated schematically in Fig. 9.16. The diagrams illustrate various ways of going from the initial state at $\mathbf{k}_v$ to the final state at $\mathbf{k}_c$. The full line is the electromagnetic transition while the dashed line is that due to the electron-phonon coupling.

These diagrams and (9.70) correspond to so-called one-phonon processes. It should be kept in mind, however, that this phonon is never actually observed (i.e., in the current vernacular, it is a *virtual* particle) and *is*

[1] F. Bloch, *Z. Physik*, **59**: 208 (1930).

[2] See A. Sommerfeld and H. A. Bethe, "Handbuch der Physik," vol. 36, no. 2, Springer-Verlag OHG, Berlin, 1933.

only a convenient way of describing a "mathematical" term such as (9.70) *which appears in a perturbation expansion.* As the expansion is carried out to higher order, successive terms appear which are likewise viewed, for convenience, as . . . two-phonon, three-phonon, . . . processes. (The analogous multiple-photon processes which occur in quantum electrodynamics are usually pictured schematically by "Feynman diagrams.")

It is clear that an analysis of optical radiation absorption by semiconductors must take account of both direct and indirect processes when

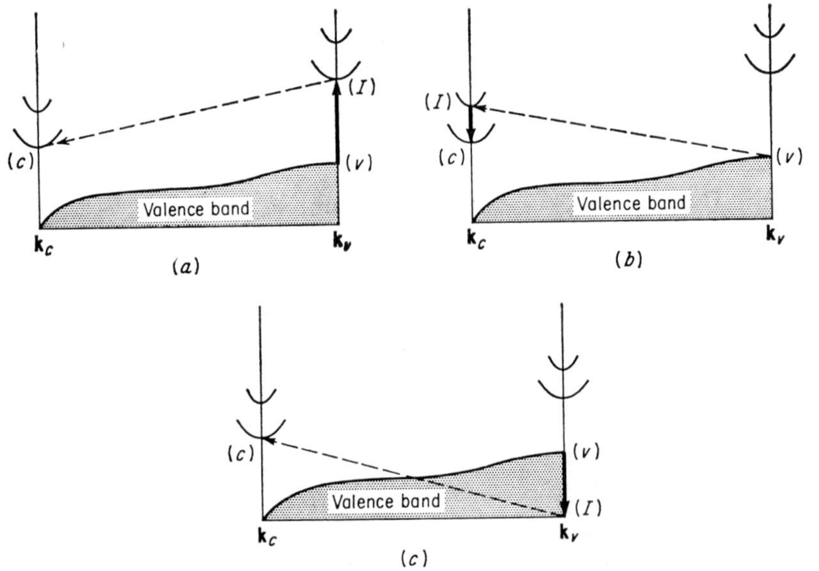

Fig. 9.16. Typical indirect transitions from the initial valence state (v) to the final conduction state (c) with $\mathbf{k}_c \neq \mathbf{k}_v$. The parabolic wells are typical vibrational states within the conduction band.

ϵ_g/h corresponds to infrared frequencies, since the lattice vibrations usually center about frequencies in this range. The band gap ϵ_g for many important semiconductors (e.g., Ge, Si, InSb) are indeed in the infrared region, thus indicating the importance of the study of the infrared absorption by semiconductors.

9.3 Contact physics

As a final application of the properties of the quasi-free-electron gas, we consider the properties of the solid-vacuum contact and the contacts between different types of solids (i.e., metal-semiconductor, n-type–p-type semiconductor).

Theory of Thermionic Emission[1]

Thermionic emission refers to the flux of electrons which evaporate thermally from a heated metal in the absence of an externally applied electric field intensity. Our object now is to calculate this flux of current (in view of the free-electron theory of metals).

First, we consider the flux of electrons across a given plane (let us say in the yz plane). According to our definition of the Fermi-Dirac distribution function, the number of electrons per volume in the element of momentum space between $\mathbf{p}$ and $\mathbf{p} + d\mathbf{p}$ can be expressed in the form

$$dn = \frac{2}{h^3} \frac{d\mathbf{p}}{e^{(p^2/2m - \epsilon_F)/kT} + 1} \qquad \text{cm}^{-3} \tag{9.71}$$

The flux of the electrons $F(p_x)$ crossing the yz plane is simply the electron velocity in the x direction multiplied by the total number of electrons per area in the yz plane. Thus, from (9.71) we have (using $v_x = p_x/m$)

$$F(p_x)\,dp_x = \frac{2p_x\,dp_x}{mh^3} \int_{-\infty}^{\infty} \int_{-\infty}^{\infty} \frac{dp_y\,dp_z}{e^{[(p_x^2+p_y^2+p_z^2)/2m - \epsilon_F]/kT} + 1} \tag{9.72}$$

Equation (9.72) is readily integrated by substituting

$$u^2 = p_y^2 + p_z^2$$
$$dp_y\,dp_z = 2\pi u\,du$$

giving

$$F(p_x)\,dp_x = \frac{4\pi p_x\,dp_x}{mh^3} \int_0^{\infty} \frac{u\,du}{e^{[(p_x^2+u^2)/2m - \epsilon_F]/kT} + 1}$$
$$= \frac{4\pi mkT}{h^3} \{\ln\,[1 + e^{-(p_x^2/2m - \epsilon_F)/kT}]\} \frac{p_x\,dp_x}{m} \tag{9.73}$$

Substituting the energy variable

$$\epsilon_n = \frac{p_x^2}{2m}$$

(where the subscript n denotes the normal to the plane of electron emission), (9.73) can be expressed in the form

$$F(\epsilon_n)\,d\epsilon_n = \frac{4\pi mkT}{h^3} \ln\,[1 + e^{-(\epsilon_n - \epsilon_F)/kT}]\,d\epsilon_n \tag{9.74}$$

Consider now the potential that binds the electron to the metal. We take, for the binding potential acting on an electron inside the metal, the average effect due to all the other charged particles on a given electron and assume that this is a constant $(-V_0)$. As the elec-

[1] See, for further reading, R. H. Fowler and E. A. Guggenheim, "Statistical Thermodynamics," p. 477, Cambridge University Press, New York, 1956.

tron is withdrawn from the surface of the metal, it sets up an image charge of opposite polarity in the metal and thus must continue to exert energy in order to escape until the effect of its image disappears. (This, of course, happens at an infinite separation because of the infinite range of Coulomb forces.) It is shown from the method of images (developed in electromagnetic theory[1]) that if the plane $x = 0$ locates

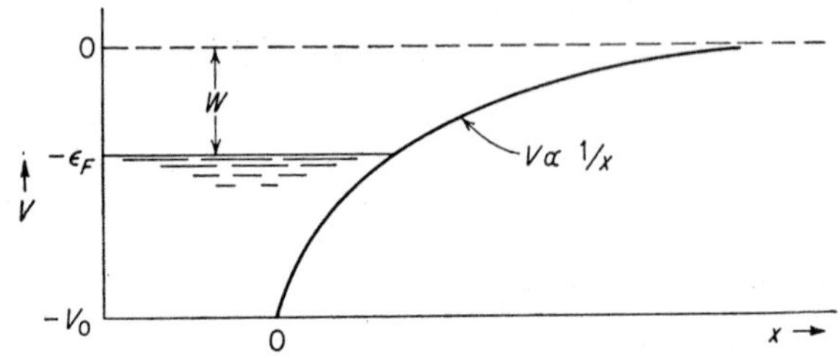

Fig. 9.17. Potential energy for electrons in a heated metal. The surface of the metal is at $x = 0$. The work function is W and ϵ_F is the Fermi energy.

the surface of the metal,

$$V = -\frac{e^2}{4x} \tag{9.75}$$

is the potential energy, x units away from its surface. Combining (9.75) with the potential energy

$$V = -V_0 \qquad \text{for } x \leq 0 \tag{9.75$'$}$$

inside the metal, we have the pictorial diagram of the electron potential energy given in Fig. 9.17.

The energy required to remove from the metal an electron which is at the top of the Fermi sea is called the *work function* and will be denoted by W.

The general expression for the current density of electrons leaving the surface of the metal is

$$j = e\int F(\epsilon_n)D(\epsilon)\,d\epsilon_n \tag{9.76}$$

where $F(\epsilon_n)$ is the number of electrons per square centimeter per second with energy ϵ_n that move across the yz plane (i.e., the flux derived above) and $D(\epsilon)$ is the probability that these electrons will penetrate the surface barrier potential W. The latter is called the *barrier transmission coefficient.*

[1] See, for example, W. R. Smythe, "Static and Dynamic Electricity," McGraw-Hill Book Company, Inc., New York, 1950.

Substituting (9.74) into (9.76), we have

$$j = \frac{4\pi mkTe}{h^3} \int_0^\infty D(\epsilon) \ln [1 + e^{-(\epsilon_n - \epsilon_F)/kT}] \, d\epsilon_n \tag{9.77}$$

The transmission coefficient has the following values:

$$D(\epsilon) = 0 \qquad \text{for } \epsilon < |V_0| = \epsilon_F + W \tag{9.78a}$$

$$= 1 - \rho \qquad \text{for } \epsilon \geq |V_0| \tag{9.78b}$$

where ρ is the coefficient of reflection of electrons on the outside striking the surface of the metal. Equation (9.78*a*) follows from the infinite range of the image potential for electrons inside the potential well. Equation (9.78*b*) follows from (1) the neglect of lattice vibrations and (2) the quantum-mechanical theorem which states that the transmission coefficients over any potential barrier are necessarily the same for electrons (of a given energy) moving in either direction,[1] i.e.,

$$D_{1\to2}(\epsilon) = D_{2\to1}(\epsilon) \tag{9.78c}$$

Substituting (9.78) into (9.77), we have

$$j = \frac{4\pi mkTe}{h^3} (1 - \rho) \int_{\epsilon_F + W}^\infty \ln [1 + e^{-(\epsilon_n - \epsilon_F)/kT}] \, d\epsilon_n \tag{9.79}$$

Finally, the integral in (9.79) may be evaluated by expanding the integrand about ln 1 = 0. That such an expansion is valid is seen as follows: At the lower limit

$$\epsilon_n^{(0)} = \epsilon_F + W$$

giving

$$\epsilon_n^{(0)} - \epsilon_F = W \ (\simeq 2 \text{ to } 6 \text{ ev}) \gg kT \tag{9.80}$$

Thus, at the lower limit

$$e^{-(\epsilon_n - \epsilon_F)/kT} \ll 1 \tag{9.81}$$

and, of course, as ϵ_n increases, the inequality becomes even stronger. In view of (9.81), we substitute

$$\ln [1 + e^{-(\epsilon_n - \epsilon_F)/kT}] \simeq e^{-(\epsilon_n - \epsilon_F)/kT}$$

giving

$$j = \frac{4\pi mkTe}{h^3} (1 - \rho) \int_{\epsilon_F + W}^\infty e^{-(\epsilon_n - \epsilon_F)/kT} \, d\epsilon_n$$

$$= \frac{4\pi m(kT)^2 e}{h^3} (1 - \rho) e^{-W/kT} \equiv AT^2 e^{-W/kT} \tag{9.82}$$

where A is defined to be the temperature-independent factor. The last part of Eq. (9.82) is *Richardson's equation* for thermionic emission.

[1] See R. H. Fowler, *Proc. Cambridge Phil. Soc.*, **25:** 193 (1929); Fowler and Guggenheim, *loc. cit.*

The temperature dependence given above is in quite accurate agreement with experimental data, and the latter may be used to measure the work function W. The experimental thermionic emission of tungsten is shown in Fig. 9.18. The data correspond to a work function of 4.54 ev and a reflection coefficient $\rho = 0.5$.

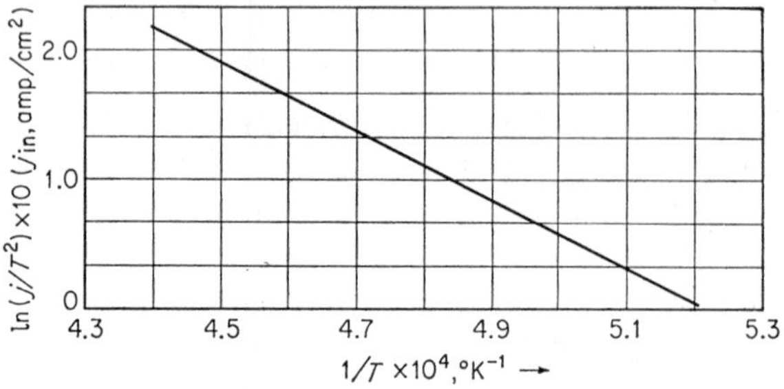

Fig. 9.18. Thermionic emission of tungsten as a function of the absolute temperature. The experimental curve corresponds to $\rho = \frac{1}{2}$, $W = 4.5$ ev. (*After R. H. Fowler and E. A. Guggenheim, "Statistical Thermodynamics,"* p. 480, *Cambridge University Press, New York,* 1956.)

Schottky Emission[1]

Suppose now that, in addition to the temperature effect on the electron emission, a strong electric field intensity $\mathcal{E}_0$ is applied. In this case, the surface barrier (Fig. 9.17) must change since (9.75) must now be replaced by

$$V = \frac{-e^2}{4x} - e\mathcal{E}_0 x \qquad x > 0 \tag{9.83}$$

(see Fig. 9.17).

From (9.83) we have, after maximizing the external potential energy,

$$\frac{dV}{dx} = 0 = \frac{e^2}{4x_m^2} - e\mathcal{E}_0$$

or

$$x_m = \frac{1}{2}\left(\frac{e}{\mathcal{E}_0}\right)^{1/2} \tag{9.84}$$

with

$$V_m = \frac{-e^2}{4x_m^2} - e\mathcal{E}_0 x_m = -e(e\mathcal{E}_0)^{1/2} \tag{9.85}$$

From Fig. 9.19, we see that the limits of integration in (9.79) must change to the range $\epsilon_F + W - e(e\mathcal{E}_0)^{1/2}$ to ∞, since the transmission coefficient is now

$$\begin{aligned} D(\epsilon) &= 0 \qquad &\text{for } \epsilon_n < \epsilon_F + W - e(e\mathcal{E}_0)^{1/2} \\ &= 1 - \rho \qquad &\text{for } \epsilon_n > \epsilon_F + W - e(e\mathcal{E}_0)^{1/2} \end{aligned} \tag{9.86}$$

[1] See, for further reading, R. H. Fowler, "Statistical Mechanics," Sec. 11.3, Cambridge University Press, New York, 1936; W. Schottky, *Z. Physik*, **18**: 63 (1923).

Substituting (9.86) into (9.79) and again using the inequality (9.81), we have for the resulting current

$$\begin{aligned} j_{te} &= \frac{4\pi m(kT)^2 e}{h^3}(1-\rho)e^{-[W-e(e\mathcal{E}_0)^{1/2}]/kT} \\ &\equiv AT^2 e^{-[W-e(e\mathcal{E}_0)^{1/2}]/kT} \end{aligned} \tag{9.87}$$

Our earlier statement that electrons are never actually free of the metal because of the infinitely long barrier no longer holds in the presence

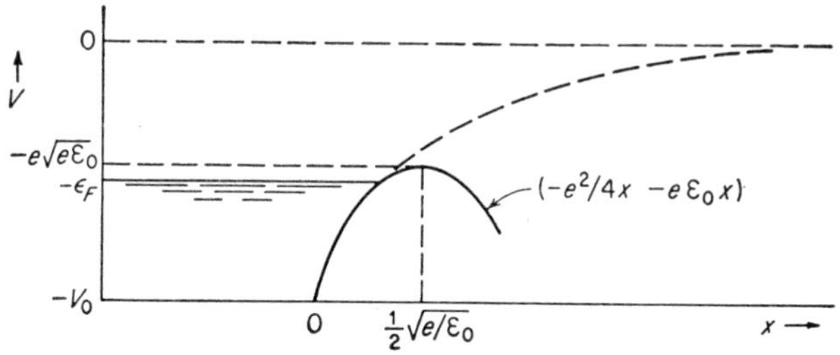

Fig. 9.19. Potential energy for electrons in a heated metal in the presence of an external field $\mathcal{E}_0$.

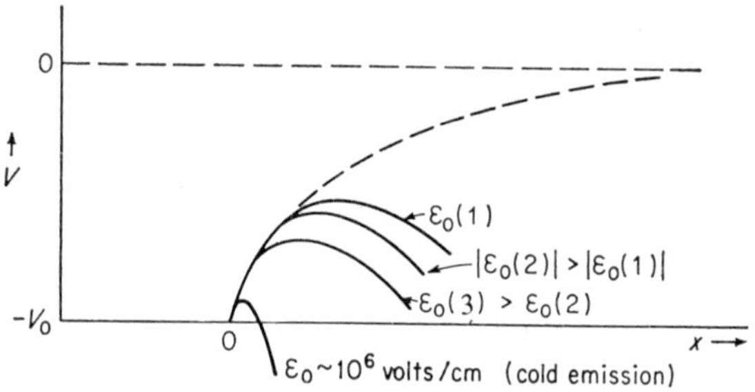

Fig. 9.20. Surface barriers as a function of the applied electric field intensity $\mathcal{E}_0$. The tunnel effect increases with $|\mathcal{E}_0|$.

of an electric field, and electrons will indeed tunnel through the barrier (illustrated in Fig. 9.19). This quantum-mechanical *tunnel effect* is known as barrier penetration. As $\mathcal{E}_0$ is increased, the difference between V_{max} and ϵ_F decreases and the tunnel effect thereby increases the flux of electrons leaving the metal. In particular, when the applied field reaches the order of 10^6 volts/cm, the tunnel effect becomes so large that an electron cascade occurs with the resulting current emission becoming independent of temperature. This phenomenon, known as *cold emission*, is illustrated in Fig. 9.20.[1]

[1] See Fowler, *ibid.*, p. 357.

Two Different Metals in Contact[1]

Let us now consider the equilibrium conditions for two different metals which are brought into contact and thereby determine some of the qualitative properties of such a contact.

Two different metals are characterized by different Fermi energies and work functions. The Fermi sea for each of two typical metals (in the separated state) is shown in Fig. 9.21. Suppose now that the

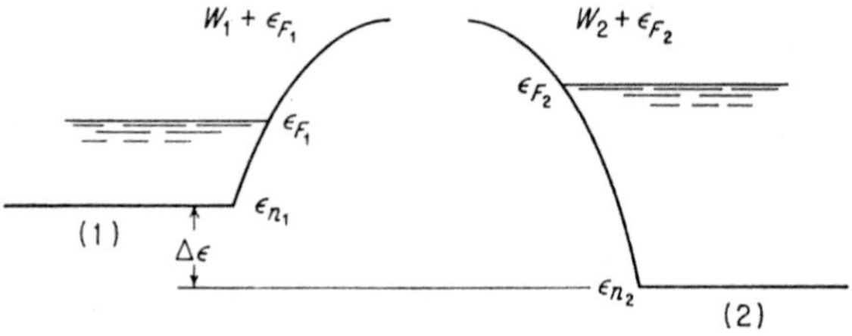

Fig. 9.21. Separated metals with work functions W_1, W_2 and Fermi energies ϵ_{F_1} and ϵ_{F_2}.

metals are brought close enough so that the mean free path of the conduction electrons belonging to each of the metals is much longer than the separation between the metals. In this case there will be a flow of electrons across the contact. Let us now assume that thermodynamic equilibrium is reached for the two-metal system. Under these conditions, the flux of electrons with a given energy which cross over from metal (1) to metal (2) must be the same as the flux of electrons with the same energy that cross over from metal (2) to metal (1). Thus

$$F_1(\epsilon_1 = \epsilon) = F_2(\epsilon_2 = \epsilon) \tag{9.88}$$

where

$$\epsilon_i = \epsilon_{n_i} - V_{0_i} \qquad i = 1, 2 \tag{9.89}$$

is the total electron energy and ϵ_{n_i} is the kinetic energy of the electrons of the ith metal that cross into the other metal. Equation (9.88) can also be expressed in the form

$$F_1(\epsilon_{n_1})D(\epsilon)_{1\to 2} = F_2(\epsilon_{n_2})D(\epsilon)_{2\to 1} \tag{9.90}$$

where the electron fluxes are expressed as a function of the kinetic energy while the transmission coefficient depends on the total energy ϵ. Combining (9.90) with (9.78*c*) and (9.74), we have (at equilibrium)

$$\ln\,[1 + e^{-(\epsilon_{n_1}-\epsilon_{F_1})/kT}] = \ln\,[1 + e^{-(\epsilon_{n_2}-\epsilon_{F_2})/kT}] \tag{9.91}$$

[1] See, for further reading, N. F. Mott & R. W. Gurney, "Electronic Processes in Ionic Crystals," Oxford University Press, Fair Lawn, N.J., 1940.

Since (as we see in Fig. 9.21)

$$\epsilon_{n_2} = \epsilon_{n_1} + \Delta\epsilon$$

Eq. (9.91) takes the form

$$\ln\left[1 + e^{-(\epsilon_{n_1}-\epsilon_{F_1})/kT}\right] = \ln\left[1 + e^{-(\epsilon_{n_1}+\Delta\epsilon-\epsilon_{F_2})/kT}\right] \tag{9.92}$$

and the arguments of the exponentials are thereby equal. Thus

$$\Delta\epsilon = \epsilon_{F_2} - \epsilon_{F_1} \tag{9.93}$$

This means that, at thermodynamic equilibrium, the Fermi energies for the metals in contact are aligned (see Fig. 9.22).

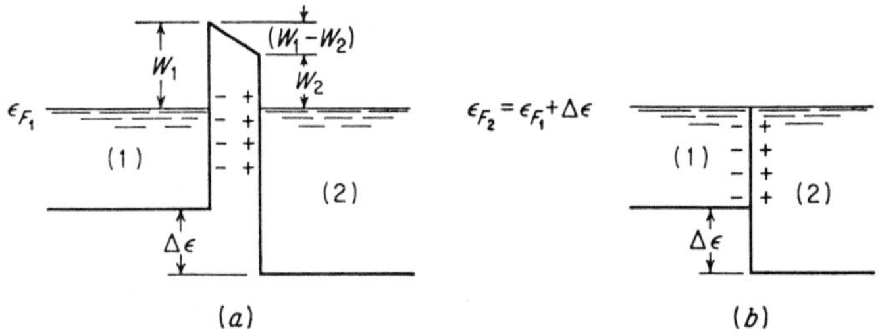

Fig. 9.22. Two metals in contact. The pictures (*a*) and (*b*) show finite and infinitesimal (~ 10 Å) separations between the two metals.

The alignment of the Fermi levels entails a transfer of electrons from the metal that has a higher Fermi energy (in the separated state) to the other metal. Such a transfer of electrons thereby leaves the former metal positively charged while the latter becomes negatively charged. Thus, an electric dipole layer is set up between the metals. The added energy that the electron requires to cross this layer is called the *contact potential energy* (see Fig. 9.22*a*). It is clear that this potential difference is just equal to the difference between the work functions of the respective metals.

As the separation between the metals diminishes, so does the contact potential, until the limit of perfect contact when it disappears, leaving an infinitesimally thin electric dipole layer (see Fig. 9.22*b*). It is clear that an electron crossing over from (1) to (2) gains kinetic energy and therefore speeds up whereas one which goes across the barrier in the opposite direction slows down. In fact, for constant energy

$$\tfrac{1}{2}mv_1^2 = \tfrac{1}{2}mv_2^2 + \Delta V_0 = \tfrac{1}{2}mv_2^2 - \Delta\epsilon$$

or

$$v_1 = \left(v_2^2 - \frac{2\,\Delta\epsilon}{m}\right)^{1/2} < v_2$$

Figure 9.22*b* corresponds to the case of metallic conductivity and occurs in practice when the gap between the metals is less then about 10 Å. If the gap were larger, an application of a sufficiently large voltage could wipe out the contact barrier and thereby give rise once again to metallic conductivity.

The Contact Rectifier

The metal contact, such as is described by Fig. 9.22, acts as a rectifier; i.e., the application of a voltage with one polarity causes a large current flow whereas an opposite polarity voltage causes a very small current flow. This can be seen as follows: If the effect of field emission is

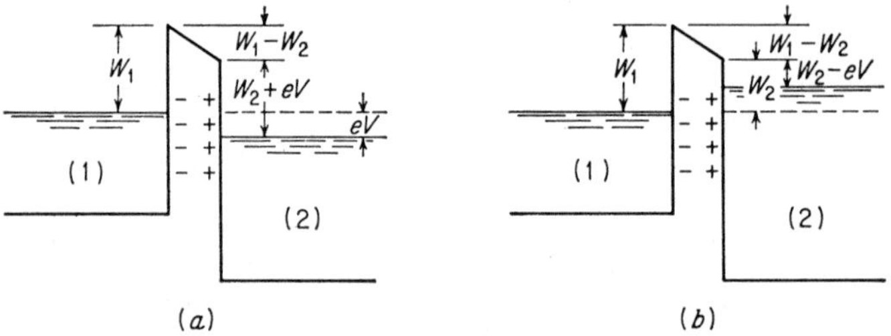

Fig. 9.23. Metal-metal contact under the application of a voltage V (*a*) in the backward direction and (*b*) in the forward direction.

neglected, the current density for electron flow from (2) → (1) (Fig. 9.23) decreases when a voltage $(-V)$ is applied in the backward direction, since the contact potential is thereby increased.

The current density is, according to (9.82),

$$j_{2\to1} = AT^2e^{-(W_1+eV)/kT} \tag{9.94}$$

The current flow from (1) to (2) is still given by (9.82) with $W = W_1$. Thus the net current flow in the direction of the applied voltage [i.e., from (1) to (2)] is

$$j_b = j_{1\to2} - j_{2\to1} = AT^2e^{-W_1/kT}(1 - e^{-eV/kT}) \tag{9.95}$$

On the other hand, if the voltage is applied in the forward direction (that is, $+V$), the potential barrier is thereby decreased, and the net current flow in the direction of the applied voltage is (see Fig. 9.23*b*)

$$j_f = j_{2\to1} - j_{1\to2} = AT^2e^{-W_1/kT}(e^{eV/kT} - 1) \tag{9.96}$$

It is clear from Fig. 9.23*b* that the applied voltage in the forward direction is limited by the inequality

$$W_1 - |eV| > W_2 \tag{9.97}$$

or

$$|eV| < (W_1 - W_2)$$

Combining (9.95) and (9.96), we obtain the characteristic voltage-current curve for the contact rectifier shown in Fig. 9.24.

A typical example is the selenium rectifier, which is made up by coating a selenium disk with some other metallic alloy. These selenium cells are stacked in series to obtain a rectifier with a desired voltage rating and then the desired number of stacks are connected in parallel to obtain a desired current rating. Such rectifiers used in circuits so as to convert alternating to direct current are practical when voltages do not exceed around 200 volts.

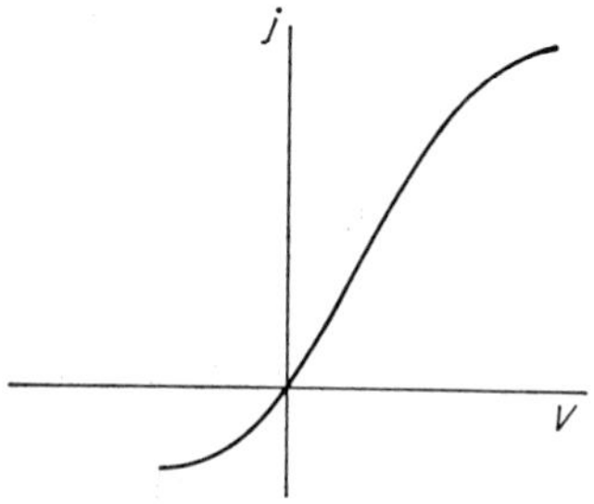

Fig. 9.24. Current-voltage characteristic curve for a contact rectifier. With $V > 0$ the current is limited by the potential difference $|W_1 - W_2|$; when $V < 0$, the current is limited by W_1 alone.

Metal–n-type Semiconductor Junction

The analogous diagram to Fig. 9.21, when a metal and an n-type semiconductor are apart, is shown in Fig. 9.25.

As the two materials are brought together, electrons flow from the n-type semiconductor into the metal if $W_{sc} < W_m$ until the Fermi levels are aligned (just as it happened in the previous case of two metals). A space charge is thereby set up at the junction, and the energy-band scheme about the junction (analogous to Fig. 9.23) is shown in Fig. 9.26.

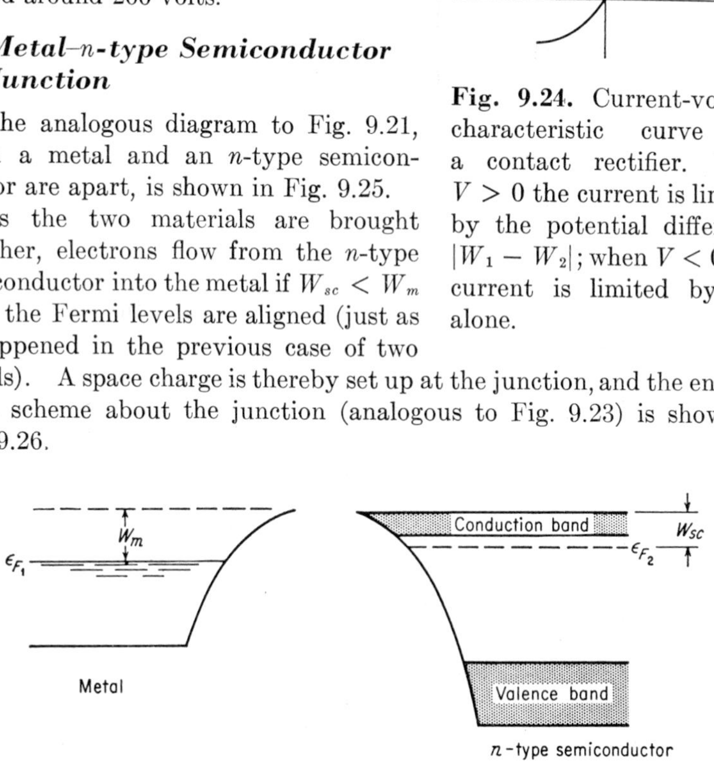

Fig. 9.25. Separated metal and semiconductor.

It is clear that, as electrons flow from (2) into (1), the positively charged donor ions are no longer neutralized by their (donated) conduction electrons, and those ions within an effective layer (of characteristic thickness λ) of the surface, present a barrier to the flow of electrons. Thus, the valence and conduction bands bend upward near the junction, as shown in Fig. 9.26.

If, now, a voltage is applied to the junction so as to raise the semiconductor energy levels relative to the metal (i.e., voltage in the forward direction), the barrier height, viewed by electrons in the semiconductor, becomes lowered by eV, that is, it becomes $(W_m - W_{sc} - eV)$,

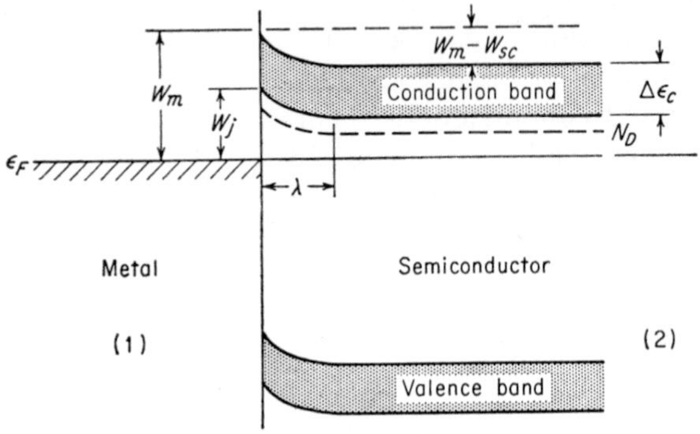

Fig. 9.26. Metal–*n*-type semiconductor junction. λ is the penetration depth of the space charge.

while the barrier height to metallic electrons is still W_j (see Fig. 9.26). On the other hand, if a voltage is applied in the backward direction, the barrier to semiconductor electrons increases while that to metallic electrons still remains the same. Then, an applied voltage in the forward direction produces a large current from semiconductor to metal while a backward voltage induces a small current in its direction (i.e., metal to semiconductor). Thus, a metal–*n*-type semiconductor also acts as a rectifier with a typical voltage-current characteristic curve shown in Fig. 9.24.

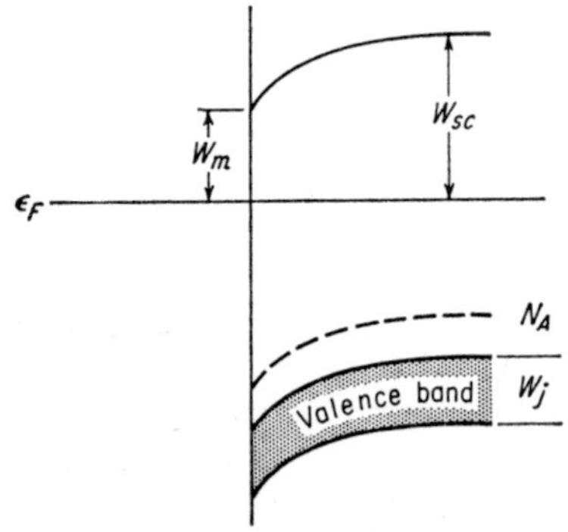

Fig. 9.27. Metal–*p*-type semiconductor junction.

Metal–p-type Semiconductor Junction

This device behaves in the same way as the metal–*n*-type junction except that it is the backward voltage that increases the current whereas the forward voltage decreases it. The energy-level diagram analogous to Fig. 9.26 is shown in Fig. 9.27. In this case $W_{sc} > W_m$ and the bands bend downward at the junction. The latter happens because, as the electrons flow from the metal into the semiconductor, the acceptor states of the impurity atoms are occupied, producing a negative space charge near the junction. This reduces the hole concentration in the valence band near the junction, and the negative space charge in turn lowers the potential energy for holes, near the junction, relative to the remainder of the semiconductor. In the same way as before, such a junction acts as a rectifier.

The p-n Junction

Suppose now that we join two semiconductors, one n-type and the other p-type. The junction, called a *p-n junction*, also acts as a rectifier. Consider the potential energy for holes $V(h)$ as a function of distance across the junction (Fig. 9.28). In the bulk of the p-type semiconductor, the positive holes and acceptor ions neutralize each other, and in the n-type material the electrons and donor ions neutralize each other. At the junction the electrons of the n region and holes of the p region must remain separated in order to maintain charge neutrality (i.e., each may not diffuse into the other material). In order to keep them apart, an electric field intensity must exist at the junction. Such a field is established by the initial diffusion of holes into the n region, leaving behind a negative-ion layer, and electrons diffusing into the p region, leaving behind a positive-ion layer. Thus, an electric dipole layer polarized in this way offers a sharp barrier to further hole penetration at the junction (Fig. 9.28). However, there is a finite probability that holes will annihilate by combining with conduction electrons of the n-type material (with subsequent photon emission), thereby causing a small current in the direction from (1) to (2). This is called the recombination current and is denoted by j_r. When the system is in thermal equilibrium, the recombination current from (1) to (2) is balanced by a current moving from (2) to (1), due to holes which, because of thermal fluctuations, flow into the n-type material. This current is denoted by j_g (see Fig. 9.28).

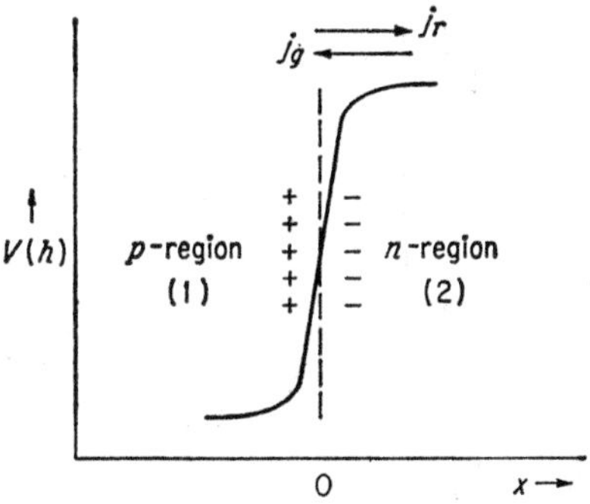

Fig. 9.28. The p-n junction. Potential energy is plotted as a function of distance from the center of the junction (at $x = 0$).

Suppose, now, that a voltage is placed across the junction which makes the n region more negative and the p region more positive. Such a voltage makes it more difficult for holes to approach the electrons of the n material and thereby decreases the recombination current j_r. On the other hand, j_g is not affected by the applied voltage since current flow from (2) to (1) does not depend on the height of the potential barrier. The fraction of holes that contribute to the recombination current are now cut down by the Boltzmann factor $e^{-eV/kT}$, representing that fraction of holes which gain sufficient energy (that is, $-eV$) to combine with the electrons of the n material. Thus, the new recombination current is

$$j_r = j_r^{(0)} e^{-eV/kT} = j_g e^{-eV/kT} \tag{9.98}$$

where $j_r^{(0)}$ is the recombination current when no voltage is applied (see Fig. 9.29*a*).

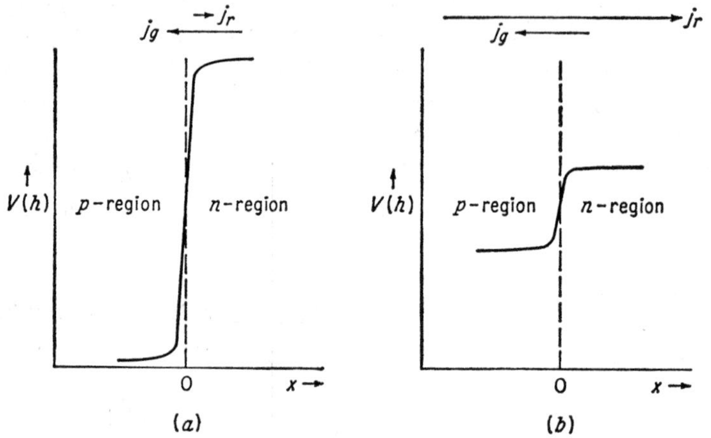

Fig. 9.29. Hole potential across a *p-n* junction for (*a*) forward bias voltage and (*b*) backward bias voltage.

If, now, the voltage applied makes the n region less negative and the p region less positive, the opposite effect happens, and the recombination current becomes

$$j_r = j_r^{(0)} e^{eV/kT} = j_g e^{eV/kT} \tag{9.99}$$

In the first case (Fig. 9.29*a*), the net current from (2) to (1) is

$$j_{2\to 1} = j_g - j_r = j_g(1 - e^{-eV/kT})$$

while in the second case (Fig. 9.29*b*), the net current from (1) to (2) is

$$j_{1\to 2} = j_r - j_g = j_g(e^{eV/kT} - 1) \tag{9.100}$$

Thus we see that the *p-n* junction acts as a rectifier. It is observed that as the temperature is decreased, the ratio of currents

$$j_{1\to 2}/j_{2\to 1}$$

and thus the rectifying action, increases.

In the preceding discussions of the properties of a single contact between unlike solids, we have indicated the basic rectifying action that results from the adjustment of the Fermi energy levels of each material to the other at thermodynamic equilibrium. As a final example of an application of different materials in contact, we shall consider the voltage amplification that is produced by the point-contact transistor.

The Point-contact Transistor[1]

An example of a point contact transistor is the arrangement of two point-contact electrodes in close proximity on the upper face of a small crystal of n-type germanium. A large-area electrode is fixed to the base of the crystal, constituting a low resistance contact (Fig. 9.30). One of the point contacts is biased positively with respect to the base electrode,

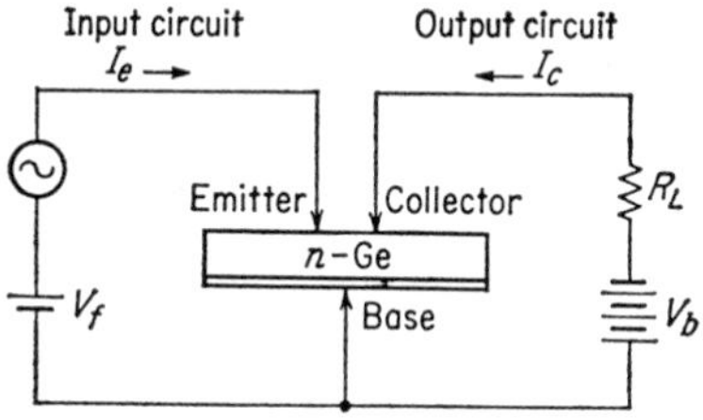

Fig. 9.30. Point-contact-transistor circuit.

allowing current to pass in the forward direction. This electrode is called the *emitter* and, together with the base electrode, the bias voltage V_f, and the input signal, constitutes the input circuit of the device.

The second contact is biased negatively (with $|V_b| > |V_f|$) with respect to the base electrode. This contact is called the collector and, together with the base electrode, load resistance, and its bias voltage, constitutes the output circuit.

If a small signal voltage is applied in the input circuit, a much larger voltage appears across the load resistance and a voltage and power gain are thereby achieved, along with a small current amplification.

The explanation follows from the properties of the energy bands of the different materials at the contacts (see Fig. 9.31).

At the emitter contact, the top of the (full) valence band of Ge is curved upward for the same reasons as discussed previously [i.e., an electric dipole layer is set up because of the flow of electrons across the contact from Ge into the emitter metal (see Fig. 9.26)]. The upward slope of the energy bands of Ge results from the backward bias voltage on the collector contact.

Since the band gap for Ge is small (~0.75 ev), the top of the valence band of Ge comes very close to the Fermi level of the emitter metal. Consequently, the electrons in the (full) valence band of Ge are readily

[1] See J. Bardeen and W. H. Brattain, *Phys. Rev.*, **75**: 1208 (1949).

excited from the semiconductor into the metal. But this is equivalent to the emission of positive holes from the emitter into the semiconductor. If these holes have sufficient thermal energy to overcome the barrier $x_1 \rightarrow x_2$ (Fig. 9.31), they can escape into the bulk of the semiconductor. The potential at x_2 is kept near the electrode base potential by the low resistance path to the base electrode. The application to the emitter electrode of a potential which is positive relative to the base electrode

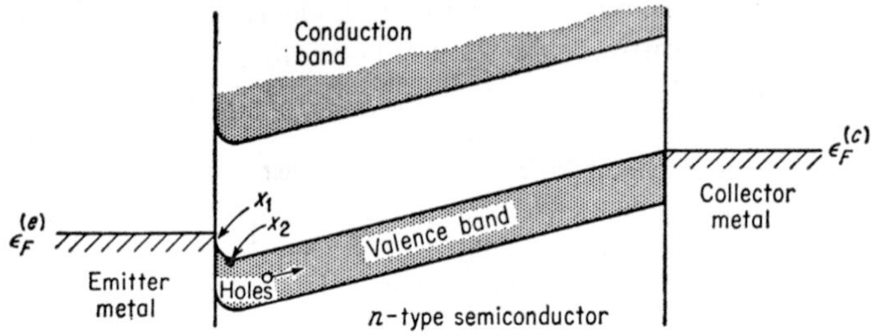

Fig. 9.31. Energy-band diagram for an n-type intrinsic transistor (such as Ge).

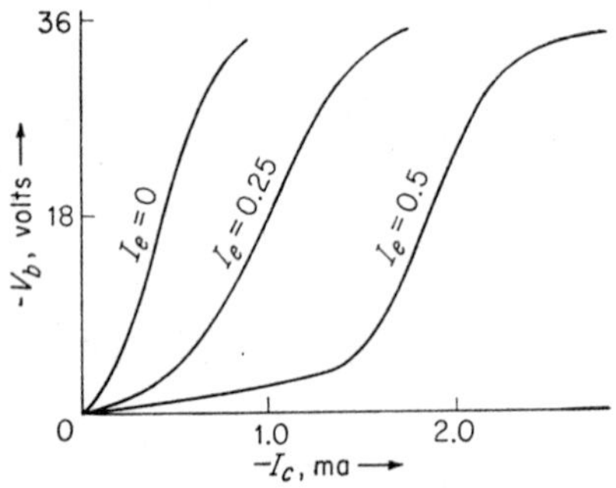

Fig. 9.32. Characteristic voltage-current curves for a point-contact transistor. [*After J. Bardeen and W. H. Brattain, Phys. Rev.,* **75:** 1208 (1949).]

decreases the height of the potential $V(x_1) - V(x_2)$ and thereby increases the flux of holes into the semiconductor. Since the collector electrode is biased negatively with respect to x_2, positive holes are attracted to the collector. Modulation of the injected hole current is thereby obtained by modulation of the emitter voltage.

A large part of the hole current that reaches the collector contact flows into the contact, contributing to the current in the output circuit. The collector contact is made of a metal which provides a high resistance to the flow of electrons from the metal to the semiconductor but a very low resistance to the flux of holes from the semiconductor into the metal. It is clear that the flow of holes into the collector contact is equivalent to the flow of extra electrons into the semiconductor in the high-resistance direction. The extra flow of electrons in the high-resistance direction thereby gives rise to a voltage amplification. Thus we see that the transistor performs the same function of voltage amplification and modulation with an input signal as does the vacuum triode tube.

It is, of course, clear that the point-contact transistor is effective only if the injected holes at the emitter can get to the collector before they are annihilated. Such a requirement demands high hole mobility and small separation of the emitter and collector contacts. The semiconductor Ge fulfills the former requirement quite well.[1] Typical voltage-current characteristic curves for a point-contact transistor are shown in Fig. 9.32.

Summarizing this chapter, we have discussed the applications of the quasi-free-electron theory partly from a quantitative and partly from a qualitative point of view. We have considered the important solids known as semiconductors and have discussed some of the techniques which are used in studying their band structure and electrical properties. The derivation of Richardson's equation for thermionic emission then followed as an illustration of the application of the free-electron theory of metals, and some qualitative discussion of the physics of contacts was then given. The latter is of great practical importance in a study of the technology of *solid state electronics*. Since this is a subject in itself, the discussion here was intended only as an illustration of the qualitative features of solid state rectifiers and amplifiers; the reader who is interested in a more quantitative description is referred to the literature.

Up to the present time, we have been using the one-electron approximation in discussing the properties of the quasi-free-electron model. Such a model is inadequate in accounting for the cohesive energy of such a solid, since this is found to depend sensitively on the collective behavior of the electron gas. For this reason we shall devote the following chapter to a discussion of the theories that lead to the cohesive energy of solids described by the quasi-free-electron model but shall take some account of the interaction between the electrons themselves.

[1] The transistor described here is the original one which was invented by Bardeen and Brattain, *ibid.*

10 the cohesive energy of conducting solids

ON A THEORETICAL development of the physical implications of the metallic bond (discussed in the four preceding chapters) has provided an explanation for many of the properties of conducting solids. Finally, we shall devote this chapter to the fundamental question which pertains to the actual mechanism responsible for the cohesive aspect of the metallic bond.[1] Thus, we wish to answer the question: What is the cause of the binding effect of a charged-particle system made up of a periodic array of positive ions immersed in a sea of (charge-neutralizing) electrons?

Still maintaining our assumption that the motion of the constituent ionic cores may be neglected and taking account only of the electrostatic forces in the crystal, we find that the hamiltonian describing the system of N (static) singly ionized atoms and their "freed" valence electrons has the form

$$\hat{\mathcal{H}} = \hat{T} + \hat{\mathcal{H}}_{II} + \hat{\mathcal{H}}_{Ie} + \hat{\mathcal{H}}_{ee} \tag{10.1}$$

where

$$\hat{T} = -\frac{\hbar^2}{2m}\sum_{i=1}^{N}\nabla_i^2 \qquad \nabla_i \equiv \frac{\partial^2}{\partial x_i} + \frac{\partial^2}{\partial y_i} + \frac{\partial^2}{\partial z_i} \tag{10.2}$$

is the total electron kinetic energy operator,

$$\hat{\mathcal{H}}_{II} = \sum_{j \neq i = 1}^{N} \frac{e^2}{|\mathbf{R}_i - \mathbf{R}_j|} \tag{10.3}$$

is the Coulomb-interaction operator for all pairs of ions,

$$\hat{\mathcal{H}}_{Ie} = \sum_{i,j} \varphi(|\mathbf{R}_i - \mathbf{r}_j|) \tag{10.4}$$

is the Coulomb-interaction operator appropriate to the electron-ion

[1] It should be reemphasized that the *metallic* state of a crystal refers to that state in which there is bonding due to the quasi-free motion of electrons throughout the crystal. Such a state occurs (to some degree) in all solids.

coupling, and

$$\hat{\mathcal{H}}_{ee} = \sum_{i \neq j = 1}^{N} \frac{e^2}{|\mathbf{r}_i - \mathbf{r}_j|} \tag{10.5}$$

is the Coulomb operator appropriate to electron-electron interactions.

The first term, $\hat{\mathcal{H}}_{II}$, describes the total repulsion of the entire array of positively charged ions, while the second term $\hat{\mathcal{H}}_{Ie}$ represents the binding effect of the electron sea to the positive-ion lattice. The last term $\hat{\mathcal{H}}_{ee}$ describes the effect on the total energy of the system due to the correlation of the positions of each of the constituent electrons. Clearly, the expectation value of $\hat{\mathcal{H}}$, representing the total energy of the system, must represent a binding effect (that is, $<\hat{\mathcal{H}}> < 0$) in order to describe the energy of the solid as cohesive.

Historically, the first calculations which were carried out completely neglected the electron-electron interactions and gave a fair degree of agreement with the measured values for cohesive energies of the alkali metals. The most successful of these calculations were those of Wigner and Seitz;[1] their theory will be outlined below. Closer agreement was then reached when the electron-electron interactions were taken into account. The first of these calculations leading to the so-called correlation energy was carried out by Wigner and Seitz[2] and by Wigner.[3] Their theoretical development used the one-electron approximation (which, of course, we have also used thus far in the text). The more recent calculations of the correlation energy give even better agreement with the data; they are based on the abandonment of the one-electron approximation for a collective approach. Recent approaches that consider the collective behavior of a degenerate electron gas are those of Bohm and Pines[4] and of Sawada, Brueckner, Fakuda, and Brout.[5] In this chapter we shall outline only the Bohm-Pines treatment of the many-electron problem. This is principally to indicate the importance of the role played by electron correlations in the cohesive energy of metals with a very physical picture. Actually, the approach taken by Sawada et al.[5] is more general and contains the Bohm-Pines results as a limiting case. The former approach, however, makes use of techniques developed originally for handling the elementary particle interactions in relativistic field theories in terms of special types of convergent perturbation expansions and will not be described here. Although the finer details of these

[1] E. P. Wigner and F. Seitz, *Phys. Rev.*, **43:** 804 (1933); **46:** 509 (1934).

[2] *Ibid.*

[3] E. P. Wigner, *Phys. Rev.*, **46:** 1002 (1934).

[4] D. Bohm and D. Pines, *Phys. Rev.*, **82:** 625 (1951); **85:** 338 (1952); **92:** 609 (1953); D. Pines, *Phys. Rev.*, **92:** 626 (1953).

[5] K. Sawada, K. A. Brueckner, N. Fakuda, and R. Brout, *Phys. Rev.*, **108:** 507 (1957).

theories are somewhat more advanced than most of the material in this text, they are *mentioned* here because field-theory techniques have led to some very important contributions to our understanding of certain aspects of solid state theory. In particular, they have been used in recent theories of superconductivity[1] as well as in the derivation of the correlation energy of a degenerate electron gas.

The presentation of the many-electron problem given here could serve as an *introduction* to the many-body problem (especially for those who are interested in pursuing this aspect of theoretical physics in more detail).

10.1 The Wigner-Seitz theory

The Hartree derivation of the energy levels and their corresponding wave functions for a many-electron atom is outlined in many texts.[2] It is recalled that such a calculation is based on the one-electron approximation. That is to say, we study the behavior of only one electron at a time, subject to the influence of an average ("smeared out") potential due to all the other electrons in the system. This average potential, acting on the ith electron at $\mathbf{r}$, is due to the charge density of all other electrons

$$\rho_e = -e \sum_{j \neq i = 1}^{n} |\psi_j|^2 \tag{10.6}$$

and has the form

$$\varphi_j(\mathbf{r}) = -e \sum_{i \neq j = 1}^{n} \int \frac{|\psi_i(\mathbf{r}')|^2}{|\mathbf{r} - \mathbf{r}'|} \, d\mathbf{r}' \tag{10.7}$$

The wave equations for each of the n particles then form a set of n coupled equations

$$\begin{aligned}
\hat{\mathcal{H}}(1)\psi(1) &= \varphi_1(\psi_2, \ldots, \psi_n) \; \psi(1) \\
\hat{\mathcal{H}}(2)\psi(2) &= \varphi_2(\psi_1, \psi_3, \ldots, \psi_n)\psi(2) \\
&\;\;\vdots \\
\hat{\mathcal{H}}(n)\psi(n) &= \varphi_n(\psi_1, \ldots, \psi_{n-1}) \; \psi(n)
\end{aligned}$$

where $\hat{\mathcal{H}}(i)$ represents that part of the hamiltonian independent of $(\psi_1, \ldots, \psi_{i-1}, \psi_{i+1}, \ldots, \psi_n)$ and φ_i is defined in Eq. (10.7).

In the case of the atom, n is a relatively small number and thus

[1] We refer to the theories of J. Bardeen, J. R. Schreifer, and L. N. Cooper, *Phys. Rev.*, **108**: 1115 (1957), and of N. N. Bogoliubov, in N. N. Bogoliubov, V. V. Tolmacev, and D. V. Shirkov, "New Method in the Theory of Superconductivity," Chapman & Hall, Ltd., London, 1959.

[2] See, for example, F. Seitz, "The Modern Theory of Solids," p. 333, McGraw-Hill Book Company, Inc., New York, 1940.

the number of coupled wave equations is small. These wave equations are solved together for a consistent set of wave functions (and in accordance with the Pauli exclusion principle in the Hartree-Fock calculation).

The case of the conducting solid differs from the atomic case in that n (i.e., the number of electrons) is a very large number.

In the first (Hartree) approximation, the exchange interaction (which appears because of the antisymmetrization of the wave function; see Chap. 5) is neglected. In this case, and in view of our neglect of the correlated electron-electron interactions, the wave function for the "free" electron gas is given by the product function

$$\Psi_H = \psi_{\mathbf{k}_1}(\mathbf{r}_1)\psi_{\mathbf{k}_2}(\mathbf{r}_2) \cdots \psi_{\mathbf{k}_n}(\mathbf{r}_n) \equiv \prod_{i=1}^{n} \psi_{\mathbf{k}_i}(\mathbf{r}_i) \tag{10.8}$$

where $\psi_{\mathbf{k}_i}(\mathbf{r}_i)$ has the Bloch form, i.e.,

$$\psi_{\mathbf{k}_i}(\mathbf{r}_i) = u_{\mathbf{k}_i}(\mathbf{r}_i)e^{i\mathbf{k}_i\cdot\mathbf{r}_i} \tag{10.9}$$

Thus the charge density at the site of the ith electron is

$$\rho_e + \rho_I = -e \sum_{j=1}^{n} |u_{\mathbf{k}_j}e^{i\mathbf{k}_j\cdot\mathbf{r}_j}|^2 + \rho_I \tag{10.10}$$

where ρ_I is the charge density of the positive-ion background.

The Wigner-Seitz calculation is carried out by filling up the entire space of the crystal with identical polyhedra and assuming that (for a monovalent metal) there is only one electron in a given polyhedron at a time, together with the positively charged ion. Thus we must consider the interaction between (1) the polyhedra themselves (i.e., the contribution of ρ_I) and (2) the interaction within each polyhedron. Since the polyhedra are electrically neutral, we should expect that, if they are nearly spherically symmetric, the former interaction is very small in comparison with the latter. Using this argument, Wigner and Seitz initially neglect the interaction between the polyhedra and consider the electron energy to have the form

$$\epsilon(\mathbf{k}) = \epsilon_0 + \frac{\hbar^2k^2}{2m} \tag{10.11}$$

where ϵ_0 is the energy eigenvalue of the single electron which happens to be in the field of a crystalline ion within one of the polyhedra. The second term on the right-hand side of (10.11) is its kinetic energy. The procedure then is to evaluate ϵ_0 by setting $\mathbf{k} = 0$ and solve the Schroedinger equation, subject to the boundary condition that the slope of the wave function vanish at the faces of the polyhedron. This condition is necessary in order that the wave function (whose interpretation requires that its value and first derivatives be continuous) be precisely the same throughout each polyhedron of the crystal.

Consider, for example, the body-centered-cubic sodium lattice. The polyhedra are constructed by inserting planes bisecting the lines of centers between a given ion and each of its eight nearest and six next-nearest neighbors. The resulting polyhedron is the (14-sided) truncated octahedron (shown in Fig. 10.1).

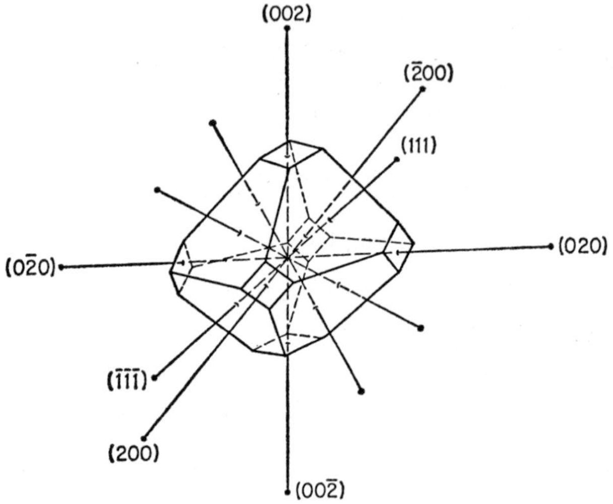

Fig. 10.1. Wigner-Seitz polyhedron for the body-centered-cubic lattice—a truncated octahedron.

If now, in the first approximation, the polyhedron is replaced by a sphere of equal volume

$$\Omega = \frac{4\pi}{3} r_s^3 \tag{10.12}$$

where Ω is the volume of the polyhedron of a single cell, then r_s is a measure of the electron density, i.e.,

$$r_s = \left(\frac{3\Omega}{4\pi}\right)^{1/3} = \left(\frac{3}{4\pi n}\right)^{1/3} \tag{10.13}$$

where n is the number of electrons per volume. The boundary condition for the wave function of the electron in the polyhedron is

$$\frac{\partial\psi}{\partial \mathbf{n}} = 0$$

where $\mathbf{n}$ is a direction normal to any of the faces of the polyhedron. This boundary condition is now replaced by

$$\left(\frac{\partial\psi}{\partial r}\right)_{r=r_s} = 0 \tag{10.14}$$

The boundary condition (10.14) is then combined with the Schroedinger equation [using the *s*-state potential $V_0(r)$]

$$\left\{\frac{1}{r^2}\frac{\partial}{\partial r}\left(r^2\frac{\partial}{\partial r}\right) + \frac{2m}{\hbar^2}\left[\epsilon_0 - V_0(r)\right]\right\}\psi(\mathbf{r}) = 0 \tag{10.15}$$

[where $\psi(\mathbf{r}) = u_0(\mathbf{r})$ according to (10.9), since $\mathbf{k} = 0$] to arrive at the energy eigenvalues ϵ_0. The way in which this is accomplished is to

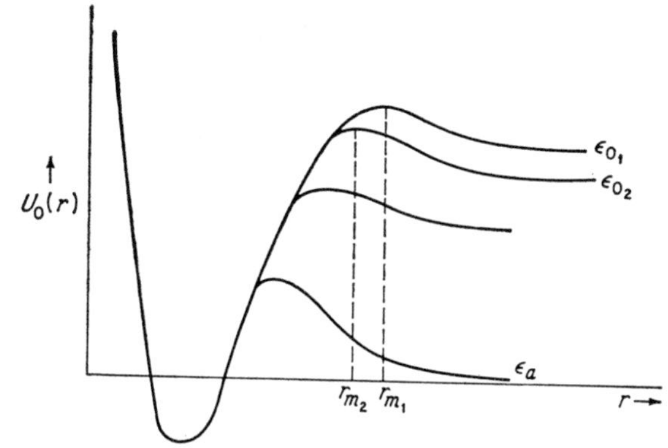

Fig. 10.2. Family of curves showing the behavior of the electron wave function $u_0(r)$ vs r as a function of ϵ_0. The free-ion energy eigenvalue is denoted by ϵ_a.

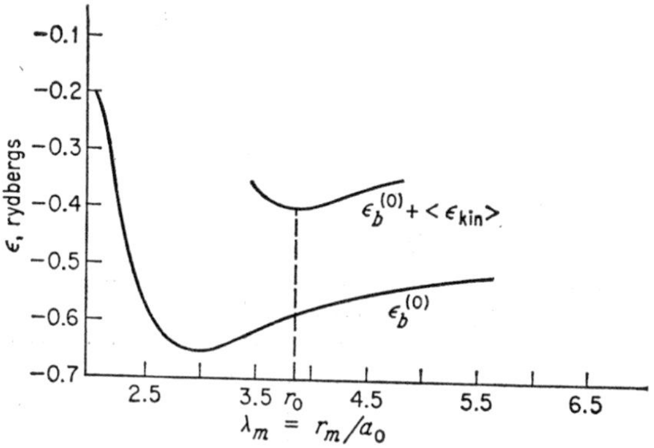

Fig. 10.3. The binding energy ϵ_b and the ground-state eigenvalue ϵ_0 for Na as a function of the radius of the Wigner-Seitz sphere. Energy is in units of rydberg constants. [*After T. S. Kuhn and J. H. van Vleck, Phys. Rev.*, **79**: 382 (1950).]

substitute for $V_0(r)$ the *free*-ion potential and numerically integrate (10.15) for different values of ϵ° (see Fig. 10.2). Wherever the second maximum in the curve occurs is called r_m and the corresponding energy values ϵ_0 are then plotted vs r_m. The resulting curve of ϵ vs r_m contains a minimum [curve (1), ($\epsilon_b^{(0)}$), Fig. 10.3]. Finally, the total energy ϵ_b is obtained by adding the average kinetic energy of the valence electron (at $T = 0°K$) to $\epsilon_b^{(0)}$. The latter quantity was shown in Chap. 6 [Eq. (6.47)] to be

$$<\epsilon_{\text{kin}}> = \frac{3}{5} n\epsilon_F^{(0)} = \frac{3}{5}\left(\frac{3}{2}\right)^{2/3} \pi^{2/3} \frac{\hbar^2}{2m} \frac{n}{r_m^2} \tag{10.16}$$

Adding (10.16) to the numerically obtained curve and taking account of (10.13) give the corrected behavior of ϵ vs r [curve (2), Fig. 10.3]. The minimum of this curve then corresponds to the energy eigenvalue at the equilibrium sphere radius r_s. Further work on perfecting the calculation of cohesive energy in the Wigner-Seitz approximation was carried out by Kuhn and Van Vleck[1] (whose results for Na are shown in Fig. 10.3) and by Brooks.[2] These methods do not require an explicit knowledge of the ion core potential or a numerical integration of the radial wave function.

The lattice parameter r_0 is obtained from the value of (r_s/a_0) calculated above. Since the bcc lattice contains two atoms per cell, the lattice parameter is obtained from the relation

$$2\left(\frac{4\pi}{3} r_s^3\right) = r_0^3$$

or

$$r_0 = \left(\frac{3}{8\pi}\right)^{1/3} r_s \tag{10.17}$$

In this way, the calculated lattice parameters of the Wigner-Seitz model may be compared with the observed values. The calculated values of Brooks are compared with the measured values in Table 10.1. Although

TABLE 10.1 *A Comparison of the Calculated Lattice Parameters with the Measured Values for the Alkali Metals**

Metal	*Lattice parameter r_0, Å* Calculated	Measured	*Percentage error*
Li	3.40	3.46	−1.73
Na	4.27	4.25	+0.47
K	5.16	5.24	−1.53
Rb	5.45	5.60	−2.68
Cs	5.74	6.05	−5.13

* After H. Brooks, *Phys. Rev.*, **91:** 1027 (1953).

the agreement indicated is not bad for the lattice parameters, the final results obtained from these calculations for the cohesive energy is not good. Let us now consider the origin of the cohesive energy.

[1] T. S. Kuhn and J. H. van Vleck, *Phys. Rev.*, **79:** 382 (1950).
[2] H. Brooks, *Phys. Rev.*, **91:** 1027 (1953).

The solution of the Schroedinger equation (10.15) differs from the free-ion equation only in the replacement of the boundary condition (10.14) for that which occurs in the free-ion case,

$$\psi(r = \infty) = 0$$

Thus the calculated binding energy $\epsilon_b^{(0)}$ (see Fig. 10.3) is indeed not equal to the ionization energy of the free atom. Rather, $\epsilon_b^{(0)}$ represents the amount of energy that is required to remove an electron (with the wave vector $\mathbf{k} = 0$) from the crystal. If $\mathbf{k} = 0$ occurs at the edge of the Brillouin zone, the difference between $\epsilon_b^{(0)}$ and the free-atom ionization energy ϵ_a must represent a contribution to the cohesive energy of the solid. This difference

$$\epsilon_{bc} = \epsilon_b^{(0)} - \epsilon_a \tag{10.18}$$

is frequently referred to as the *boundary correction* energy.

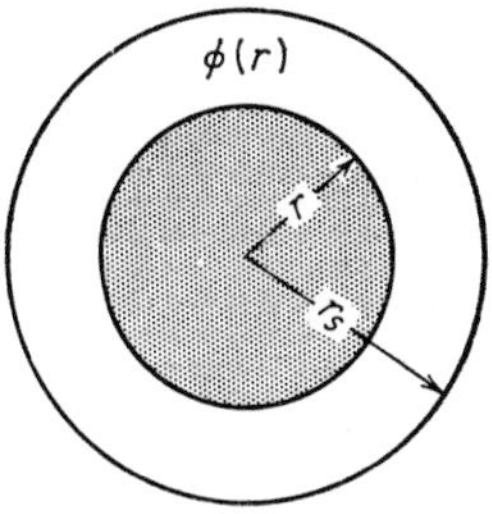

Fig. 10.4. Wigner-Seitz spherical cell with uniform charge distribution.

Finally, a more accurate approach to the estimated Hartree approximation (i.e., neglecting exchange forces) can be accomplished only by abandoning the assumption (of the original Wigner-Seitz model) that only one electron appears in a cell (i.e., a polyhedron) at a time and replacing it with a uniform charge distribution throughout the cell, determined by the wave function (10.8), but still neglecting the interaction between the polyhedra themselves. If we again assume a sphere of radius r_s to contain a *uniform* charge distribution, the potential energy at any internal point r is

$$\varphi(r) = \frac{eQ(r)}{r} + e\int_r^{r_s} \frac{\rho\, dV}{r} \tag{10.19}$$

where ρ is the uniform charge distribution, i.e.,

$$\rho = \frac{e}{(4\pi/3)r_s^3} \tag{10.20}$$

and $Q(r)$ is the total charge contained in the (inner) sphere of radius r, that is,

$$Q(r) = \left(\frac{4\pi}{3}r^3\right)\rho \tag{10.21}$$

Combining (10.19) to (10.21), we have

$$\begin{aligned}\varphi(r) &= e\left[\frac{4\pi}{3}\rho r^2 + 2\pi\rho(r_s^2 - r^2)\right] \\ &= \frac{3}{2}\frac{e^2}{r_s}\left[1 - \frac{1}{3}\left(\frac{r}{r_s}\right)^2\right] \end{aligned} \tag{10.22}$$

The average potential energy due to this electron-electron interaction within the Wigner-Seitz sphere is then

$$\bar{\varphi} = \frac{\frac{1}{2}4\pi \int_0^{r_s} \varphi(r) r^2 \, dr}{(4\pi/3) r_s^3} = 0.6 \frac{e^2}{r_s} \tag{10.23}$$

The factor of $\frac{1}{2}$ is introduced so that each of the electron pairs is counted only once.

The cohesive energy calculated thus far is then given by

$$\epsilon_{\text{coh}}^{(H)} = \epsilon_{bc} + <\epsilon_{\text{kin}}> + \bar{\varphi} \tag{10.24}$$

where ϵ_{kin} is given by (10.16) and $\bar{\varphi}$ by (10.23). The calculated values of ϵ_{bc} for the alkali metal are given, together with $\epsilon_{\text{coh}}^{(H)}$ and the measured values, in Table 10.2.

If we now introduce the dimensionless parameter

$$\lambda_s = \frac{r_s}{a_0}$$

where

$$a_0 = \frac{\hbar^2}{me^2}$$

is the first Bohr radius, and define energy in units of rydberg constants,

$$1 \text{ rydberg} = \frac{1}{2} \frac{me^4}{\hbar^2} = \frac{\alpha^2}{2} (mc^2) \qquad (\alpha \equiv \text{fine structure constant})$$

then (10.24) takes the form

$$\epsilon_{\text{coh}}^{(H)} \simeq \epsilon_{bc} + \frac{2.21}{\lambda_s^2} + \frac{1.20}{\lambda_s} \qquad \text{rydbergs} \tag{10.25}$$

We see from Table 10.2 that the calculated values of the cohesive energy in the Hartree approximation [Eq. (10.25)] are not only far different in magnitude from the measured values but also they do not indicate any binding at all (that is, $\epsilon_{\text{coh}}^{(H)}$ is positive instead of negative).

The large repulsion instead of attraction results from the feature of the Hartree approximation which gives a wave function of such a nature as to imply that the electrons are (on an average) much closer to each other than they actually are. This is because no consideration is given to the correlation of the electron positions and spins.

If we now invoke the Pauli exclusion principle, the situation should improve, since the implication of this principle is that electrons of equal kinetic energy and parallel spins cannot come arbitrarily near each other. In the Hartree-Fock approximation account is taken of the parallel electron spins by antisymmetrizing the system wave function (10.8). Thus

$\Psi_{H\text{-}F}$ is the Slater determinant

$$\Psi_{H\text{-}F} = \sqrt{\frac{1}{N!}} \begin{vmatrix} \psi_{\mathbf{k}_1}(\mathbf{r}_1) & \psi_{\mathbf{k}_2}(\mathbf{r}_1) & \cdots & \psi_{\mathbf{k}_N}(\mathbf{r}_1) \\ \psi_{\mathbf{k}_1}(\mathbf{r}_2) & \psi_{\mathbf{k}_2}(\mathbf{r}_2) & \cdots & \psi_{\mathbf{k}_N}(\mathbf{r}_2) \\ \cdots & \cdots & \cdots & \cdots \\ \psi_{\mathbf{k}_1}(\mathbf{r}_N) & \cdots & \cdots & \psi_{\mathbf{k}_N}(\mathbf{r}_N) \end{vmatrix} \tag{10.26}$$

The effect of this modification on the cohesive energy of the system is to introduce the (extra) exchange energy (see Chap. 5 for a discussion of exchange energy) which, in turn, keeps electrons apart. In order to calculate this term, we can, without very much loss of accuracy, take for $\psi_{\mathbf{k}}(\mathbf{r})$ the plane-wave solution

$$\psi_{\mathbf{k}}(\mathbf{r}) = \frac{1}{\sqrt{V}} e^{i\mathbf{k}\cdot\mathbf{r}} \tag{10.27}$$

The exchange integral then takes the form[1]

$$\begin{aligned} \epsilon(\mathbf{k},\mathbf{k}') &= -\int \psi_{\mathbf{k}}^*(\mathbf{r}_1)\psi_{\mathbf{k}'}^*(\mathbf{r}_2) \frac{e^2}{|\mathbf{r}_1 - \mathbf{r}_2|} \psi_{\mathbf{k}}(\mathbf{r}_2)\psi_{\mathbf{k}'}(\mathbf{r}_1)\, d\mathbf{r}_1\, d\mathbf{r}_2 \\ &= -\frac{1}{V^2}\int e^{i(\mathbf{k}-\mathbf{k}')\cdot(\mathbf{r}_1-\mathbf{r}_2)} \frac{e^2}{|\mathbf{r}_1 - \mathbf{r}_2|}\, d\mathbf{r}_1\, d\mathbf{r}_2 \\ &= -\frac{4\pi e^2}{V} \frac{1}{|\mathbf{k}-\mathbf{k}'|^2} \end{aligned} \tag{10.28}$$

The minus sign indicates a decrease in the electron-electron interaction because of the Pauli principle.

If $\mathbf{k}$ is the wave vector for a given electron, then $\mathbf{k}'$ is an index denoting wave vectors for all other electrons in the metal. The total exchange interaction acting on a single electron is then obtained by summing $\epsilon(\mathbf{k},\mathbf{k}')$ over all $\mathbf{k}'$. A summation with respect to points in $\mathbf{k}$ space is equivalent to an integration, according to the prescription[2]

$$\sum_{\mathbf{k}} \rightarrow \frac{V}{(2\pi)^3} \int d\mathbf{k} \tag{10.29}$$

[1] The integration in (10.28) is most readily carried out by the Fourier-transform method. The last part of this equation is recognized to be the Fourier transform of the Coulomb potential.

[2] This can be seen to be compatible with the uncertainty principle, since the latter allows only one electron at a time (with a given spin) to occupy the unit of phase space h^3 [$= (2\pi\hbar)^3$]. Thus the total possible number of states is just the total volume of phase space divided by $(2\pi\hbar)^3$. Consequently (using the De Broglie relation $\mathbf{p} = \hbar\mathbf{k}$), we have

$$\sum_{\mathbf{k}} \rightarrow \frac{V}{(2\pi\hbar)^3} \int d\mathbf{p} = \frac{V}{(2\pi)^3} \int d\mathbf{k}$$

Using (10.29), the total exchange energy acting on a single electron is

$$\frac{1}{2}\sum_{\mathbf{k}'} \epsilon(\mathbf{k},\mathbf{k}') = -\frac{e^2}{2\pi^2}\int^{\mathbf{k}_F} \frac{d\mathbf{k}'}{|\mathbf{k}-\mathbf{k}'|^2}$$

$$= -\frac{e^2}{2\pi^2}\int_0^{2\pi} d\varphi \int_0^{\pi} \sin\theta\, d\theta \int_0^{k_F} \frac{k'^2\, dk'}{k^2 + k'^2 - 2kk'\cos\theta} \qquad (10.30)$$

where k_F is the Fermi wave vector, i.e.,

$$k_F = \sqrt{\frac{2m\epsilon_F^{(0)}}{\hbar^2}} \qquad (10.31)$$

The right-hand side of Eq. (10.30) is readily integrated, giving

$$\epsilon(\mathbf{k}) = (2)(\tfrac{1}{2})\sum_{\mathbf{k}'} \epsilon(\mathbf{k},\mathbf{k}') = \frac{e^2 k_F}{\pi}\left(2 + \frac{k^2 - k_F^2}{kk_F}\ln\frac{|k_F - k|}{k_F + k}\right) \qquad (10.32)$$

The factor 2 is inserted in (10.32) to take account of the two spin states of electrons which occupy the state $\psi_{\mathbf{k}'}$.

Finally, the total exchange energy is obtained by summing $\epsilon(\mathbf{k},\mathbf{k}')$ over all electrons (making sure to count each pair only once). Using (10.29) and (10.32), we have

$$\epsilon_{ex} = \frac{1}{N}\sum_{\mathbf{k}}\sum_{\mathbf{k}'} \epsilon(\mathbf{k},\mathbf{k}') = -\frac{2e^2 k_F^4}{(2\pi)^3} \qquad (10.33)$$

Finally, in the Hartree-Fock approximation, the cohesive energy is obtained by adding ϵ_{ex} [Eq. (10.34)] to $\epsilon_{\text{coh}}^{(H)}$ [Eq. (10.25)], with

$$\epsilon_{ex} \simeq -0.458\,\frac{e^2}{r_s}\ \text{ergs/electron} = -\frac{0.916}{\lambda_s}\ \text{rydbergs/electron} \qquad (10.34)$$

Clearly, the account taken of the correlation in electron position in the Hartree-Fock approximation improves the agreement between theory and experiment and gives a net binding effect. Nevertheless, as we see in Table 10.2, the agreement between the magnitudes of the theoretical and experimental values (for the alkali metals) is still poor.

The discrepancy which remains will be shown below to result from our neglect, thus far, of the correlations of the electron positions (apart from the exchange energy discussed above). The resulting energy, due to electron-electron interactions, is commonly referred to as the *correlation energy.* Strictly speaking, this contribution to the cohesive energy can be determined only by treating the many-electron problem in a rigorous fashion. Although it is impossible to carry out the rigorous calculation by present-day techniques, methods of approximating the correlation energy have been investigated. Some of the work was done initially by Wigner and Seitz themselves[1] and, as mentioned before, most recently techniques due to Bohm and Pines[2] and Brueckner[3] have also shown much promise.

TABLE 10.2 *Cohesive Energy of the Alkali Metals (at $T = 0°K$) in the Hartree and Hartree-Fock Approximations. Energy Is Measured in Units of Rydberg Constants.** ϵ_{bc} *Is the Boundary Correction Energy [Eq. (10.18)]*

Metal	λ_s	ϵ_{bc}	$\epsilon^{(H)}$	$\epsilon^{(H\text{-}F)}$	$\epsilon(meas)$
Li	3.22	−0.272	+0.232	−0.0530	−0.114
Na	3.96	−0.222	+0.211	−0.0212	−0.081
K	4.87	−0.161	+0.175	−0.0134	−0.0705
Rb	5.18	−0.149	+0.166	−0.0106	−0.0590
Cs	5.57	−0.137	+0.156	−0.0091	−0.0585

* 1 rydberg/electron = 3.12×10^{-3} kcal/mole.

The Wigner-Seitz method of determining the correlation energy is to alter the two-body wave function

$$\Psi = \frac{1}{N!}\begin{vmatrix} \psi_1(\mathbf{x}_1) & \cdots & \psi_1(\mathbf{x}_N) \\ \cdots & \cdots & \cdots \\ \psi_N(\mathbf{x}_1) & \cdots & \psi_N(\mathbf{x}_N) \end{vmatrix} \begin{vmatrix} \psi_1(\mathbf{y}_1) & \cdots & \psi_1(\mathbf{y}_N) \\ \cdots & \cdots & \cdots \\ \psi_N(\mathbf{y}_1) & \cdots & \psi_N(\mathbf{y}_N) \end{vmatrix} \tag{10.35}$$

($\mathbf{x} \equiv \mathbf{r}, \uparrow$; $\mathbf{y} \equiv \mathbf{r}, \downarrow$; and $\uparrow\downarrow$ refer to the spin states) to the form

$$\Psi = \frac{1}{N!}\begin{vmatrix} \psi_1(\mathbf{y}_1, \ldots, \mathbf{y}_N, \mathbf{x}_1) & \cdots & \psi_1(\mathbf{y}_1, \ldots, \mathbf{y}_N, \mathbf{x}_N) \\ \cdots & \cdots & \cdots \\ \psi_N(\mathbf{y}_1, \ldots, \mathbf{y}_N, \mathbf{x}_1) & \cdots & \psi_N(\mathbf{y}_1, \ldots, \mathbf{y}_N, \mathbf{x}_N) \end{vmatrix} \cdot \begin{vmatrix} \psi_1(\mathbf{y}_1) & \cdots & \psi_1(\mathbf{y}_N) \\ \cdots & \cdots & \cdots \\ \psi_N(\mathbf{y}_1) & \cdots & \psi_N(\mathbf{y}_N) \end{vmatrix} \tag{10.35'}$$

in order to take account of the statistical correlation in the interactions between electrons of opposite spins. In (10.35′) the coordinates $(\mathbf{y}_1, \ldots, \mathbf{y}_N)$ in the first Slater determinant are treated as parameters; the purpose of the calculation is to determine the best wave function from a minimization of the energy. The method makes use of the

[1] E. P. Wigner and F. Seitz, *Phys. Rev.*, **46:** 509 (1934); Wigner, *loc. cit.; Trans. Faraday Soc.*, **34:** 678 (1938).

[2] Bohm and Pines, *loc. cit.*

[3] Sawada, Brueckner, Fakuda, and Brout, *loc. cit.* Also, for a recent compilation of many of the important papers in this field, along with discussion, see D. Pines, "The Many Body Problem," W. A. Benjamin, Inc., Publishers, New York, 1962.

Rayleigh-Schroedinger perturbation expansion in powers of e^2. The calculation gives for the correlation energy

$$\epsilon_{\text{corr}} = -\frac{0.88}{r_s + 7.8} \quad \text{rydbergs} \tag{10.36}$$

When this result is added to the Hartree-Fock result, good agreement is obtained with the measured cohesive energies of the alkali metals (see Table 10.3).

10.2 The Bohm-Pines theory

The Collective Description of a Many-particle System

The treatment of the particle-particle interactions in a dense electron gas is greatly complicated by the fact that the mechanism of interaction (i.e., the Coulomb interaction) is of a long-range character. Thus it is not generally possible to simplify the calculation by considering only a small region of space surrounding any given particle. In the (B-P) treatment an extra approximation, just as extreme but opposite to that of the individual electron model, is introduced which considers the behavior of the entire electron gas *as a whole.* Thus, besides the degrees of freedom associated with the motion of the individual particles, extra degrees of freedom associated with the *collective* behavior of the electron gas are introduced. These give rise to a description in which electrons, beyond some screening radius r_c of any given electron, act cooperatively on that electron, while the individual-particle aspects are important for radii smaller than r_c. The collective modes of behavior of the electron gas are associated with *plasma oscillations*[1] with characteristic frequencies ω_p, and their energy quanta ($\hbar\omega_p$) are commonly called *plasmons.*

The object of the Bohm-Pines treatment is to describe the many-electron hamiltonian

$$\mathcal{H}(\mathbf{r}_1,\mathbf{r}_2, \ldots ,\mathbf{r}_N,\mathbf{p}_1,\mathbf{p}_2, \ldots ,\mathbf{p}_N) = \sum_i \frac{p_i^2}{2m} + \sum_{i<j} \frac{e^2}{r_{ij}}$$

and its eigenfunctions and eigenvalues in terms of a formulation which involves new canonically conjugate variables ($\mathbf{Q}_1, \ldots ,\mathbf{Q}_i, \ldots ,$ $\mathbf{P}_1, \ldots ,\mathbf{P}_i, \ldots$) which refer to the collective degrees of freedom of the electron gas. These are called the *plasma degrees of freedom* and their number n' must be determined.

Before outlining the Bohm-Pines development, let us consider some general features of collective behavior. The first question which arises

[1] The metal is usually identified as a high-density plasma. It differs from a normal gas plasma, of course, not only in particle concentrations but also, in the gas plasma, the neutralizing positive-ion background is mobile whereas in the metal it is not.

is: What physical mechanism is responsible for the screening action in a dense electron gas? Such action was first discussed by Debye and Huckel[1] and results from charge fluctuations and the high mobility of the constituent electrons of the gas. Consider a momentary fluctuation in the equilibrium position of any given electron which is influenced by the average electrostatic field of all other electrons of the gas. Such a position fluctuation would correspond to a charge imbalance in the region of that electron and a subsequent attempt by other electrons to rush into the area in order to restore charge balance. Because of their high mobility and kinetic energy (associated with their thermal energy), the electrons are not able to stop in the desired region and will therefore overshoot their mark. Subsequently they will turn around and try once again. The continuation of this process constitutes collective oscillatory motion. The amount of "overshoot" has a lower limit which is the radius of a sphere that screens the given (misbehaving) electron from the attempts of its fellow electrons to correct the improper situation.

Mathematically we may view this process as follows: Suppose that a negative charge qV is introduced (at a point which we call the origin) inside a metal (viewed as a plasma). The destruction of charge neutrality at this point, because of the momentary fluctuation in particle concentration, thereby decreases the electron (number) density by δn. Therefore, the net change in charge density at this point is $q - e\delta n$. The effective electrostatic potential is then a solution of Poisson's equation

$$\nabla^2 \varphi = 4\pi(q - e\delta n) \tag{10.37}$$

If n_0 is the equilibrium electron (and ion) concentration (i.e., in the absence of a position fluctuation) at a temperature T and if the excitation energy $e\varphi \ll kT$ and n is sufficiently low to allow the use of the classical statistical approximation for the distribution function, then

$$\delta n = (n_0 e^{e\varphi/kT} - n_0) \simeq n_0 \left(\frac{e\varphi}{kT}\right) \tag{10.37'}$$

Combining (10.37) with (10.37′), we have

$$\left(\nabla^2 + \frac{4\pi n_0 e^2}{kT}\right) \varphi = 4\pi q \tag{10.38}$$

The particular solution of (10.38) is (in a unit volume)

$$\varphi = \frac{q}{r} e^{-r/\lambda_c} \tag{10.39}$$

where

$$\lambda_c = \left(\frac{kT}{4\pi n_0 e^2}\right)^{1/2} \tag{10.40}$$

[1] P. P. Debye and E. Huckel, *Z. Physik*, **24:** 185 (1923).

is called the *Debye length*. Thus we see that the introduction of a density fluctuation in the plasma has the effect of screening a given particle from all others in such a way that, at a distance λ_c from this particle, the normal Coulomb potential has to be decreased by the fraction e^{-1}.

The plasma frequency associated with this action may be approximated by considering the equation of motion of the ith electron in the presence of the density fluctuation. If the amount of "overshoot" of the ith electron of the gas in the region of the fluctuation (at time t) is $\mathbf{r}(t)$, the effective electric field intensity acting on the ith electron is

$$\mathbf{\mathcal{E}} = 4\pi e n_0 \mathbf{r}(t)$$

where n_0 is the average (time-independent) electron concentration. The equation of motion for the ith electron is then

$$m\ddot{\mathbf{r}}(t) = -e\mathbf{\mathcal{E}} = -4\pi e^2 n_0 \mathbf{r}(t) \tag{10.41}$$

or

$$\ddot{\mathbf{r}}(t) + \omega_p^2 \mathbf{r}(t) = 0$$

where

$$\omega_p = \left(\frac{4\pi e^2 n_0}{m}\right)^{1/2} \tag{10.42}$$

is the frequency of the plasma oscillation. It is noted that for a gaseous plasma, where $n_0 \sim 10^{12}$ cm^{-3}, $\nu_p = \omega_p/2\pi \sim 10^4$ Mc/sec is in the microwave region, whereas in metals, where $n_0 \sim 10^{22}$, $\nu_p \sim 10^9$ Mc/sec which is in the infrared region of the spectrum.

The plasma itself may be treated either in terms of the equations of motion of the particle density fluctuations of the system or in terms of the independent-particle aspects of the plasma. As mentioned earlier, the Bohm-Pines treatment takes the former approach. Let us now consider this treatment in more detail.

In order to predict the equations of motion of density fluctuations in the plasma, it is convenient, because of the periodic boundary conditions imposed on the electron wave functions, to describe our system in $\mathbf{k}$ space rather than $\mathbf{r}$ space. The potential energy for the interaction between the ith and jth electrons may be expanded in a Fourier series (in a box of unit volume with periodic boundary conditions) in the standard way, and we obtain [see (10.28)]

$$\varphi(|\mathbf{r}_i - \mathbf{r}_j|) = \frac{e^2}{|\mathbf{r}_i - \mathbf{r}_j|} = 4\pi e^2 \sum_{\mathbf{k}}{}' \frac{1}{k^2} e^{i\mathbf{k}\cdot(\mathbf{r}_i - \mathbf{r}_j)} \tag{10.43}$$

The equation of motion for the ith electron

$$m\ddot{\mathbf{r}} = -\nabla\varphi$$

then takes the form

$$\ddot{\mathbf{r}}_i \equiv \dot{\mathbf{v}}_i = -\frac{4\pi e^2 i}{m} \sum_{\mathbf{k},j}{}' \frac{\mathbf{k}}{k^2} e^{i\mathbf{k}\cdot(\mathbf{r}_i - \mathbf{r}_j)} \tag{10.44}$$

The prime in the summation signs of Eqs. (10.43) and (10.44) denotes that the term with $j = i$ is excluded from the sum. In (10.43) the sum over $\mathbf{k}$ is identical to a sum over electrons (of a given spin), since there is only one such electron in the state $\psi_{\mathbf{k}}$.

In the same way, the particle density $n(\mathbf{r})$ is Fourier-decomposed with the corresponding Fourier coefficients given by

$$n_{\mathbf{k}} = \int n(\mathbf{r}) e^{-i\mathbf{k}\cdot\mathbf{r}} \, d\mathbf{r} \tag{10.45}$$

If it is now assumed that we are dealing with point particles, then

$$n(\mathbf{r}) = \sum_i \delta(\mathbf{r} - \mathbf{r}_i) \tag{10.46}$$

where $\delta(\mathbf{r} - \mathbf{r}_i)$ is the three-dimensional Dirac delta function $[\delta(x - x_i)\delta(y - y_i)\delta(z - z_i)]$ [see Eqs. (7.6) to (7.8) for properties of the delta function].

Substituting (10.46) into (10.45) and carrying out the integration, we have

$$n_{\mathbf{k}} = \sum_j e^{-i\mathbf{k}\cdot\mathbf{r}_j} \tag{10.47}$$

Thus we see that n_0 is the mean electron concentration (recalling that all calculations refer to a unit volume), and $n_{\mathbf{k}}$ ($\mathbf{k} \neq 0$) describes fluctuations about n_0.

The equations of motion of $n_{\mathbf{k}}$ are obtained by differentiating (10.47) implicitly with respect to time, giving

$$\dot{n}_{\mathbf{k}} = -i \sum_j (\mathbf{k} \cdot \mathbf{v}_j) e^{-i\mathbf{k}\cdot\mathbf{r}_j}$$

and

$$\ddot{n}_{\mathbf{k}} = -\sum_i [(\mathbf{k} \cdot \mathbf{v}_i)^2 + i(\mathbf{k} \cdot \dot{\mathbf{v}}_i)] e^{-i\mathbf{k}\cdot\mathbf{r}_i} \tag{10.48}$$

Combining (10.48) with (10.44), we have

$$\ddot{n}_{\mathbf{k}} = -\sum_i (\mathbf{k} \cdot \mathbf{v}_i)^2 e^{-i\mathbf{k}\cdot\mathbf{r}_i} - \frac{4\pi e^2}{m} \sum_{\substack{\mathbf{k}',i,j \\ \mathbf{k}'\neq 0}} \frac{(\mathbf{k} \cdot \mathbf{k}')}{k^2} e^{i(\mathbf{k}'-\mathbf{k})\cdot\mathbf{r}_i} e^{-i\mathbf{k}\cdot\mathbf{r}_j} \tag{10.49}$$

The next step in the calculation is to consider separately those terms in the summation over $\mathbf{k}'$ [in the last part on the right-hand side of (10.49)], where $\mathbf{k} = \mathbf{k}'$ and where $\mathbf{k} \neq \mathbf{k}'$. When $\mathbf{k} = \mathbf{k}'$, the sum over i is independent of $\mathbf{r}_i$ and gives n_0. When $\mathbf{k} \neq \mathbf{k}'$, there is indeed a dependence in the sum on $\mathbf{r}_i$. This involves the phase factors $e^{-i(\mathbf{k}'-\mathbf{k})\cdot\mathbf{r}_i}$. Since there is a very large number of particles at random locations, these terms (summed over $\mathbf{k}' \neq \mathbf{k}$) tend to cancel each other and, in the first approximation, the Bohm-Pines treatment neglects them. This is called the *random-phase approximation.* Thus the equation of motion (10.48) takes the approximate form

$$\ddot{n}_{\mathbf{k}} = -\sum_i (\mathbf{k} \cdot \mathbf{v}_i)^2 e^{-i\mathbf{k}\cdot\mathbf{r}_i} - \frac{4\pi n_0 e^2}{m} \sum_i e^{i\mathbf{k}\cdot\mathbf{r}_i}$$

or, using (10.42) and (10.47),

$$\ddot{n}_{\mathbf{k}} = \sum_i (\mathbf{k} \cdot \mathbf{v}_i)^2 e^{-i\mathbf{k}\cdot\mathbf{r}_i} - \omega_p^2 n_{\mathbf{k}} \tag{10.50}$$

The first term on the right-hand side of (10.50) does not describe collective behavior; rather it corresponds to the contribution of the thermal motion of individual particles to the density fluctuations. The frequency contribution associated with each of the particles is $\omega_i = \mathbf{k} \cdot \mathbf{v}_i$, where $\mathbf{v}_i$ is the linear velocity of the ith particle. These frequencies cover a whole spectrum. On the other hand, the second term on the right-hand side of (10.50) describes each constituent electron of the entire gas, to contribute the same frequency ω_p to the density fluctuations.

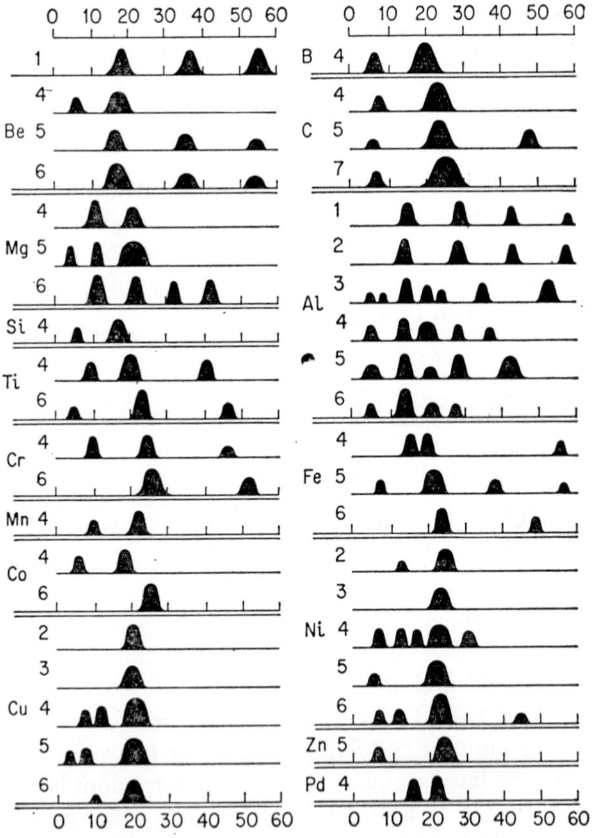

Fig. 10.5. Experimental results on characteristic energy losses in solids. The units of energy are electron volts. The code numbers refer to results that are reported in the following publications: (1) G. Ruthemann, *Naturwissenshaften,* **29**: 648 (1941); **30**: 145 (1942); *Ann. Physik,* **2**(6): 113 (1948); (2) W. Lang, *Optik,* **3**: 233 (1948); (3) G. Möllenstedt,

Thus the latter is a *collective* behavior whereas the former is an individual-particle behavior. (Figure 10.5 shows characteristic energy losses in solids due to absorption by plasma oscillations.) They are both, in principle, present at all times. However, we may use the criteria of the relative magnitudes of their average values to determine when one or the other will predominate. If

$$\frac{4\pi n_0 e^2}{m} \gg \langle(\mathbf{k}\cdot\mathbf{v}_i)^2\rangle_{\text{av}} \tag{10.51}$$

the electron gas will tend to behave collectively, whereas the individual-particle aspects become important if this inequality is reversed.

If the velocity distribution is maxwellian at a temperature T, (10.51) takes the form

$$k^2 \ll \frac{12\pi n_0 e^2}{m\langle\mathbf{v}_i^2\rangle_{\text{av}}} = \frac{4\pi n_0 e^2}{kT} = \lambda_c^{-2} \tag{10.52}$$

where λ_c is the Debye length defined in Eq. (10.40). The inequality (10.52) is equivalent to the statement that the collective features of the electron gas will predominate so long as the mean De Broglie wavelength

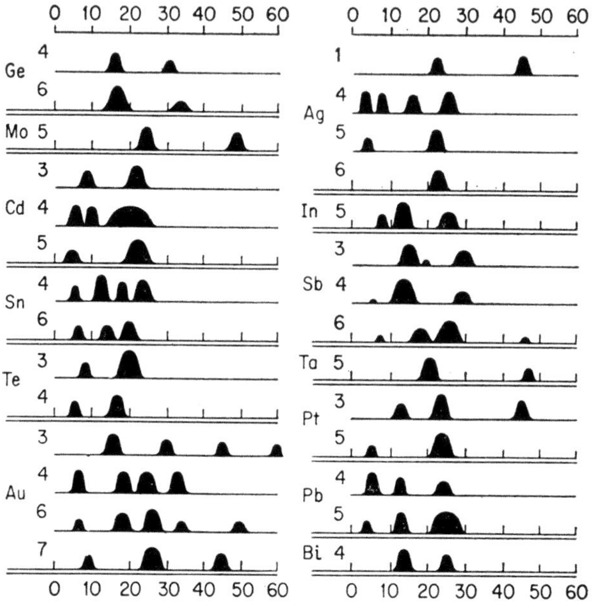

Optik, **5**: 499 (1949); (4) L. Marton and L. B. Leder, *Phys. Rev.*, **94**: 203 (1954); (5) W. Kleinn, *Optik*, **11**: 226 (1954); (6) H. Watanabe, *J. Phys. Soc. Japan*, **9**: 920 (1954); (7) D. Gabor and G. W. Jull, *Nature*, **175**: 718 (1955). *(From D. Pines in F. Seitz and D. Turnbull (eds.), "Solid State Physics," vol.* 1, *Academic Press Inc., New York*, 1955.)

of the particles is long compared with a screening radius λ_c. If the probability interpretation of the electron wave functions is used, this means that, so long as the interacting electrons cannot be localized within a sphere or radius λ_c, they will behave collectively. On the other hand, if the kinetic energy is sufficiently high that many wavelengths can fit into the Debye sphere (i.e., the sphere of radius λ_c), then the individual-particle aspects become more important than the collective aspects of the gas.

Also, from (10.52) we see that collective behavior is preferred when the electron concentration n_0 is large and when the temperature is low. Physically, this is because the former corresponds to a large degree of coupling between the constituent electrons of the gas and the latter diminishes the random thermal motion of the particles.

Summarizing, we see that the plasma frequency in (10.50) (derived above in the random-phase approximation) is the same as that obtained from the cruder analysis used in arriving at (10.42).

Plasma Degrees of Freedom and Collective Coordinates

Thus far, we have described the electron gas in a metal in terms of the density fluctuations $n_{\mathbf{k}}$, and we have seen that these "field coordinates" incorporate both collective and individual-particle features of the electron gas. Thus they would not properly serve as "pure" collective coordinates. The Bohm-Pines treatment attempts to transform the hamiltonian of the system (in terms of these coordinates) by means of canonical transformation[1] from the appropriate set of field coordinates that represent extra degrees of freedom in the system, to the normal coordinates which describe the independent modes of collective behavior *separately* from the individual-particle behavior of the gas. This means that we wish to determine the system wave function to have the product form

$$\Psi(\mathbf{r}_1,\mathbf{r}_2, \ldots ,\mathbf{r}_n,Q_1, \ldots ,Q_{n'}) = \psi_p(\mathbf{r}_1, \ldots ,r_n)\chi_{\text{coll}}(Q_1, \ldots ,Q_{n'}) \tag{10.53}$$

where ψ_p describes the individual-particle behavior and depends on the $3n$ particle coordinates, while χ_{coll} describes the collective behavior of the gas and depends on n' collective coordinates. Since the total number of degrees of freedom ($3n$) cannot be changed, n' subsidiary conditions on the functions χ_{coll} must be introduced in order to maintain a total of $3n$ independent coordinates in the mathematical description.[2]

[1] See, for example, H. Goldstein, "Classical Mechanics," chap. 8, Addison-Wesley Publishing Company, Inc., Reading, Mass., 1953.

[2] The Bohm-Pines treatment does not completely succeed in arriving at wave functions which satisfy their subsidiary conditions, but they do explain why the functions derived do, indeed, lead to reasonable values for energies and other physical properties of the electron gas.

The hamiltonian describing the individual-particle behavior may be expressed [in view of (10.43) and (10.47)] as follows:

$$\mathfrak{H} = \sum_i \frac{p_i^2}{2m} + 2\pi e^2 \sum_{\mathbf{k}} \frac{n_{\mathbf{k}} n_{\mathbf{k}}^*}{k^2} - 2\pi n e^2 \sum_{\mathbf{k}} \frac{1}{k^2} \tag{10.54}$$

In (10.54), the second term includes the so-called *self-energy* (that is, $\mathbf{k} = 0$) and the third term subtracts it off again.

The new set of collective coordinates are the canonically conjugate variables, satisfying the usual commutation relation

$$[P_{\mathbf{k}}, Q_{\mathbf{k}'}] = i\hbar \delta_{\mathbf{k}\mathbf{k}'} \tag{10.55}$$

and these coordinates commute with the ordinary electron spatial and momentum variables. The collective coordinates are chosen to represent a *real longitudinal* field $\mathbf{A}(\mathbf{r})$ since the collective behavior arises from the Coulomb potential. Its Fourier decomposition is

$$\mathbf{A}(\mathbf{r}_i) = \sqrt{4\pi c^2} \sum_{\mathbf{k}} \hat{\boldsymbol{\varepsilon}}_{\mathbf{k}} Q_{\mathbf{k}} e^{i\mathbf{k}\cdot\mathbf{r}_i} \tag{10.56}$$

where

$$Q_{\mathbf{k}}^* = -Q_{-\mathbf{k}} \tag{10.56$'$}$$

ensures the reality of $\mathbf{A}$ and $\hat{\boldsymbol{\varepsilon}}_{\mathbf{k}}$ is a unit polarization vector in the direction of $\mathbf{k}$. The field $\mathbf{A}(\mathbf{r}_i)$ is to be identified with the longitudinal vector potential of the electromagnetic field acting on the ith particle in the gas.

From (10.56), the corresponding electric field intensity is

$$\begin{aligned} \boldsymbol{\mathcal{E}}(\mathbf{r}_i) &= -\frac{1}{c}\frac{\partial \mathbf{A}(\mathbf{r}_i)}{\partial t} = -\sqrt{4\pi} \sum_{\mathbf{k}} \hat{\boldsymbol{\varepsilon}}_{\mathbf{k}} \dot{Q}_{\mathbf{k}} e^{i\mathbf{k}\cdot\mathbf{r}} \\ &= \sqrt{4\pi} \sum_{\mathbf{k}} \hat{\boldsymbol{\varepsilon}}_{\mathbf{k}} P_{-\mathbf{k}} e^{i\mathbf{k}\cdot\mathbf{r}} \end{aligned} \tag{10.57}$$

and the hamiltonian, equivalent to (10.54), takes the form

$$\mathfrak{H}' = \frac{1}{2m} \sum_i \left[\mathbf{p}_i + \frac{e}{c}\mathbf{A}(r_i)\right]^2 + \frac{1}{8\pi} \int \boldsymbol{\mathcal{E}}^2(\mathbf{r})\, d\mathbf{r} - 2\pi n e^2 \sum_{\mathbf{k}} \frac{1}{k^2} \tag{10.58}$$

Combining (10.58) with (10.56) and (10.57), we have

$$\begin{aligned} \mathfrak{H}' = \sum_i \frac{p_i^2}{2m} &+ \frac{e}{m}\sqrt{4\pi} \sum_{i,\mathbf{k}} \hat{\boldsymbol{\varepsilon}}_{\mathbf{k}} \cdot \left(\mathbf{p}_i - \frac{\hbar\mathbf{k}}{2}\right) Q_{\mathbf{k}} e^{i\mathbf{k}\cdot\mathbf{r}_i} \\ &+ \frac{2\pi e^2}{m} \sum_{i,\mathbf{k}'\mathbf{k}} \hat{\boldsymbol{\varepsilon}}_{\mathbf{k}} \cdot \boldsymbol{\varepsilon}_{\mathbf{k}'} Q_{\mathbf{k}} Q_{\mathbf{k}'} e^{i(\mathbf{k}+\mathbf{k}')\cdot\mathbf{r}_i} - \frac{1}{2}\sum_{\mathbf{k}} P_{\mathbf{k}} P_{-\mathbf{k}} - 2\pi n e^2 \sum_{\mathbf{k}} \frac{1}{k^2} \end{aligned} \tag{10.59}$$

Combining (10.59) with the subsidiary conditions on the wave function

$$\Omega_{\mathbf{k}} \Psi = 0 \qquad \text{for all } \mathbf{k} \tag{10.60}$$

where

$$\Omega_{\mathbf{k}} = P_{-\mathbf{k}} - i\frac{4\pi e^2}{k^2} \sum_i e^{-i\mathbf{k}\cdot\mathbf{r}_i} \tag{10.61}$$

leads to the correct equations of motion for the electrons. ($\Omega_{\mathbf{k}}$ is a Fourier component of $\nabla \cdot \mathbf{\varepsilon} - 4\pi\rho$. Thus, as required, the subsidiary conditions maintain the form of Maxwell's equations.)

The equivalence of the hamiltonian operators (10.59) and (10.54) may be seen by applying the unitary transformation

$$\Psi = S\Phi \tag{10.62}$$

with

$$S = \exp\left(-\frac{2e^2}{\sqrt{\pi}\,\hbar}\sum_{i,\mathbf{k}}\frac{1}{k}\,Q_{\mathbf{k}}e^{i\mathbf{k}\cdot\mathbf{r}_i}\right) \tag{10.63}$$

Problem

It will be left as an exercise for the reader to show that the subsidiary condition (10.60) then becomes

$$P_{-\mathbf{k}}\Phi = 0 \qquad \text{for all } \mathbf{k}$$

and that, if Φ is independent of $Q_{\mathbf{k}}$,

$$\hat{\mathfrak{H}} = S^{-1}\hat{\mathfrak{H}}'S \tag{10.64}$$

where $\hat{\mathfrak{H}}$ and $\hat{\mathfrak{H}}'$ are given by (10.54) and (10.59), respectively.

Thus the new degrees of freedom are associated with canonically conjugate variables which are the coefficients of the Fourier decomposition of the longitudinal vector potential field and their respective time derivatives. The number of these new (collective) degrees of freedom is limited by the fact that collective action takes hold only when $\lambda > \lambda_c$, or, equivalently, when $|\mathbf{k}| < |\mathbf{k}_c|$ (where $|\mathbf{k}_c| = 2\pi/\lambda_c$). The number of collective degrees of freedom is then defined as

$$n' = \frac{1}{(2\pi)^3}\int^{\mathbf{k}_c} d\mathbf{k} = \frac{k_c^3}{6\pi^2} \tag{10.65}$$

It is necessary at this point to modify the hamiltonian (10.59) so that the summation over $\mathbf{k}$, involving the canonically conjugate variables $(Q_{\mathbf{k}},P_{\mathbf{k}})$, be restricted to $k < k_c$. It is done by restricting the sum in the unitary transformation S [Eq. (10.63)] to $k > k_c$. This leads to the following hamiltonian:

$$\begin{aligned}\hat{\mathfrak{H}} = \sum \frac{p_i^2}{2m} &+ \sqrt{4\pi}\,\frac{e}{m}\sum_{i,k<k_c}\hat{\boldsymbol{\varepsilon}}_{\mathbf{k}}\cdot\left(\mathbf{p}_i - \frac{\hbar\mathbf{k}}{2}\right)Q_{\mathbf{k}}e^{i\mathbf{k}\cdot\mathbf{r}_i}\\ &+ \frac{2\pi e^2}{m}\sum_{i,k,k'<k_c}\hat{\boldsymbol{\varepsilon}}_{\mathbf{k}}\cdot\hat{\boldsymbol{\varepsilon}}_{\mathbf{k}'}Q_{\mathbf{k}}Q_{\mathbf{k}'}e^{i(\mathbf{k}+\mathbf{k}')\cdot\mathbf{r}_i} - \frac{1}{2}\sum_{k<k_c}P_{\mathbf{k}}P_{-\mathbf{k}}\\ &+ 2\pi e^2\sum_{\substack{k>k_c\\ i\neq j}}\frac{e^{i\mathbf{k}\cdot(\mathbf{r}_i-\mathbf{r}_j)}}{k^2} - 2\pi ne^2\sum_{k<k_c}\frac{1}{k^2}\end{aligned} \tag{10.66}$$

with the associated subsidiary conditions

$$\Omega_{\mathbf{k}}\Psi = 0 \qquad k < k_c \tag{10.67}$$

Next, in the third term on the right-hand side of (10.66) we separate those terms with $\mathbf{k} + \mathbf{k}' = 0$ from the terms with $\mathbf{k} + \mathbf{k}' \neq 0$. The former gives

$$\frac{2\pi n e^2}{m} \sum_{k<k_c} Q_{\mathbf{k}} Q_{-\mathbf{k}} = \frac{\omega_p^2}{2} \sum_{k<k_c} Q_{\mathbf{k}} Q_{-\mathbf{k}} \tag{10.68}$$

while the latter is

$$\frac{2\pi e^2}{m} \sum_{k,k'} \hat{\boldsymbol{\varepsilon}}_{\mathbf{k}} \cdot \hat{\boldsymbol{\varepsilon}}_{\mathbf{k}'} Q_{\mathbf{k}} Q_{-\mathbf{k}} e^{i(\mathbf{k}+\mathbf{k}')\cdot\mathbf{r}_i} \tag{10.69}$$

Once again, the random-phase approximation is evoked and the contribution (10.69) is neglected. Thus, combining (10.68) with the fourth term on the right-hand side of (10.66), we have a contribution to $\hat{\mathcal{H}}$ which takes the form of a set of independent harmonic oscillators, each characterized by the plasma frequency ω_p. Denoting this operator by $\hat{\mathcal{H}}_{\text{coll}}$, we have, in view of (10.56′),

$$\hat{\mathcal{H}}_{\text{coll}} = -\tfrac{1}{2} \sum_{k<k_c} (|P_{\mathbf{k}}|^2 + \omega_p^2 |Q_{\mathbf{k}}|^2) \tag{10.70}$$

This set of oscillators represents the collective modes of the many-electron system.

We can now express $\hat{\mathcal{H}}$ in the approximate form

$$\hat{\mathcal{H}} = T + \hat{\mathcal{H}}_I + \hat{\mathcal{H}}_{\text{coll}} + \hat{\mathcal{H}}_{sr} + \hat{\mathcal{H}}_{se} \tag{10.71}$$

where T is the total kinetic energy of the electrons. The second term,

$$\hat{\mathcal{H}}_I = \sqrt{4\pi}\,\frac{e}{m} \sum_{k<k_c} \hat{\boldsymbol{\varepsilon}}_{\mathbf{k}} \cdot \left(\mathbf{p}_i - \frac{\hbar}{2}\mathbf{k}\right) Q_{\mathbf{k}} e^{i\mathbf{k}\cdot\mathbf{r}_i} \tag{10.72}$$

describes a (linear) coupling of each electron with the collective field of the remaining electrons. $\hat{\mathcal{H}}_{\text{coll}}$ is the "pure collective field term" discussed above, and

$$\hat{\mathcal{H}}_{sr} = 2\pi e^2 \sum_{\substack{k>k_c \\ i\neq j}} \frac{e^{i\mathbf{k}\cdot(\mathbf{r}_i-\mathbf{r}_j)}}{k^2} \tag{10.73}$$

represents a short-range contribution to the Coulomb interaction. When the summation over $\mathbf{k}$, indicated in (10.73), is carried out, we have

$$\hat{\mathcal{H}}_{sr} = \frac{1}{2} \sum_{i\neq j} \frac{e^2}{|\mathbf{r}_i - \mathbf{r}_j|} \left[1 - \frac{2}{\pi} S_i(k_c|\mathbf{r}_i - \mathbf{r}_j|)\right] \tag{10.74}$$

where
$$S_i(y) \equiv \int_0^y \frac{\sin y}{y}\,dy$$

A comparison of $\hat{\mathcal{H}}_{sr}$ with the ordinary Coulomb potential e^2/r and the "Yukawa-type" potential (10.39) (which was obtained from the earlier analysis of Debye and Huckel) is shown in Fig. 10.6.

The last term

$$\hat{\mathcal{H}}_{se} = -2\pi n e^2 \sum_{k<k_c} \frac{1}{k^2} \tag{10.75}$$

is the *self-energy* term introduced previously.

Summarizing, we see that the hamiltonian for the many-electron system may be expressed (in the random-phase approximation) in terms of three parts, one part ($\hat{\mathcal{H}}_p$) representing the individual-particle behavior,

$$\hat{\mathcal{H}}_p \equiv T + \hat{\mathcal{H}}_{sr} + \hat{\mathcal{H}}_{se} \tag{10.76}$$

one part, $\hat{\mathcal{H}}_{\text{coll}}$, representing the collective behavior, and the third part

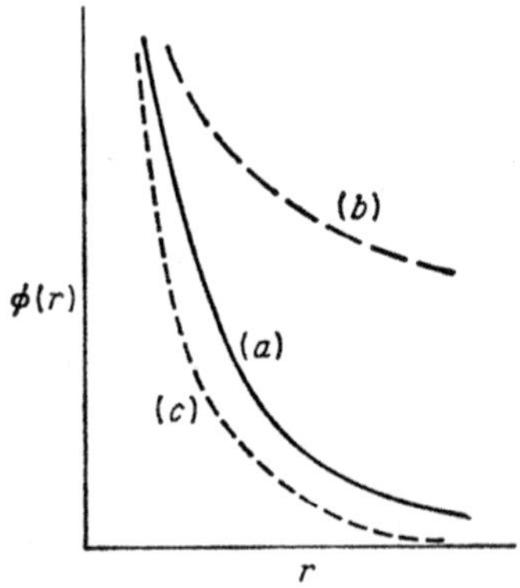

Fig. 10.6. A comparison of $\hat{\mathcal{H}}_{sr}$ (*a*) with the ordinary Coulomb potential e^2/r (*b*) and with a cutoff Coulomb potential $(e^2/r)e^{-k_c r}$ (*c*).

$\hat{\mathcal{H}}_I$ representing a coupling between the individual particles and collective fields of the system.

The presence of the interaction term $\hat{\mathcal{H}}_I$ in $\hat{\mathcal{H}}$ means that, unless this term can be neglected, we have not yet provided a purely collective description. The final transformation to independent collective modes is carried out by Bohm and Pines with the use of perturbation theoretic canonical transformation theory.[1] They find that so long as terms of the order

$$\frac{\beta^2}{2\lambda_s}$$

with $\beta = \dfrac{k_c}{k_F}$ (k_c to be determined)

$$k_F = \sqrt{\frac{2m\epsilon_F}{\hbar^2}} \qquad (\epsilon_F = \text{Fermi energy})$$

[1] This technique along with a more detailed discussion of the material in this section is in D. Bohm and D. Pines, *Phys. Rev.*, **93:** 609 (1953).

and higher, can be neglected, the (final) form of the hamiltonian may be transformed into

$$\hat{\mathcal{H}}_{\text{new}} = T\left(1 - \frac{\beta^3}{6}\right) + \hat{\mathcal{H}}_{\text{coll}} + \hat{\mathcal{H}}_{se} + \hat{\mathcal{H}}_{sr}$$
$$- \left\{\pi\left(\frac{e}{m}\right)^2 \sum_{\substack{k<k_c \\ i\neq j}} \frac{[\hat{\varepsilon}_{\mathbf{k}} \cdot (\mathbf{p}_i - \hbar\mathbf{k}/2)][\hat{\varepsilon}_{\mathbf{k}} \cdot (\mathbf{p}_j + \hbar\mathbf{k}/2)]}{\omega[\omega - (\mathbf{k}\cdot\mathbf{p}_j)/m - \hbar^2/2m]} e^{i\mathbf{k}\cdot(\mathbf{r}_i - \mathbf{r}_j)} + \text{c.c.}\right\} \quad (10.77)$$

where c.c. stands for complex conjugate, and where the new frequency of the collective oscillations, denoted by ω, is given by the dispersion relation

$$1 = \frac{4\pi e^2 n_0}{m} \sum_i \frac{1}{[\omega - (\mathbf{k}\cdot\mathbf{p}_i)/m]^2 - (\hbar k^2/2m)^2} \quad (10.78)$$

The form of the hamiltonian (10.77) no longer has any terms which depends on both the collective and the individual-particle coordinates; thus it represents a truly separated hamiltonian.

The n' subsidiary conditions, accompanying the new hamiltonian, now take the form

$$\left\{\sum_i \frac{\omega^2}{\omega^2 - [(\mathbf{k}\cdot\mathbf{p}_i)/m - \hbar k^2/2m]^2}\right\} \Psi_p = 0 \qquad k < k_c \quad (10.79)$$

where Ψ_p is the part of the wave function dependent only on particle coordinates.

It is interesting to note that the first (kinetic energy) term in (10.77) implies that the electron mass has been increased to

$$m' = \frac{m}{1 - \beta^3/6}$$

This is interpreted by asserting that m' is not the inertial mass of a "bare" electron. Rather, it describes the inertial property of a "bare" electron surrounded by a "plasmon field." The latter is analogous to the conventional quantum-electrodynamical description of a "bare" electron surrounded by a photon field. In our case we would think of the electron's continual emission and absorption of virtual plasmons instead of virtual photons.

The last term appearing in $\hat{\mathcal{H}}_{\text{new}}$ is an electron-electron interaction and is very weak in comparison with the other terms. As pointed out by Bohm and Pines, it represents that part of the screened interaction which is effective beyond the screening length. Thus its influence on the electron behavior is of negligible importance.

Summarizing, the Bohm-Pines formalism describes the density fluctuations in an electron gas in terms of plasma oscillations.

As remarked earlier, the Bohm-Pines treatment is not able to develop a wave function that precisely satisfies the subsidiary conditions (10.79). On the other hand, they do find that the ground-state energy for the electron gas is rather insensitive to the degree to which these subsidiary conditions are satisfied. Thus, it is argued that one property of the electron gas which should be given quite accurately by their treatment is the correlation energy. Let us now consider the correlation energy which is predicted by Pines.[1]

The Correlation Energy of Degenerate Electron Gas

In the first approximation, the short-range term $\mathcal{H}_{sr}$ is treated as small, so that the unperturbed ground-state wave functions are taken to have the form (10.53),

$$\Psi_0 = \chi_c^{(0)}\psi_p^{(0)}$$

where $\psi_p^{(0)}(\mathbf{r}_1, \ldots ,\mathbf{r}_n)$ is the ordinary Slater determinant (10.26) in which the elements are the free-particle wave functions for the ground state of the system. The other factor in (10.53) (that is, $\chi_c^{(0)}$) is a product of one-dimensional harmonic-oscillator wave functions (for the ground state), one for each of the n' wave vectors up to $k = k_c$. Thus, using this wave function, the mean long-range energy per electron, determined by the hamiltonian

$$\hat{\mathcal{H}}^{(lr)} = T\left(1 - \frac{\beta^3}{6}\right) + \hat{\mathcal{H}}_{\text{coll}} + \hat{\mathcal{H}}_{se} + \hat{\mathcal{H}}_{ex} \tag{10.80}$$

is

$$\epsilon = \epsilon_F' + \epsilon_{\text{coul}} + \epsilon_{ex}^{sr} \tag{10.81}$$

where

$$\epsilon_F' = \frac{3}{5}\frac{\hbar^2 k_F^2}{2m}\left(1 - \frac{\beta^3}{6}\right) \tag{10.82}$$

$$\epsilon_{\text{coul}} = -\frac{e^2}{\pi}\beta k_F + \frac{n'}{n}\frac{\hbar}{2}\langle\omega\rangle_{\text{av}} \tag{10.83}$$

and

$$\epsilon_{ex}^{sr} = -2\pi e^2 \sum_{\substack{k,k'<k_F \\ |\mathbf{k}-\mathbf{k}'|>\beta k_F}} \frac{1}{|\mathbf{k} - \mathbf{k}'|^2} \tag{10.84}$$

In the first term, $\frac{3}{5}\epsilon_F$ is the mean kinetic energy for a degenerate gas (see Chap. 6). The average plasma frequency $\langle\omega\rangle_{\text{av}}$ is obtained by averaging ω [Eq. (10.78)] over all $k < k_c$, giving

$$\langle\omega\rangle_{\text{av}} = \omega_p[1 + 3\alpha(1 + \tfrac{3}{10}\beta^2)] \tag{10.85}$$

where

$$\alpha = \left\langle\left(\frac{\mathbf{k}\cdot\mathbf{p}_i}{m\omega}\right)^2\right\rangle_{\text{av}} \simeq \frac{1}{2}\frac{\beta^2}{\lambda_s} \tag{10.86}$$

(The last approximate equality is obtained by Bohm and Pines.[2])

[1] D. Pines, in F. Seitz and D. Turnbull (eds.), "Solid State Physics," vol. I, Academic Press Inc., New York, 1955.

[2] D. Bohm and D. Pines, *Phys. Rev.*, **92:** 609 (1953).

Thus, ϵ_{coul} reduces to

$$\epsilon_{\text{coul}} = \frac{0.866\beta^3}{\lambda_s^{3/2}} - \frac{1.222\beta}{\lambda_s} \quad \text{rydbergs} \tag{10.83'}$$

The last term in (10.81) (ϵ_{ex}) is the exchange energy which arises from $\hat{\mathcal{H}}_{sr}$ [Eq. (10.74)]. The sums over **k** and **k**′ are carried out for all electrons with parallel spins and within the Fermi distribution, so that $|\mathbf{k}' - \mathbf{k}| > k_c \equiv \beta k_F$. This restriction arises from the fact that the *short-range* interactions are confined to De Broglie wavelengths shorter than λ_c. In this way, (10.84) is evaluated by Pines,[1] giving

$$\epsilon_{ex}^{sr} = -\frac{0.916}{\lambda_s}\left(1 - \frac{4}{3}\beta + \frac{\beta^2}{2} - \frac{\beta^4}{48}\right) \quad \text{rydbergs} \tag{10.87}$$

The long-range part of the correlation energy is obtained by subtracting from (10.87) the cohesive energy which is calculated in the Hartree-Fock approximation, except for the term $\bar{\varphi}$ [Eq. (10.23)] (since the latter is being replaced in the Bohm-Pines treatment). Thus,

$$\epsilon_{\text{corr}}^{lr} = \epsilon_F' + \epsilon_{\text{cuol}} + \epsilon_{ex}^{sr} - (<\epsilon_{\text{kin}}> + <\epsilon_{ex}>) \tag{10.88}$$

and, from Eqs. (10.16) and (10.33),

$$<\epsilon_{\text{kin}}> + <\epsilon_{ex}> = \frac{3}{5}\epsilon_F - \frac{0.916}{\lambda_s} = \left(\frac{2.21}{\lambda_s^2} - \frac{0.916}{\lambda_s}\right) \quad \text{rydbergs} \tag{10.89}$$

Combining (10.88) and (10.89), we have [using (10.87)]

$$\epsilon_{\text{corr}}^{lr} = \frac{0.866\beta^3}{\lambda_s^{3/2}} - \frac{0.458\beta^2}{\lambda_s} + \frac{0.019\beta^4}{\lambda_s} \quad \text{rydbergs} \tag{10.90}$$

Next, the parameter β must be determined. Pines[2] argues that the value of β which leads to an energy consistent with the best wave function for the many-body system is that value which minimizes $\epsilon_{\text{coll}}^{lr}$. Further, in the minimization, the term in β^4 is neglected, and he thereby obtains

$$\beta_{\min} = 0.353\lambda_s^{1/2} \tag{10.91}$$

giving

$$\epsilon_{\text{corr}}^{lr} = -(0.019 - 0.0003\lambda_s) \quad \text{rydbergs} \tag{10.92}$$

From (10.91) and (10.65), we have for the ratio of collective degrees of freedom to the total number of degrees of freedom

$$\frac{n'}{3n} = 0.0073\lambda_s^{3/2} \tag{10.93}$$

It is interesting to note that for cesium $\lambda_s = 5.57$ and $n'/3n \sim 10$ per cent and that this value decreases for the lighter metals.

[1] D. Pines, *Phys. Rev.*, **92**: 626 (1953).

[2] In Seitz and Turnbull (eds.), *op. cit.*

As a further correction to the long-range correlation energy, Pines[1] estimated the contribution from the electron-plasma interaction. He finds, treating it as a perturbation, that this contributes an extra (-0.004 rydberg) to $\epsilon_{\text{corr}}^{lr}$ (using $\beta = 0.353\lambda_s^{1/2}$), giving for the final value

$$\epsilon_{\text{corr}}^{lr} = -(0.023 - 0.0003\lambda_s) \qquad \text{rydbergs} \tag{10.94}$$

Finally, we must take account of the short-range contribution to the correlation energy. This is a repulsive term, keeping electrons further apart than would normally occur and reducing the energy of the system. Pines[2] finds that the short-range correlation energy for electrons of antiparallel spin contributes (according to second-order perturbation theory)

$$_{(a)}\epsilon^{sr}(\mathbf{k},\uparrow;\mathbf{k}',\downarrow) = -\sum_{\boldsymbol{\kappa}>\mathbf{k}_c} \left(\frac{4\pi e^2}{\kappa^2}\right)^2 \frac{m}{\hbar^2\boldsymbol{\kappa}\cdot(\mathbf{k}-\mathbf{k}'+\boldsymbol{\kappa})} \tag{10.95}$$

where the sum is restricted to

$$|\mathbf{k}' - \boldsymbol{\kappa}|, |\mathbf{k} + \boldsymbol{\kappa}| > k_F \tag{10.96}$$

according to the Pauli exclusion principle. $_{(a)}\epsilon^{sr}(\mathbf{k},\mathbf{k}')$ is then summed over all $\mathbf{k}'$ (i.e., the electrons with antiparallel spin) and averaged over all $\mathbf{k}$ (i.e., electrons in the Fermi distribution), giving

$$_{(a)}\epsilon_{\text{corr}}^{sr} = -\frac{3}{16\pi^5}\frac{1}{k_F^3}\frac{\int d\boldsymbol{\kappa}\int d\mathbf{k}\int d\mathbf{k}'}{\kappa^4\boldsymbol{\kappa}\cdot(\mathbf{k}-\mathbf{k}'+\boldsymbol{\kappa})} \qquad \text{rydbergs} \tag{10.97}$$

where the regions of integration are specified by (10.96) and

$$|\mathbf{k}|, |\mathbf{k}'| < k_F \qquad |\boldsymbol{\kappa}| > k_c \tag{10.98}$$

Next, the short-range correlation energy for electrons with parallel spins is computed in the same way, giving

$$_{(p)}\epsilon_{\text{corr}}^{sr} = -\frac{3}{16\pi^5}\frac{\int d\boldsymbol{\kappa}\int d\mathbf{k}\int d\mathbf{k}'}{\boldsymbol{\kappa}\cdot(\mathbf{k}-\mathbf{k}'+\boldsymbol{\kappa})\hbar^2}\left[\frac{1}{\kappa^4} - \frac{f(\mathbf{k}-\mathbf{k}'+\boldsymbol{\kappa})}{\kappa^2(\mathbf{k}-\mathbf{k}'+\boldsymbol{\kappa})^2}\right] \tag{10.99}$$

where
$$f(x) \equiv \begin{cases} 0 & x < k_c \\ 1 & x > k_c \end{cases}$$

and the regions of integration are the same as specified in (10.96) and (10.98).

Pines argues that (10.99) is indeed quite small in comparison with the other terms in the perturbation expansion. He obtains the result

$$\epsilon_{\text{corr}}^{sr} \sim {}_{(a)}\epsilon_{\text{corr}}^{sr} = -(0.0254 - 0.0626\ln\beta + 0.00637\beta^2) \qquad \text{rydbergs} \tag{10.100}$$

[1] *Ibid.*

[2] D. Pines, *Phys. Rev.*, **92**: 626 (1953).

Using Eq. (10.91) in (10.100), we have

$$ {}_{(a)}\epsilon_{\text{corr}}^{sr} = -(0.095 - 0.0313 \ln \lambda_s + 0.0008\lambda_s) \qquad \text{rydbergs} \qquad (10.100') $$

Thus, according to Pines, the total correlation energy is

$$ \epsilon_{\text{corr}} = {}_{(a)}\epsilon_{\text{corr}}^{sr} + \epsilon_{\text{corr}}^{lr} = -(0.114 - 0.0313 \ln \lambda_s + 0.0005\lambda_s) \qquad \text{rydbergs} \qquad (10.101) $$

and the cohesive energy is the sum of (10.101) with $\epsilon^{(H\text{-}F)}$. A comparison of this result with the experimental observations is demonstrated in Table 10.3, where the improvement over the ordinary individual-particle Hartree-Fock calculation is indicated.

TABLE 10.3 *Cohesive Energy of the Alkali Metals. (Energy Is in Units of Rydberg Constants.)*

$$ \epsilon_{\text{coh}} = \epsilon^{(H\text{-}F)} + \epsilon_{\text{corr}} \begin{cases} (\text{WIGNER}) \equiv \text{Eq. (10.36)} \\ (\text{B-P}) \equiv \text{Eq. (10.101)} \end{cases} $$

Metal	$\epsilon^{(H\text{-}F)}$	$\epsilon_{\text{coh}}(Wigner)$	$\epsilon_{\text{coh}}(B\text{-}P)$	$\epsilon_{\text{coh}}(meas)$
Li	−0.0530	−0.123	−0.129	−0.114
Na	−0.0212	−0.087	−0.092	−0.081
K	−0.0134	−0.0734	−0.0784	−0.0705
Rb	−0.0106	−0.0688	−0.0736	−0.0590
Cs	−0.0091	−0.0643	−0.0702	−0.0585

Another method of handling the many-electron problem in metals is due to the techniques developed by Brueckner and his collaborators. In a paper by Sawada et al.[1] the results obtained by Pines are duplicated with a different approach. The latter avoids the arbitrary introduction of a cutoff distance (separating the region of mutual electron-electron separations where collective action is important from that where individual-particle action is important). The cutoff of the Pines theory appears naturally in the Sawada formalism, and in the limit where it becomes infinite (low density) the correlation energy is unaffected. The techniques used in the Sawada calculation are analogous to those of quantum field theory and will not be discussed here.

In later work by Nozières and Pines,[2] it is shown how the Pines expansion for the correlation energy becomes identical with that obtained by Sawada et al.[3] It is also shown by Nozières and Pines how their

[1] Sawada et al., *loc. cit.*

[2] P. Nozières and D. Pines, *Phys. Rev.*, **111**: 442 (1958).

[3] Actually, Nozières and Pines show an equivalence with the result of Gell-Mann and Bruecker [*Phys. Rev.*, **106**: 364 (1957)]. This was, however, shown to be equivalent to the results of Sawada et al. by the latter authors.

result, for realistic metals, is related to another (different) approach, due to Hubbard,[1] that gives very similar results for the correlation energy.

In conclusion, it should be emphasized that while the approximation techniques of Bohm and Pines (or Sawada et al. or Hubbard) give numerical results that are in fair agreement with the observations (to within ~15 per cent), this work is presently in the early stages and will require a more rigorous treatment of the many-body problem before more conclusive statements can be made about the actual underlying nature of the many-electron system.

[1] J. Hubbard, *Proc. Roy. Soc.* (*London*), *Ser. A*, **240:** 539 (1957); **243:** 336 (1958).

appendix A
Kramers' theorem[1]

The well-known theorem due to Kramers[2] states that the energy levels of a system containing an odd number of spin one-half particles (i.e., a Fermi-Dirac system) will have an even-fold degeneracy if the hamiltonian which characterizes the system is invariant under a reversal of the signs of all linear and angular momenta. The latter operation is equivalent to a reversal of the sense of time; thus the proof of Kramers' theorem is based on the validity of the "law" of time-reversal invariance of physical phenomena.[3]

We now proceed to prove this theorem with the aid of the Wigner-Eckart theorem. The latter theorem utilizes the fact that the spherical harmonics transform as the irreducible representations of the rotation group.

We take as an example a paramagnetic crystal and assume (as we did in Chap. 4) that a given magnetic ion is subjected to an average crystalline potential due to its surroundings, which may be characterized by the multipole expansion in $\varphi_{\lambda\mu}$ and $\bar{\varphi}_{\lambda\mu}$ [Eqs. (4.9) and (4.10)]. These moments in turn depend on linear combinations of the spherical harmonics.[4]

It is a consequence of the Wigner-Eckart theorem[5] that the matrix elements of the functions (Y_λ^μ) (in the JM basis of representation) are given by the product of the M dependent part of the Clebsch-Gordan coefficient and a coefficient that is independent of M (i.e., the eigenvalue of the z component of the angular-momentum operator J). Thus

$$\int \psi^*(\gamma JM) Y_\lambda^\mu \psi(\gamma' J'M')\, d\mathbf{r} = \langle \gamma J \| Y_\lambda^0 \| \gamma' J' \rangle \langle J'\lambda M'\mu | J\lambda J'M \rangle \quad (A.1)$$

[1] The derivation given in this appendix is based on unpublished work by A. Mencher, M. Sachs, and R. Satten.

[2] H. A. Kramers, *Proc. Acad. Sci. Amsterdam*, **33:** 959 (1930).

[3] Some implications of a breakdown of this law in electromagnetic interactions have been discussed by M. Sachs, *Ann. Phys. (N.Y.)*, **6:** 244 (1959), and M. Sachs and S. L. Schwebel, *Ann. Phys. (N.Y.)*, **8:** 475 (1959).

[4] The result obtained in this appendix applies generally to any system that is characterized by angular-momentum variables.

[5] See, for example, A. R. Edmonds, "Angular Momentum in Quantum Mechanics," Chap. 5, Princeton University Press, Princeton, N.J., 1957.

where γ denotes the set of all simultaneously measurable quantities other than the angular momentum J and its component M. The right-hand side of (A.1) vanishes unless

$$M = M' + \mu \qquad J = J' + \lambda - \nu$$

where ν is an integer between zero and the smaller of 2λ and $2J'$. The quantity $<J'\lambda M'\mu|J\lambda JM>$ is the M-dependent part of the Clebsch-Gordan coefficient. This is discussed by Edmonds[1] and by Sachs.[2] (In the latter paper these coefficients are given explicitly in terms of the quantum numbers that are appropriate for the application to solid state problems.)

The Clebsch-Gordan coefficient has the following useful symmetry property:

$$<J'\lambda M'\mu|J\lambda JM> = (-1)^{J+\lambda-J'}<J'\lambda - M' - \mu|J\lambda J - M> \quad \text{(A.2)}$$

The crystal potential is expressed most generally according to Eq. (4.4) as

$$-e\varphi_c = \sum_{\lambda=0}^{\infty} \sum_{\mu=0}^{\lambda} \Phi_{\lambda\mu}$$

Since the crystalline potential is a real function, it follows that each moment

$$\Phi_{\lambda\mu} = (\Lambda_{\lambda\mu}^{(r)} Y_\lambda^\mu + \Lambda_{\lambda-\mu}^{(r)} Y_\lambda^{-\mu}) + i(\Lambda_{\lambda\mu}^{(i)} Y_\lambda^{+\mu} + \Lambda_{\lambda-\mu}^{(i)} Y_\lambda^{-\mu}) \quad \text{(A.3)}$$

must also be real. Consequently, from the properties of the spherical harmonics, we must have

$$\Lambda_{\lambda\mu}^{(r)} = (-1)^\mu \Lambda_{\lambda-\mu}^{(r)} \qquad \Lambda_{\lambda\mu}^{(i)} = (-1)^{\mu+1} \Lambda_{\lambda-\mu} \quad \text{(A.3')}$$

(where $\Lambda_{\lambda\mu}^{(r)}$ and $\Lambda_{\lambda\mu}^{(i)}$ are the real and imaginary components of $\Lambda_{\lambda\mu}$). It then follows from (A.1) to (A.3′) that

$$\int \psi^*(\gamma JM)\Phi_{\lambda\mu}\psi(\gamma' J'M')\, d\mathbf{r} = (-1)^{J-J'+\mu+\lambda}[\int \psi^*(\gamma J - M)\Phi_{\lambda\mu}(\gamma' J' - M')]^* \quad \text{(A.4)}$$

The hermitian character of the total crystal potential φ_c requires that

$$\int \psi^*(\gamma JM)\varphi_c\psi(\gamma' J'M')\, d\mathbf{r} = [\int \psi^*(\gamma' J'M')\varphi_c\psi(\gamma JM)\, d\mathbf{r}]^* \quad \text{(A.5)}$$

We now proceed to prove Kramers' theorem by making use of the symmetry properties of the matrix representation of φ_c as expressed in Eqs. (A.4) and (A.5).

Assume that

$$\psi = \sum_{\gamma JM} \alpha(\gamma JM)\psi(\gamma JM) \quad \text{(A.6a)}$$

[1] *Ibid.*
[2] M. Sachs, *J. Phys. Chem. Solids*, **15**: 291 (1960).

is a linear superposition of orthonormal functions that represents an eigenvector of the total hamiltonian $\mathcal{H}_0 - e\varphi_c$ (where $\mathcal{H}_0$ is the free-ion hamiltonian). It will be shown that

$$\psi' = \sum_{\gamma JM} \alpha'(\gamma JM)\psi(\gamma JM) \tag{A.6b}$$

where $$\alpha'(\gamma JM) = (-1)^{J+M+p_\gamma}\alpha^*(\gamma J\ -M)$$

and where $(-1)^{p_\gamma}$ is the parity contained in the set γ, is also an eigenvector of $\mathcal{H}_0 - e\varphi_c$ which corresponds to the same eigenvalue as does ψ. In addition, it will be shown that ψ and ψ' are orthogonal *when the angular momentum has a half-integer value* (i.e., when the angular momentum describes a Fermi-Dirac system). (This is, of course, the case when the number of electrons in an atom is odd.) The demonstration of this result then represents a proof that the energy eigenvalues of a Fermi-Dirac system in a static field are at least 2-fold degenerate (and are generally even-fold degenerate) and therefore is a proof of Kramers' theorem.

Substituting the linear superposition of eigenstates given by Eq. (A.6*a*) for the eigenvector into the Schroedinger equation $\mathcal{H}\psi = \epsilon\psi$ and making use of the orthonormal properties of the functions $\psi(\gamma JM)$, the following equation is obtained:

$$\sum_{\gamma' J' M'} \alpha(\gamma' J' M') \int \psi^*(\gamma JM)(\mathcal{H}_0 + \Phi_{\lambda\mu})\psi(\gamma' J' M')\, d\mathbf{r} = \epsilon\alpha(\gamma JM) \tag{A.7}$$

The summation in Eq. (A.7) extends over all possible values of γ', J', M', λ, and μ with $M \leq J$, $\mu \leq \lambda$.

Again, let $\mathcal{H}_0 - e\varphi_c$ operate on ψ', making use of the defined transformation given by Eq. (A.6*b*) and the symmetry relation given by Eq. (A.4). We thus obtain

$$\begin{aligned} \Sigma\int\psi^*(\gamma JM)(\mathcal{H}_0 + \Phi_{\lambda\mu})\psi(\gamma' J' M')\, d\mathbf{r}\, \alpha'(\gamma' J' M') &= \epsilon'\alpha'(\gamma JM) \\ &= \Sigma(-1)^{J'+M'+p'_\gamma}\alpha^*(\gamma' J'\ -M')\int\psi^*(\gamma JM)(\mathcal{H}_0 + \Phi_{\lambda\mu})\psi(\gamma' J' M')\, d\mathbf{r} \\ &= \Sigma(-1)^{J+M+p'_\gamma+\lambda}\alpha^*(\gamma' J'\ -M')\int\psi^*(\gamma J\ -M) \\ &\qquad (\mathcal{H}_0 + \Phi_{\lambda\mu})\psi(\gamma' J'\ -M')\, d\mathbf{r} \end{aligned} \tag{A.8}$$

This equation can be modified by replacing the dummy index $-M' \rightarrow M'$ and also by making use of the fact that, for nonvanishing matrix elements, $p_\gamma + p_{\gamma'} = \lambda$. The resulting equation is

$$\begin{aligned} \epsilon'\alpha'(\gamma JM) = (-1)^{J+M+p_\gamma}\Sigma\alpha^*(\gamma' J' M')\int\psi^*(\gamma J\ -M) \\ (\mathcal{H}_0 + \Phi_{\lambda\mu})\psi(\gamma' J' M')\, d\mathbf{r} \end{aligned} \tag{A.9}$$

It follows from taking the complex conjugate of Eq. (A.7) and noting that ϵ is real that the right-hand side of Eq. (A.9) is equal to $\epsilon(-1)^{J+M+p_\gamma}$ $\alpha^*(\gamma J\ -M)$. Making use of the identity given by Eq. (A.6*b*), Eq. (A.9) becomes

$$\epsilon'\alpha'(\gamma JM) \equiv \epsilon'(-1)^{J+M+p_\gamma}\alpha^*(\gamma J\ -M) = \epsilon(-1)^{J+M+p_\gamma}\alpha^*(\gamma J\ -M) \tag{A.10}$$

thereby establishing the equality between ϵ and ϵ'. Thus, the eigenvector ψ' is an eigenvector of $\mathfrak{H}_0 - e\varphi_c$ and does indeed correspond to the same eigenvalues as does the eigenvector ψ.

It will now be shown that the eigenvectors ψ and ψ' are orthogonal when each magnetic ion contains an odd number of electrons. The scalar product of ψ and ψ' is given, with the aid of Eq. (A.6*b*), by the following equation:

$$\begin{aligned}\int (\psi')^*\psi \, d\mathbf{r} &= \sum_{\gamma JM}\sum_{\gamma' J' M'} \alpha(\gamma JM)\alpha'^*(\gamma' J' M') \int \psi^*(\gamma' J' M')\psi(\gamma JM)\, d\mathbf{r} \\ &= \sum\sum \alpha(\gamma JM)\alpha'^*(\gamma' J' M')\delta(\gamma\gamma')\delta(JJ')\delta(MM') \\ &= \sum (-1)^{J+M+p_\gamma}\alpha(\gamma JM)\alpha(\gamma J\ -M)\end{aligned} \tag{A.11}$$

If the ion contains an odd number of electrons, then J and M are half-integer values, and if $J + M$ is an even integer, $J - M$ is an odd integer.

Thus, when J has a half-integer value the above summation over all positive and negative values of M vanishes, thereby establishing the linear independence of ψ and ψ'. Consequently, *if the hamiltonian which characterizes the interaction between a system containing an odd number of spin one-half particles and an external field is invariant under time reversal and conserves parity,* the eigenfunctions ψ and ψ' belong to the same eigenvalue ϵ and the scalar product

$$\int \psi'^*\psi \, d\mathbf{r} = 0$$

so that the energy levels of the system are at least 2-fold degenerate.[1] The eigenstates ψ and $\psi' = K\psi$ are called *Kramers degenerate states.*

The operator K, which transforms an eigenvector ψ, into its corresponding degenerate eigenvector ψ', has the following $(2J + 1)$-dimensional matrix representation

$$(K_{MM'}) = [(-1)^{J+M}\delta_{M',-M}]K_0 = -\begin{pmatrix} & & & & 1 \\ & & & -1 & \\ & & 1 & & \\ & -1 & & & \\ \cdot & & & & \\ \cdot & & & & \end{pmatrix} K_0 \tag{A.12}$$

[1] It can also happen that, for an even number of electrons, an eigenstate can have a degenerate Kramers' state, since in special cases ψ and its Kramers' conjugate ψ' can be orthogonal for single-valued representations (e.g., the states belonging to the complex conjugate irreducible representations of $\mathbf{C}_3$).

where M takes the values $J, J - 1, \ldots, -J$ and where K_0 represents the operation of taking the complex conjugate. Since Kramers degeneracy is a result of the time-reversal invariance of the hamiltonian and since $\psi' = K\psi$, K must represent the time-reversal operator. The reader may verify this statement by comparing the time-reversed solution $\psi_{JM}(-t)$ of the Schroedinger equation with $K\psi_{JM}(t)$.

These properties of the time-reversal operator were first discussed by Wigner[1] in a general discussion of the time-reversal properties of the Schroedinger equation; they have also been discussed by R. G. Sachs[2] and by K. H. Hellwege.[3]

It is interesting that, if along with an average *smeared-out* crystalline potential one considers an additional interaction of the type $\sum_{i<j} \mathcal{H}(i,j)$ [a term, such as (5.26), which couples paramagnetic atoms in a crystal], a simple extension of the above proof can be given, which shows that, for an odd number of Fermi-Dirac systems, each energy state for the entire ensemble has a Kramers degenerate state, whereas this is no longer the case when the number of Fermi-Dirac systems is even.

[1] E. Wigner, *Goettingen Nachr.*, p. 546, 1932; "Group Theory and Its Application to Quantum Mechanics and Atomic Spectra," chap. 26, Academic Press Inc., New York, 1959.

[2] R. G. Sachs, "Nuclear Theory," App. 3, Addison-Wesley Publishing Company, Inc., Reading, Mass., 1953.

[3] K. H. Hellwege, *Ann. Physik*, **4**: 95 (1948).

appendix B statistical mechanics and the density matrix

As indicated in the preface, it is assumed in this text that the reader is acquainted with some of the elements of statistical mechanics. However, since the density-matrix method is a very powerful way of approaching quantum statistics and since this method is not outlined in most texts on solid state theory, we shall describe it here. Following this, we shall derive the distribution functions and some of the features of degenerate quantum-mechanical systems.

The density matrix Present-day quantum mechanics is a linear theory, based on a probabilistic interpretation which has an underlying *assertion*, the *principle of linear superposition*. According to this principle, the eigenvectors ψ of a hamiltonian $\hat{\mathcal{H}}$, i.e., the solutions of the Schroedinger equation

$$\hat{\mathcal{H}}\psi = i\hbar \frac{\partial \psi}{\partial t} \tag{B.1}$$

may always be expressed as a linear superposition of any complete orthonormal set $\{\psi_m\}$ of eigenstates of the system. Putting the time dependence into the coefficients of such an expansion, ψ is expressed in the form

$$\psi(\mathbf{r},t) = \sum_m c_m(t)\psi_m(\mathbf{r}) \tag{B.2}$$

The *quantum-mechanical average* of any quantity Q is then[1]

$$\begin{aligned} <Q> &= \int \psi^* \hat{Q} \psi \, d\mathbf{r} \\ &= \sum_m \sum_n c_m^*(t) c_n(t) Q_{mn} \end{aligned} \tag{B.3}$$

where

$$Q_{mn} \equiv \int \psi_m^* \hat{Q} \psi_n \, d\mathbf{r} \tag{B.4}$$

and $\hat{Q}$ is the quantum-mechanical operator associated with the observable.

In actual physical systems, the eigenvector ψ refers to one of a large number of microscopic elements that make up the macroscopic whole

[1] See, for example, L. I. Schiff, "Quantum Mechanics," McGraw-Hill Book Company, Inc., New York, 1955.

(e.g., the constituent atom of a solid). Thus we may express ψ for the ith atom as

$$\psi^{(i)} = \sum_m c_m^{(i)}(t)\psi_m(\mathbf{r}) \tag{B.2$'$}$$

We can now calculate the *observable* by taking the ensemble average of $<Q>$ for the entire macroscopic system. Thus, we take for the observed quantity

$$Q_{obs} = \frac{1}{N}\sum_{i=1}^{N} <Q^{(i)}> = \frac{1}{N}\sum_{i=1}^{N}\sum_m\sum_n c_m^{(i)*}(t)c_n^{(i)}(t)Q_{mn} \tag{B.5}$$

Defining the density matrix ρ as the array of elements

$$\rho_{nm} \equiv \frac{1}{N}\sum_{i=1}^{N} c_m^{(i)*}(t)c_n^{(i)}(t) \tag{B.6}$$

Eq. (B.5) takes the form

$$\begin{aligned} Q_{obs} = \sum_m\sum_n \rho_{nm}Q_{mn} &= \sum_n (\rho Q)_{nn} \\ &\equiv \text{Tr}\,(\rho Q) \end{aligned} \tag{B.7}$$

The feature of this method of calculating observables that makes it powerful is the fact that the trace (Tr) of ρQ is independent of the particular basis functions that originally defined the matrices ρ and Q. This can be seen as follows: It is readily verified that

$$\text{Tr}\,(TS) = \text{Tr}\,(ST) \tag{B.8}$$

Calling $ST = A$ and *assuming that each of these matrices has an inverse,* $T = S^{-1}A$, and Eq. (B.8) takes the form

$$\text{Tr}\,(S^{-1}AS) = \text{Tr}\,(A) \tag{B.8$'$}$$

Assume now that $\psi' = S\psi$ defines a new orthonormal set of basis functions. Here, ψ is expressed as an n-element column and S is an $n \times n$ matrix that "reshuffles" the elements of this column to give the elements of the transformed wave function ψ'.

Since

$$\int \sum_i |\psi_i|^2\,d\tau \equiv \int \psi^\dagger\psi\,d\tau = 1 = \int \psi'^\dagger\psi'\,d\tau = \int \psi^\dagger(S^\dagger S)\psi\,d\tau$$

we must require that S be a unitary matrix, i.e.,

$$S^\dagger = S^{-1} \tag{B.9}$$

The notation used is $S^\dagger_{ij} \equiv S^*_{ji}$ (the hermitian adjoint of S). Similarly,

$$\psi = \begin{pmatrix} c_1\psi_1 \\ \cdots \\ c_n\psi_n \end{pmatrix} \qquad \psi^\dagger = (c_1^*\psi_1^* \cdots c_n^*\psi_n^*)$$

Combining Eq. (B.9) with the definitions of the matrices ρ and Q, we have in the new (primed) basis of representation

$$\rho' = S^{-1}\rho S \qquad Q' = S^{-1}QS$$

and $$\mathrm{Tr}\,(\rho'Q') = \mathrm{Tr}\,(S^{-1}\rho SS^{-1}QS) = \mathrm{Tr}\,(S^{-1}\rho QS)$$

Using Eq. (B.8), we then have

$$\mathrm{Tr}\,(\rho'Q') = \mathrm{Tr}\,(S^{-1}\rho QS) = \mathrm{Tr}\,(\rho Q)$$

Q.E.D.

Thus a knowledge of the matrices of ρ and Q in the most convenient basis of representation would allow a calculation of the observable Q_{obs}. The most convenient basis of representation is usually that one which diagonalizes the density matrix. This corresponds to the case where ρ commutes with the hamiltonian of the system (and therefore represents a stationary quantity, simultaneously measureable with the energy of the system). To see this, we combine Eq. (B.6) with the Schroedinger equation (B.1) and the complex conjugate of the Schroedinger equation. This gives[1]

$$\frac{\partial \rho}{\partial t} + \frac{1}{i\hbar}[\rho,\hat{\mathcal{H}}] = 0 \tag{B.10}$$

With the basis functions that diagonalize $\hat{\mathcal{H}}$, its matrix representation is

$$(\mathcal{H}) = \begin{pmatrix} \epsilon_1 & 0 & \cdots & 0 \\ 0 & \epsilon_2 & & \\ \cdot & & \cdot & \\ \cdot & & & \cdot \\ \cdot & & & \cdot \\ 0 & & & \epsilon_n \end{pmatrix} \tag{B.11}$$

[1] The equation of motion for ρ [Eq. (B.10)] is the quantum-mechanical analogue of Liouville's equation in classical statistical mechanics

$$\frac{\partial \rho^{(c)}}{\partial t} + \{\rho,H\} = 0$$

where $\{\rho,H\}$ is the Poisson bracket and H is the classical hamiltonian of the system. It is a well-known property in quantum mechanics that the expectation value of the commutator $<[\rho,\hat{\mathcal{H}}]>$, expanded in a power series in $\hbar$, takes the form of the Poisson bracket $\{\rho,H\}$ in the classical limit (that is, $\hbar = 0$). This is required by the correspondence principle.

With (B.11), $<[\rho,\hat{\mathcal{H}}]> \equiv <\rho\hat{\mathcal{H}} - \hat{\mathcal{H}}\rho> = 0$ only if ρ is also diagonal. This case corresponds to the representation of ρ as

$$\rho = \begin{pmatrix} \omega_1 & 0 & \cdots & 0 \\ 0 & \omega_2 & & \\ \cdot & & \cdot & \\ \cdot & & & \cdot \\ \cdot & & & & \cdot \\ 0 & & & & \omega_n \end{pmatrix} \tag{B.12}$$

where $\rho_{nm} = 0$ for $n \neq m$ and

$$\rho_{nn} = \omega_n = \frac{1}{N} \sum_{i=1}^{N} |c_n^{(i)}|^2$$

is the probability that the nth cell of the ensemble is occupied. The type of ensemble described associates a constant energy value with each cell (this is the Gibbs canonical ensemble).

Energy and Entropy

With (B.7), (B.11), and (B.12), the energy of the ensemble is *the constant*

$$E = \text{Tr}\,(\rho\hat{\mathcal{H}}) = \sum_n \epsilon_n\omega_n \tag{B.13}$$

Also, from (B.7) and with $Q = 1$, we must have

$$\text{Tr}\,(\rho) = \sum_n \omega_n = 1 \tag{B.14}$$

The condition (B.13) incorporates the first law of thermodynamics. The second law of thermodynamics is incorporated into the definition of entropy in terms of the density matrix[1]

$$S = -k\,\text{Tr}\,(\rho \ln \rho) = -k \sum_n^n \omega_n \ln \omega_n \tag{B.15}$$

where k is Boltzmann's constant. Von Neumann[2] shows that S is a function that is always positive and is a maximum for a system that is in thermodynamic equilibrium (i.e., a system that is undisturbed by any outside system, such as a measuring apparatus).

[1] This follows from expressing the entropy in terms of the *most probable distribution* of the elements of the ensemble among its states. Denoting the latter quantity by P, Boltzmann's classical expression for entropy is (with $\omega = 1/P$)

$$S = \overline{k \ln P} = -k\,\overline{\ln \omega} = -k \sum \omega_n \ln \omega_n$$

[2] J. von Neumann, "Mathematical Foundations of Quantum Mechanics," Princeton University Press, Princeton, N.J., 1955.

In the limit when a system is in "pure state," i.e., when there is perfect order, we have $\omega_m = 1$, $\omega_{n \neq m} = 0$,

$$\rho = \begin{pmatrix} 0 & & & & & & & & \\ & \cdot & & & & & & & \\ & & \cdot & & & & & & \\ & & & 0 & & & & & \\ & & & & 1 & & & & \\ & & & & & 0 & & & \\ & & & & & & \cdot & & \\ & & & & & & & \cdot & \\ & & & & & & & & 0 \end{pmatrix}$$

In this case, $S = 0$ since $\operatorname{Tr}(\rho \ln \rho) = 0$.

In the other extreme, when a system is in any one of Nd states, each with equal probability $\omega_n = 1/d$, we have

$$\rho = \begin{pmatrix} 1/d & & & & & \\ & 1/d & & & & \\ & & \cdot & & & \\ & & & \cdot & & \\ & & & & \cdot & \\ & & & & & 1/d \end{pmatrix}$$

and

$$S = -k \operatorname{Tr}(\rho \ln \rho) = -kNd\left(\frac{1}{d} \ln \frac{1}{d}\right) = Nk \ln d \tag{B.16}$$

Thus, if ϵ_J is the energy of each constituent atom of the system of N atoms and if the state of each atom is $(2J + 1)$-fold degenerate (i.e., each of the $2J + 1$ eigenvectors corresponds to the same energy ϵ_J), then

$$S = Nk \ln (2J + 1) \tag{B.17}$$

(This case was discussed in the text in Chap. 5.)

In view of (B.13), (B.14), and the fact that S, given by (B.15), is a maximum at equilibrium, we have

$$\delta\left(\sum_n \omega_n\right) = \sum_n \delta\omega_n = 0 \tag{B.18}$$

$$\delta E = \sum_n \epsilon_n \delta\omega_n = 0 \tag{B.19}$$

$$\delta S = \sum_n (\ln \omega_n + 1)\delta\omega_n = 0 \tag{B.20}$$

We now take an arbitrary linear combination of these variations, giving

$$\Sigma \delta\omega_n[(\ln \omega_n + 1) + \lambda + \mu\epsilon_n] = 0$$

where λ and μ are the *Lagrange multipliers* to be determined.

Since $\delta\omega_n$ cannot vanish arbitrarily, its coefficient must vanish, or

$$\ln \omega_n = -1 - \lambda - \mu\epsilon_n$$

giving

$$\omega_n = e^{-1-\lambda-\mu\epsilon_n}$$

In view of (B.14), we have

$$e^{1+\lambda} = \sum_n e^{-\mu\epsilon_n}$$

and

$$\omega_n = \frac{e^{-\mu\epsilon_n}}{\sum_n e^{-\mu\epsilon_n}}$$

The entropy of the system then takes the form

$$S = -k \sum \omega_n \ln \omega_n = -\frac{k}{Z} \sum_n e^{-\mu\epsilon_n}(\ln e^{-\mu\epsilon_n} - \ln Z)$$

$$= \frac{-k}{Z} \sum_n e^{-\mu\epsilon_n}(-\mu\epsilon_n - \ln Z) = k\mu E + k \ln Z \qquad \text{(B.21)}$$

where

$$Z = \sum_n e^{-\mu\epsilon_n} = \text{Tr}\,(e^{-\mu\mathcal{H}}) \qquad \text{(B.22)}$$

is called the *partition function*. The last part of Eq. (B.22) expresses Z in the more general form of the trace of a matrix that may or may not be diagonal, according to the set of basis functions that are used to define it. $\mathcal{H}$ is the hamiltonian for the entire ensemble, and ϵ_n are its eigenvalues.

Because of the complexity that is introduced when the elements of a system are coupled in pairs (or more), it is generally impossible to evaluate Z exactly. (This is discussed in Chap. 5 in relation to magnetism.)

The identification of the constant μ with the absolute temperature may be made by considering the expression for entropy that is determined from thermodynamical considerations:

$$S = \frac{E - F}{T} \qquad \text{(B.23)}$$

where the constant $(1 + \lambda)kT$, denoted by

$$F = -kT \ln Z \qquad \text{(B.24)}$$

is the "free energy" of the system. Thus, comparing (B.21) to (B.23),

$$\mu = \frac{1}{kT}$$

and using this result, the weighting function for the nth state is

$$\rho_{nn} = \omega_n = \frac{e^{-\epsilon_n/kT}}{Z} \tag{B.25}$$

An example of an application of (B.7) is to the calculation of the magnetization of an ensemble. In this case

$$Q_{obs} \equiv \mathbf{M} = \operatorname{Tr}(\rho\boldsymbol{\mu}) = \sum_n \sum_m \mu_{nm}\rho_{mn} \tag{B.26}$$

where the matrix element of a constituent magnetic moment is

$$\mu_{nm} = \frac{e\hbar}{mc}\int \psi_n^*\mathbf{J}\psi_n\,d\mathbf{r}$$

and $\mathbf{J}$ is the angular-momentum operator for one of the *magnetic* elements of the system.

If it is possible to choose the set of basis functions that diagonalize the density matrix, then, with (B.25), Eq. (B.26) takes the form

$$\mathbf{M} = \frac{\sum_n \boldsymbol{\mu}_{nn}e^{-\epsilon_n/kT}}{\sum_n e^{-\epsilon_n/kT}} \tag{B.27}$$

If an external magnetic field is applied, the energy eigenvalues ϵ_n depend linearly on this field as

$$\epsilon_n = \epsilon_n^{(0)} + \frac{e\hbar}{mc}\mathbf{J}\cdot\mathbf{H}$$

(where $\epsilon_n^{(0)}$ denotes the energy eigenvalue with $\mathbf{H} = 0$), and the magnetic susceptibility tensor is, by definition,

$$\chi_{ij} = \frac{\partial M_i}{\partial H_j} \tag{B.28}$$

Quantum Statistics of Degenerate Systems

The derivation of the distribution function [Eq. (B.25)] depended on the assumption that the elements of the ensemble are distinguishable (i.e., each of them can be *tagged*). However, as we have discussed in the text (Chap. 6), the proper conditions of dense particle concentration and low temperature in a quantum-mechanical system can lead to the indistinguishability of the constituent elements. In this case, there are still two possibilities as far as the distribution of the elements among the states of the system is concerned. One of these corresponds to the case where an added restriction is imposed that prevents more than one element occupying one particular state. This restriction, the *Pauli exclusion principle,* applies (*according to observation*) to systems of particles whose inherent angular momentum (divided by $\hbar$) is a half-integer, e.g., electrons, protons, He^3 nuclei, etc. The resulting statistics are called *Fermi-Dirac,* and the particles are called *fermions.* In the second case of indistinguishability of the particles, no restriction is placed on the number of elements that can occupy a given state. The resulting distribution is called Bose-Einstein, and the particles are called *bosons.*

To illustrate how the distribution changes from one type of statistics to the other, consider two particles to be distributed among three states that we shall call ψ_a, ψ_b, ψ_c.[1] In the case of the classical (Boltzmann) system the two particles are distinguishable and therefore can be *tagged.* We shall call them α_1, α_2. In the other two cases we cannot attach subscripts to α. The distribution is indicated in Table B.1.

TABLE B.1 *A Comparison of the Distribution of Two Particles among Three States According to Boltzmann, Bose-Einstein, and Fermi-Dirac Statistics*

	Boltzmann			*Bose-Einstein*			*Fermi-Dirac*		
States	ψ_a	ψ_b	ψ_c	ψ_a	ψ_b	ψ_c	ψ_a	ψ_b	ψ_c
	α_1	α_2	0	α	α	0	α	α	0
	α_2	α_1	0						
	α_1	0	α_2	α	0	α	α	0	α
	α_2	0	α_1						
	0	α_1	α_2	0	α	α	0	α	α
	0	α_2	α_1						
	α_1,α_2	0	0	α,α	0	0	Forbidden		
	0	α_1,α_2	0	0	α,α	0			
	0	0	α_1,α_2	0	0	α,α			

Fermi-Dirac statistics Consider that the energy ϵ_r of an ensemble corresponds to the distribution of n_r indistinguishable elements among g_r states. The total number of ways of distributing the n_r elements among the g_r states with *only one element allowed per state* is just the number of ways of taking g_r things n_r at a time. This is the binomial coefficient,

$$P_r^{(F\text{-}D)} = \binom{g_r}{n_r} \equiv \frac{g_r!}{(g_r - n_r)!n_r!} \tag{B.29}$$

Considering, then, the entire array of distinct energy levels of the ensemble $\epsilon_1, \epsilon_2, \ldots, \epsilon_r, \ldots$ corresponding to the independent probabilities of distribution $P_1, \ldots, P_r, \ldots$, the probability for the distributions

[1] See R. D. Cowan, *Am. J. Phys.*, **25:** 463 (1957).

corresponding to all energy levels is

$$P^{(F\text{-}D)} = \prod_s P_s^{(F\text{-}D)} = \prod_s \frac{g_s!}{(g_s - n_s)!n_s!} \tag{B.30}$$

Once again, for the *most probable* distribution, we take the variation of the entropy to vanish. Since $S \propto \ln P^{(F\text{-}D)}$, we then require

$$\begin{aligned} \delta \ln P^{(F\text{-}D)} &= \delta \sum_s [g_s \ln g_s - f_s \ln f_s - (g_s - f_s) \ln (g_s - f_s)] \\ &= \sum_s \left[\ln \left(\frac{g_s - f_s}{f_s}\right)\right] \delta n_s = 0 \end{aligned} \tag{B.31}$$

where we use the notation

$$(n_s)(\text{most probable}) \equiv f_s$$

and the Stirling approximation

$$\ln N! \simeq N(\ln N - 1) \qquad N \gg 1 \tag{B.32}$$

has been used.

Combining (B.31) with (B.18) and (B.19) we have

$$\sum_s [\ln \frac{g_s - f_s}{f_s} - \alpha - \beta\epsilon_s] \,\delta n_s = 0$$

Since δn_s is arbitrary, its coefficient must vanish, thereby yielding the result

$$f_s = \frac{g_s}{e^{\alpha + \beta\epsilon_s} + 1} \tag{B.33}$$

The distribution function

$$\frac{f_s}{g_s} = \frac{1}{e^{\alpha + \beta\epsilon_s} + 1} \tag{B.34}$$

is then the probability that the *state* with energy ϵ_s will be occupied (with *either* spin state of spin one-half particles). When either of the two spin states of a spin one-half particle is equally probable, the factor 2 appears in g_s.

We shall now determine the constants α and β from thermodynamical considerations. To do this, we consider once again the expression for the entropy in terms of the distribution probability that has been maximized.

$$S^{(F\text{-}D)} = k \ln P^{(F\text{-}D)}$$

With (B.30) and (B.32),

$$\ln P^{(F\text{-}D)} = \sum_s [g_s \ln g_s - (g_s - n_s)\ln(g_s - n_s) - n_s \ln n_s]$$

Substituting for n_s its most probable value f_s [given by Eq. (B.34)] we have

$$\ln P^{(F\text{-}D)} = \sum_s \frac{\alpha g_s}{e^{\alpha+\beta\epsilon_s}+1} + \sum_s \frac{\beta\epsilon_s g_s}{e^{\alpha+\beta\epsilon_s}+1} + \sum_s g_s \ln(e^{-\alpha-\beta\epsilon_s}+1)$$

$$= \alpha N + \beta E + \sum_s g_s \ln(e^{-\alpha-\beta\epsilon_s}+1) \tag{B.35}$$

where N is the number of constituent elements of the system and E is the internal energy. The first two terms on the right side of (B.35) follow respectively according to the definitions of the distribution function and the total internal energy E. Thus, the entropy of a Fermi-Dirac gas takes the form

$$S^{(F\text{-}D)} = k\alpha N + k\beta E + k\sum_s g_s \ln(e^{-\alpha-\beta\epsilon_s}+1) \tag{B.36}$$

Since the last term on the right-hand side of (B.36) is constant, we have, allowing changes to occur in N and E,

$$dS = k\alpha\, dN + k\beta\, dE$$

Thus, keeping the volume constant,

$$\alpha = \frac{1}{k}\left(\frac{\partial S}{\partial N}\right)_{E,V} \qquad \beta = \frac{1}{k}\left(\frac{\partial S}{\partial E}\right)_{N,V} \tag{B.37}$$

Let us call the entropy, internal energy, and volume per particle, s, u, and v, that is,

$$S = Ns \qquad E = Nu \qquad V = Nv$$

Using the thermodynamical relationship

$$T\,ds = du + p\,dv \tag{B.38}$$

and allowing the number of particles to change, i.e.,

$$dS = N\,ds + s\,dN$$

Eq. (B.38) takes the form

$$T\,dS = dE + p\,dV - \epsilon_F\,dN \tag{B.39}$$

where the constant

$$\epsilon_F = pv + u - Ts \tag{B.40}$$

is the *Fermi energy* (or the thermodynamic potential) referred to extensively in Chaps. 6 to 10.

From (B.39) we have

$$\left(\frac{\partial S}{\partial E}\right)_{V,N} = \frac{1}{T} \qquad \left(\frac{\partial S}{\partial V}\right)_{E,N} = \frac{p}{T} \qquad \left(\frac{\partial S}{\partial N}\right)_{E,V} = \frac{-\epsilon_F}{T} \tag{B.41}$$

Comparing these relationships with (B.37), we finally arrive at the constants that were to be determined:

$$\alpha = -\frac{\epsilon_F}{kT} \qquad \beta = \frac{1}{kT} \tag{B.42}$$

so that the Fermi-Dirac distribution function takes the form

$$\frac{f_s}{g_s} = \frac{1}{e^{(\epsilon_s - \epsilon_F)/kT} + 1} \tag{B.43}$$

as given in the text. Also, as indicated in the text, this function takes the classical Boltzmann form in the *nondegenerate limit* (i.e., the 1 in the denominator can be neglected in this limit).

The equation of state of the Fermi-Dirac gas follows from combining Eqs. (B.40) (multiplied through by N), (B.42), and (B.36). Thus,

$$\frac{pV}{kT} = \sum_s g_s \ln\left[1 + e^{-(\epsilon_s - \epsilon_F)/kT}\right] \tag{B.44}$$

is the equation of state of an *ideal* degenerate Fermi-Dirac gas.

Bose-Einstein statistics In this case, we have once again (associated with the energy ϵ_r) n_r indistinguishable particles to be distributed among g_r states. The difference is that any number of the particles are allowed in any of the g_r states. Consequently, we can consider the n_r particles to be broken up into different *groups* to be distributed among the states (this is in contrast to the *single* particle in each of the states in the Fermi-Dirac case). Each of these groups may then be considered separated from each other by a partition between each two of the g_r states. Since there are $g_r - 1$ partitions, there are $g_r - 1$ groups into which the n_r particles are divided. Thus, the total number of ways in which the n_r particles can be distributed in this way is just the number of ways of taking $g_r - 1 + n_r$ (partitions and particles) n_r at a time. This is the binomial coefficient

$$P_r^{(B\text{-}E)} = \binom{g_r - 1 + n_r}{n_r} \equiv \frac{(g_r - 1 + n_r)!}{(g_r - 1)!n_r!}$$

and the total distribution (for all energy levels) is

$$P^{(B\text{-}E)} = \prod_s \frac{(g_s - 1 + n_s)!}{(g_s - 1)!n_s!} \tag{B.45}$$

Following the same procedure as above for the Fermi-Dirac gas, we find that the Bose-Einstein distribution function takes the form

$$\frac{f_s}{g_s} = \frac{1}{e^{(\xi+\epsilon_s)/kT} - 1}$$

where the constant

$$\zeta = pv + u - Ts$$

is the thermodynamic potential for the Bose-Einstein gas. Once again, the Bose-Einstein distribution function takes the classical Boltzmann form in the nondegenerate limit. Similar to the results obtained above for the Fermi-Dirac case, the equation of state of the *ideal* Bose-Einstein gas is

$$\frac{pV}{kT} = -\sum_s g_s \ln\left[1 - e^{-(\xi+\epsilon_s)/kT}\right]$$

Summarizing, the distribution function for any system takes the general form

$$\frac{f_s}{g_s} = \frac{1}{ce^{\epsilon_s/kT} + \delta} \qquad \delta = \left\{\begin{array}{ll} +1 & \text{Fermi-Dirac} \\ -1 & \text{Bose-Einstein} \\ 0 & \text{Boltzmann} \end{array}\right\} \text{statistics}$$

appendix C general properties of the S matrix

Some general properties of the scattering matrix are readily determined from two fundamental assumptions. These are (1) the invariance of the expectation values of observables under the time reversal of the Schroedinger wave equation and (2) the conservation of the number of particles.

If we let the time $t \to -t$, the wave equation transforms as follows:

$$\mathcal{H}\psi(t) = i\hbar \frac{\partial\psi(t)}{\partial t} \to \mathcal{H}\psi(-t) = -i\hbar \frac{\partial\psi(-t)}{\partial t} \tag{C.1}$$

Also, the complex conjugate of the wave equation is[1]

$$\mathcal{H}\psi^*(t) = -i\hbar \frac{\partial\psi^*(t)}{\partial t} \tag{C.2}$$

Comparing the right-hand side of (C.1) with Eq. (C.2), we see that, for time-reversal invariance, we must have

$$\psi(-t) = \psi^*(t) \tag{C.3}$$

In (C.2) and (C.3) ψ^* refers (most generally) to the complex conjugate of each element of a column function, i.e.,

$$\psi^* \equiv \begin{pmatrix} \psi_1 \\ \cdots \\ \psi_n \end{pmatrix}^* = \begin{pmatrix} \psi_1^* \\ \cdots \\ \psi_n^* \end{pmatrix} \tag{C.4}$$

According to the definition of the S matrix,

$$\psi(t) = S\psi(-t) \tag{C.5}$$

[1] For the sake of simplicity, we have assumed $\mathcal{H}$ to be a *real* operator. Actually, the restriction imposed is that $\mathcal{H}$ be hermitian (that is, $\tilde{\mathcal{H}}^* = \mathcal{H}$) to ensure the reality of the energy expectation values. When $\mathcal{H}$ is diagonal, hermiticity corresponds to reality. The results obtained above are, however, readily derived in the more general case of the nondiagonal hermitian hamiltonian.

where t and $-t$ correspond to the asymptotic limits of the distant future and remote past when the scattered particle may be considered as *free.* Thus, with (C.3) and (C.5),

$$\psi^*(-t) = \psi(t) = S\psi(-t) = SS^*\psi^*(-t)$$

so that

$$SS^* = 1 \tag{C.6}$$

or

$$S^* = S^{-1}$$

Thus, as a consequence of time-reversal invariance, the *inverse* of the S matrix is its *complex conjugate* matrix.

If the number of particles are conserved in time, then, according to the definition of the wave function,

$$\int \sum_i |\psi_i(-t)|^2 \, d\mathbf{r} \equiv \int \psi^\dagger(-t)\psi(-t) \, d\mathbf{r}$$
$$= \int \psi^\dagger(t)\psi(t) \, d\mathbf{r} \tag{C.7}$$

where ψ_i are each of the elements of the column [Eq. (C.4)], and $\psi_{ij}^\dagger \equiv \psi_{ji}^*$, that is

$$\begin{pmatrix} \psi_1 \\ \cdot \; \cdot \; \cdot \\ \psi_n \end{pmatrix}^\dagger \equiv (\psi_1^* \; \cdot \; \cdot \; \cdot \; \psi_n^*)$$

With (C.5), the right-hand side of (C.7) becomes[1]

$$\int \psi^\dagger(-t)S^\dagger S\psi(-t) \, d\mathbf{r}$$

Thus,

$$S^\dagger S = 1 \tag{C.8}$$

or

$$S^\dagger = S^{-1}$$

Therefore, it is a consequence of the assumption that the number of particles is conserved, along with the probabilistic interpretation of the wave function, that the S matrix must be unitary [i.e., obey Eq. (C.8)].

Combining (C.6) and (C.8), we observe that the S matrix is equal to its own transposed matrix, i.e.,

$$S = S^{tr} \qquad S_{ij}^{tr} \equiv S_{ji} \tag{C.9}$$

[1] It is easily verified that $(S\psi)^\dagger = \psi^\dagger S^\dagger$.

name index

subject index